ENCYCLOPEDIA OF THE BIOSPHERE

Humans in the World's Ecosystems

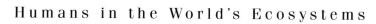

ENCYCLOPEDIA OF THE BIOSPHERE

VOLUME 1: Our Living Planet

Project Director

Ramon Folch

Assistant Project Director

Josep M. Camarasa

GALE GROUP

Detroit
San Francisco
London
Boston
Woodbridge, CT

ENCYCLOPEDIA OF THE
BIOSPHERE

For an outline of the contents of each volume
consult the Thematic Index in the back of that volume

Encyclopedia of the Biosphere is an 11-volume work that treats the bioclimatic zones of the planet Earth and their corresponding biomes, and covers the settlement and use of these areas and systems by humans, as well as the problems that this has led to. This work has been planned in accordance with the principles of UNESCO's MAB (Man and Biosphere) Programme, under whose patronage it has been prepared.

ENCYCLOPEDIA OF THE BIOSPHERE

Project Director

Ramon Folch
UNESCO/FLACAM Professor of Sustainable Development
Secretary-General of the Spanish Committee of the UNESCO/MAB

Assistant Project Director

Josep M. Camarasa
Member of the Spanish Committee of the UNESCO/MAB Programme

Editorial Advisory Committee

Francesco di Castri
Head of Research of the CNRS [Montpellier]
Former Assistant General Director of UNESCO's Environmental Coordination Programmes [Paris]

Mark Collins
Director at the World Conservation Monitoring Centre [Cambridge]

Ramon Margalef
Professor emeritus of Ecology of the University of Barcelona

Gonzalo Halffter
Director of the Institute of Ecology [Xalapa, Veracruz]

Pere Duran Farell
Founder member of the Club of Rome
President of the Spanish Chapter of the Club of Rome [Barcelona]

Alpha Oumar Konaré
Former President of the International Council of Museums [Bamako]

The original Catalan edition of this work was accomplished (1993-98) with the conceptual assistance and logistics of the United Nations Educational, Scientific, and Cultural Organization (UNESCO).
The positions held by the Authors, the Project Director, the Assistant Project Director and the members of the Editorial Advisory Committee refer to the period when the series was first prepared.

Catalan-language edition (volume 1): 1993
Biosfera. Els humans en els àmbits ecològics del món
Enciclopèdia Catalana

English-language edition (volume 1)**: 2000**

Editor: **ERF - Gestió i Comunicació Ambiental, SL** (Barcelona)
Director: **Ramon Folch**
Chief Editor: **Caterina López**
Editorial Team: **Josep M. Palau, Marina Molins**
Updating: **Josep M. Camarasa**

Publisher: **The Gale Group** (Farmington Hills, MI)
Art Directors: **Cynthia Baldwin, Martha Schiebold**
Editorial Coordinators: **Christine Jeryan, Pamela Proffitt**

Translation
Quartet

Revision
Vernon Heywood
Ph. D., D. Sc., Professor emeritus, The University of Reading

English-language edition distributed to all markets worldwide by The Gale Group
27500 Drake Rd.
Farmington Hills, MI 48331-3535
U.S.A.

Printed by PRINTER, Indústries Gràfiques S.A. (Barcelona)

ISBN 0-7876-4506-0 (complete set)
ISBN 0-7876-4507-9 (volume 1)

Foreword

Where do the animals, plants, and microbes dwell? Which, among these forms of life, photosynthesize and thus make energy from the sun and food from the air available to us? These and so many other questions are answered in dazzling color photographs and authoritative prose as the world's natural splendor reveals itself in these eleven volumes of the *Encyclopedia of the Biosphere*. From the angled landscapes of frigid Antarctica, past the lush glory of the tributaries of Amazonia, and on to the corn and wheat fields that feed our growing population, these descriptions of islands, caves, deciduous forests, and California chaparral enlighten us. We begin to understand how local habitats depend on what we so easily dismiss and misunderstand: the details of their geological and biological context. We see how our living world far transcends the large, familiar forms of life in their native setting. The flora (plants) and fauna (animals) only supplement their ancestors, the smaller, less familiar forms of life: bacteria, protoctists (algae, slime molds, ciliates, and their kin) and fungi, such as yeasts and mushrooms. No longer can the bounty of the ever-changing environment be taken for granted or treated as a mere backdrop for human affairs. And today, no better, more complete, or accessible description of life and its environment exists. Here the entire biosphere — the place where life exists and evolves—is represented in all its glory and never-ending surprise.

The chroniclers of nature's splendor, our authors—scientists, land managers, and environmental educators —live in and around the 357 biosphere preserves throughout the world associated with Man and Biosphere (MAB) Programme. These activists in the UNESCO (The United Nations Educational, Scientific and Cultural Organization) MAB Programme inform us of each unique specific habitat and its natural history. Together they have written original descriptions of their tropical forests, temperate woodlands, upland lakes, karstic terrains, desert landscapes, open prairies, mountainous highlands, rocky seashores or other land or waterscape. These dedicated public servants and their colleagues have lived in, studied, and protected the land and waters of our prodigious Earth as they worked to produce this decade-long labor of environmental love. The *Encyclopedia of the Biosphere*, under the direction of Dr. Ramon Folch and his team of experts, primarily Dr. Josep M. Camarasa, shines with clear prose illuminated by scientific accuracy. In the midst of rapidly shrinking natural resources and obliteration of nonhuman habitats, they and myriad other collaborators produced a remarkably accessible international account of the natural world. From the beginning Enciclopèdia Catalana sought to make this monumental project available to readers around the world. Even in the Catalan language the quality of the first few volumes, as works in progress, was recognized and "Biosfera" was strongly recommended to be published in the English language by many members of the Ecology and Evolution section of the United States National Academy of Sciences.

With such a talented pool of authors, the level of scholarship and the accuracy of this multi-volume work is matched only by its readability, inclusiveness, and beauty. As a unique description of our world at the beginning of the third millennium, the legacy of this work will extend to generations yet to come. At the end of the millennium, this *Encyclopedia* will generate historical interest as our descendants ponder the biosphere prior to its "development" by *Homo sapiens*. The *Encyclopedia of the Biosphere* is meant as a reference not only for students and their teachers but for professional biologists, geologists, and other scholars and nature lovers who share concern for the health of our home planet. The publisher welcomes any comments or corrections so that this comprehensive description of the Earth's living surface may maintain its stature as a scientific account of great responsibility. After all, herein is described the same biosphere upon which each of us entirely depends for the perpetuation and fulfillment of our lives.

Baruch S. Blumberg, Director, NASA Astrobiology Institute, United States of America

Niles Eldredge, American Museum of Natural History, New York, United States of America

Ricardo Guerrero, University of Barcelona, Spain

Malcolm Hadley, Division of Ecological Sciences, UNESCO, Paris, France

Wolfgang Krumbein, University of Oldenburg, Germany

Andrei V. Lapo, VSEGEI (All-Russian Geological Research Institute), St. Petersburg, Russia

Antonio Lazcano Araujo, Autonomous University of Mexico, Mexico

Thomas Lovejoy, Smithsonian Institution, Washington, D.C., United States of America

James E. Lovelock, independent scientist, United Kingdom

Lynn Margulis, University of Massachusetts-Amherst, MA, United States of America

Eugene P. Odum, Institute of Ecology, University of Georgia, GA, United States of America

Peter Raven, Missouri Botanical Garden, St. Louis, MO, United States of America

Jan Sapp, York University, Ontario, Canada

David Suzuki, University of British Columbia, Vancouver, B.C., Canada

Crispin Tickell, Chancellor of the University of Kent at Canterbury, United Kingdom

Jorge Wagensberg, Museum of Science, Barcelona, Spain

Malcolm Walter, Macquarie University, Sydney, Australia

Peter Westbroek, University of Leiden, The Netherlands

Edward O. Wilson, Harvard University, Cambridge, MA, United States of America

Preface

The Gale Group, in collaboration with Enciclopèdia Catalana, is pleased to present the *Encyclopedia of the Biosphere. Humans in the World's Ecosystems.* This 11-volume reference set, first published in Catalan in 1998, is an original, authoritative publication composed by a team of international authors writing under the auspices of UNESCO's Man and the Biosphere (MAB) Programme. *Encyclopedia of the Biosphere* features comprehensive coverage of the earth's major biomes, their characteristics, and their operations. Moreover, it explains for students and general researchers how these ecosystems have been transformed by human activity, while presenting the main species of the planet.

Each volume of *Encyclopedia of the Biosphere* begins with a foreword that introduces the reader to a biome and concludes with a thematic index, an index of terms, and an exhaustive bibliography, including the writings of *Encyclopedia of the Biosphere*'s own contributors. The text in each volume is clearly organized into four distinct sections covering the ecosystem's environmental factors; plant and animal ecology; human influences and uses; and biosphere reserves. Volume 11 provides a comprehensive overview of the history of the concept of the biosphere along with a survey of the men and women who have made significant contributions to its study and preservation. In addition, Volume 11 serves as a cumulative index to the entire set, making it easy for the researcher to find information quickly and efficiently.

Readers will especially value the *Encyclopedia of the Biosphere*'s profuse illustrations (maps, diagrams, charts) and nearly 4,000 four-color photographs. Special sections that focus on narrower topics (e.g., polar exploration, Eskimo art) are sprinkled generously throughout every volume.

Through words and pictures, *Encyclopedia of the Biosphere* will help students and general researchers understand the importance of—and gain an appreciation for—the ecological realities of the world.

The Gale Group
2000

Historical justification of the Catalan version

The 20th century is nearing its end. The frontier that the year 2000 represents is about to be crossed, and being so near it has lost much of its symbolic nature. The third millennium, as it leaves the realm of fiction to be entered into our diaries, is already part of our daily lives and is therefore difficult to reconcile with futuristic visions. Indeed, none of the forecasts made about the turn of the millennium includes imminent cosmic disaster, perhaps because science, the resplendent daughter of these last 10 centuries, is now breaking new ground and has gradually, though admittedly only to a small extent, blunted the edge of the enormous gullibility which tends to typify the human race.

Nonetheless, it is quite a paradox, since the Earth we live on has never been through such a sensitive phase before: not so much because the millennium is changing, but because we humans are not changing enough. Mean and selfish as ever, but also more powerful, we exalt in our condition as highly intelligent but not very rational beings. As the millenium changes, the Earth is replete with knowledge but lacks a measure of prudence. Freed from the dark superstitions of the past, we now have every right to feel afraid, for we are faced with concerns that are genuinely disturbing. This inbuilt threat has not fallen from heaven, but is developing the world over. The new millennium is an ecological "hinge," a decisive turning point.

Let us look at the evidence. The consciences of a number of illustrious minds began to stir in the middle of the 1960s. Some chose the path of prophetic denunciation, others that of study, to seek new solutions. They were all, however, bound to coincide, like two rivers flowing into the same estuary. The United Nations Conference on the Human Environment, held in Stockholm in 1972, sounded the first warning *urbi et orbi.* The United Nations Conference on the Environment and Development (UNCED), which took place in Rio de Janeiro in 1992, confirmed, once and for all, the seriousness of the environmental problem. The 20 years between these two conferences were a period of growing ecological conflict and progressive social and scientific reaction.

In the literature, that infallible testimony of human progress and concern, the publication of *Only One Earth* in that turning-point year of 1972, readily comes to mind. This was a compendium produced by René J. Dubos, an Americanized Frenchman, and American Barbara Ward, at the request of Maurice F. Strong, who was Secretary-General of both the Stockholm and Rio conferences. Other landmark publications were *A Blueprint for Survival*, by the Englishman Edward Goldsmith, also editor of *The Ecologist* magazine, and the publication, in 1974, of the essay entitled *La crise*, by the Dutchman Sicco L. Mansholt, former President of the Commission of the European Economic Community. *La crise* was based on his own experience and on a celebrated report on the limits of economic growth commissioned from the Massachusetts Institute of Technology by the Club of Rome. These key texts were preceded by the prophetic *Silent Spring* (1962), by the American Rachel Carson, and the distinguished and all too often forgotten *Avant que nature meure* (1964) by the Frenchman Jean Dorst. These were immediately followed by works like *Natura: ús o abús?*, perhaps better known by its subtitle *Llibre blanc de la gestió de la natura als Països Catalans* (1976), put together by about a hundred authors associated with the Catalan Institute of Natural History, and which I myself coordinated. These led to works that gradually moved away from simply and agonizingly cataloging our offenses against nature and towards suggesting, increasingly, an alternative system of global management. We only have to think of the influential *Our Common Future* (1987), the report of the World Commission for the Environment and Development, under the auspices of the United Nations and presided over by the Norwegian Gro Harlem Brundtland, or the indispensable *World Conservation Strategy* (1980), a joint production of the IUCN, the WWF and UNEP, followed 10 years later by *Caring for the Earth. A Strategy for Sustainable Living*, from the same organizations. In the introductory note to a work like this one, we could not fail to mention *Gaia: A New look at Life on Earth* (1979) by the British chemist James E. Lovelock, an essay in which he not so much proposed a global vision of the Earth, but a unitary perception of the planet as functioning like one large macroorganism.

All these major works are an eloquent testimony and a reflection of intense activity by institutions and associations the world over. We have already mentioned the Club of Rome, founded by the Italian Aurelio Peccei in 1968 as a kind of high comission to consider our future, IUCN (International Union for the Conservation of Nature and Natural Resources, today IUCN—The World Conservation Union), founded in 1948; WWF (World Wildlife Fund), set up in 1961; and UNEP (United Nations Environment Programme), established in 1972 by the General Assembly of the United Nations. But there is another initiative that ought to be mentioned, and which we have deliberately left to the end, namely the Man and Biosphere (MAB) Programme, which was set up in 1971 by UNESCO as an expression of a then-innovative methodological approach that aimed to make human activities compatible with the conservation and wise use of natural resources. The emphasis was on humans working together with nature, neither for it nor against it, neither destroying it nor subjugating it, but simply using it in a rational manner. It proposed a new methodology, born out of a new, initially subversive attitude, which ended up becoming the accepted approach. Thus what was initially a daring MAB approach has become accepted as orthodox. It had to be like this: if we want to master the present, we have to have invested in the past to ensure the future.

I believe it is pertinent and opportune in this Preface to remind ourselves of these matters and of the history of their development, not least because *Biosfera* fully supports the spirit of the MAB program, in that it aims to be a distillation of the literature of the entire socio-scientific process to which we have just alluded. *Biosfera. Els humans en els àmbits ecològics del món* is the modern way of understanding the Earth's ecological present, of explaining its past and catching a glimpse of its future, by telling the fascinating story of this strained, yet rich, dialogue between humans and their environment. The idea of excluding the human race from explanations of ecology, or of seeing it merely as disturbing the natural order of things, in fact contains a serious epistemological error that has been repeated time and again. It is also a strategic error, because it means blaming ourselves unilaterally and excluding ourselves from a cultural heritage of which we, by definition, are the only recipients. *Biosfera* is a bibliographical compilation of the decade of the '90s and should be considered as such in the future. If anything, it might be thought of as ahead of its time.

Aims, level and scope

Biosfera aims to show the relationships between humankind and the great bioclimatic dominions of the Earth, as well as the ecological systems that these determine—the so-called biomes. In this way, the work has three simultaneous objectives. The first is to present the Earth's great ecosystems and biomes, such as forests, savannahs, and deserts, and to explain their characteristics and how they function. The second is to consider the effects of human actions on these systems, from cultivation of crops and other constructive modifications to problems of environmental degeneration. As part of this effort, integrated management is discussed, as represented by the "biosphere reserves" referred to in the UNESCO/MAB Programme. Third, the book is a way of organizing and describing all these phenomena. It aims to introduce the most notable species, in the style of classic works of natural history, but with a more dynamic focus and in an up-to-date context. *Biosfera*, then, hopes to provide a new ecological vision of planet Earth that is both global and modern.

The present work is aimed at professionals and students of the earth and life sciences, as well as all educators, naturalists, environmentalists and ecologists, or those who are simply interested in the natural sciences, biogeography, ecology, or ethnology. It is a serious work which, while not being abstruse, uses a specialized language. It is a work which is neither trivial nor trivializing, yet it is not so erudite as to be inaccessible. In the words of Stephen Jay Gould:

> "I believe—as Galileo did when he wrote his two greatest works as dialogues in Italian rather than didactic treatises in Latin, as Thomas Henry Huxley did when he composed his masterful prose free from jargon, as Darwin did when he published all his books for general audiences—that we can still have a genre of scientific books suitable for and accessible alike to professionals and interested lay people. The concepts of science, in all their richness and ambiguity, can be presented without any compromise, without any simplification counting as distortion, in language accessible to all intelligent people." (From the Preface to *Wonderful life: The Burgess Shale and the Nature of History*, 1989.)

In accordance with this philosophy, the work has been produced by a group of educated people who are not specialists in all possible environmental areas, and they are, therefore, in the same situation as the majority of readers of books on the subject. Indeed, this is also true for the majority of life scientists, who cannot be specialists in all branches of the subject at the same time: for example, agronomists will find the zoological information useful; entomologists will appreciate the climatic considerations; and geographers may benefit from the ethnographical data that the work contains. It aims, then, to be a reference manual, rigorous in its treatment but at the same time comprehensible, giving a new perspective by being a compendium of scattered information that, though part of current knowledge, is in practice often hard to find.

Biosfera naturally covers the whole world. Because of this huge area of study, certain themes will necessarily receive a rather summary treatment. This could be mistaken by an inattentive reader for deliberate superficiality. In practice, very few Australian botanists, for example, are familiar with the tundra mastofauna, while there cannot be many Canadian oceanographers capable of describing the fynbos of southern Africa. All these professionals, undoubted experts in their own particular field (which they will no doubt find insufficiently treated in the work), will probably obtain valuable insights into areas that are not strictly their province. The challenge of compressing information on the entire planet into only 10 volumes will of necessity lead to some rather brief examinations, but this is also one of the work's virtues—everyone will find everything here. They will also find a global vision which puts a specific piece of information into context. In this case, the selectively chosen trees will allow the reader to see the deliberately schematic wood.

The Earth's 15 great biomes or bioclimatic areas are all examined in *Biosfera*, as are the seas and oceans and Antarctica, which are given as much space as the biomes proper. Each biome is first given a generic treatment (general bioclimate, the characteristics of its flora, fauna and ecology, world distribution, and so on) together with an introduction to its major flora and fauna (plants and animals that can be singled out for their numbers or characteristics) and to the racial groups of human beings in these areas (native and non-native). This is followed by a consideration of the exploitation of its biodiversity (the most characteristic native timber and other natural products, the most typical crops, indigenous livestock, etc.) and the environmental problems caused by human intervention. Lastly, certain good examples of biosphere reserves are covered, as well as other legally protected areas that are of special interest.

Viewed in this way, *Biosfera* is offered as an instrument to support environmental education, which is so badly needed today. Apart from being a channel for scientific information and communication, *Biosfera* is also intended to be a pedagogical tool. The spirit of MAB is also alive and well in this area of education, and the treatment of the subject in these volumes reflects the concerns of the MAB/UNESCO Programme. For this reason, if only as a tribute the positive side of the Rio Conference, allow me to include some excerpts from a lecture that UNESCO commissioned me to give as part of the Scientific Program of the Conference:

"Educating is more complicated, and above all more important, than simply informing. Scientists, who necessarily produce information in order to obtain and interpret data, tend to believe that knowledge educates, but this is not entirely true. Education establishes a model for behavior based on information, but this is then subjected to a system of moral values. It is for this reason that ecological research for its own sake cannot solve the planet's environmental problems. Research informs, but it does not educate...Environmental education, on the other hand, is an instrument that society can use to convert scientific information on the environment into positive attitudes as far as use and management of the planet are concerned, in other words, into educational norms of behavior. But environmental education is not merely a new branch of natural science teaching; rather, it is a pedagogical movement which brings together ecological, technological, sociological, and economic learning in order to foster sensible and positive attitudes in environmental management. If we look at the current way of the world, this sort of pedagogical activity is unthinkable without the cooperation and teamwork of researchers, teachers, and communicators. Thus, in practice, research, communication, and education are all concepts linked together."

This is exactly the case with *Biosfera.*

Development of the concept and editorial structure

In publishing terms, *Biosfera* is both a continuation and a break. In 1984, Enciclopèdia Catalana, S.A., the publishing arm of the Fundació Enciclopèdia Catalana, began publication of a voluminous *Història Natural dels Països Catalans*, a 15-volume work, a project that had been entrusted to me two years previously, based on an earlier proposal first conceived in 1978. The last of these volumes appeared in 1992, which is why we can speak of continuity. Indeed, the *Història Natural dels Països Catalans* and *Biosfera* will have followed on one from the other and stayed in the same editorial hands without a significant break. But we are also justified in speaking of a break, as the two works correspond to very different publishing propositions.

The *Història Natural dels Països Catalans*, the product of a broadly based editorial cooperation (with more than 300 contributors), enthusiastically and warmly received by the public (with more than 30,000 regular subscribers), and worthy of any serious reader's interest, was originally intended for domestic use. The geographical area that it covers, rather than the fact that it was published only in Catalan, limits its readership to those interested in the territory in question, although this obviously does not prevent the educated or curious, no matter what their origin, from dipping into its pages. *Biosfera* is quite the opposite. It is directed at the whole world, being conceived from the very beginning as a work without frontiers. Under the aegis of UNESCO and initially published by Enciclopèdia Catalana S.A., it arose out of a multilingual team of authors and editors, so that it is difficult to say in which language it was originally conceived. It is better like that: everyone can feel that it is his or her own, just as the world itself belongs to everyone.

Whatever the case, the project was originally a Catalan one. It was born out of a proposal which I presented to ECSA in 1989 and a couple of subsequent initial projects that were prepared throughout 1990. Having agreed to work on the preparation and hypothetical development of the project with Josep M. Camarasa—a colleague and friend from our university days in the early '60s—ECSA gave the final go-ahead on December 17, 1990. The final project, finished on April 15, 1991, was approved on July 1, and work began immediately thereafter. The same editorial team that was responsible for the *Història Natural dels Països Catalans*, with Montserrat Comelles as Chief Editor, initially took on the project.

A provisional but detailed list of contents was established, and an Editorial Advisory Board was set up to oversee and revise the text, to propose contributors from around the world, and generally to assist in the conceptual direction of the work. The Board, consisting of Francesco di Castri, then Assistant Director-General for Co-ordination of Environmental Affairs at UNESCO; Mark Collins, then Head of the Habitats Data Unit of the World Conservation Monitoring Center; Pere Duran Farell, President of the Spanish section of the Club of Rome; Gonzalo Halffter, Director of the Mexican Institute of Ecology, Alpha Oumar Konaré, President of the International Council of Museums; and Ramon Margalef, Emeritus Professor of Ecology at the University of Barcelona, was constituted on February 5, 1992 at the head office of the Fundació Enciclopèdia Catalana. However, the *Biosfera* project had already received approval from UNESCO and had been through its first baptism of fire in the international publishing market. Indeed, the Spanish Committee of the MAB/UNESCO Programme, chaired by Tomás Azcárate and with myself as Secretary-General, knew about the initiative and gave it its total support from the earliest stage of the initial project (1990). The entire *Biosfera* operation was then presented to the MAB Programme International Coordinating Committee, which, at its 11th Plenary Session held in Paris November 12-18, 1990, decided to validate the project, incorporating it into the educational activities of the Programme. Later, in 1991, the governing body of UNESCO itself decided to give its backing to the work. The project made its debut in the international publishing world at the 43rd Frankfurt Book Fair in October 1991, where the first versions in languages other than Catalan were projected.

Biosfera has followed a collective editorial policy. Dozens of specialists have been invited to participate, or will be as the publication of the work advances. Nevertheless, only a restricted number of the potential authors will end up contributing, and for obvious reasons. The Management Board has only one concern in this respect: that the various themes are covered correctly. The efforts of the editorial team have been concentrated in obtaining suitable texts, rather than spreading commissions around all the distinguished writers of the world. Indeed, the desire to produce a comprehensive and comprehensible synthesis has been placed above all others. Therefore, editing of the originals by the editorial staff is very important. For this reason, and in order to ensure the smooth progress of the project, the authors' identification with the work's central philosophy is essential. It goes without saying that anything that is good in *Biosfera* can be attributed to them, while errors can only be put down to the limitations of the editorial team, in other words, the Management Board.

Layout of the texts and illustrations

The bulk of the information contained in *Biosfera* appears in the body of the text, and is formatted in a conventional way. Nevertheless, an elaborate, and deliberately unconventional, system of headings has been designed to help orient the reader. Headings in this book are often phrases which have more in common with marginal notes or the rubric of older books than with the commonly found, strictly academic headings. But there are two other sources of information, the inserts outside the main text, and the illustration captions.

The inserts outside the text provide complementary information that is related to the main theme being covered and supplements the basic expository narrative. They are sometimes historical anecdotes or references, or information which is not strictly ecological, while at other times they are comments on flora, fauna, geology, or ethnography that, if left in the main text, would only succeed in interrupting the flow of the central argument. In any case, these inserts, more unconventional than the main text, constitute a colorful vehicle for a variety of information that enriches the body of the work as well as making it livelier. The captions to the illustrations, as well as documenting the pictures to which they refer, also contain various explanations and comments that are just as informative.

In fact, all the illustrations are informative by their very nature. This is how it should be, although one has to admit that sometimes the spectacular nature of photographs tends to overshadow the concepts that they are intended to illustrate. In a work like *Biosfera*, this risk is particularly great. However, it has always been a strict rule of this work to avoid spectacular solutions, however great the temptation. The illustration is always at the service of the text, without merely becoming its iconographic twin. Indeed the opposite is often true, and the illustration explains concepts that have been deliberately excluded from the text. It is then that the interest in discursive captions becomes more obvious. It goes without saying that tables, histograms, and graphs complete the picture, complementing both the text and the illustrations. Finally, there are also the usual and useful indices, bibliographies, and appendices.

Biosfera is essentially a reference work, but it can also be read straight through. There are two ways of getting into the work: thematically, by looking in the relevant index, which leads the reader to information on a particular theme (for example, the structure of forests, the fauna of the tundra, or the ethnic groups of the Sahara); or, alphabetically, also by using the appropriate index, which makes it possible to locate a particular animal, plant, ethnic group, or phenomenon, either through its common or scientific name. Having an alphabetical access also allows the work to be used as a specialized glossary, especially in the field of ethnobiology. Thus, as well as providing the essential scientific nomenclature of animals and plants, *Biosphere* also gives their accepted everyday names and, in many cases, the common names in the original languages.

Acknowledgements

The acknowledgements section is dedicated first and foremost to those authors who appear in the credits for each volume. Our thanks must go to them, and to the members of the Editorial Advisory Board and the entire editorial team. Authors, contributors, and, of course, photographers and illustrators all compose that essential human team without which this work could not even have been started. A special mention must go to M. Antònia Miserachs, who was responsible for the layout and page design. Her work was crucial in giving a formal quality to the work, which underlines its conceptual intention and is present on every page.

Decisive roles have also been played by the Fundació Enciclopèdia Catalana S.A. and DIGEC, the latter being responsible for marketing the work in Catalonia. Promoting a work of these proportions is an act of faith for which we are sincerely grateful. But it is also a contribution to the cause of the environment and a valuable addition to the very necessary process of developing our environmental conscience. The technical and production departments of ECSA have also been most professional and efficient, and should be acknowledged here.

Finally, we owe a special debt of gratitude to UNESCO and its MAB Programme. We are especially grateful for the support they have given the work, but particularly for their invaluable contribution in promoting the global nature of the biosphere as the framework for human activity. Many ecologists would not now be able to work without this conceptual framework, and *Biosfera*, in particular, would probably not exist. As the third millennium gradually approaches, full of doubts and uncertainties, this global concept does at least give us reason for hope.

Dr. Ramon Folch
Project Director
1993

1

Our Living Planet

Jaume Bertranpetit
Josep M. Camarasa
Lluís Ferrés
Ramon Folch
Ricard Guerrero
Ramon Margalef
Lynn Margulis
Rosa M. Poch
Jaume Porta

and

Albert Garriga
Arnald Marcer
Dorion Sagan

THE GALE GROUP

The authors and collaborators - volume 1

Jaume Bertranpetit
Professor of Anthropology at Stanford University [USA]

Josep M. Camarasa
Member of the Spanish Committee of the MAB/UNESCO Programme

Lluís Ferrés
Doctor in Biology

Ramon Folch
Secretary-General of the Spanish Committee of the MAB/UNESCO Programme

Ricard Guerrero
Professor of Microbiology at the University of Barcelona

Arnald Marcer
Technical Collaborator in the Department of the Environment, Autonomous Government of Catalonia

Ramon Margalef
Emeritus Professor of Ecology at the University of Barcelona

Lynn Margulis
Professor in Botany at the University of Massachusetts-Amherst [USA]

Rosa M. Poch
Doctor in Soil Science of the University of Ghent [Belgium]

Jaume Porta
Professor of Soil Science of the University of Lleida

Dorion Sagan
Member of Sciencewriters-Amherst [USA]

EDITORIAL TEAM

DIRECTOR: **Ramon Folch**, Doctor of Biology
ASSISTANT DIRECTOR: **Josep M. Camarasa**, Doctor of Biology
CHIEF EDITOR: **Montserrat Comelles**, Graduate in Biology
EDITOR: **Cristina Junyent**, Graduate in Biology
ART DIRECTION: **Rosa Carvajal, Miquel Monge**, Graduates in Geography, **Mikael Frölund**
DESIGN AND PAGE-MAKING: **Toni Miserachs**
ADMINISTRATIVE SECRETARIES: **Maria Miró**, **Mònica Díaz**

EDITORIAL DIRECTOR: **Jesús Giralt**
PUBLICATION MANAGER FOR MAJOR PROJECTS: **Josep M. Ferrer**
HEAD OF PRODUCTION: **Francesc Villaubí**

Introduction

The idea that the biosphere, that is to say the whole ensemble of living matter and the limited layer of the Earth's surface where life is possible, is a single entity that can be studied in its entirety is a relatively new one. The ebbs and flows of thought that have shaped our knowledge of nature did not include the word biosphere until little over a century ago, and indeed the concept was not taken seriously by the academic world until the last 25 years. When the Austrian geologist Eduard Suess first coined the word *biosphere* in 1883, in his work *Die Entstehung der Alpen (The Formation of the Alps)*, he could not have suspected the scientific, social, and political implications that his neologism would have in the closing stages of the second millennium. The publication of Vladimir Vernadski's work on the biosphere in the '20s, first in Russian (1926) and later in French (1929), had little influence. A book like this first volume of *Encyclopedia of the Biosphere*, which aims to be a general introduction to the concept of a biosphere and to describe its general characteristics, its history, its workings, and above all the peculiar role that humankind has played in it, has, therefore, few precedents. For this reason, the usual mixed sentiments of joy and fear that one experiences on seeing the text published irrevocably in print, are in this case felt more acutely.

Today there is much talk about the biosphere, ecology, and the environment. Yet, as often happens with fashionable isssues, people talk about more than they actually know, and their words reflect a strange mixture of frivolity and fear, confusing biosphere with natural parks, ecology with pollution, and the environment with meteorology. And these are only the most favorable cases, for there is no shortage of prophets of doom (and opportunists), ranging from those who speak of the biosphere as if it were some threat to progress, and of ecology as if it were an extremist and subversive ideology, to those who turn the biosphere into a god, with ecologists as the clergy of the new faith being persecuted by the infidels. Few people see (and this is surely due to a lack of proper information) the true dimension of the biosphere concept, as Vladimir Vernadski intended it, at the end of the 1920s, or as modern ecologists around the world now understand it. The concept of the biosphere embraces the essential functional interdependence of all living things, including the human race, and their inevitable dependence on the great flows of energy and materials that affect not just the Earth as a whole, but every single living creature, including human beings.

The view that life on our planet can be conceived of as a single whole, a view we owe to Vernadski and that pervades contemporary ecological studies, is drawn from very different schools of thought that are, at times, contradictory. We find it in the romantic and liberal progressivism of Alexander von Humboldt or the mystic humanism of Lev Tolstoy, by way of the positivist rigor of the physiologists of the Claude Bernard school or the biochemists, from Priestley to Pasteur, not to mention Ingen-Housz, Martí Franquès, or Liebig. Then there are the great naturalists of the 19th century like Lyell, Darwin, and Dokuchayev, with their strongly inductive approach based on observation. Even if it would be difficult today to share Vernadski's blind faith in science as a motor of progress and treasure house of absolute truths, we can admire the way he was able to synthesize elements of such different origins into single theory. It was received with indifference at first, but it was to become one of the foundations of modern global ecology. It is updated in the pages of this volume. Here you will find Vernadski's biosphere: "that unique region of the earth's crust where life exists," where hundreds of thousands of species act as "transformers which convert cosmic radiation into active, terrestrial energy." Thus, "all life, all living material can be considered as an indivisible whole within the mechanism of the biosphere," whose natural upper limit is the ozone layer that protects the very existence of life. Living material, organisms, and the space they occupy: this is what we understand as the biosphere. But we are also concerned with just how all these organisms occupy this space. We want to explore which organisms live there, under what conditions with what effects they live, how they interact, which strategies they employ, and how they are affected by temporary or permanent changes in the environment.

The biosphere is not a static reality. The first part of this volume takes us through the biosphere's history, starting with its physical support, the planet itself, and its different inert layers. The formation and drifting of continents and seas, and chemical and physical changes in the atmosphere, have at times preceded, and at other times accompanied or followed, changes in the biosphere. The history of the biosphere, in precise terms, from the first organic syntheses to the consolidation of the human race as the dominant species, has been written by Lynn Margulis and Ricard Guerrero. Margulis, one of the world's leading authorities on microbial evolution, and Guerrero have prepared a text that is directed at the non-specialist reader, and which is a fascinating journey through the thousands of millions of years of the evolution of life right up to the emergence of our own species.

The dynamism of the biosphere does not manifest itself only at an evolutionary scale but is also present in our everyday life, in processes which are repeated with more or less regularity, in cycles and flows, in changes in the organization of the elements that shape them, and in the relationship among them. All of this, which belongs to the field of ecology, has been covered by Ramon Margalef in the second part of this volume. His text, like all his writings, is full of wisdom and, at the same time, guile. *Encyclopedia of the Biosphere*'s indebtedness to Ramon Margalef, however, goes much further than the large helpings of science (and cunning) that he has poured into his text. It also goes beyond what we owe him as a member of the Editorial Advisory Board. *Encyclopedia of the Biosphere* owes its very existence to Ramon Margalef's many years of leadership in the scientific community, out of which this project is born. All of us in Catalonia who have studied ecology over the last 25 years have looked and continue to look on him as our mentor, and we hope that this will be the case for many years to come. Many of the ideas that support *Encyclopedia of the Biosphere*, and especially in this first volume, are unashamedly and unequivocally Margalef's, or have at least been filtered through the optimistically sceptical, imaginatively rigorous, and enormously creative vision of this emeritus anarchist.

For better or for worse, the irruption of our species into the biosphere, particularly since the Industrial Revolution, has signaled an unprecedented break in some aspects of this functionalism. As human beings, we play a unique role in the biosphere, and for this reason we bear special responsibilities as far as the rest of the biosphere is concerned. This is the subject matter of the third part of this volume. Its middle chapters, written by Jaume Bertranpetit, cover the biological evolution of hominids in general, and of our own species in particular. The first chapter, written by Ramon Folch and Jaume Bertranpetit, is a summary of what our species has in common with the rest of the biosphere and what singles us out from the point of view of ecological functionalism. The last chapter, written by Josep M. Camarasa with the occasional marginal note by Ramon Margalef, tackles the question of the biosphere's evolution under the stamp of human societies and technological change.

The last part, written by Lluís Ferrés and Jaume Porta, describes the main factors, basically climate and soil, which determine the distribution of different types of biomes on the Earth's surface. It also provides a general description and territorial distribution of these biomes and ends with an outline of the present situation of the biosphere as a whole. It serves as a general introduction to the descriptions of the different biomes that will appear in successive volumes of *Encyclopedia of the Biosphere*.

The illustrations are an essential element of *Encyclopedia of the Biosphere*. Although the contents of this first volume are very different from those of later volumes, the illustrations are no less important. Miquel Monge was responsible for the process of selection. The map of the world's biomes represents the beginnings of a fruitful relationship between ECSA and the Habitats Service and Geographical Information System of the World Conservation Monitoring Center (WCMC) in Cambridge (Great Britain).

Our list of thanks to those persons and institutions who have helped in the publication of this volume begins with the WCMC, particularly Director Mark Collins, who is also a member of *Encyclopedia of the Biosphere's* Editorial Advisory Board. We should also mention above all the other members of the Editorial Advisory Board, who have gladly given their services whenever asked, and the contributing authors, whose participation goes much farther than their texts and suggestions for illustrations. We would also like to thank all those people and institutions who have provided us with documentation or who have offered to read the draft versions of some parts of the volume. They include Jordi Corbera (Department of Dynamic Geology, Geophysics and Paleontology in the Faculty of Geology at the University of Barcelona), Jordi Cunillera (Department of Meteorology and Astronomy in the Faculty of Physics at the University of Barcelona University), Dianne Edwards (University of Wales College in Cardiff), Alexei Ghilarov (Department of Vertebrate Zoology and General Ecology in the Faculty of Biology at Moscow University), April Goebel (National Geographic Society), Peter Grinevald (University of Geneva), Joan Guimerà (Department of Dynamic Geology, Geophysics and Paleontology in the Faculty of Geology at the University of Barcelona), B.J. Hopkins (Department of Meteorology at the University of Reading), Xavier Luri (Department of Meteorology and Astronomy in the Faculty of Physics at the University of Barcelona), Maria Dolors Llopart (Barcelona Museum of Folk Art, Industry and Traditions), Andreu Roca ("Frullato" string quartet), Antoni Roca (The History of Science Work Group at the Institute of Catalan Studies), Antoni Serra (Department of Invertebrate Zoology in the Faculty of Biology at the University of Barcelona), William Shear (Hampden-Sydney College), Oriol Vinyes (Generalitat de Catalunya's Cartographic Institute), Jutta Voss (Alfred Wegener Institute for Polar and Marine Research), Richard Walter (Éditions Nuit et Jour) and Natalie Wellis (Weldon Owen Publishing).

Dr. Josep M. Camarasa
Assistant Project Director
1993

The Earth's living mantle

Like the rose swept away by the torrent,
Like the mimosa flake tossed in the breeze,
So is your life under the firmament.

Joan Salvat-Papasseit
Óssa Menor (1925)

1
The history of the biosphere

1. The evolution of the planet Earth

1.1 From prehistoric times to the present day

Before we start to look at the biosphere's history we must first take a look at the history of its physical support, the planet Earth. We must examine its structure, which requires an explanation of plate tectonics. Plate tectonics determine the configuration and the distribution of continents and oceans and have varied more than we think throughout geological times. These process greatly affect the climatic and atmospheric conditions to which all organisms are subject. We must also look at the shaping of the Earth's crust by atmospheric and organic agents, which has also contributed to the diversification and modification of habitats. Finally, we will analyze the variations in these phenomena, including those that are the consequence of the action of living beings themselves.

The formation of the planet

According to the most generally accepted hypotheses of recent years, the universe as a whole, including our galaxy, is some 14,000 million years old. The Sun and the planetary system that surrounds it, of which the Earth is a part, were not, however, formed until some 4,600 million years ago. This came about as the result of the greater part of a cloud of dust and interstellar gas condensing to create the Sun, and through the accretion of the remainder in the form of protoplanets that began to revolve around it.

One of those protoplanets, after a period in which frequent collisions with other bodies and energy from the radioactive disintegration of short-lived isotopes maintained it in a molten state, cooled down and separated into a solid crust and a gaseous atmosphere. And so this planet on which we all live, together with many other beings that share with humans all the properties we call life, came about. Thus, our planet, the Earth, has a history of some 4,600 million years, although it did not cool down and become stable until some 3,900 years ago, at the end of the Hadean eon.
At the beginning of the Earth's history, there were no living beings. Today we know of fossil bacteria, which differ little from present-day bacteria and date back some 3,500 million years. There are even older examples that are still being studied. So the biosphere probably began to take shape sometime between these two remote milestones, separated by a thousand million years, at some stage during the Archaean eon, which covers the period from 3,900 to 2,500 million years ago. However, this was a very different biosphere from the one we know today, as were the configuration of the Earth's surface and the environmental conditions that affected its organisms.

The atmosphere, for example, had a completely different composition and series of properties from those of the present day. It was basically composed of water vapor, nitrogen, and carbon dioxide. It lacked oxygen, and so was a reducer instead of an oxidizer. Much less energy reached the Earth from the Sun than it does today. The distribution of continents and oceans was also very different, and the only living beings were microorganisms similar to certain groups of present-day bacteria. Today's biosphere is largely the result of the action of those same organisms over the last 4,000 million years, although the planet's own geological dynamics and other factors, completely independent of life, have also shown their influence, at times in an extremely dramatic manner.

The Earth's present structure

In the earliest stages of its formation, the Earth was subjected to a shower of celestial objects of all sizes. The material from these objects added to what had already been condensed, a process called accretion. It was also subjected to radiation from the disintegration of short-lived radioactive isotopes that were initially present in its core, and to the increase in temperature derived from the compression of the initial materials under the weight of those more recently incorporated. The Earth reached extremely high temperatures, at least more than 2,912°F (1,600°C) on the surface and progressively higher nearer the center. Under these conditions, all the materials that are today solid remained in liquid or molten form. The heaviest atoms, like iron and nickel, have tended to concentrate

1 The Milky Way, a galaxy to which the planet Earth belongs, was formed, according to current views, about 14 thousand million years ago. On clear nights, away from the lights of the great cities, one can notice straightaway the densest part of the Milky Way as a whitish path in the sky, from which it derives its name. The galaxy is of the spiral type, with a mass equivalent to 2×10^{14} solar masses, with 100 billion stars and a diameter of some 80,000 light-years. In our galaxy, the sun is situated in the arm of Orion, and on the equatorial plane is 27,000 light-years distant from the center of the galaxy. The whole revolves around an axis which passes through its center.
[Photo: TCL-Index]

2 The calendar of the different stages of development of the planet Earth since its creation. The universe, our galaxy, and the planet Earth, have neither always existed nor remained the same. Human beings, one of the living beings who have existed the least time on Earth, have reconstructed in broad terms the evolutionary history of the planet, but there are still many enigmas that have to be resolved. The history of the appearance of life on earth and its later expansion, as far as we know it today, is of absorbing interest.
[Diagram: Jordi Corbera, based on various sources]

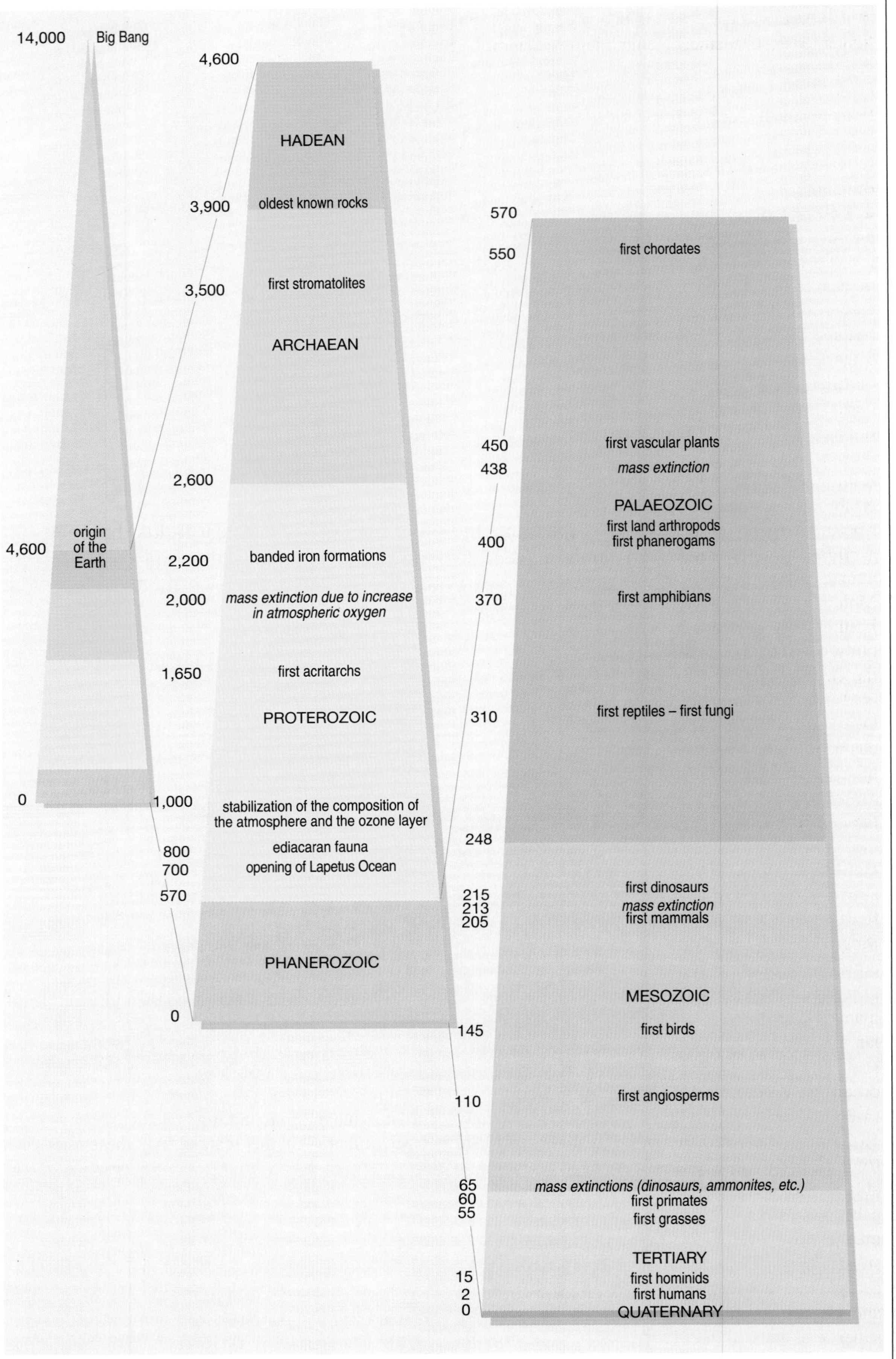

at the Earth's center, constituting a core, while the lighter ones, like silicon, aluminium, calcium, and carbon, have tended to remain on the surface. As the planet has progressively cooled, these lighter atoms have eventually formed a crystalline crust.

Between the nucleus, or core, and the crust, we can differentiate an intermediary layer with peculiar physical characteristics that we call the *mantle*. Nitrogen and the so-called noble gases (helium, neon, argon, etc.) formed a gaseous *atmosphere*. Other gases from volcanic eruptions, the impact of objects coming from space, and chemical reactions on the Earth's surface became incorporated into this atmosphere at a later stage. The whole planet, then, can be seen as a series of different concentric layers, or levels, with different densities and other physical properties, dating from between 4,400 and 4,300 million years ago.

Using seismological techniques we have been able to establish two major discontinuities within the Earth. The one nearest the surface, the so-called *Mohorovicic discontinuity* (or *Moho* for short), named after the Croatian seismologist Andrija Mohorovicic who discovered it in 1909, separates the Earth's crust from the mantle. The second discontinuity, called the *Gutenberg discontinuity*, named after the German geologist Beno Gutenberg who discovered it in 1914, separates the mantle from the core. One part of the upper mantle, the deepest part, is characteristically both less dense and more flexible than the part nearest the surface, and is thus called the *asthenosphere*. The part nearest the surface, which is the lightest and most rigid, is called the *lithosphere*.

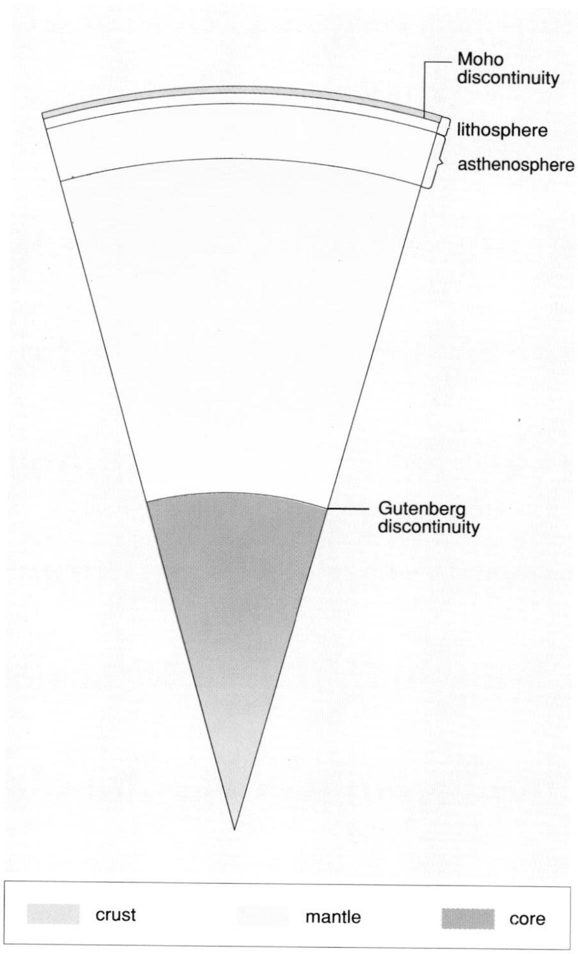

3 The terrestrial crust, the outermost layer of the Earth, is made up of two different parts. The lower, of basaltic composition, some 6 mi (9 km) thick, forms the floors of the oceans and the base on which the continental masses are formed. The continents, formed principally by granitic rocks, constitute the upper, much thicker layer—some 22-28 mi (35-45 km). Below the lithosphere, that is, underneath the crust and the upper layer, there is a zone in a state of partial fusion called the asthenosphere. The base of the asthenosphere, which is found at a depth of between 250-435 mi (400 and 700 km), makes contact with the inner part of the terrestrial globe, called the mesosphere, where the material becomes rigid again. It is thought that the solid nucleus of the Earth is made up of materials in which nickel, iron, sulphur and silica predominate.
[Diagram: Editrònica, from various sources]

Until about 1950, the prevailing image of the Earth's structure was that of a perfectly spherical symmetry from the center to the Moho discontinuity and a more irregular and complex distribution of materials on the crust. However, since the second half of the 20th century, it has become clear that both the crust and the mantle layers that are nearest the surface are irregular. The depth of the Moho discontinuity is not constant, nor is the thickness of the crust. Under the oceans the depth of the Moho discontinuity is 3-5 mi (5-8 km), while under the continents it is generally 18-25 mi (30-40 km). It can be as much as 40 mi (65 km) under large mountain ranges and considerably thinner under large collapsed structures, the so-called rifts, which we will cover in greater detail later on. However, even though it does not correspond to substantial differences in composition, we must accept that the discontinuity between the lithosphere and the asthenosphere—that is, between the solid superficial part of the Earth, which includes the crust and the outer part of the upper mantle to a depth of 44-93 mi (70 and 150 km), and the asthenosphere, which is more plastic and with a base that reaches depths of 250-435 mi (400-700 km)—is more important for the consequences it has in shaping the planet's surface than the seismic discontinuities that were detected previously.

The composition of the lithosphere as a whole, despite the great variety of rocks on its surface, is very similar to that of granite, a rock which is made up, essentially, of two different types of minerals: quartz (silicon dioxide) and feldspars (silicates of aluminium linked with those as sodium, potassium, calcium, or barium). These are much lighter than olivine (magnesium and iron silicates), which is the basic mineral in the mantle. All these materials become compacted into pieces of a variety of thicknesses, shapes, and sizes. The pieces move very slowly in relation to each other and are called *lithospheric plates*. The movements of these plates are possible due to the flexibility of the asthenosphere (over which it could be said that they float and drift) and the fact that it is less dense.

1.2 Drifting plates

The Earth's crust

The Earth's crust is composed of two shells—the continental and oceanic crusts. The thicker and more permanent *continental crust* corresponds to the continental areas in the geological sense of the word. This includes the continents themselves, but also the continental shelves and many of the islands. Its thickness varies from one place to another, but averages about 22 mi (35 km); exceptionally it can exceed 37 miles (60 km) under certain mountain ranges or become as thin as 12 mi (20 km) under some depressions. At the edges of the continental areas, generally coinciding with the shelves and submerged continental slopes, it tapers off to nothing and is substituted by the *oceanic crust*. This basically corresponds to the oceanic floor and the volcanic islands that emerge from them and is denser and thinner than the continental one. It has an average thickness of 4.5 mi (7 km) and only exceptionally exceeds 6 mi (10 km).

As we have already said, both the continental and the oceanic crusts—even though they are clearly separated from the upper mantle by the Moho discontinuity, in which the phenomena of reflection and refraction of seismic waves take place—are solidly connected with the upper, solid part of this discontinuity. The upper mantle is thinner under the oceanic crust than under the continental crust and also has slightly different physical properties. Without any variation in composition, the upper mantle rests on the asthenosphere. Some of the asthenosphere's material is molten and behaves like a ductile, though somewhat viscous, material, which is what makes the movement of lithospheric plates possible.

Plate tectonics

In the space of a very few years (practically between 1965 and 1971), plate tectonic theory has moved from being a daring hypothesis to one of the paradigms on which modern geological science is based. If it is true that even before the First World War the German meteorologist, Alfred Wegener, had formulated the hypothesis of continental drift based on geophysical, stratigraphic, palaeontologic, palaeoclimatologic, and biogeographical arguments, his ideas were generally rejected until, in the early 1960s. It was at this time that the research of the North American geophysicists Harry Hess and Robert S. Dietz, namely the process of seafloor spreading from oceanic ridges, was recognized. The initial evidence from the central Atlantic ridge and confirmation from the Pacific ridge, an ocean which has traditionally been considered very ancient, led Hess to formulate the hypothesis that convection cells in the fluid part of the mantle acted like a conveyor belt, spreading the oceanic floors outward from the axes of the ridges (under which were found the hot ascendent branches of the convection cells). They became hung under the marginal cavities, toward which the cold descendent branches of those convection cells descended. Ceaseless volcanic eruptions continued to add new rocky material from the mantle, and so prevented an even broader separation of the two edges of the ocean floor, which move in opposite directions.

Although this phenomenon manifests itself in the center of oceans, this does not mean that it has no effect on the continents. In fact, it was from the Canadian geologist J. Tuzo Wilson's observation in 1965 that the "conveyor belts" postulated by Hess and Dietz could be connected with a network of

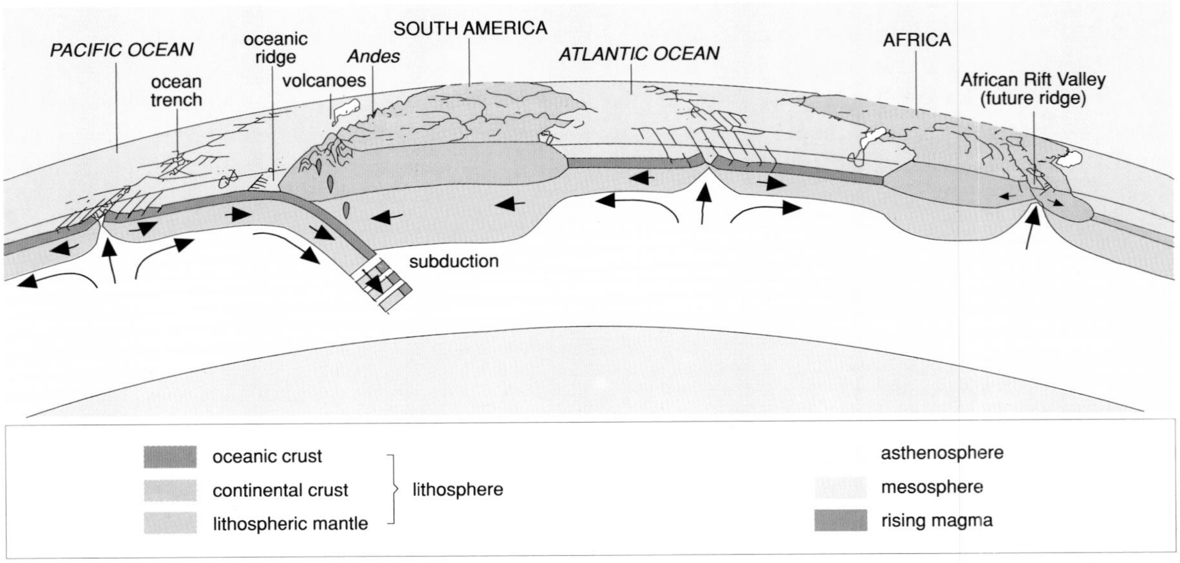

4 The process of separation of South America and Africa through the progressive enlargement of the Atlantic, due the formation of lithosphere in the central-Atlantic ridge, proves that the terrestrial crust is formed by a mosaic of plates separated by ridges, trenches, or faults. The formation of new crust in the oceanic ridges and the corresponding disappearance of the old crust into the trenches are the phenomena that originate continental drift. As the formation of new lithosphere has to be compensated for by the destruction of lithospheric material. *[Diagram: Albert Martínez, from various sources]*

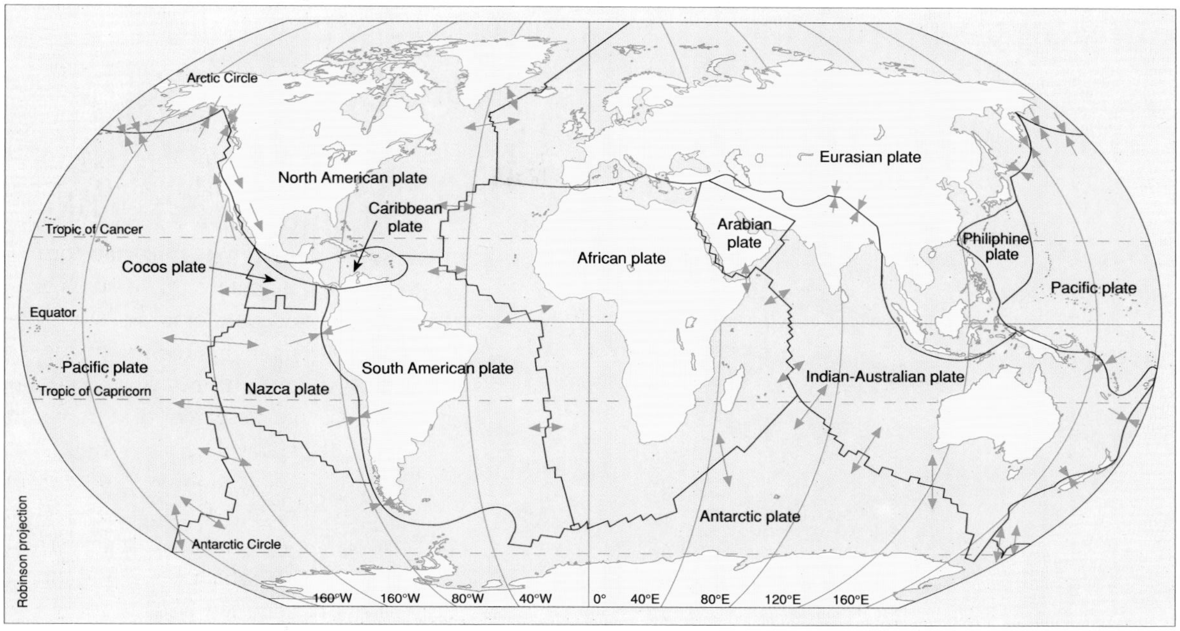

5 Arrangement of the different lithospheric plates. The lithospheric plates together comprise a mosaic of spherical domes that encircle the Earth. These plates vary in thickness between 31 and 93 mi (50 and 150 km), and move at a speed of a few centimeters a year. Throughout the history of the Earth, the shape and number of lithospheric plates, as well as their relative movements, have been changing as larger plates break up into smaller ones or join together to form even larger ones. Wegener's theory of lithospheric plates replaced earlier theories about the structure of the Earth.
[Diagram: Editrònica, from various sources]

6 The German geophysicist and meteorologist Alfred Lothar Wegener (1880-1930), based on observations made previously on the outline of the African and South American continents and using concepts from geophysics, geology, plaeontology, and palaeoclimates, formulated the hypothesis of continental drift. In 1912, in a lecture, Wegener made his hypothesis public for the first time. That same year he published the Gusic concepts hypothesis and in 1915, they were presented in book form (*Die Entstehung der Kontinente und Ozeane*), Revised editions were published in 1920, 1922, and 1929. The first reactions to his ideas were ones of scepticism, and although some of his followers improved and added to them, it was not until the beginning of the 1950s that doubts were raised about the earlier hypothesis regarding the state of solidification of the Earth.
[Photo: Alfred Wegener - Institut für Polar und Meerforschung]

faults dividing the Earth's surface into a number of rigid plaques, that he began to develop the theory of plate tectonics. This would very soon be confirmed by a whole series of archaeamagnetic, stratigraphic, oceanographic, and geochemical data.

Plate tectonic theory has important repercussions on the biosphere and its history, whose setting it modifies, though at a speed of only about an inch (a few centimeters) per year. Generally it is recognized that there are eight principal plates and a group of smaller plates that occupy the whole of the Earth's surface and that are slowly displaced relative to each other.

Contact between the plates

The boundaries between the plates are tectonically active and are of three types. The types correspond to three different kinds of relative movement of the plates in contact. The first type of plate margin includes those that are called *constructive*, or *of accretion*; these are the type of boundaries that we have already described, in which a "new" lithosphere is being generated through the outflow of mantle materials. This is the case in all oceanic ridges, even of those parts that have emerged, as is the case of Iceland, for example.

A second type of boundary between plates covers the so-called *convergent margins* or *destructive boundaries*, although strictly speaking there is only lithosphere destruction in the case of subduction. Subduction happens with boundaries in which a plate overlaps with another in such a way that the

7 The principal contacts between the lithospheric plates are of three types: convergent, divergent and transforming. The convergent contacts arise from a collision between two plates. They can be of three different types, according to the types of crust that come into contact: oceanic crust with oceanic crust, as happens in zones of island arcs; oceanic crust with continental crust, as in the west coast of South America; continental crust with continental crust, as in the Himalaya or the Alpine-Pyrenean range. Divergent plates are ones that separate. The most typical examples are the oceanic ridges where new material appears responsible for the creation of the oceanic crust. The zones of continental crust where there is a thinning that suggests the future separation of a new ridge, may also be considered divergent contacts, as in the area of the lakes of the Rift Valley. A lateral movement takes place between the transforming contacts, the most characteristic example being the faults that cut through the oceanic ridges in an almost perpendicular manner. It has to be noted too that these faults may affect the oceanic crust and/or the continental crust, as in the concrete case of the San Andreas fault on North America.
[Diagram: Albert Martínez, from various sources]

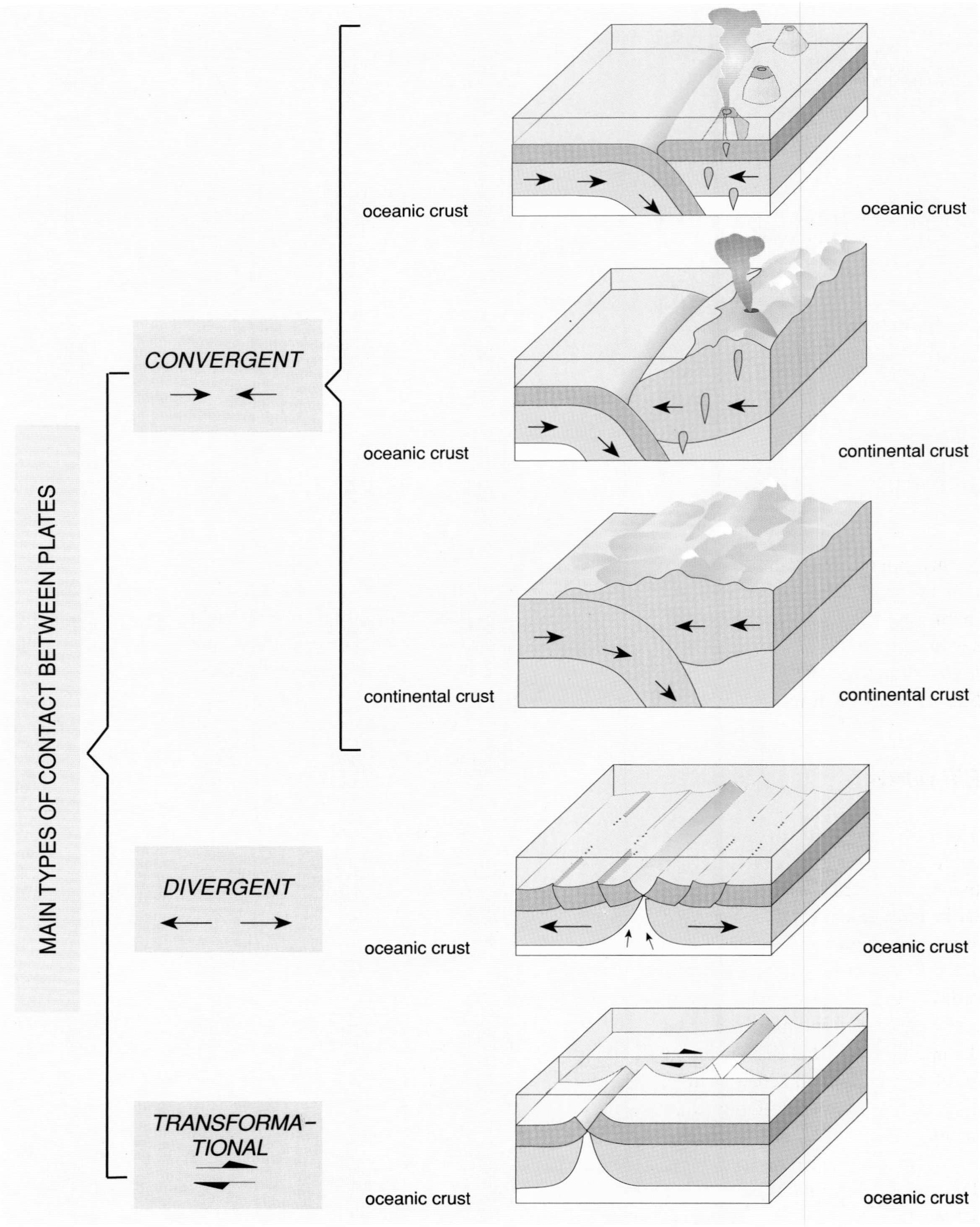

one underneath is driven downwards towards the center of the asthenosphere, below the oceanic trenches or the arcs of islands and volcanic mountains that cross them. At the other convergent plate margins, through a series of complex overlappings, the lithosphere thickens through a collision process. Examples of subduction are the northern boundaries of the Pacific plate, where two arcs of typical volcanic islands are bounded either by the trenches of the Aleutian Islands or of the Kuril Islands. An example of collision is the boundary of India—in fact a fragment of the old austral continent of Gondwana—with the Euroasiatic plate, which has led to the formation of the Himalayas.

The third type of boundary between plates includes those that are called *transform* or *conservative margins*, where there are only lateral displacements without formation or destruction of the lithosphere.

8 The African Rift zone, which extends from the great lakes of East Africa, Ethiopia, the Red Sea and reaches the north of Palestine, and the European rift zone which goes from the valley of the lower Rhine to the sea of Alborán, are areas where possibly the fracturing of a plate is taking place. The breaking of the plates and the formation of subplates takes place because the rigid material of which they are made is subject to pressures and mechanical forces. These forces are transmitted towards the interior of the plates and produce elastic distortions of various degrees which can end up producing fractures. Breaks can also take place as a result of the differential warming of the lithosphere due to unequal distribution of radioactive material, a consequence of the existence of convection currents in deep zones of the asthenosphere. In fact, the Earth's ocean depths stem from a process of fragmentation of a single plate, the Pangaea, at the beginning of the Mesozoic. *[Photo: Emory Kristof / National Geographic Society]*

In many places, they cut the axes of oceanic mountain ranges and are more or less perpendicular to them. These margins are therefore places of intense seismic activity. They are also marked by *transform faults*, the most famous of which is probably that of San Andreas Fault in California.

Rift valleys

The overall rigidity of the plates does not totally exclude other methods of deformation at their edges that results from contacts between plates, in particular in areas called rifts. Intracontinental rifts are long areas (sometimes as long as thousands of miles) that are rather narrow (in general, tens to hundreds of miles but often narrower). These rift zones are characterised by a thinning of the continental crust and the upper mantle that lies underneath and a structure of blocks individualized by faults. The blocks can dropped, raised, or tilted, but as a whole, a rift zone is depressed in relation to its edges to such an extent that it can be invaded by the sea or covered by lakes. The zones have a lateral extension—in other words a type of elongation or divergent movement of its sides—and, at the same time, the asthenosphere rises to levels nearer the surface. This has a double implication; it causes a mechanical weakness in the plate and is also an important flux of heat. Both factors generate conditions that are favorable to volcanic and seismic activity.

The processes associated with the formation of intracontinental rift zones can be stabilized at a given moment in their evolution. On the other hand, they can continue until the tearing of the plate in which they have been formed. If the break remains limited, an area of the continental crust replaces the interior of a plate. Its floor can then fill up with oceanic-type materials, as happens with the basins of the Caspian and Black Seas or those of the marginal seas of the eastern coast of Asia (Bering, Okhotsk, Japan, Eastern China, Southern China, Sulu, Celebes), or dome basins of the Mediterranean. If the process is not stopped, it can lead to the fragmentation of the plate and formation of new oceanic spaces. It was a process of fragmentation of this type, at the start of the Mesozoic era some 250 million years ago, which, starting from a single, large continental plate, led to the formation of the oceanic floors that we find on Earth today, as well as the successive configurations of emerged lands and oceans, from that period to the present day.

In the same way that plate movements affect the distribution of continents and oceans, they also indirectly affect the climate and the distribution of living beings and their diversity. When a rift process is set in motion and the continents begin to sink at the edges of the rift, the elevation of large blocks of land can take place [an example would be the case of the Ethiopian Plateau, with heights of more than 13,000 ft (4,000 m)]. This can cause a drop in sea level and lead to a more continental climate in the emerged lands. In contrast, when continental fragmentation is complete, the climate in the emerged lands becomes more maritime; in any case, any modification of the distribution of land masses and seas effect changes in atmospheric fluxes.

Time: The fourth dimension in geology

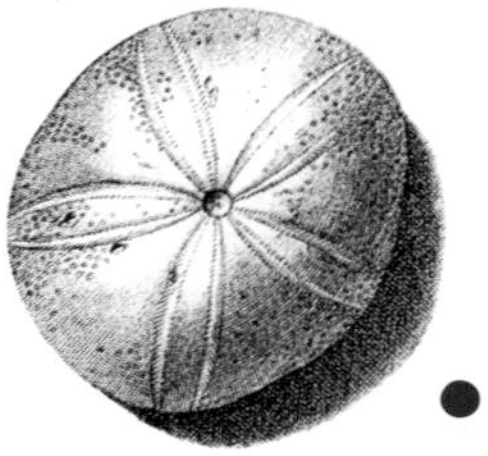

Measurements of time with which we are familiar, like hours, days, months, years, and even centuries, appear insignificant in the face of the study of the Earth's history. Geological periods are extremely long, and that is why time represents a fourth geological dimension.

Astronomical clock of Prague [AGE Fotostock]

On a human scale, we see the landscape and the geography of our planet as more or less permanent. We consider rocks to be inert elements about which, from time to time, we receive news of a landslide, an earthquake, or a volcanic eruption. The gradual elevation of a mountain range, the relentless erosion of surfaces, or the widening gap between the shores of an ocean necessarily go unnoticed, simply because they occur at a pace that only geological observation is capable of detecting. The formation of waterways requires tens and even hundreds of years, glaciation thousands, continental drift millions, and the formation of the atmosphere thousands of millions of years. The earliest *Homo sapiens* appeared about 300,000 years ago, one fifteen thousandth part of the time the Earth has existed and one fifty thousandth part of the time the Universe has existed.

From medieval times to the 19th century, there were many interpretations about the creation of the Universe that, in keeping with the Bible, attempted to explain why there were large deposits of sediments or, indeed, why there were maritime fossils in mountain environments. The resulting stories were full of supernatural disturbances and phenomena, since the whole history of the planet had to be compressed into a period of only 4,000 years.
Gradually, however, an idea began to take shape: the idea that the forces that must have acted in the ancient past were the same as those that are working today. As these forces operate very slowly, it is clear that they must have needed many millions of years to shape the morphology and structure of Earth's surface today. Thus, the time dimension acquired major importance. All in all, the central aim of geological research is to gain knowledge about the Earth's evolution from the very beginning, through a period of time that appeared to be extraordinarily long.

For several generations of geologists, biological dating was the only relative dating system available to guide them through this long period of time. The changes that had taken place as a result of biological evolution had been recorded in the fossil record pertaining to each sediment, allowing the boundaries of great periods of geological history to be established. It was not until the first third of the 20th century that radiactive dating, based on the measurement of the rates of radiactive decay of certain radioactive isotopes in rocks, allowed absolute and extremely accurate dating to be done. However, the scale of the events that these two systems are capable of dating is very different because they are founded on very different premises. The use of the two together has been compared to trying to arrange an appointment between two individuals, one of whom has a stopwatch that counts the seconds, while the other has a watch with only an hour hand.

Ammonites (*Arnioceras semicostatum*) [Sinclair Stammers - Science Photo Library / AGE Fotostock]

Geologists relate rapid processes, like eruptions or earthquakes, to the apparent movement of the Sun (daily time). For extraordinarily slow processes, like the evolution of the atmosphere, they use radioactive decay. Between them, there is the geological time scale, against which the movement of the continents, the formation of mountain ranges, the reversals of the Earth's magnetic field, the evolution of fossil species, and ice ages are recorded. On this time scale, the main points of reference are the specific rock sequences that constitute the most important record of geological history. If we study such a complex history in detail, the fluctuations in the process become apparent. Among the thousands of fluctuations that generate "background noise" (slight variations in sea level, the rate of separation between continents and the speed of erosion) we can find, although not very often, indications of great events. The trace they have left behind is, however, often very discrete when compared to the enormous consequences they must have had. Thus, such noteworthy events as the closure of the connection between the Atlantic and the Mediterranean at the end of the Miocene Epoch and its subsequent opening would have had an insignificant effect on the global cycle. Likewise, the formulation of certain hypotheses about massive extinction at the end of the Cretaceous Period arose with the discovery of some abnormally high levels of iridium in an argillaceous deposit just 0.8 in (2 cm) thick, separating the older Mesozoic from the younger Cenozoic era.

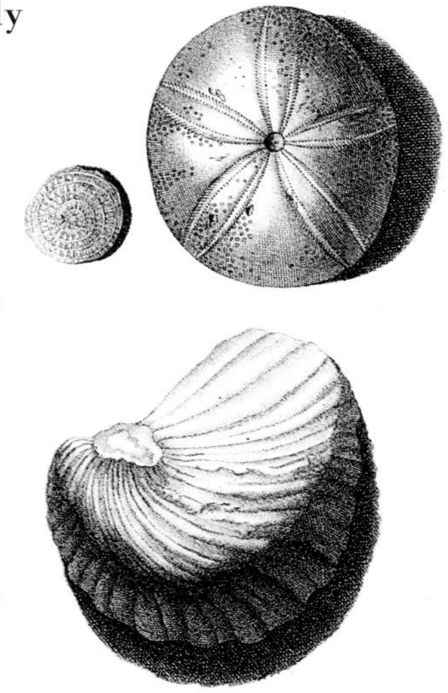

Engraving by the botanist, Antoni Josep Cavanilles [Jordi Vidal / Institut Botànic de Barcelona]

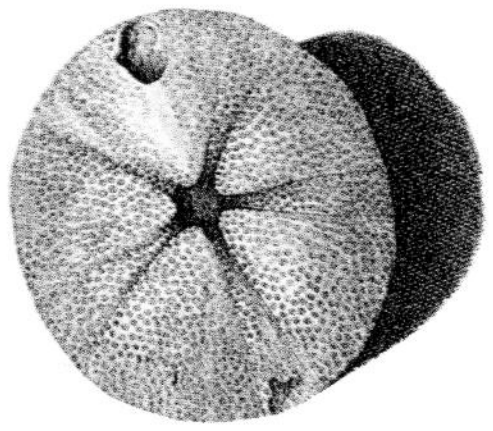

Measurement of geological time by applying different geochronological techniques (radioactive decay, fission traces, fossil corals, varves, etc.) has enabled us to move beyond simple rock dating to more accurate quantitative measurements. This has opened the doors to our understanding of vast periods of the Earth's history in which time is measured in millions of years.

1.3 The formation of the continents

The oldest lands

We know hardly anything of the distribution of land and water masses at the beginning of the biosphere's history. The oldest known sedimentary rocks, those of the *Isua Formation* in southwest Greenland and the adjacent coast of Labrador, are about 3,900 million years old, according to different methods of dating. They seem to have been deposited in shallow coastal waters. We do not, however, know if the land from which the sediments were derived was a large continent or an island, or if it was the only dry ground or if there were other areas.

The discovery of the oldest sedimentary rocks in the world in the Isua formation was followed by finds of rocks of between 3,500 and 3,800 million years old in various sites in southern Africa, North America, western Australia, Yakutskaya, India and the Antarctic but, as in the case of the Isua formation, one can only be sure the materials that formed the sediments had been deposited on a solid crust in a marine environment, that the proportion of oxygen in the atmosphere had to be low, and that the temperatures could not have been too different from today's, assuming that water existed in a liquid state. On the other hand, studies of the relative concentrations of the normal carbon isotope ^{12}C and of the non-radioactive heavy isotope ^{13}C in Late Proterozoic sediments of Spitsbergen, South Africa, and northeastern Canada indicated there was a concentration of oxygen in the atmosphere at that time that was comparable to that of the Phanerozoic age.

Other authors have suggested the hypothesis of a whole series of relatively small, discontinuous continental masses floating over the mantle all around the Earth's equator and partially covered by the waters of the oceans. Preserved Archean rocks are the remains of some of these hypothetical continental masses. On the other hand, there is no evidence of the hypothetical basaltic crust that covered the floor of the oceans. According to this hypothesis, in Archaean times, fragments of silicate scoria, lighter than the upper mantle, would have come up to the mantle's surface and, transported by drift via the mantle's convection processes, would have grouped together in ever greater "continental" masses, in a manner that reminds us of the accretional growth of planets. The oceanic crust, on the other hand, under the effects of much more vigorous mantle convection than at present, must have experienced an active

9 The Oldest sedimentary rocks in the world are found in the south east of Greenland. The study of the Isua formation, rocks some 3,900 million years old, provides us with very valuable information about the former distribution of the continents and about the deposition of the first marine sediments. This lead us to believe that the materials were deposited on a sold marine base, the proportion of oxygen in the atmosphere was low, and that the temperatures allowed water to exist in a liquid state. Some 3,800 million years ago there was already a solid crust emerging, and on top of this crust various sediments and volcanic were deposited. In addition, the atmosphere was rich in CO_2 and water vapor which moderated the global temperature. A substantial hydrosphere, which along with other heating and eroding agents, led to the production of sediments, their transport, and deposition in the sea. Some 3,800 millions years ago, the rocks were submitted to temperatures and pressures that were so high that no fossils in them remained intact. But life may have left traces in Isua: carbon, a key element of life, is abundant in some rocks and could be the result of bacterial photosynthesis. The carbon in the rocks of Isua is found in the form of graphite, which is produced when schists are submitted to high pressures and temperatures. If this graphite was related to the photosynthetic bacteria of the mires, the origins of life would be as old as the origins of the surface of the Earth. *[Photo: James L. Amos / National Geographic Society]*

10 The rocks of Oscar Range in the extreme north of Western Australia are formed by Proterozoic material. During the intense plutonic and volcanic activity that took place in the Archaean practically 60% of the continental mass of the planet was formed. These rocks, formed in the Proterozoic, which are associated with volcanic activity, provide a great deal of information when studied using palaeomagnetic orientation techniques, since in many cases they are found to be little altered. Palaeomagnetism confirms the tectonics of the plates and the reversals of polarity of the terrestrial magnetic field: the rocks which were formed in the same period have the same polarity throughout the world. *[Photo: AF Photographic Library / Zadoya]*

recycling on a small scale towards the interior of the upper mantle. This would explain why there is no trace of Archaean oceanic crust, only rocks of volcanic origin with a predominance of iron and magnesium (mafic) minerals, sometimes considerable areas of young sedimentary rocks derived from the reorganization of these volcanic rocks (greywackes or shales), mostly deposited in oceanic environments. Despite this, considerable lateral and rotational movements, which remind us of those of present-day plate tectonics, began to take place on these continental masses before the end of the Archean Period. Data collected in North America show movements of 45 degrees latitude between the end of the Archean and beginning of Proterozoic Eras.

The Proterozoic continents

With the beginning of the Proterozoic Era (nearly 3,000 million ago in southern Africa, 2,800 million in western Australia and between 2,700 and 2,600 million on the Canadian Shield), the situation changes considerably. Sixty percent of present continental mass already existed at the end of this initial period of the Proterozoic era and between 20-25% more was added, probably in the form of intrusive rocks in the mountain-forming processes which took place between 1,900 and 1,700 million years ago.

The Lower Proterozoic Era, up to some 2,000 or 1,900 million years ago, was a time of growth for the continental crust and, in particular, for the coastal shelves. Both in these and in the continental basins, an extensive record of sedimentation and volcanic activity accumulated, interrupted intermittently by fragments of basaltic dykes and by bands folded between the nuclei of the *shelves*, or *cratons*. This, and the apparent derivation of the dust which took place at this time, lead us to conclude that the processes of plate tectonics had already begun. Similarly, the first definite evidence of climatic changes also began to appear in the materials of this era (the oldest recorded glaciation). There are also signs of a rich and varied bacterial flora, and of the evolution of the atmosphere, which the action of these organisms determines.

In the Late Proterozoic Era, signs of plate tectonics almost identical to those of the present day are numerous and irrefutable, and, according to a provisional reconstruction, the distribution of continental masses 1,250 million years ago would have been not only very different from the present one, but almost the opposite, as most of the emerged lands lay in the southern hemisphere. These lands include parts of what are today Africa, Antarctica, Arabia, Central Asia, Australia, Europe, and southern China. Only part of the materials of that period preserved today in Siberia, at the extreme east of the Russian Federation and in northern

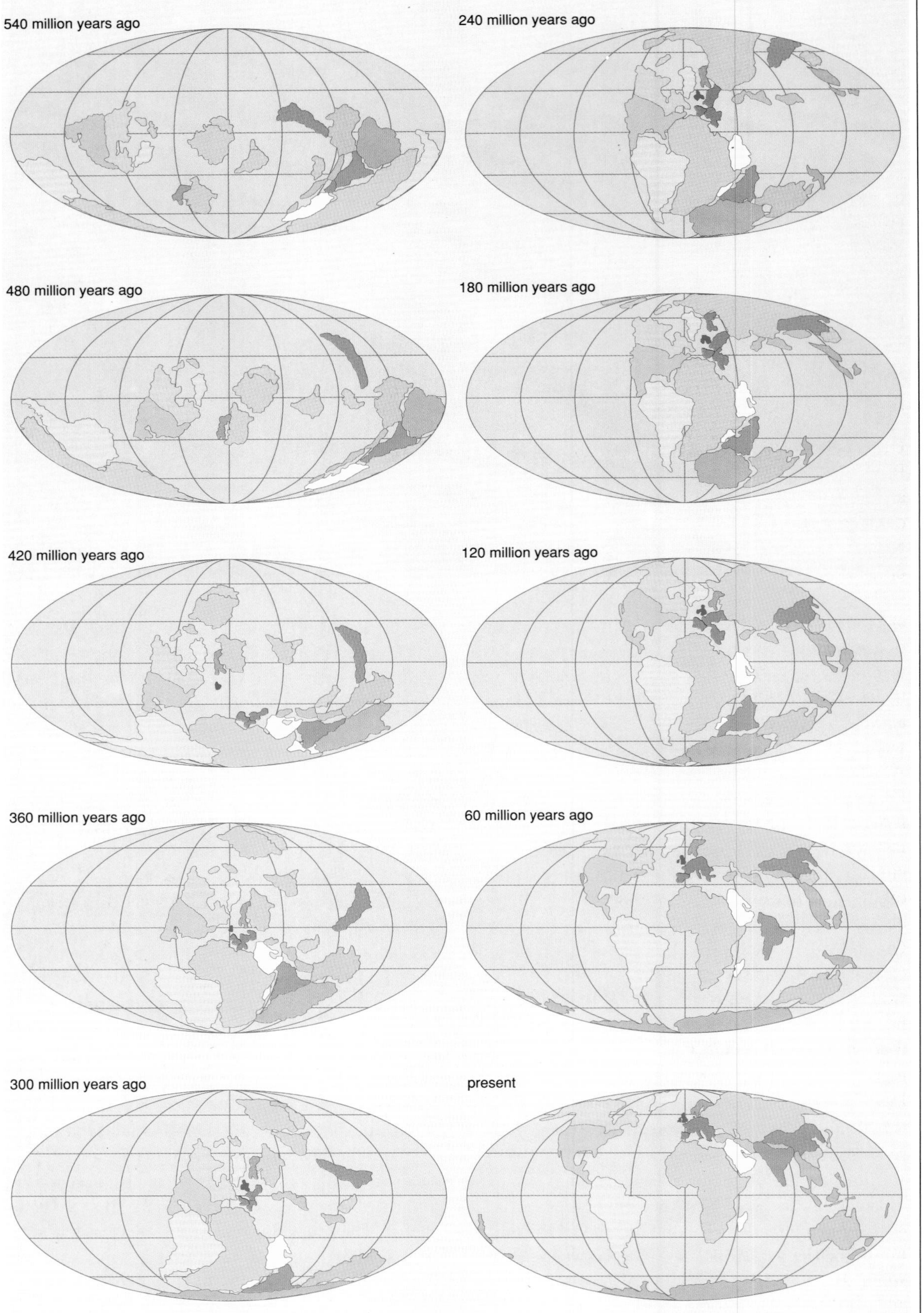

11 The movement of the lithospheric plates during the history of the Earth has shaped the continents and affected the formation of the oceans and seas which separate them. It appears that during the Upper Proterozoic the greater part of the emerged lands that comprise present day Africa, Antarctica, Arabia, central Asia, Australia, Europe and south China, were situated in the southern hemisphere. They formed a single continental mass, the first Pangaea. During the Cambrian, Pangaea was broken up and an ocean called Lapetus appeared. Towards the Ordovician, the land masses were distributed nearer the equator, in small groups, and in a large continent, Gondwana, made up of present day Africa, South America, Antarctica, Arabia, Australia and India. After the Silurian, Laurasia and Gondwana drew closer to each other until they united in a single continent, the second Pangaea. The subsequent breaking up of this continent—surrounded by a single ocean Panthalassa—together with the later formation of new oceans and the uplifting of mountain ranges, led to the arrangement of land and sea that we see today. In the Lower Jurassic, a new sea, the Tethys, began to form near the equator between the two continents, thus beginning the creation of the South Atlantic by the fragmentation of Gondwana, and the formation of the North Atlantic by the break up of Laurasia (Cretaceous). At the end of the Eocene, Antarctica separate from the other southern continents, while the collision of India with the Eurasiatic plate began; this led to the upraising of the Himalaya. During the Miocene, the coming closer of the African and Eurasiatic plates led to the beginning of the closure of the Tethys sea. *[Diagram: Editrònica, from various sources]*

China, were clearly located in the northern hemisphere, while the two parts of the American continent were practically on the equator, with the longest axes in an east-west position as opposed to the north-south position they occupy today. This southern distribution of the emerged lands would have been even more marked during the course of the Proterozoic Era, until the African plate was situated in a position not very different from the one that the Antarctic occupies today, and most of the others gathered around it, forming a single continental whole, a first Pangaea. This was different from the continent of the same name which we mentioned earlier, which was broken into fragments at the end of the Secondary Era. According to this hypothesis, that would be a second Pangaea or Pangaea II.

From the first Pangaea to Gondwana

During the Precambrian and Cambrian periods, Pangaea would have begun to break up into fragments and, between the North American-Greenland plate on one side and the north European and Siberian-Mongolian plate on the other, a new ocean would have opened up, called Iapetus. Toward the beginning of the Ordovician period (some 500 million years ago), available paleomagnetic data seem to confirm the existence of a series of small continental masses mostly distributed in latitudes close to the Equator, and a single continent of larger dimensions, somewhat to the south, but also basically equatorial. This is Gondwana, which would have encompassed what is today Africa, South America, the Antarctic, Arabia, Australia, and India. Progressive separation of the continents and new movements of most of the emerged lands toward tropical latitudes during the Cambrian period had certain climatic consequences and, very probably, could explain in part the sudden explosion of new life forms during this period, a subject to which we will return. On the other hand, from the Ordovician Period onward, a new phase of growth of the continents would have begun, in which the Iapetus ocean would have closed again and most of the emerged lands and their continental platforms would have gathered together to form just two continental masses: one—Laurasia—mainly tropical and more fragmented, and the other—Gondwana—mainly southern and subject to a glacial climate.

This was probably how the Earth's geography looked at the beginnings of the Silurian Period (some 440 million years ago). Laurasia and Gondwana, though, would have moved closer and closer to each other and, during the Permian Period (some 250 million years ago), they would have finally joined to form one large continental mass, Pangaea II, from which our present continents derive.

From the time when the heart of Pangaea II's large continental plate began to fracture and with the successive opening of new oceans and the formation of mountain ranges of the alpine cycle, the available data are much more definite, as the continental crust has not joined together again into one large plate. It seems that an arm of the sea, the Tethys, did not begin to open up again in a latitude near to the Equator, between Gondwana and Laurasia, until the Late Jurassic Period (some 200 million years ago), nor did the configuration of the coasts of the world's one existing ocean (Panthalassa) change excessively. In the same way, the formation of the whole continental crust into one plate created instability, and the mechanical forces resulting from it produced numerous fractures and rift formation processes, as well as significant seismic and volcanic activity and the individualization of small microplates at the edges of the continents. The large fractures, though, like the one that caused the opening of what is now the Atlantic ocean, did not begin until the late Jurassic period. The fragmentation of the southern continent of Gondwana reached its climax during the Cretaceous Period (some 100 million years ago). The South Atlantic had already begun to form, and the Antarctic (still attached to Australia and the extreme south of America), Australia, India, and Madagascar were then separated from southern Africa.

The break-up of Gondwana

It was not until the end of the Eocene period, some 40 million years ago, that the Antarctic separated from the other neighboring southern continents and became isolated near the South Pole. This had considerable climatic consequences, not only on a local level, but also on a global one, due to the birth of the circum-Antarctic cold ocean current. This period also saw the beginnings of the collision of India with the Euroasiatic plate, as well as the formation of the Himalayas and the Central Asian plateaus. During the Miocene period, the Tethys sea gradually became closed off through the progressive approach of and later collision between the African plate (or Afro-Arabic, bearing in mind that the continental mass included the Arabic peninsula) and the Euroasiatic one. First, the Afro-Arabic plate moved to the north-east and drew closer to the Euroasiatic one, until both continents, Afro-Arabic and Euroasiatic, became joined towards the end of the mid-Miocene period (some 12 million years ago), through a line which roughly follows the present mountain ranges of the Taurus Mountains, the Kurdistan mountains, and the

12 The Alps (above) belong to the post-Palaeozoic mountains of the modern world which were formed during the Miocene. The alpine orogenesis, (mountain building) which gave rise to most of today's south European mountain ranges, is the result of the rotation of the African plate and its collision with the European plate. At different times during the Cenozoic, the mountains of the Atlas, the Pyrenees, the Alps and their European extensions, arose, and with them the Flysch deposits, characteristic of the Alpine deformation. Later erosion gave rise to the alpine, characteristic post-tectonic sedimentary product. The most recent alpine movement dates back some five million years, and it dried out all the remaining shallow seas which remained in the European continent, including the Parisian basin, while the glaciations have given a definitive shape to the historical landscape. The opening of the Straits of Gibraltar (at the end of the Miocene, beginning of the Pliocene, some five million years ago), allowed the Mediterranean sea (above) to fill again with Atlantic water. It had dried up during the Messianian period. In effect, the climatic and geographical history of the Mediterranean is linked to the plate tectonics and climatic fluctuations of the Neogene. The coming together of Africa and Asia, together with the consolidation of the Eurasiatic microplates, had given shape to the old link of the Tethys between the Indian and Atlantic oceans. Between six and a half and six million years ago, when gradual convergence reduced the Straits of Gibraltar to their present width, the growth of the Antarctic ice had already lowered the water level below that connection. This was the cause of a series of drying out and flooding that took place between six and a half and five million years ago. *[Photo: H. Kanus/ Firo Foto / AGE Fotostock]*

Zagros range. A new rotation of the African plate and the consequent collision with Europe led to—apart from some episodes of the Alpine orogenesis (beginning of mountain formation), from which most of the mountain ranges in today's southern Europe have originated—the transformation of Tethys into a large, closed sea with only sporadic communications with other basins. This has been called Paratethys, which subsequently divided into a series of enormous inland salt lakes, from the Vienna basin to the Caspian depression, the latter being a last remnant of this southern European Miocene geography. More to the south, the complex movements of microplates between Europe and Africa opened a chain of new oceanic basins that was to shape the Mediterranean and, though only later, would connect with the Black Sea, another descendent of the old Tethys, although until the Neogene period, between 13 and 14 million years ago, it maintained sporadic communications with the Indian Ocean and with Paratethys.

Recent history

Towards the end of the Miocene age some 6 million years ago, during the so-called Messinian crisis, it appears that the Baetic and Rifian straits, which connected the western Mediterranean with the Atlantic ocean were closed from these larger bodies of water. This was a result of the new convergent movements between the African and Euroasiatic plates and the general fall in the oceans' levels, resulting from the formation of the Antarctic ice cap. The first drying up of the Mediterranean then took place.

The climatic fluctuations of the period, during the following 600,000 years, meant that periodically the Mediterranean basin partly filled and emptied, as a result of which enormous volumes of salt deposits accumulated (calculations estimate 6% of all the salts of all the oceans). Meanwhile, almost simulta-

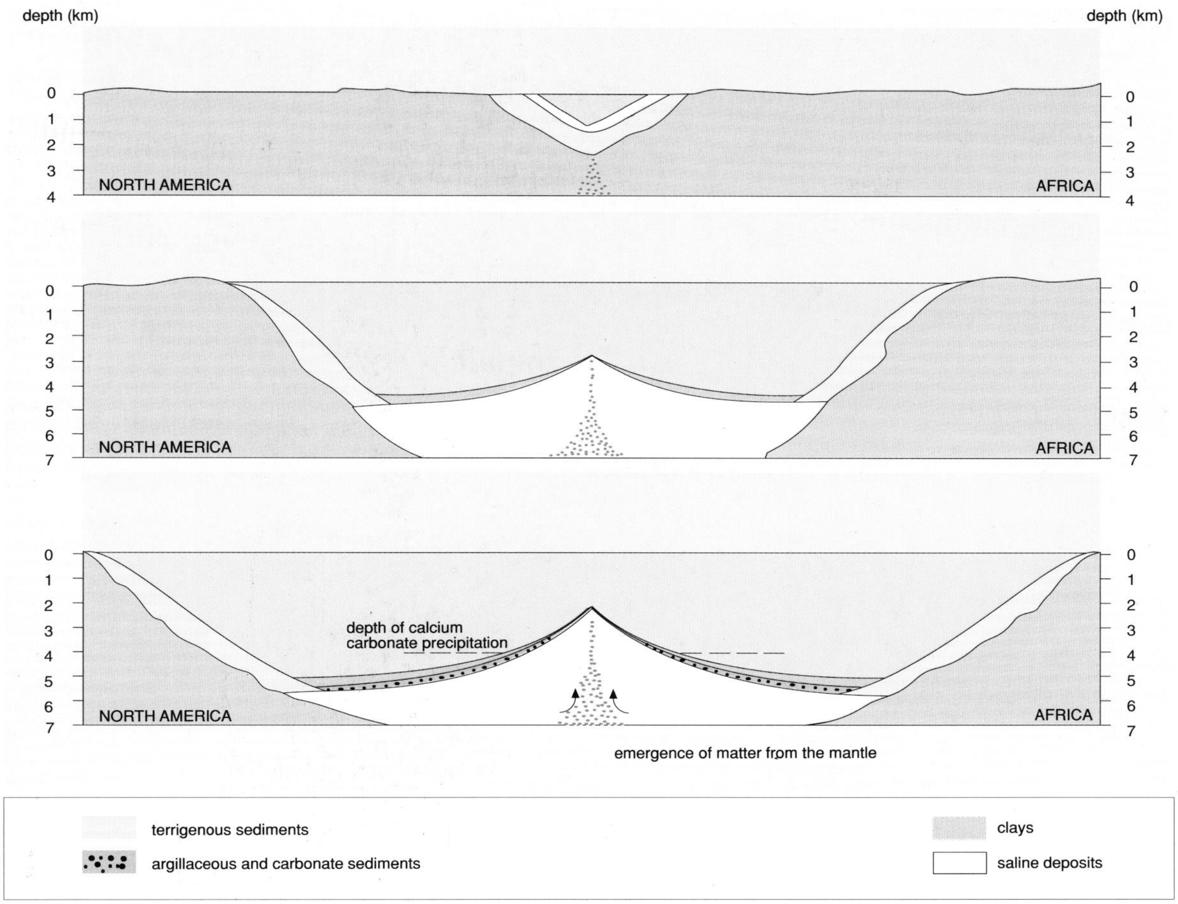

13 The widening of the ocean deeps became evident for the first time in the central ridge of the Atlantic. The North Atlantic and the South Atlantic did not open up during the same epoch, since Laurasia broke up before Gondwana. North America separated from Africa in the mid-Jurassic (about 165 million years ago), while the formation of the South Atlantic occurred 125 millions years ago. The beginning of the break up took place in circumstances like those of the present day African rift, with vulcanism, tectonic expansion and salt lakes. Saline sediments were deposited, in shallow waters, in the margins of the continents, and deposits that were rich in organic matter would later give rise to the oil fields that border the Atlantic, such as those of Venezuela or Nigeria. As the ocean deeps expanded, an accumulation of calcareous deposits was produced near the ridge and detritus near the continents, and between the two, fine materials.
[Diagram: Biopunt, from various sources]

neously, at the east of the Afro-Arabic plate, the Great Rift began to open, laying the foundations of the Red Sea.

The end of the Miocene and the beginning of the Pliocene, some five million years ago, were marked by two singular and opposite events: on the one hand, the end of the Messinian crisis with the definitive opening of the Straits of Gibraltar, leading to the last refilling of the Mediterranean sea; on the other hand, the establishment of the definitive connection between North and South America by means of the central American isthmus.

After this, the present pattern of the distribution of land and sea masses was practically complete, except for relatively small movements of tectonic plates that have been active in more recent times and, also, the growth of the oceanic crust that continues producing the large submarine ridges or present-day rift areas and subduction phenomena. In fact, if a satellite or a space ship had been able to take a picture of the Earth from space two million years ago, just before the ice age, we would not observe many differences from a similar picture taken today.

1.4 The crust of the ocean floors

The ocean floors that exist today are, for the most part, relatively recent and have their origin in the axes of the mid-oceanic ridges, the margins between the tectonic plates in which new crust is formed. We have already indicated that these boundaries are divergent and that their edges are moving away from each other. They are doing so at a rate of only about an inch (a few centimeters) per year, but this separation is sufficient to produce a reduction in the pressure of the mantle lying underneath, in such a way that part of this relatively fluid upper mantle can push its way up to the surface in the form of basaltic magma.

Oceanic ridges

Most geologists accept that molten magma accumulates in magmatic chambers at the base of the crust, where the different fractions become separated. One part is crystallized and goes to make up the rocks at the crust's base: peridotites (olivine-type rocks) under the Moho discontinuity and gabbro (a more granular version of peridotites) above it. Another part remains molten and rises as far as the surface at some point along the 37,000 mi (60,000 km) of oceanic ridges

14 The ridges of the ocean deeps bring material from the mantle to the Earth's crust. The proof that the oceanic basin is refilling is found when we study the age of the rocks that make up the crust: they are always younger than the rocks found near the marine ridges, and much older than those that are further distant, especially those found in subduction zones, that is, where the crustal material returns to the Earth's mantle. The movement of materials ensures that the bottom of the ocean is always moving, albeit very slowly on a human time scale. Further proof that the continents are in motion comes from palaeontology. *[Photo: J. Edmond / MIT]*

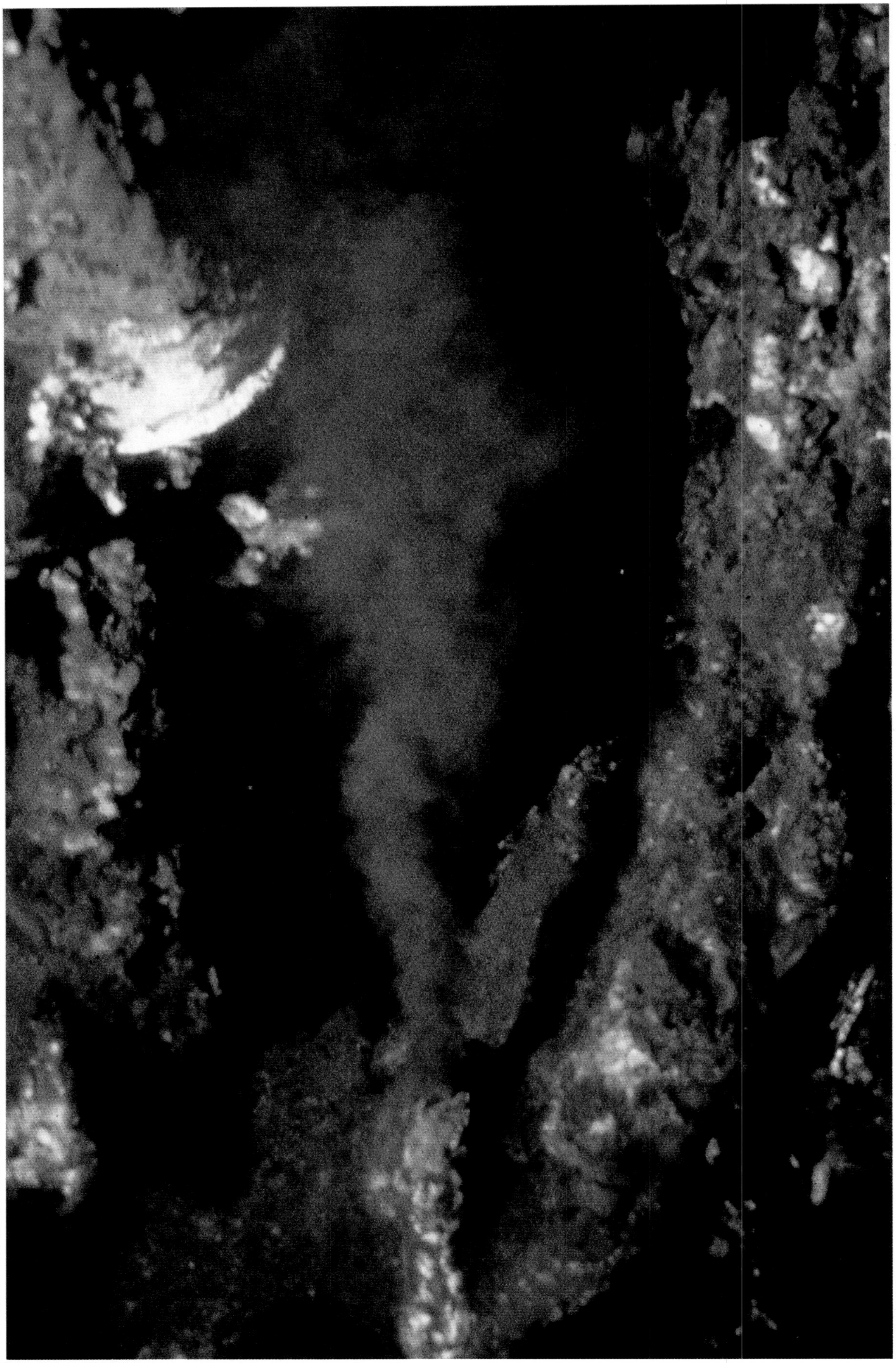

in the form of basaltic lava, sliding through the ridges' slopes and solidifying there in the form of laminar basaltic outflows or pillow lavas. As the divergence of the plates does not stop, the formation of magmatic chambers and the incorporation of new extrusive material is constant. The tension caused by the continuous movement of the plates can lead to the formation of fissures and faults parallel to the axis of the ridge's crest, in the materials that have already been produced by the newly formed crust. This can also cause the formation of transform faults, which, in order to adapt to the geometry of the Earth's surface, adopt the same movements as plates that, once solidified, would otherwise be too rigid to move on an almost spherical surface.

Sea water penetrates the cracks and fissures produced by these tensions and by the cooling of the magmas, making the crust grow. Sea water below the crust is heated, dissolving the soluble compounds that may exist in the rock through which it. Once heated, it then returns to the surface, bearing materials extracted from the rock, in particular metallic ions, and is expelled through chimneys near the ridge. These outlets are a peculiar habitat in which, despite the lack of sunlight, communities of organisms (only discovered in 1977) prosper, and where the primary producers are not plants but chemo-autotrophic bacteria.

Subduction of the oceanic plates

As the oceanic crust moves away from the ridge, it cools and contracts. In this way it increases its density and, as it floats on the asthenosphere, this increase in density means that the crust sinks; the older the oceanic plate, the more it sinks. During its growth process, the oceanic crust—given that the Earth's volume has to remain relatively constant—sooner or later meets another plate, which can be either continental or oceanic. Since, as we have already said, the deformation possibilities of the plates are small, the only mechanism that allows the Earth to maintain a relatively constant volume is subduction of one of the colliding plates' mantles under another. If the expanding oceanic plate collides with a continental plate, which is thicker and denser, the subduction is always of the oceanic plate below the continental one.

Subduction is a complex phenomenon and is of great importance in the shaping of the Earth's surface. We find seismic, volcanic, and orogenic (mountain-forming) phenomena in subduction zones. Along the boundary where subduction takes place, oceanic trenches and arcs of islands form. Earthquakes and volcanoes are frequent phenomena in these areas, as is the case along the northern and eastern Pacific coasts, from the Aleutian Islands to New Zealand, through the Kuril Islands, Japan, the Ryukyu Islands, Taiwan, the Philipines, the Moluccas, New Guinea, and the Melanesian and western Polynesian archipelagoes. In fact, earthquakes with a focus deeper than 60 mi (100 km) only occur in subduction zones. This appears to be the case because only there do the subducted lithospheric plates enter the asthenosphere in a substantial way and reach depths of up to 400 mi (700 km). Both the shifting of the subducted oceanic plate, with the continental plate lying on top, and the penetration within the asthenosphere take place through an enormous concentration of mechanical forces that result in either in new fractures or in movements along some of the old ones, triggering seismic waves at very great depths.

In the course of subduction, the temperatures in the zones of contact between plates increase considerably. The subducted oceanic crust has accumulated water throughout its long trajectory from the axis of the oceanic crest where it started, and its materials are subjected to ever higher temperatures. This water tends to help in the crust's fusion, first in the subducted plate and later, when it has partially migrated to the plate lying on top, on this one. This explains the substantial presence of volcanic activity in the areas of subduction mentioned above, often associated with the formation of mineralogical deposits that are a result of the selective concentration of certain chemical elements in the crust, facilitated by the migration of water from the great depth to which subduction has transported it.

1.5 The current configuration of the emerged lands

The convergent boundaries, whether there are subduction processes like the ones we have just described or collision processes between two continental plates, are precisely the places where processes of orogenesis, or the formation of mountains, take place. The characteristics of the orogens differ from one case to another, and the collision is often preceded by subduction. If this is the case, characteristic structures from one and the other situation are combined in the orogens. The orogenesis of the Andes, for example, has come about through a subduction process, while that of the Himalayas, the Alps, or the Pyrenees have come about through collision processes.

15 In the collision of the Indian plate with Asia, the northern edge of the former stayed below the Asiatic plate, which led to the uplift of the Himalaya. The process of building this mountain chain began some 150 million years ago, when a large mass of land (the plate that supported the continent that today we call India), was displaced to the north and collided with the southern part of another continental mass: Eurasia. The collision ended some 60 million years ago; traces of the titanic movement remain in the oceanic zones nearest the continent. *[Diagram: Biopunt, from various sources]*

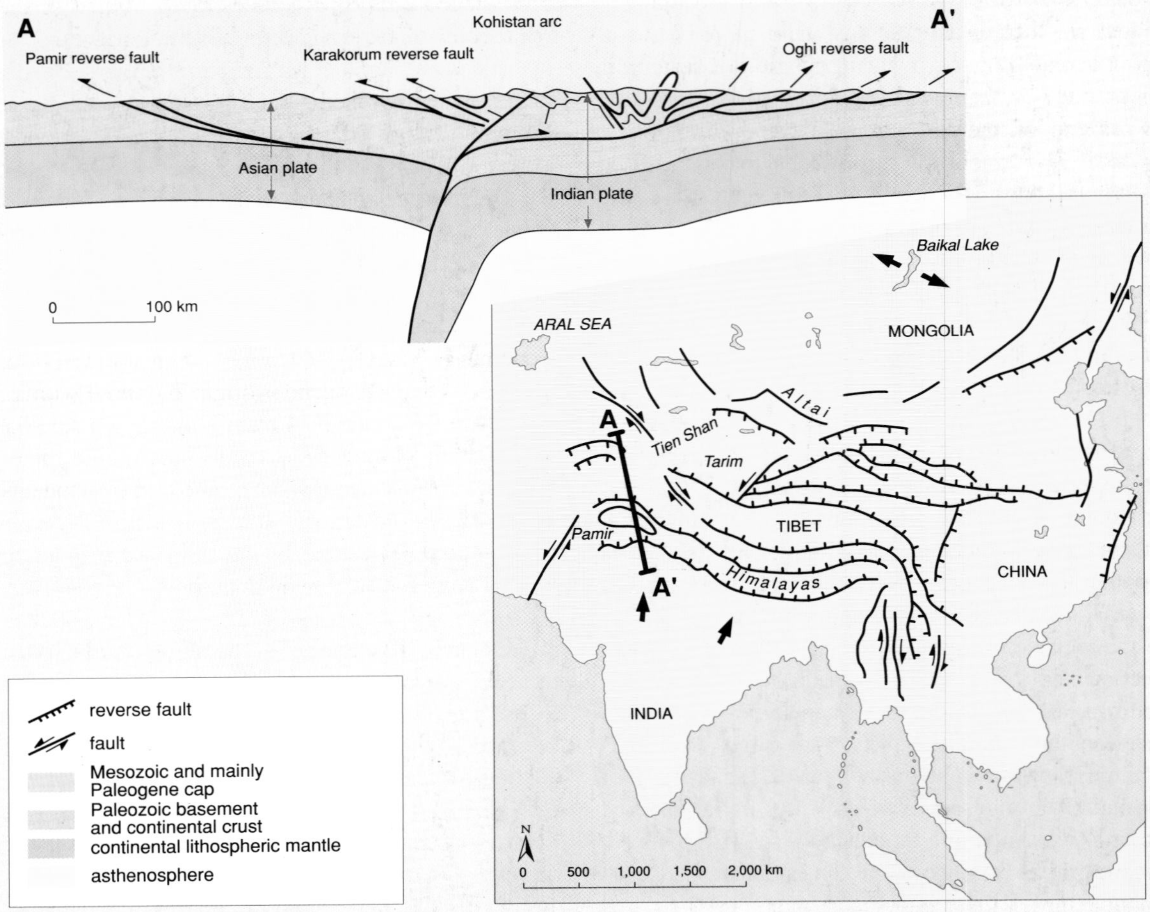

Mountains that grow and basins that fill

Orogenic processes

We have already referred to the characteristics of subduction processes (volcanoes, deep seismic activity). These always produce chains of mountains, such as the Andes or Sierra Madre mountain ranges or the Rocky Mountains (which are known as *cordillera* type mountains). They also product strings of island arcs, typical examples of which are the islands of Japan or Indonesia, with altitudes of nearly 13,000 ft (4,000 m) [Mount Fuji, on Honshu, Japan, 12,388 ft (3,776 m); Kerinci, on Sumatra, 12,483 ft (3,805 m)], all of which have many volcanoes on their highest peaks.

In the case of collision processes, the materials of the two plates involved are both parts of the continental crust. Therefore, as they are lighter, they cannot be dragged up to the asthenosphere as happens with oceanic crust plates in subduction processes. From this we get an ever more complex structure of the orogen, with the successive production of layers as well as a considerable thickening of the continental crust in a fairly broad zone (of the order of tens to hundreds of miles) all along the collision front. On the other hand, as the deformation continues to expand on both sides of the collision front, and fractures and the overlapping of the layers become generalized, the boundary between the two initial plates becomes differentiated on a wider front between the numerous compartments that are shaped through fracture phenomena. These continue to settle, converge, and slide laterally against each other. The front becomes an ever broader band with intense seismic activity that can exceed 60 mi (100 km) on both sides of the initial collision front. The most striking example of this is the Tibetian-Himalayian group of mountains, at the contact point between the Eurasiatic plate and India. Another example is the contact point between the African and Euroasiatic plates in the Mediterranean region, with its group of mountain ranges including, in particular, the Alps, and which is complicated even further by the fact that between these two plates, territories corresponding to old intermediate microplates are interwoven.

Erosion and sedimentation

When we look at the Earth's relief as it is today, apart from the history of the formation of structural units, both on the scale of the fundamental tectonic plates and on the level of the structures resulting from their interactions, we must bear in mind how these structures have come about through erosion processes and the filling of depressed areas with sediments. Each physiographical unit is the result of a particular geological history, and is characterized by a particular series of rocks, a characteristic structure and shape which are the result of a succession of old and recent geomorphological processes.

In general terms, we could say that the morphology of the relief, which is the result of tectonic processes, is slowly though unequally modified, depending on the sites and the characteristics of the surface rocks, through the action of atmospheric agents and living organisms. The disintegrated fragmentary materials of the rock are transported to depressions, where they become sediments. On a geological time scale, these sedimentary materials can later become involved in orogenic movements, which then place them once again in high reliefs shaped in turn by erosive agents as part of a huge recycling process. In fact, today, around two thirds of continental surface rocks are of recent origin, in other words sedimentary, and only about a third of the continental surface contains rocks which are a direct result of old tectonic processes—the so-called *cratons* or *shields*, which make up the oldest cores of the emerged continental masses.

The processes involved in this recycling of continental materials include erosion, transport, and sedimentation, as well as the processes of metamorphosis of sediments deposited in large trenches and subjected to high temperatures and pressures, transportation of continental materials trapped in collision processes between continental plates toward the mantle, or occasional contributions from the mantle through volcanic phenomena. There is a close relationship between processes with an exogenous origin and those with an endogenous origin in the formation of the continental crust. This mixture of two types of processes suggests there are two basic components. The first components are sediments whose chemical composition is the result of complex erosion processes and of a filtering process between the different chemical elements, using water—both a corrosive and separating agent—as a medium. The second components are magmatic products coming from the mantle, which produce basaltic-type material. The whole can be altered, eroded, sifted, and transported, giving rise to sediments that can produce intrusions of magmatic rock, and the cycle can repeat over and over again. Out of this alliance between sediments, product of water and of sky, of magmas, and of internal fire was borne the continental Earth, from which life arose. An example of ancient Sumerian mythologies revisited!

16 The Grand Canyon is a pass excavated out of sedimentary materials by the Colorado river in the State of Arizona. It is 217 mi (350 km) long and from 4-18 mi (6-29 km) wide, with blocks from 2,297-5,577 ft (700-1,700 m) high. It was declared a National Park in 1919, with an area of 1,007 mi^2 (2,610 km^2). In the region between the Grand Canyon and the valley of the Rio Verde, the history of the earth can be contemplated on a gigantic scale: its walls present the oldest rocks —Archaeozoic, Proterozoic and Palaeozoic, and in them the remains of amphibians and reptiles, primitive fish, trilobites, brachiopods and many other fossils can be found.
[Photo: A. Tovy / Index]

Rocks with fossil remains and sediments

Scenes in England by Isaac Taylor (1882) [Ann Ronan at Image Select]

All rocks, because they are the product of a process, carry information about their genesis. They contain physical, chemical, and geological information, as well as biological information. In fact some rocks contain remains of ancient living organisms. Sometimes these rocks are nothing less than a compact amalgam of such remains.

and consequent binding together of larger ones) gives rise to sedimentary rock. Paleontology looks to sedimentary rocks for signs of previous life that developed, like the sedimentary processes themselves, in the uppermost layer of the Earth's crust. Whole individuals, fragments of bones, twigs and shells, leaves and grains of pollen, coprolites (fossil excrement) and footprints are the very scarce remnants of past biospheres, of life trapped in strata. However, if the rocks that contain these fossils are subjected to a fairly high degree of metamorphism (through pressure and/or temperature), the information becomes blurred, gradually distorted, and finally lost.

The study of a rock with small cavities and very small crystals, just formed, provides us with information about the rock's magmatic origin. This also tells us that the rock had a rapid cooling-down period, which probably occurred on the outside of the Earth's crust. The presence of large, well-formed crystals fitted into each other, on the other hand, shows that there was freedom of molecular movement (of probable magmatic origin) and a slow decrease in the energy that made the arrangement possible (internal cooling down). Parallel to this, the study of exogenous rocks, formed on the surface as a result of processes employing solar energy, allow us to discover the traces of the processes by which they originated. These are sedimentary processes which, as if there had been a rain of fragmented rocks, wash down sediments into the basins as they run out of energy. The lithification (changing into stone) of incoherent sediments (decrease of porosity, loss of water by compression, precipitation of soluble substances,

Dolichopod (long-legged) fly preserved in amber
[Gunter Ziesler / Bruce Coleman Limited]

The fossilization of an organism or its remains requires a quick burial in a finely grained sediment (sand, silt, clay, fine volcanic ash, etc.) to protect it from erosion, oxygen, and aerobic bacteria. Aquatic environments, which act as deposit basins for land environments, are best for fossiliztion. That is why the most abundant and well-preserved fossils are of sea and lake origin. Decomposition by other organisms and microorganisms, on the other hand, makes preservation unlikely in land environments. Only the driest and coldest environments, those which are most hostile to life, offer good preservation opportunities, whether mummification in deserts and steppes or freezing in ice. Apart from these physical requirements, some special chemical conditions are necessary to allow the replacement or substitution of organic molecules by mineral compounds.

When the organism already contains mineral matter, preservation is very simple, so long as the circulation of water through the pores is minimal. Silicified trunks or carbonized organic matter are examples of fossilization through chemical change. Molds, or impressions, whether external or internal, are also considered to be fossils of an organism and, as such, are examples of indirect preservation. In exceptional cases, preservation may even extend to the "soft parts" of an organism: leaves and insects in amber, bacteria and cyanophyta in silica nodules, entire woolly rhinoceroses in ice, and various animals in tar or mummified in desert environments. Fossil traces of the presence of organisms can also be found—their habitats and movements (worm borings, mollusc tracks), regurgitated or defecated (coprolitic) remains, eggs, etc. These indirect samples preserved between the strata are generically called *ichnofossils*.

The spores of cryptogams and the pollen of phanerogams form a special case among fossilized remains. The resistance offered by their walls has favored good preservation, allowing their structures and fine internal sculpturing to be studied and allowing the organisms to be classified into different families and genera. In such a way, correlations between the sediments can be obtained, and attempts to reconstruct—if only in a very fragmentary way—the vegetation of the past can be made.

Fossil fern (*Pecopteris unita*) [Jordi Vidal / ECSA]

Fossil fern (*Pecopteris polymorpha*) [Jordi Vidal / ECSA]

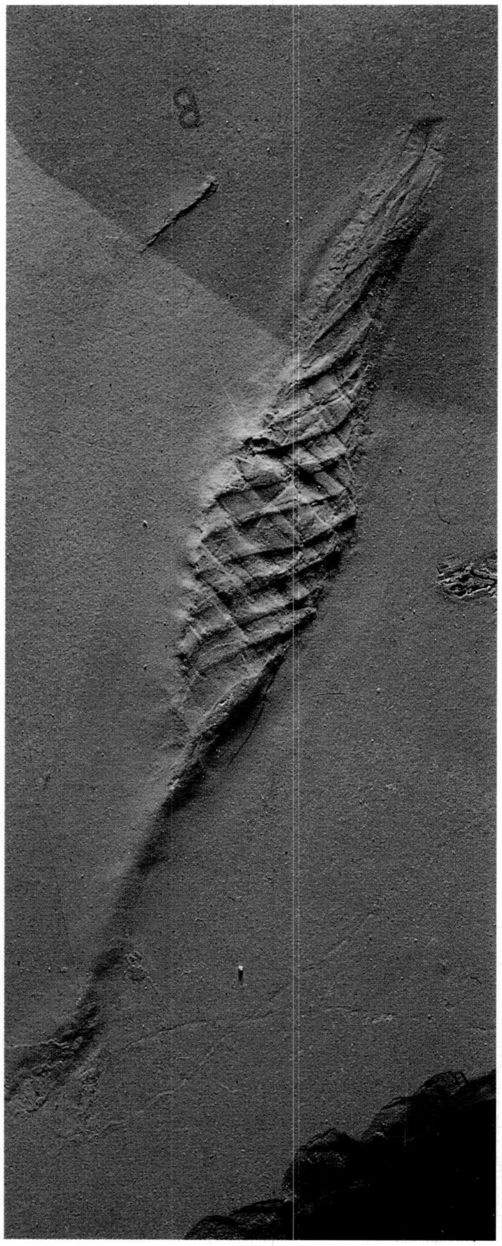

Egg case of selachian [Jordi Vidal / ECSA]

The study of marine and lake sediments shows their changes throughout history. The filling of pools, which normally happens at a rate of 0.2 mm per year on average, limits the record to relatively short periods. Thus, the majority of lake systems in northern temperate zones is very recent. Their sediments only record the last 10,000 years of history. Only very old lakes, located in tectonic subsidence basins like the Miocene Period lake in Cerdanya (Pyrenees) or lake Biwa (Japan), allow a careful search to be made for taphocoenoses (subterranean communities) up to several million years old. It is worth noting, however, that sediment is always a very incomplete archive that includes just that fraction of the initial community that managed to pass through the filter of preservation. Lakes act as collectors for pollen (and microspores in general) from the surrounding vegetation. In such a way, high levels of grass and amaranthaceous pollen, as well as an increase in fine matter and signs of eutrophication, can be interpreted as unmistakable signs of human presence.

Advances in paleontological knowledge played an important role in the development of the geologic discipline of stratigraphy. In 1830, Charles Lyell established an initial relationship between the strata and fossils found in them. The fossils appeared in an orderly fashion within the stratigraphical sequence, and they followed one another in a very strict way in accordance with the principle of superimposition. Each unit was identifiable through its characteristic assemblage of fossils. Some "key" fossils were selected and used to compare the relative ages of the strata, allowing chronostratigraphical units to be established within a general scale of time units. The massive extinctions that could be seen among the strata, as well as other quite remarkable changes, were useful in outlining the limits of great periods in geological history.

Fossils have also helped to confirm the plate tectonics theory, as the same plant and vertebrate fossils can be found in continents that are currently separated. The fossil record has therefore allowed us to get closer to the origins of life and follow its course of evolution. By going back in time, major changes can be found in some groups, while others remain virtually unchanged. That is why some of today's species have been called "living fossils," because of their close relationship to extinct groups. Examples are for such noteworthy species as the ginkgo (*Ginkgo biloba*), a Chinese tree that existed during the Carboniferous Period, or the coelacanth (*Latimeria chalumnae*), a fish that was thought to have disappeared during the Cretaceous Period but is today confined to the waters of the Comoros.

Trilobites (*Phacobs potieri*) [Jordi Vidal / MGB]

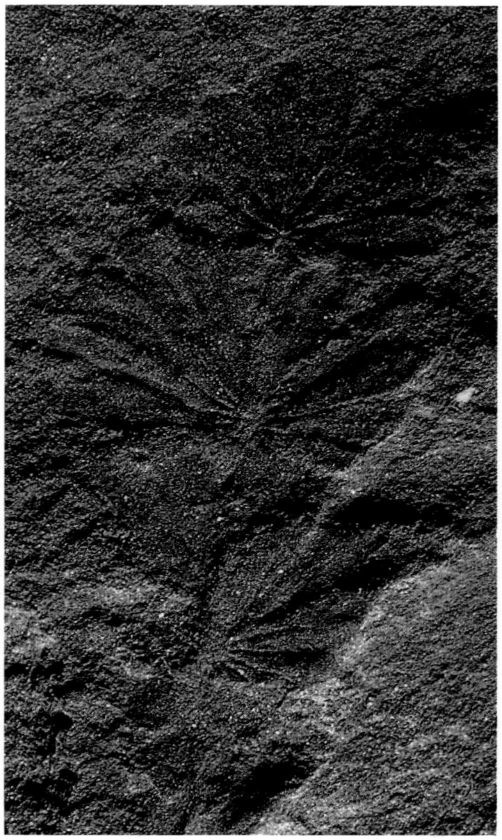

Fossil horsetail (*Annularia sphenophylloidea*) [Jordi Vidal / ECSA]

Fossil fish (*Diplomystus*) [Martin Land -Science Photo Library / AGE Fotostock]

17 Before the Cretaceous, some 140 million years ago, the coasts of County Kerry, in the south-west of Ireland (the westernmost projection of the Eurasian continent) were joined to the present day east coasts of North America. In both zones coastal lowlands and low gentle hills have been formed; in these areas agriculture is well developed because of the fertile soils and their ease of cultivation. Also in these low coastal zones, Artesian wells can be sunk because the rainwater penetrates through them. *[Photo: Photothèque Stone International]*

The emerged continental masses

At a global level, in the course of the Earth's history, the continents have increased in surface area and volume. Continental growth began some 4,000 million years ago, the age of the oldest continents, and remained constant until some 1,000 million years ago. Around that date, growth slowed until 500 million years ago, when it reached a virtually stationary state, in which any increase in the continents' mass was more or less compensated by the destruction and transport to the mantle of an equivalent mass. The present distribution of continents and oceans on our planet represents a remarkable asymmetry on either side of the equator. While in the northern hemisphere, emerged lands predominate over the seas (although the northern polar cap is occupied by an oceanic basin), to the south of the equator oceans predominate, even though the polar cap here is occupied by a continent, the Antarctic. A "continental" northern hemisphere can thus be contrasted with an "oceanic" southern hemisphere.

The northern hemisphere

To the north of the equator we find Eurasia, North and Central America, the two northern thirds of Africa, the northern part of South America, and several large islands or archipelagoes, among which the most important are Greenland and Iceland, the Canadian, Norwegian (Svalbard, Jan Mayen), and Russian Arctic archipelagoes, the island arcs which, from the Aleutian Islands to the Moluccas, follow the western Pacific coasts (the Kuril Islands, the Japanese archipelago, the Ryukyu Islands, Taiwan, the Mariana Islands, the Philipines and Palau), Hawaii and the Micronesian archipelagoes, to the center of the Pacific, Newfoundland, the British Isles, the Faroe Islands, the Bermudas, the Antilles, and Macaronesian archipelagoes in the Atlantic, the islands of the Mediterranean and Socotra, Sri Lanka and the archipelagoes of the northern Indian Ocean (the Laquedives, Maldives, Andaman and Nicobar Islands). In the East Indies, Borneo, Celebes, and Sumatra straddle the equator, with their northern part in the northern hemisphere.

The Eurasiatic continent

Eurasia, with more than 20 million sq mi (52 million sq km), is the Earth's largest continental mass. At 43 degrees latitude, between the Galician Costa da Morte (9ºW longitude) and the coast of the Russian region of Primorsky (135ºE), it measures more than 7,000 mi (11,000 km) from west to east. In the Arctic Circle more than 5,000 mi (8,000 km) separate the Norwegian coast (13 degrees E) and the Chukchi peninsula, near the Bering Strait (190 degrees E). The greatest distance between north and south is the 5,300 mi (8,500 km) around longitude 104 degrees E, between the Taymyr Peninsula, in northern Siberia (77 degrees N near Cape Chelyuskin) and the Malacca Peninsula (between 1 and 2 degrees N on the coast of the Strait of Singapore). The greater part of the present surface of Eurasia was the largest fragment of the old continent of Laurasia, from which, as we have seen, northern America became separated in the Cretaceous period, with the opening of the northern Atlantic basin.

Similarly in the south, a part of the Mediterranean region, the Arabian peninsula, and the Indian and Iranian plains have become incorporated into Eurasia in more recent times (after the opening of the North Atlantic). These were part of the old southern continent of Gondwana that, in its contacts with the initial Eurasiatic continental mass, formed powerful orogens, from the Baetic mountains in the south of the Iberian Peninsula to as far as the Himalayan regions, which are still characterized today by considerable seismic activity. Other Eurasiatic orogens also correspond to fusions (older in this case) between great blocks of lithosphere (the solid rock of the Earth) that have gone to make up the present extensive Euroasiatic block: the Urals, between Europe and Siberia; the Verkhoyansk mountain range, between Siberia and the Kolyma block; the Altai mountains, the Sayan mountains and Yablonovy between Siberia and the Tarim and Sino-Korean blocks; the Yunnan and Guizhou plateaus and the border mountains between Tonkin and Guangxi Zhuang, on the boundary between the Chang Yiang (Yangtze) block and that of South East Asia, etc. From Kamchatka to Borneo and the Molucca Islands, the garlands of volcanically and seismically active island arcs, which follow the eastern edge of Eurasia, are an indication of the subduction of the Pacific plate under the Eurasiatic plate.

North America

The other large continental unit of the northern hemisphere, basically consisting of the rest of the divided continent of Laurasia, is North America, measuring more than 9 million sq mi (24 million sq km) in area if we include Greenland, the Canadian Arctic archipelago, central America, and the Antilles. Its largest east-west dimension, some 3,000 mi (5,000 km), is around 52 degrees N latitude between the coast of the Labrador Peninsula (56°W) and the British Colombian coast (128°W). However, the continent sharpens considerably towards the south, and at the latitude of the mouth of the River Grande (25°N), it hardly exceeds 750 mi (1,200 km). Leaving Central America, east of the Isthmus of Tehuantepec, the maximum dimension of North America in a north-south direction—more than 3,700 mi (6,000 km)—lies between 95-97 degrees W, between the northern extreme of the Boothia Peninsular, Canada, at 72 degrees latitude north, and the southern coast of the Mexican state of Oaxaca, at 16°N. At the western edge of the continent, the subduction of the Pacific plate pushed up a major mountain range, which over the last 200 million years has been joined, from the mouth of the River Mackenzie to the western Sierra Madre, by a series of large blocks of lithosphere (lithospheroclasts). Their origin is still being discussed, but they were far from what was the western coast of Laurasia when the North Atlantic opened up. These additional blocks—there are more than a hundred of them—are different from the neighboring rocks of the old North American shield because of their geological characteristics, the fossils that they contain, and their palaeomagnetic properties. During the last 200 million years, they have completed the complex relief of the western façade of North America. Even today, a part of this western façade, to be more precise the Lower California Peninsula and the part of California situated to the west of the San Andreas fault, is sliding northwards at a speed of some 2 in (5 cm) per year in relation to the rest of the continent. This piece was the last of these lithospheroclasts to join the continent, and is in fact still attached to the neighboring Pacific Ocean plate.

The Meso-American isthmus

At the southern extreme of North America there is a tectonically complex area that is also very active volcanically and seismically. It includes Central America and the Antilles, as well as the Caribbean shore of South America. Central America's narrow stretch of land, which goes from the Mexican states of Oaxaca and Veracruz to the Columbian and Panamanian confines of Darién and which, in some areas, is less than 60 mi (100 km) wide and only over 310 mi (500 km) in a few places, is the result of the subduction of the Cocos plate under the Caribbean plate, and the southern end of the North American plate. The Antilles themselves, in particular the Virgin Islands and Trinidad and Tobago, are another arc of islands which are characteristic of the boundaries between plates.

The southern hemisphere

Straddling the equator, South America and Africa are the two largest fragments of the old continent of Gondwana. Since the collision between the African and Euroasiatic plates, which led to the formation of all the Alpine chains and the opening of the Atlantic, Africa has remained much more tied to Eurasia, to the point that many old geography books juxtaposed an Old Continent (or Old World) which encompassed Europe (which can only be considered a separate continent because of the Eurocentrism of its inhabitants), Asia, and Africa, with a New Continent (or New World) comprising the Americas, along with a Very New Continent that was Australia. We have already noted that oceans dominate the southern hemisphere. Apart from the southern parts of Africa and South America, the only two continents that are entirely in the south are Australia and Antarctica, both isolated in the midst of wide expanses of ocean. Both resulted from the fragmentation of the old southern continent of Gondwana and initially, at the beginning of the

18 In the frontier between Brazil, Argentina, and Paraguay, in the southern limits of the pre-Cambrian Brazilian shield, the river Iguazú falls in spectacular cascades down to the lowlands of the Paraná valley. The waterfalls, the highest of which is that of Santa Marta, with a drop of 230 ft (70 m), forms an immense amphitheatre of 2 mi (3 km) in circumference called the Iguazú falls. This river which rises in the Serra do Mar, a few from the Atlantic, describes a large number of meanders which snake their way through the araucaria woods of southern Brazil.
[Photo: R. Koskas / Photothèque Stone International]

Cretaceous Period, they separated off together from Africa and India, remaining together until the beginnings of the Cenozoic Period.

The African continent

Africa, with an area of just under 12 million sq mi (30 million sq km), stretches nearly 5,000 mi (8,000 km) from north to south, from the northern coasts of Tunisia to the southern coasts of South Africa, and its maximum width from west to east is a similar distance, from the coasts of Senengambia to the coasts of Somalia. Of all the continents, Africa is the most compact and with the most articulated coasts. It has not received accretions of alien lithospheric blocks; rather, many important blocks have separated from it, like India, Arabia, or Madagascar. Madagascar split from the African continent in the Cenozoic Period and is today separated from the African coast by the more than 250 mi (400 km) of the Mozambique channel. The Earth's most important continental rift phenomenon is still evident today in the heart of the African continent, which will inevitably lead, in a few million years, to the splitting up of Africa along the Rift Valley, from Djibouti to the lower Zambezi, into two completely separate continental masses divided by a new oceanic crust (and the probable union of the greater part with Eurasia with more extensive continental bridges than today's). The highest reliefs are situated in the north, on the boundary with the Euroasiatic plate (Atlas) and at the edges of the Great Rift (Ethiopian Highlands, Uhuru, Ruwenzori Mountains). However, on the whole, highlands dominate, with extensive plateaus between 650 and 3,000 ft (200 and 1,000 m) high. The only lowlands are the coastal plains and a part of the Sahara.

South America

South America, with more than 7 million sq mi (18 million sq km), is a more pointed continental mass in the north-south direction. More of it lies in the southern hemisphere than does Africa. If we limit ourselves strictly to the continent, disregarding the large southern island of Tierra del Fuego and the archipelagoes which surround it, South America stretches nearly 4,700 mi (7,500 km) between its northernmost point, Punta Gallinas, on the Guajira Peninsula near the border between Columbia and Venezuela, situated at 21 degrees N, and its southernmost point, Cape San Isidro, on the Chilean peninsula of Brunswick, on the northern coast of the Strait of Magellan, which almost reaches 54 degrees S (the latitude of Liverpool, Hamburg, or Minsk in the northern hemisphere). Cape Horn, on the island of the same name, lies two degrees further south (approximately the latitude of Edinburgh, Copenhagen or Moscow). Its maximum east-west dimension is of some 3,000 mi (5,000 km) between the north coast of Peru (Punta Pariñas, in the Piura area at 81 degrees longitude W) and the coast of the Brazilian states of Paraíba and Pernambuco (Cape Branco, in Paraíba, touching 35 degrees longitude W) and is situated between six and seven degrees latitude S. Like Africa, from which it became separated in the Cretaceous Period, South America is mostly made up of a shield of Pre-Cambrian materials that was part of the old southern continent of Gondwana, but its western edge is affected by the collision with the Pacific plate and the subduction of this under the South American plate. A result of this is the colossal Andes mountain range. Between this mountain range and the plains of Guyana and Brazil, and the sierras of the Venezuelan Caribbean coast, there are extensive areas of lowlands and plains that stretch from the Venezuelan and Columbian llanos in the north to Patagonia in the south.

The Antarctic

The Antarctic is the larger of the two southern hemisphere continents, and is situated on the southern polar cap. Except in a few areas (the northernmost point of the Antarctic Peninsula between 54 and 66 degrees W; small sectors of the Terre Adélie, Wilkes Land, and Queen Mary Land between 90 and 140 degrees E; and the shore line of the Napier Mountains in Enderby Land, between 50 and 60 degrees E), it extends no further north than the Antarctic Polar Circle. The continent has two very distinct parts: Greater Antarctica and Lesser Antarctica, separated by the narrowing of the lands between the Ross Sea and the Weddell Sea, following the southernmost section of the Transantarctic mountain range and which, in its narrowest sector, between the Gould Coast and Edith Ronne Land, can hardly exceed 620 mi (1,000 km) of continental land. In any event, the large ice shelves that occupy the coastal areas of these seas and the continental ice of the region do not allow us to make more than approximate measurements. Roughly speaking, we could say that the two sectors of the Antarctic are separated by the 50 degrees W and 180 degrees meridians, for which reason the Lesser Antarctica is sometimes called the Western Antarctica. Most of Antarctica's surface is permanently covered by ice (some 39,000 billion cubic yards or 30 million cu km of it), representing 90% of the total amount of ice on Earth. This ice, which is the result of snowfalls accumulated over the past 100,000 years, can reach depths of up to 15,000 ft (4,500 m), burying a good part of the Antarctic continent to below sea level. Because of these great thicknesses of ice permanently covering the Antarctic continent (more than 8,800 ft, or 2,700 m, at the South Pole), the structure of the Antarctic continent and the composition and morphology of its materials are still little known as a whole. Greater Antarctica seems to have a shield of crystalline rocks underneath the icesheet with a cover of palaeozoic and permotriassic sediments. Lesser Antarctica, particularly the Antarctic peninsula and the islands that are attached to it, seem to extend the Andean mountain range toward the south.

Australia and Oceania

Australia, with an area of 2.9 million square miles (7.5 million sq km), is a large island and the smallest continent. Completely isolated from Africa, the Americas, and Antarctica by thousands of miles of ocean and by the insular areas of Melanesia and Indonesia in southeast Eurasia, it is very unusual. Like other continents that originated from the fragmentation of Gondwana, it is basically composed of a Pre-Cambrian shield. The land is very rugged in the east due to a mountain range that stretches some 1,800 mi (3,000 km) in a north-south direction. In the west, the land is higher where it forms a plateau, than in the center, which is occupied by lowlands. The rest of the emerged lands of the southern hemisphere constitute a scattering of islands, the most important of which, in terms of size, are New Guinea, separated from the north of Australia by the Torres Strait, a stretch of sea 90 mi (150 km) wide; and the islands of the north and south of New Zealand, isolated in the middle of the Pacific, 1,200 mi (2,000 km) from Australia, 1,500 mi (2,500 km) from Antarctica, and nearly 6,200 mi (10,000 km) from the coasts of Chile. There are also the majority of the Polynesian and Melanesian archipelagoes in the Pacific, like the Galapagos Islands, Juan Fernández Islands, and Easter and Sala y Gómez islands; in the Atlantic, the islands of the southern mid-Atlantic ridge such as Ascension Island, Santa Helena, and Tristan da Cunha, the Falklands, South Georgia, and the Brazilian islands of Fernando Noronha, Rocas, Trinidade and Martin Vaz; in the Indian Ocean, the Seychelles, the Comoros, the Mascarenes, and the Chagos archipelago.

2. The history of the atmosphere and climate

2.1 An Earth without atmosphere, an atmosphere without oxygen

Strictly speaking, we cannot say that the Earth has ever been totally lacking an atmosphere, if by this we mean a covering of gases around the terrestrial crust and the oceans. The fact that a planet has an atmosphere and oceans, and the components of these, depend on three factors. First, an atmosphere depends on a planet's mass and its fluid coverings; second, its distance from the Sun (or the star at the center of its planetary system) and the emission of its energy; and finally, the properties of the elements and their compounds present on the planet. Additionally, in the case of the Earth, logic leads us to conclude that there must necessarily have been changes in its composition throughout its history.

The origin of the Earth's atmosphere

In fact, the Earth's present composition is unusual compared to the data that affect the rest of the solar system, in terms of the properties of the planet and the elements it contains. We do not know of any possible primary source of molecular oxygen, which today represents approximately one fifth of the atmosphere and, compared with the proportions of the solar atmosphere, the quantities of hydrogen, helium, and the other noble gases are very small, while that of nitrogen (78.084% in volume) is extremely high.

The low proportion of noble gases, even of the heaviest, leads us to conclude that during the Hadean period the high temperatures on the Earth's surface made our planet lose nearly all the atmosphere it had inherited from the solar nebula from which it had originated, in such a way that practically all the Earth's present fluid coverings come from secondary sources and have accumulated from that moment, some 4,300 million years ago, when its surface cooled enough for it to be able to form a solid crust.

There are only two possible sources of the Earth's fluid coverings, in the absence of life: the Earth's interior and outer space. Probably both have played a part in the composition of the Earth's present atmosphere. Volcanoes, geysers, and thermal springs constantly emit gases, in particular carbon dioxide, hydrogen sulfide, and water vapor, this was probably also the case during the Hadean era. On the other hand, between 4,200 and 3,900 million years ago, numerous bodies of matter from space crashed onto the Earth's surface. Many of these came from a ring of asteroids, and the majority must have been chondritic carbonaceous meteoroids, an accumulation of aggregates of hydrated silicates and magnetite in a matrix of complexes of organic compounds at a low temperature.

The loss of all of the Earth's molecular hydrogen during its condensation and later cooling left the planet incapable of originating organic molecules like those that we know contribute to the formation of living matter. The solution appeared in the form of an abundant source of electrons—reduced iron (Fe^{2+})—and an equally abundant source of energy, ultraviolet (UV) light. The easy photochemical oxidation of ferrous oxide to ferric oxide (Fe^{3+}), catalyzed and energized at the same time by UV radiation, enriched the atmosphere at the same time with gases like hydrogen, methane, hydrogen cyanide, water vapor, or hydrogen sulfide, while the ferric ions generated were precipitated in insoluble oxides and other complexes. This led to the first formation of iron in bands, still of a purely inorganic origin.

In any case, the existence of sedimentary rocks dating back 3,800 million years (in the formation of Isua) implies that there must already have been an atmosphere and oceans by that date, and that temperatures, wherever there was liquid water, were not all that different from present ones, even though they were relatively higher. It seems likely that they oscillated, on the whole of the planet's surface, between about 140°F (60°C) and 34-40°F (1-5°C). The greenhouse effect of an atmosphere richer in carbon dioxide than the present one probably more than compensated for the fact that the sun was less hot than it is today.

The climatology of the original atmosphere

The considerable volcanic activity, of which the rocks of the Archean age are a testimony, suggest a period with a generally misty atmosphere, with frequent cloud formations of vapor and dust coming from submarine eruptions and, from time to time, emissions of gases of volcanic origin, such as sulfur and nitrogen oxides and hydrogen sulfide. These led to conditions that were virtually optimal for the formation of "smogs" and the precipitation of acid rain, without doubt the most powerful atmospheric agent in the shaping of the Earth's surface in Archaean times. The oxygen remained low enough because ferrous oxides not only greatly exceeded ferric iron oxides in the rocks but were transported in solution by the water. However, about 3.5 billion years ago life was involved in the formation of the atmosphere. Carbon is found in rocks of that age with ratios of carbon isotopes (^{13}C to ^{14}C) that are characteristic of photosynthetic organisms.

The fact that the day was shorter, because of the greater speed of rotation and the associated effects in atmospheric and oceanic circulation and in the magnitude and frequency of the tides, may have resulted in a more marked contrast in temperatures between equatorial and polar regions. Given a distribution of continents similar to today's, there would have been a greater aridity in the more continental regions and subtropical latitudes, but since the emerged lands were much smaller in size, it is not likely that this would have happened.

The first irrefutable evidence of a wide-ranging climatic phenomenon seems to be the deposits of tillites, a product of the glaciation that occurred in the early Proterozoic, between 2,500 and 2,300 million years ago. These are found mostly in North America, in an extensive area stretching from Lake Superior to the northwest Canadian territories and to Wyoming. It is also found, though, in western Australia, South Africa, central India, Karelia, and in the region of Lake Baikal. The fact that, at least in some points in Canada, these materials of glacial origin sat on top of rocks, which seem to have been deposited under reducing conditions, and on top of other rocks, which seem to have been deposited in oxidizing conditions, has suggested the hypothesis that the cause of the glaciation might have been the failure of the mechanism maintaining the greenhouse effect on the Earth. This stopped the planet from cooling further, in conjunction with a less intense solar radiation than there is today. Perhaps such a shutdown might have been a partial consequence of the carbon dioxide assimilation by the first photosynthetic microorganisms.

2.2 Between fire and ice: ancient climatic changes

Glaciations at the end of the Proterozoic

The end of the Proterozoic, at its boundary with the Cambrian period, between 670 and 950 million years ago, was already a period with marked plate tectonic activity. It was a new episode of glaciations, possibly the most extensive succession of continental glaciations ever recorded. In this era, as already mentioned, it seems that the atmosphere already had a similar composition to today's, with a proportion of oxygen not so different from that in the air we breathe today, and that eukaryotic life was already firmly established. Four ice ages, with the corresponding interglacial intervals, followed one another and left their traces in practically all the continents, above all in Africa (which at that moment possibly occupied the area now occupied by Antarctica), southern Australia, and Scandinavia. These traces are in the form of striated and polished pavements, tillites with striated boulders, and other characteristic forms and materials.

Of the several hypotheses that have been put forward to explain the causes of these glaciations, none is fully satisfactory, but it seems that the important activity of plate tectonics, with shifts of many thousands of miles, could have played an important role.

Climatic conditions in the Paleozoic

The Cambrian began with the melting of the continental ice, caused by the drifting of the continental masses over which it had formed towards the Equator. This probably also contributed to a general warming of the planet's climate. In fact, it seems that this led to the establishment, in the Cambrian seas, of the environmental conditions necessary for an evolutionary explosion, to which reference will be made later, and also the changes in the relative distribution of the land and sea masses. Thus, for example, the opening, during the Ediacarian and Cambrian periods, of the Iapetus ocean and its subsequent closure undoubtedly had

19 The pre-Mesozoic glaciations left a deep impression on the Australian continent, and a proof of this is the striate rocks of Hallet Cove, Adelaide (above), or the tills of Flinders Range (below). These two zones are found at the edge of the Australian glacial zone. The rock that became striated by the effect of the ice masses near Adelaide (in south Australia) were formed in the glacial era of the Permian, some 280 million years ago. The tills of Flinders Range were formed by pebbles from the glacial epochs which were inserted into a sedimentary matrix. *[Photos: Reg Morrison / Auscape International]*

20 A layer of clay rich in iridium marks the boundary between the Cretaceous and the Tertiary, (in the photograph, this layer has a coin on top). The boundary between these two periods is associated with the massive extinctions at the end of the Cretaceous, which included among them the dinosaurs. However, this was not the only loss: In the same epoch the greater part of the oceanic plankton also disappeared, as well as many tropical invertebrates, and not a few terrestrial plants. Despite these losses, one should not look upon this transition as being fatal for living organisms since at the end of the Cretaceous, insects, mammals, birds, terrestrial phanerogams, fish, corals and marine molluscs underwent active diversification.
[Photo: Walter Alvarez / Science Photo Library / AGE Fotostock].

effects on the climate on a global and regional level, as well as favoring its diversification.

From the Carboniferous period onwards, the collision of the continental masses and the formation of a very extended (in north-south terms), single continent led to very distinct zonal climates that successively affected different parts of the emerged lands, because of their general continental drift. We cannot be absolutely sure whether the catastrophic mass extinction marking the end of the Palaeozoic and the beginning of the Mesozoic was caused or accompanied by some important climatic change, but there is no convincing evidence either of a far-reaching glaciation or desertification, or of any other considerable change.

Climatic conditions in the Mesozoic

What is certain, though, is that during the Triassic and the lower Jurassic there is evidence that the climate became drier in continental areas, perhaps due to the immense extension of the continents. On the other hand, in the later Jurassic period, when the Tethys sea was already well established and the Atlantic and Indian oceans were beginning to open up, there were more benign and, above all, more humid climatic conditions that characterized the Cretaceous. On the boundaries between the Cretaceous and Cenozoic periods, the time of the dramatic extinction of the dinosaurs, it seems that there was a short-lived thermal crisis that could have led to a sudden cooling of 14-18°F (8 to 10ºC), perhaps due to giant volcanic eruptions or as the result of a collision with an asteroid or large meteorite.

Without discounting any of these catastrophes, for which there is an ever-growing body of evidence, in particular of a collision with a large, extraterrestrial body, it is possible that changes in oceanic circulation could partly explain this cooling. The opening of the North Atlantic and the incorporation of the Arctic Ocean into the global oceanic circulation, the northern movement of India through the equatorial Indian ocean—where some equatorial current of very hot water could have interfered—and the general drop in sea level as new oceanic basins opened up were all factors represented a set of conditions that led to a slower oceanic circulation and a lack of nutrients in the waters.

Climatic conditions in the Cenozoic

At the boundary between the Eocene and Oligocene, about 38 million years ago, a new extinction episode occurred that, if it was not massive, was certainly very significant. The apparently sudden change in the composition of plankton species recorded in the fossil record has led us to look for its origin in a new asteroid collision, as in the case of the boundary between the Cretaceous and Cenozoic. In fact, about 40 million years ago, one of these collisions did occur, leaving a spectacular crater of more than 60 mi (100 km) in diameter near Popigai, in northern Siberia. Nevertheless, it seems to make more sense to attribute the progressive cooling of the global climate (with some fluctuations) that began to take place at that time to the climatic changes following the separation of the Antarctic continent from its neighbors and also to the disturbance of the equatorial currents of the Indian-Pacific ocean through the drift of the Indian plate.

The Oligocene seems to have been a period of thermal oscillations resulting in a general warming tendency. During the Miocene, the oscillations were maintained. In any event, we can begin to learn more about the thermal history of the Miocene, between 5 and 25 million years ago, and even more of the history of more recent periods, as they have left much more evidence. At the beginning, the tendency of the temperatures to rise from the end of the Oligocene continued, but the successive widening of the Drake Passage, between South America and the Antarctic peninsula, first some 25 million years ago and later 18 million years ago, increased the flow of cold waters around the Antarctic and episodically inverted the tendency toward a new cooling. This was followed, however, by a new warming that reached its peak in the mid-Miocene period, some 15 million years ago. After this, however, the Antarctic completed the formation of its ice cap and a new cooling began, a tendency which continued throughout the Miocene period. This became more marked during the Pliocene period and reached its height in the glaciations of the Quaternary period.

2.3 The most recent glaciations

By the beginning of the Quaternary period, about 1.5 million years ago, it had been some 200 million years, the end of the Permian period, since a true glaciation had occurred. The continental or marine areas that had occupied positions near the Earth's poles had suffered from rigorous climatic conditions and in many periods had had polar caps. In more recent times, the Antarctic, as it became isolated at the South Pole, had seen one develop during the Oligocene and Miocene periods. However, there had been no real glaciations since the Permian period.

The Quaternary glaciations

A picture of the Earth taken from space two million years ago would have appeared very similar to one taken today. The differences would consist precisely of the way that water—liquid or solid—had shaped the continent's surface and the islands. It is precisely this geography, determined by the last movements of tectonic plates, that seems to have been the origin of the great Quaternary glaciations.

We have already mentioned the isolation of Antarctica. In fact, although Antarctica has had a considerably thick ice cap for at least the last 15 million years, and despite the fact that there are permanent ice fields along its coasts and that new ones are formed regularly every winter, its present geography means that there is a natural limit to the growth of any hypothetical southern glaciation.

At the opposite end of the planet, the North Pole is directly in the middle of an ocean practically surrounded by land: the Bering Strait is narrow and shallow; the channels between the islands of the archipelago off northern Canada and the one that separates them from Greenland are also narrow, shallow, winding, and frozen over for part of the year; the Denmark Strait, between Greenland and Iceland, is no longer than 180 mi (300 km), nor is it very deep; only the stretch of sea between Iceland on the one side and the British Isles and Norway on the other, even though they are also not very deep, can be said to represent an open channel of transfer between the waters of the Arctic Ocean and the Atlantic, and it is through this that the former receives its only current of warm water, the Gulf Stream.

However, the Arctic ocean also receives water from numerous large rivers (all the great rivers of Siberia, those of northern Canada, principally the Mackenzie, and those to the north of European Russia), which drain extensive areas of North America and Eurasia. As evaporation is rather scarce, the Arctic Ocean has an excess of water (which is translated into cold currents all along the coasts of Greenland and Labrador), and, furthermore, its surface waters are less saline than those of the other oceans. The result of this is a greater ability to freeze and form permanent ice fields that reflect solar radiation towards space. In winter they grow considerably both in area and depth. Indeed, the Arctic Ocean and the lands of North America and Europe surrounding it (except perhaps the coasts of Norway and Iceland) are abnormally cold because of the peculiarities of their geography.

21 The enormous ice cliffs of Barne (Antarctica) give some idea of the important role played by water in modelling the climate of the land surface. The waters of the Antarctic, which are cold and rich in nutrients, sink and flow northwards as far as the North Atlantic, and Nova Scotia, and in the Indian and Pacific oceans they lower the temperature of the continents that they bathe. Above the Antarctic, cold air accumulates at low altitudes, and this raises the pressure locally. This higher pressure, together with the surrounding humid winds, propels the cold air towards the surrounding regions, which are warmer and with lower pressure.
[Photo: Roger Mear / Photothèque Stone International]

Because of their high latitude, the northernmost coasts of America and Eurasia present the necessary conditions so that, if conditions favorable to the accumulation of ice caps occur, these can extend southwards. We know that continental areas have more extreme temperatures (colder winters and hotter summers) than insular areas. The Antarctic, for example, before separating from the other southern continents, must have had hotter summers. Even though it had colder winters, permanent ice would not have formed until the continent became isolated and the summers became cooler. This is due to the fact that permanent ice caps cannot form if the summer is so warm that it completely melts the snow accumulated during the winter.

The origin of glaciations

For this reason, it is probable that the triggering effect of the Quaternary glaciations occurred a long way from the Arctic. One of the most consistent hypotheses would, in fact, situate it in the tropics, to be more precise in the central American isthmus, whose closure, three million years ago, would have interrupted the circulation of a hypothetical equatorial current that previously went from the Atlantic to the Pacific. The warm waters of the Gulf Stream come from the center of the Pacific, cross the Indian ocean and enter the Atlantic via the Cape of Good Hope, cross this ocean and continue along the northeast coasts of South America and the Caribbean sea, where they warm up even more, before passing through the Gulf of Mexico, where the current that today softens the climate of the western coasts of Europe originates. Before the isthmus of Panama became closed, there was nothing to stop this current in its tour round the world from returning to the Pacific through the Strait of Panama, instead of heading toward the North Pole through the Yucatan Channel. Paradoxically, this new warm current in the North Atlantic laid the foundations of the glaciations. Warmer water meant more evaporation and also more precipitation in the more northern latitudes of the Atlantic and neighboring lands. Snow began to accumulate in enormous quantities in Greenland, Scandinavia, and the Labrador Peninsula, to depths of hundreds of feet over more than 10,000 years, in a self-feeding process, given that the change of the Earth's albedo (reflective power of the snow) was translated into the absorption of fewer calories of solar radiation per surface unit.

The accumulation of solid water on the continents or in the polar cap was accompanied by a drop in the sea level, and this could have been the mechanism allowing the process to become inverted. One must bear in mind that at the height of the glaciations it seems that the Atlantic froze up as far as the latitude of New York and Galicia and that the terrestrial polar cap covered all of Canada and a great part of the north east of the present United States and, in Europe, reached the latitude of London, Berlin, Warsaw, and Kiev, so that the volume of frozen water must have been enormous. This probably interrupted the communication between the Atlantic Ocean and the Arctic basin and diverted the Gulf Stream further southward. It also caused atmospheric disturbances in the polar front, making precipitation rarer at more northern latitudes and more frequent toward the south, in the Sahara and the Sahel, which are today affected by drought. With less snowfall, the summer melting must have pushed back the ice and led to the establishment of an interglacial period.

Glacial periods

During the Pleistocene period, situations like the one described could have occurred, to a greater or lesser degree, many times. Most authors accept that there were six glacial periods with their corresponding interglacial periods, the last of which would be the present one, and all of them had oscillations that, at times, allow us to recognize sub-periods. The three oldest, the *Biber*, the *Donau*, and the *Günz*, are the most controversial and have the most uncertain dating. However, at the center of Europe, from the beginning of the *Mindel* glaciation (also called *Elster* in northern Europe and *Kansas* in North America) 400,000 years ago, they are much less controversial and we can date them with greater precision. It is, in fact, from this date that we have the first evidence of the deliberate use of fire by humans: the remains of hearths found near Nice, in the Maritime Alps, called Terra Amata; in Vertesszöllös in Hungary and in Zhoukoudian (Chou-K'ou-tien), near Beijing, China. All of these have been associated with making of stone tools, and with the remains of animal bones.

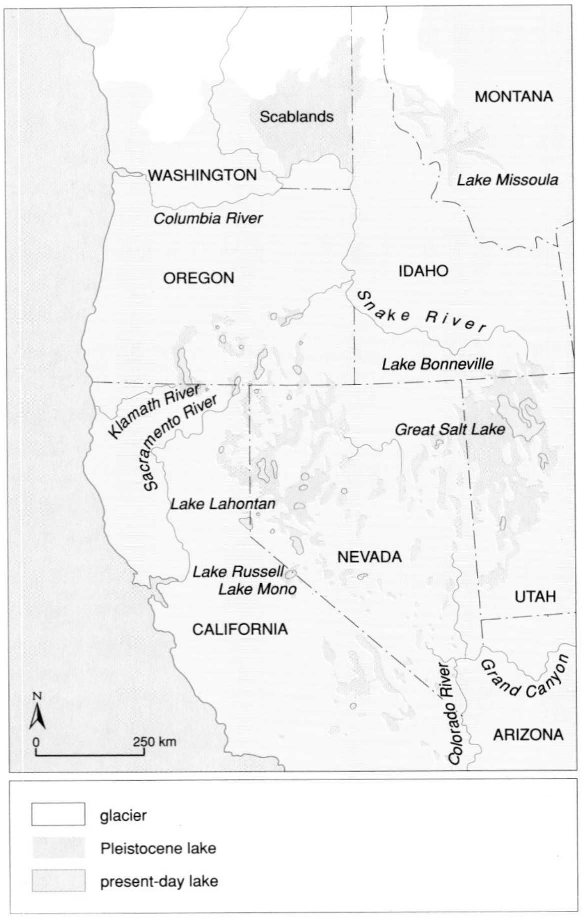

22 One of the most spectacular examples of the alteration of the Earth's surface by cycles of freezing and melting is found in the eastern part of the State of Washington, which comprises 11,583 sq mi (30,000 km^2) of basaltic terrain, slightly undulated and drained by the Columbia and Snake rivers. It is known that this is the result of sudden and repeated escape of a large quantity of water from a Pleistocene lake, which was as large as present day Ontario, Lake Misoula, which occupied the valleys of the eastern part of Montana. The flow of water released is comparable to 2,000 times the normal flow of the Colorado river in the Grand Canyon and 100 times that of the lower Mississippi in spate. These spectacular avenues are formed on large flat surfaces of Miocene lavas from which successive layers of basalt were extracted and large blocks carried away. Today comparable phenomena can be found, for example, in Alaska and Iceland, when the great dams of ice rupture and the lakes suddenly discharge all their water.
[Diagram: Biopunt, from various sources]

The Mindel glaciation lasted some 100,000 years and, after an interglacial period of some 50,000 years, about 250,000 years ago, a new glaciation started: the Riss glacial (also called the Saale in northern Europe and the Illinoian in North America). The *Riss* glacial seems to have lasted another 100,000 years and was followed by an interglacial stage of nearly 50,000 years. About 75,000 years ago, the last of the glacial stages, so far, began: the *Würm* glacial (also called *Vistula* in northern Europe and the *Wisconsin* in North America). Three stages are generally recognized in this glaciation, separated by periods of relatively mild temperatures. The first of these developed between 55,000 and 60,000 years ago, separating the stages called Würm I and Würm II and the second, the interglacial Würm II/Würm III, between 35,000 and 40,000 years ago.

The geological consequences of glaciations

As the center of the glaciations was always situated in the north Atlantic, while a large part of Europe, North America, and northwest Asia were underneath the ice, eastern Asia was not as affected by the glaciations, except in the mountainous regions. The more southern mountainous regions of Europe and North America were also centers of secondary glaciations, while the plains of central Asia and the raised mountain ranges that surround them (Himalayas, Hindu Kush, Karakoram, Tan Shan) apparently played a role in reinforcing the severity of the climate and were also important and extensive centers of glaciation. In the southern hemisphere, minor centers of glaciation were the Andes, with glaciers which reached the sea at the latitude of Chiloe (42°S) by the Pacific slopes and at Río Gallego (53°S) via the Atlantic slopes, as well as the New Zealand Alps.

In many areas of North America affected by the glaciations, ice blocked the waters of some rivers that previously had their estuaries more to the north of the glacial front, causing the formation of immense lakes, in some cases much larger than the present Great Lakes. When the ice melted and the dam broke, they produced floods of unimaginable force over a huge area. This is the case with what has been called Lake Bonneville, which was formed

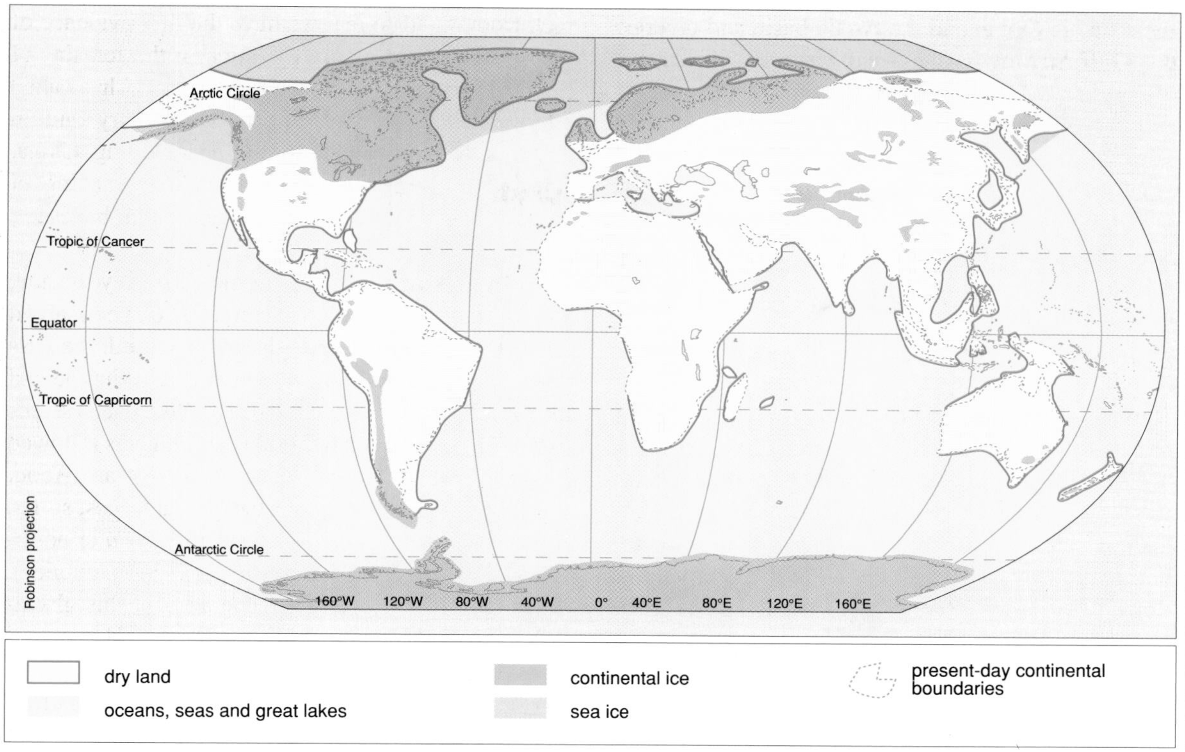

23 At the maximum extent of the Quaternary glaciations, about a third of the ice was to be found in the Antarctic and the rest mainly in the polar sector of the northern hemisphere. The total volume of ice reached about 13.4 million cubic mi (56 million cubic km). The melting of this ice could raise the sea level by some 459 ft (140 m). Moving in all directions, this ice modelled the landscape and its movements are recorded in the rocks that it covered. The flacila deposits consisted mainly of fragments of angular rock, mixed with clays or silt called till, frequently accompanied by lacustrine or fluvial sediments.
[Drawing: Editrònica, from various sources]

GLACIATIONS				CULTURES
NORTH AMERICA	ALPS		NORTHERN EUROPE	
	POST GLACIAL		Sub-Atlantic, Subboreal, Atlantic, Boreal, Preboreal	Metals; Neolithic; Mesolithic
		10		
	LATE GLACIAL			PALEOLITHIC upper: Magdalenian; Solutrian
		13		
WISCONSIN	WÜRM		WEICHSEL (+ = 3, + = 2, 1)	Aurignacian; middle: MOUSTERIAN, Périgordian
		75		
	R/W INTERGLACIAL		EEM	
		125		
ILLINOIS	RISS		SAALE (+ = 2, 1)	lower: Tayacian
	MR INTERGLACIAL		HOLSTEIN	ACHEULIAN
KANSAS	MINDEL		ELSTER (+ = 2, 1)	
		400		
	G/M INTERGLACIAL		CROMERIAN	ABBEVILLIAN
		700		
NEBRASKA	GÜNZ (?)		MENAP (+ = 2, 1)	
		900		
	D/G INTERGLACIAL		WAAL	
	DONAU		EBURON (+ = 3, + = 2, 1)	PEBBLE CULTURE
		1,700		
	B/D INTERGLACIAL		TIGLIAN	
	BIBER (?)		PRETIGLIAN	
		(?) 2.0 - 2.5 Ma		?
PLIOCENE				

24 The distribution of the ice cap during the glaciations was different in the various continents, and in each of them a different nomenclature has been applied. The table gives the equivalent names of the different periods in the various continents and their age in millions of years.
[Diagram: Editrònica, from various sources]

25 In some regions of Chad, one can find northern species that have reached there as a result of the extent of the glaciations. An example is the water flea, *Daphnia longispina*. The Pleistocene glaciations produced arctic conditions in Europe, North America and Asia (although as the center of the glaciations was north of the Atlantic, they did not reach eastern Asia). These conditions allowed species of cold climates to find refuge more to the south and in some cases they stayed there. These examples today represent relicts of the fauna that existed during the glaciations.
[Photo: Miquel Blasi (x 220)]

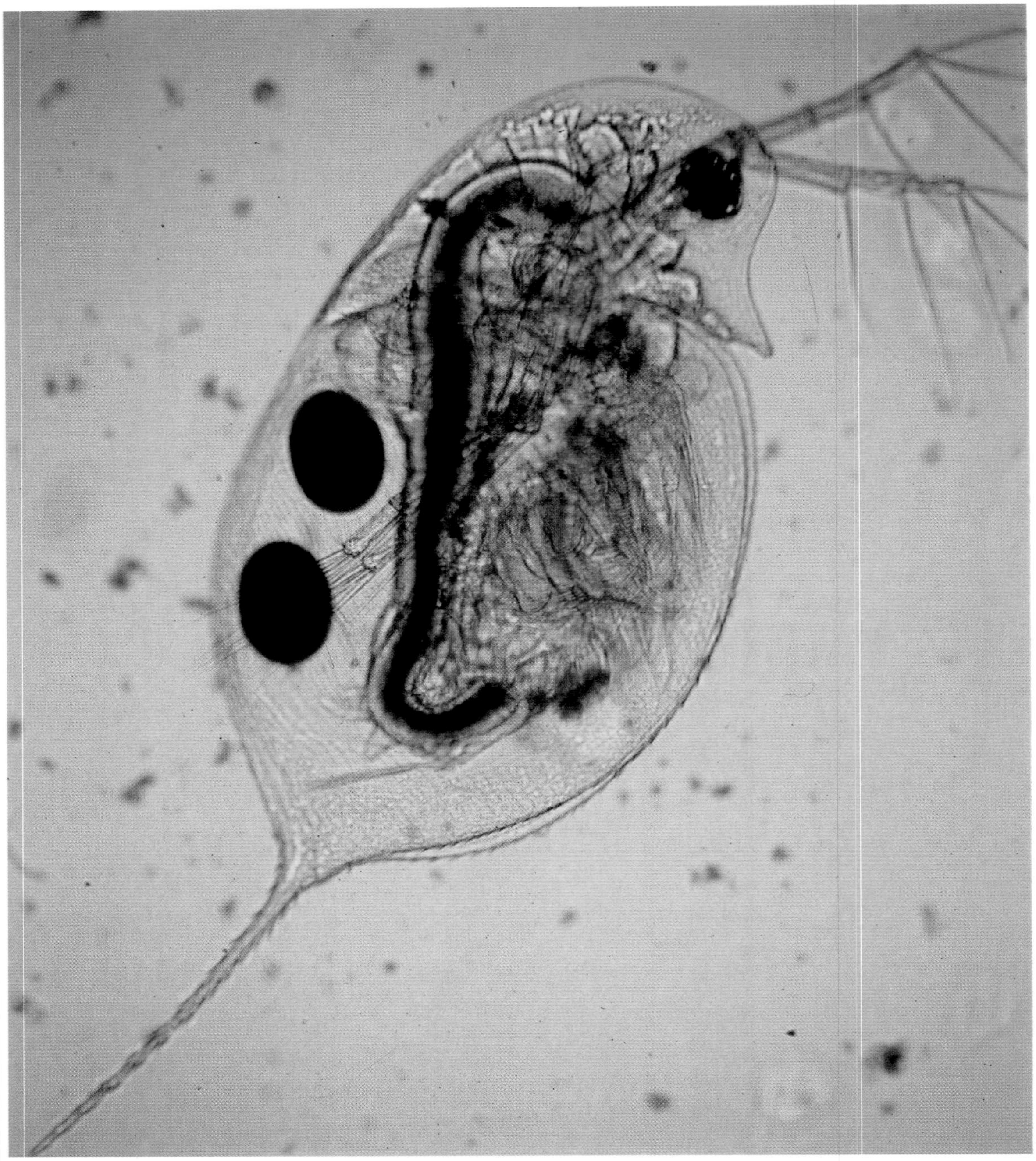

when the present valley of the Snake River was cut off by ice that came down from the mountains of today's Idaho. This lake occupied the basin at the bottom of which today we find the Great Salt Lake. The same process resulted in the appearance of the so-called Missoula Lake, a lake about the size of Ontario that formed to the north of Bonneville when ice blocked the present valley of the Columbia river. When the ice melted and the dam collapsed, Lake Bonneville excavated the gorge of the Snake River. The Missoula, as it burst its dam on several occasions over the years, caused floods with a greater flow of water than all the great rivers of today put together. These caused the formation of the so-called Channelled Scablands in Washington state, an area of some 12,000 sq mi (30,000 sq km), drained by the Columbia and Snake Rivers and, despite the only slight unevenness of the ground, covered in spectacularly eroded basaltic materials. The glacial stages were accompanied at lower latitudes by rainy periods that, associated with the lower evaporation thanks to the relatively lower temperatures, made possible, for example, the existence of great rivers right in the middle of what is today the Sahara desert, and of extensive lake basins at the foot of the mountain ranges along the western edge of North America as far south as the present-day Mexico City.

The biological consequences of glaciations

Because of these phenomena, a savannah-like vegetation covered the larger part of the area occupied today by the African and Arabian deserts, and a Mediterranean-type vegetation was still present in the western Sahara less than 5,000 years ago. Today one can still find relic species of nordic origin in many mountainous areas (Ahaggar, Tibesti) of the Sahara and even in the region of Chad where, for example, animals like the bug-like *Corixa mirandella* or the water flea *Daphnia longispina* appear, both with a much more northerly general distribution area. At the same time, the shores of the Mediterranean were populated by areas of forest comparable to those found today in the middle latitudes of Europe, while central Europe was covered in tundra and populated by a fauna of large hairy mammals, of which only the reindeer has survived.

In Europe, the southward retreat of warm-climate species during the glacials, in spite of interglacial periods of temperatures were even higher than today's and that pushed cold-climate species back to the poles or to higher altitudes, resulted in the extinction of numerous species (sometimes whole genera) of plants that had become established there during the Cenozoic. The barrier effect of the mountains in the south of the continent, as well as that of the Mediterranean sea itself, made genera like *Liriodendron*, *Catalpa*, and *Torreya* disappear from Europe, from the time of the first glaciation, and in later glacials, other plants like *Magnolia* or *Pterocarya*. Some of these genera, that, according to fossil evidence, were circumboreal in distribution before the glaciations are today restricted either to eastern Asia (*Metasequoia*, *Glyptostrobus*) or to North America (*Sequoia*, *Taxodium*).

The era of glaciations also saw the expansion of humans throughout the continents (and, starting from the last interglacial period, a time of expansion for our species, that of modern humans). The drop in sea-level facilitated the migrations of hominids, who, from their probable center of origin in Africa, moved first towards Asia and Europe and later, probably between 32,000 and 40,000 years ago, reached America and Australia. It was also a time of extinction for many mammals, like the great mammoths (*Mammuthus*), the woolly rhinoceroses (*Coelodonta*), sabre-toothed tigers (*Machairodus*), the giant American lion (*Panthera leo spelaea*, *P. leo atrox*), the horses (*Dolichohippus*) and the American camel (*Camelops*), different species of ant eaters, and giant marsupials. We cannot exclude, as one cause of these extinctions, the fact that hominid hunters had become more widespread. There were also important changes in birds, with the disappearance, for example, of the giant condor and of the majority of species of large running birds, the last of which, like the giant moa of New Zealand (*Dinornis*), disappeared in quite recent times, less than 1,000 years ago, as a direct consequence of the expansion of human populations, which did not colonize New Zealand until the eighth or ninth centuries A.D.

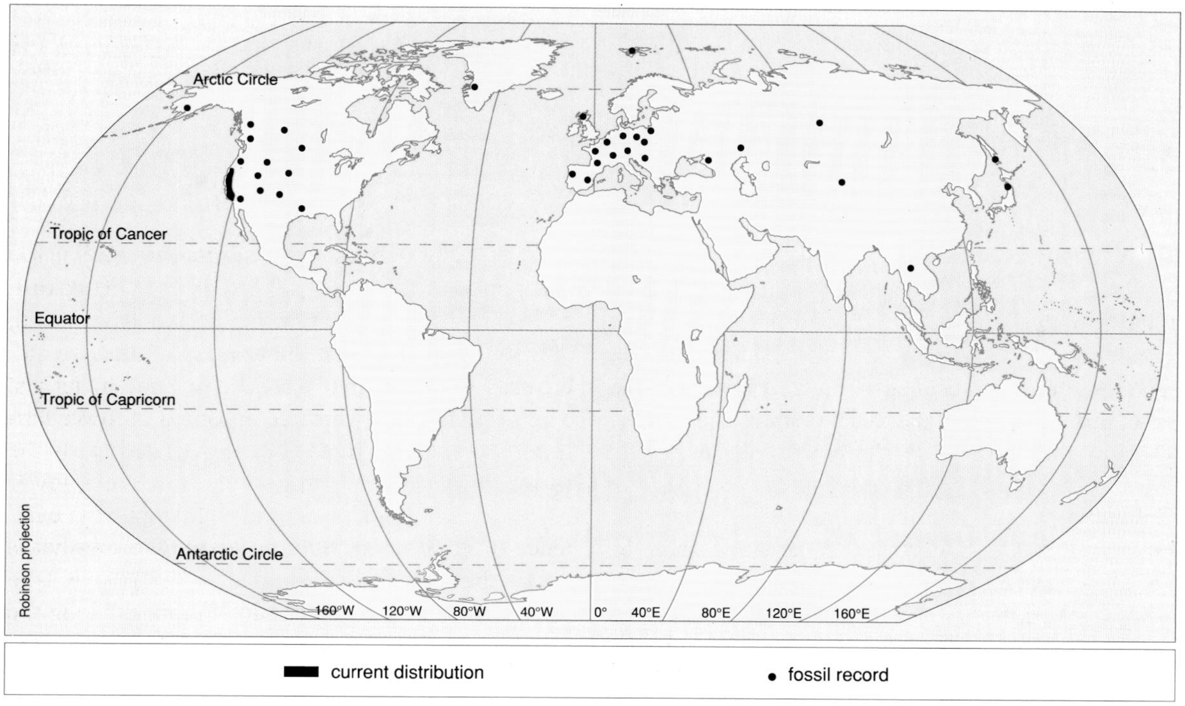

26 The predominant climate of the glacial periods is reflected in the distribution of species in the circumboreal zones, such as, the redwoods (*Sequoia*). It is believed that these trees originated in the western and central zones of North America at some time during the lower Mesozoic. The first fossil evidence was found in Manchuria and corresponded to the Jurassic. The migration of the redwoods was to reach eastern Asia and Europe, passing through Greenland. Pliocene fossils have been found SW China (26°N) and in Texas (30°N) from the Eocene; and others in areas as far north as western Greenland (70°N) and Spitzbergen (79°N), but the majority of redwood fossils have been found at latitudes between 34°N and 58°N. *[Diagram: Editrònica, from various sources]*

Frozen mammoths and other discoveries

Baby mummified mammoth (*Mammuthus*) [Novosti]

At the beginning of the 20th century, a sensational discovery was made in eastern Siberia. Two hunters who were following the trail of a reindeer on the banks of the river Berezkova when their dog brought their attention to the presence of an enormous, solid cadaver, a frozen mammoth. They hacked the very large tusks off the mammoth's huge head, which was still intact, in order to sell them for a fortune. However, the discovery of a whole cadaver was so exceptional that it could not go unnoticed or be reduced to a valuable, yet wretched, sale of ivory. In a very short time the news had travelled from the isolated town of Kolymskaja in northeast Asia to the St. Petersburg Academy, in the west of the vast Czardom. Within a few months, three scientists set off on a long journey. They went first by train to Irkutsk and, from there, traveled 3,700 mi (6,000 km) by sleigh to get to Kolymsk. On September 14, 1901, they discovered, to their amazement, the skull of the mammoth sticking out of the ice that had preserved it for so many centuries, while the rest of the body and limbs were still buried under it.

Many mammal species that were part of the primitive human's everyday life—hence the cave-paintings and other art forms of such animals—disappeared during the final glacial periods. But the very ice that caused their demise preserved some remains.

Mammoth (*Mammuthus*) from Yakutia (St. Petersburg) [Novosti]

Then, they proceeded to build a hut around the animal to provide a warm environment and melt the ice. Very gradually, enveloped in a terrible stench, they uncovered the skin, strands of long brown hair, soft flesh, etc. The animal was methodically dissected and cut into portions that were then re-frozen for transportation. All in all, a large part of the body was recovered from the frozen alluvium of the river. Even the internal organs was recovered and, at a later stage, analyzed to discover the animal's diet. Finally, on October 15, a line of sleighs set off towards St. Petersburg Museum, carrying the only mammoth that had ever been seen in modern times, albeit cut up into many pieces. Since the first discovery, other examples of frozen mammoths have been found, but none as complete as the first one. One of the later discoveries was a mammoth found in Alaska, some 22,000 years old, that miners freed from frozen mud by hosing it down with hot water. Of all elephant fossils belonging to the Quaternary Period, the mammoth (*Mammuthus* [=*Elephas*] *primigenius*) is probably the best known. Pleistocene Epoch mammoths, *Mammuthus*, coexisted with *Elephas* and *Loxodonta* groups, to which today's Asian and African elephants belong respectively. Mammoths could reach a height of 10 ft (3 m) (taller than today's elephants), and they had thick hair and huge tusks. They lived in cold areas of Europe and Asia (Siberia) during the last glacial (Würm). During this final glacial, they migrated to North America across the Bering Strait. Primitive humans hunted them for their meat, skins, and bones, and some prehistoric caves preserve cave-paintings of these animals. The woolly rhinoceros (*Rhinoceros tichorhinus*), endemic to Europe and also adapted to the glacial cold, lived at the same time as the mammoth and, for that reason, also appears in cave-paintings.

In 1967, Heinrich Erben from the University of Bonn made a proposal to his colleagues in Leningrad that bordered on science fiction: he proposed resuscitating mammoths. Erben's suggestion involved trying to obtain DNA from mammoths frozen in Siberian ice. The nuclear material was to be extracted from the best-preserved cells and used to fertilize an egg from a female elephant from which the nucleus would have previously been removed. Once fertilized, it would only have to be implanted in the elephant's womb. It would then be a matter of waiting patiently for the birth of an "extemporary" mammoth, many thousands of years after individuals of the race itself became extinct. The attempt, despite the efforts made, did not succeed. It would have been fantastic, but it is still a fantasy. It was another example, although quite a reasonable one, of how remains of the past can fire the imagination.

Mammoths (*Mammuthus*) [Mary Evans Picture Library]

Site of mammoths (*Mammuthus*) [Jim Richardson - West Light / AGE Fotostock]

On the island of Samos, Plutarch thought he had discovered the bones of the Amazons that Dionysus had killed. In Lucerne, near Randen Abbey, the origin of an enormous skeleton was open to question. There was some doubt as to whether it belonged to a giant or to an angel fallen from the sky. In 1605, a mammoth tusk was found and installed in Schwäbisch Hall (Suàbia) and next to it there was a sign asking the visitor: "Tell me, what species could this belong to?" A little later, in 1613, some enormous bones were found in the Dauphiné region that experts from both the University of Montpelier and the University of Grenoble agreed in attributing to giant humans. This caused a great deal of controversy between "those in the know" at that time and generated a pile of treatises, for and against, gigantology. It was also a good time for opportunists: a surgeon barber obtained a few bones belonging to some unknown creature from the Marquis who owned the site and took them around villages and towns proclaiming that they belonged to Theutobochus, a Germanic leader who, in Roman times, had devastated large parts of Gaul and Iberia. It was not until 1984, after the bones had gone missing, that this creature was identified by one its teeth as *Deinotherium giganteum*, a type of elephant from the Miocene Epoch. At Klagenfurt, in southern Austria, in about 1335, the skull of a woolly rhinoceros was found that, for many centuries, was thought to be a monster with all the characteristics of classical dragons. People's imaginations were quite vivid in this area. For example, a fossil vertebra of an elephant found near Munich and a mammoth molar dug up in Valence, to the south of Lyon, were said to belong to Saint Christopher.

The discovery of frozen mammoths gave rise to strange, legendary, or supernatural interpretations that, even though today may seem a little excessive, in fact attempted to find explanations that fitted in with the level of knowledge at that time. When logical analysis of these fossilized bones was still impossible, people tried to find a niche for them in their fictitious world. In such a way, the mysterious orbit in the middle of mammoth's skull (or any other elephant)—the nasal orifice—could only be interpreted as the eye socket of a mythical cyclops. Mammoth skeletons themselves have given rise to a Siberian legend about a strange being, a type of huge rat the size of a buffalo that, like a mole, used to run around below ground eating its way through wood and stone. Confined to the night because daylight would kill it, its comings and goings caused the tremors that, from time to time, rocked little hamlets. Not enough scientific reasoning, and too much cold.

2.4 The climate of the last ten thousand years

The last glaciations

The last great ice age came to an end between 20,000 and 16,000 years ago. Coinciding with this was a period of maximum aridity at tropical latitudes in Africa, Arabia, and India. Afterwards, the temperature began to rise and the ice began to retreat, at least in Europe, over a period of some 2,000 years. Magdalenian wall painting in the caves of the Pyrenean-Cantabrian region (Altamira, Lascaux, Mas d'Azil), originating right in the middle of the glaciation some 27,000 years ago, went through its most brilliant period at the beginning of this interglacial period. Later, between 11,000 and 12,000 years ago, it seems that a new cooling took place in Europe, which some authors have tried to link to the effects of the southward advance of cold waters and tabular icebergs, resulting from the thaw of the polar cap, an advance that would have triggered an intense circulation of cold and humid winds on the continent. This was the so-called late ice age, which ended some 10,000 to 11,000 years ago with what is known as the Dryas phase.

The climate of modern times

The end of the Dryas also marked the end (at least so far) of the glaciations and the beginning of the Holocene. From a geological point of view, the Holocene is the age that embraces modern, postglacial times. From an archaeological and cultural point of view, it also marks roughly, the boundary between the Paleolithic and the early Neolithic cultures. In some areas of the world, the first signs of what has since been called the Neolithic revolution, which began in this era, were found.

The thawing of snow and formation of flooded areas

About 10,000 years ago, a series of large expanses of fresh water began to form at the foot of the southern front of the retreating ice. One of these, situated to the northeast of North America, was the origin of the present-day North American Great Lakes. From another, the lake then situated to the south of Scandinavia and separated from the Atlantic by the Danish isthmus (the level of the Atlantic ocean was then much lower than it is today), the Baltic sea formed; this took place once the level of the sea had risen as a consequence of the melting of the ice, allowing it to connect to the Atlantic, first via an arm of the sea that occupied the present-day central plains of Sweden, and finally through the modern Danish straits.

In southern Europe, it was the epoch in which a vegetation of deciduous forests began to develop, similar to the one that currently predominates in central Europe. This is evidence of temperatures that were still below present ones but with much higher rainfall. As the ice retreated and the temperatures rose, the vegetation continued to advance northward, invading areas previously occupied by more or less tree-filled steppes, conifer forests, and tundra. The arrival of this type of vegetation in the present-day British Isles, which had had its own glacial cap until shortly before, has been documented at about 8,500 years ago.

The thermal maximum or Atlantic phase

Progressive warming was maintained, in general, until 5,000 years ago, when a thermal maximum was reached with average temperatures higher than present, and when marine waters reached their highest level of recent geological times. Deciduous vegetation expanded during this period throughout the whole of Europe, and the situation was similar on the Atlantic seaboard of North America, although floristically richer. On the other hand, more southerly areas were becoming progressively drier. Thus, for example, on the Barcelona Plain, situated at 41° latitude on the western Mediterranean coast, pollen analysis from 8,600 years ago reveals a mixed vegetation of oaks (by far the most dominant), hazel, cork oaks, and pines. Nevertheless, even though these trees were dominant, we can observe a considerable increase in pollen from characteristically Mediterranean species like wild olive trees, junipers, and lentiscus in samples from 7,400 years ago. In samples without precise dating, but probably between 6,500 and 7,000 years old, we can observe traces of cereal-like grass pollen, which mark the beginning of agricultural activity by human groups in this area. These data fit in with those known for other parts of western Europe. Finally, between 3,500 and 5,000 years ago, the oak was displaced in the whole of the western Mediterranean, surviving only in marginal areas and in more humid conditions than normal, while the holm oak became dominant and the Mediterranean pine forests became more widespread, as did the scrub of kermes oak and dwarf palms.

On the other hand, in the Sahara, the climatic optimum in temperate latitudes coincided with the end of a sub-luvial period that lasted until 4,500 years ago,

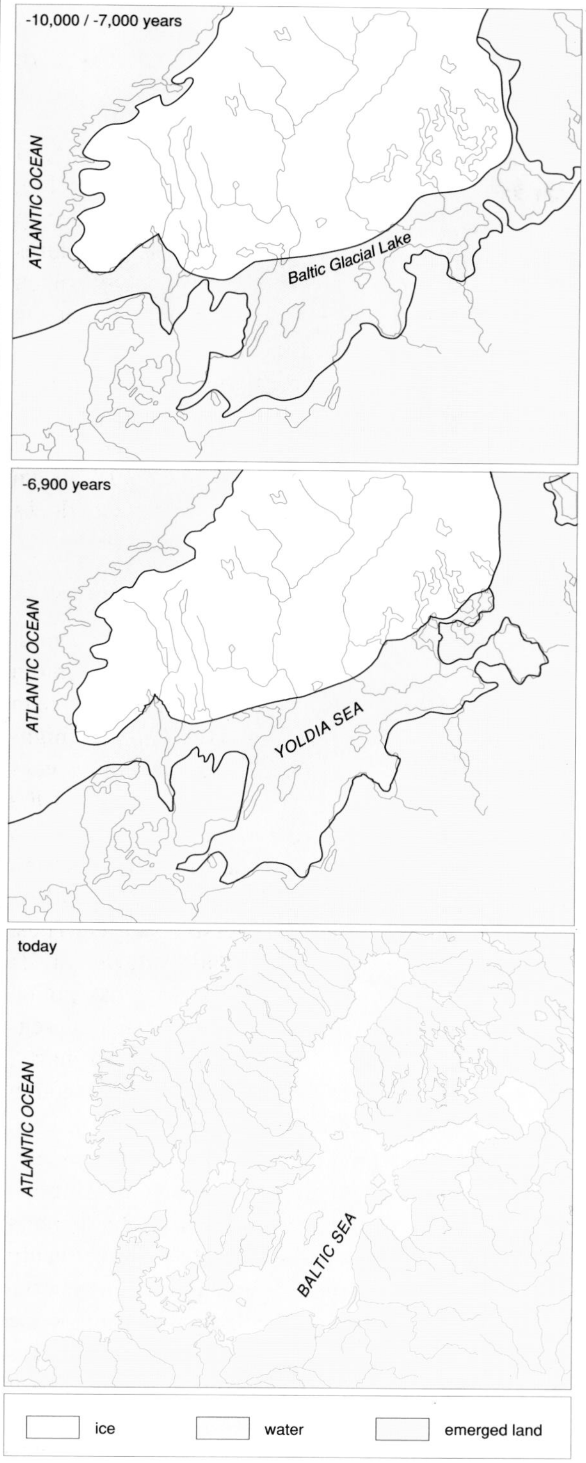

27 The formation of the Baltic sea began after the maximum glacial period (some 6,000 years ago), when the Würmian ice began to retreat and a brief warming occurred (some 15,000 to 14,000 years ago), the first of those that alternated with the various cold periods until the thermic optimum 5,000 years ago. The general mildening of the climate led to the melting of the ice in Scandinavia, and from about 10,000 years ago large areas of fresh water were formed south of the ice cap, one of which gave rise to the glacial Baltic lake. From about 8,000 years ago, the ice cap retreated from western Norway and increased volume in the Baltic lake. About 7,000 years ago, (a period in which the lands of the future British Isles became separated), the lake, which exceeded the present day dimensions of the Baltic sea, overflowed and linked up to the west with the North Sea, and to the east with the White Sea, and thereby became the sea of Yoldia (6,900 years ago), which did not last more than 60 years. Later it was converted into Lake Ancil, which connected with the North Sea, and it was bigger than the Baltic. With the rise of the sea level starting about 7,000 years ago, the fjords of Norway have been formed and the present day geography of the coasts established. Some 5,300 years ago Lake Ancil overflowed and again joined up with the sea. It ceased to be freshwater and became the Litorina Sea, which was warmer than the Yoldia and more saline than the Baltic. About 5,000 years ago, a period of maximum sunshine (the climatic optimum), the Litorina sea had wide beaches full of molluscs. *[Diagram: Biopunt, from various sources]*

during which period, as we have said, a Mediterranean-type vegetation dominated. Between 7,000 and 5,500 years ago, the first signs of the domestication of bovine livestock appear in the Saharan area. For the past 4,000 years, though, coinciding with the expansion of shepherd peoples, the drying of the Saharan climate has progressed rapidly and almost without interruption. At Tanezrouft, in the south of Algeria, millstones weighing 450-650 pounds (200-300 kg) have been found, evidence of a 3,000 year-old sedentary settlement. Probably in no other place in the world, except those places directly affected by the advances and retreats of ice, have climatic controls played such an important role in transforming of the way of life of their human populations.

Also, when rainfall dropped between 4,000 and 3,000 years ago, the contrasts between dry and rainy seasons became more accentuated in the tropical latitudes of Africa and South America. Some present day biogeographical data, such as the distribution of certain species of birds in the Amazon, would seem to suggest that the equatorial forests would have shrunk during the driest periods of the glacial stages to areas divided up by extensive penetrations of tropical vegetation adapted to conditions with a lower rainfall. The areas would have had more accentuated seasonal changes, which isolated them sufficiently to allow species differentiation to take place.

After the climatic optimum, some continental areas of Eurasia (Aralo-Caspian basin), North America (Great Basin), or Australia (the Lake Eyre region) underwent a drying of the climate, although not one as drastic as that of the African Sahara desert. In the Aralo-Caspian basin (the Caspian Sea), despite the important contributions of all its tributary rivers, [mainly those of the Volga and the Ural and, until some 2,300 years ago, the Oxus (the present-day Amu Darya), which, through a chain of lakes and small pools and the now dry canal of Uzboi, led into the southern basin of the Caspian sea], the intense evaporation over the last 4,000 years has led to the fall in the level of this sea that today lies 85 ft (26 m) below that of the Mediterranean. Two thousand three hundred years ago, at the time of the Asiatic conquests of Alexander the Great (331-323 B.C.), it was some 65 ft (20 m) higher, and in the east it nearly reached as far as the present-day Aral Sea (now even shallower than the Caspian, but mainly because of human intervention). To the north it went as far as the foot of the Volga Heights (Privilzskaia Vozvysennost) and the southern Urals. In the Great Basin of North America, the evaporation of the old Bonneville lake resulted in the Great Salt Lake, as well as a whole group of smaller lakes and basins that flood whenever there is heavy rain. Lake Eyre is also the remnant of a much larger lake.

The time when the climatic optimum occurred (around 5,000 years ago) was also marked, as we have said, by the most important sea-level movements of the Quaternary period. The average sea-level, known as the eustatic level, reached a point

28 The progressive warming of the Earth after the last Pleistocene glaciation, led, in part, to the drying out of very extensive lacustrine (lake) areas, such as Lake Eyre in Australia, where there are remains of salt encrustations of halophytes that lived in colder periods during the past. The origin of Lake Eyre is tectonic, and it has remained as a lake for more than 100 million years, even though it shares sedimentary strata with neighboring salt pans in which large numbers of deposits have been found that are rich in fossils of megafauna. Today the saline sediments form a 16 ft (5 m) thick layer. *[Photo: Waynes Lowler / Auscape International]*

roughly 10 ft (3 m) above today's level, so that many coastal plains throughout the world were covered by shallow marine waters. In the following 2,000 years, between 3,000 and 5,000 years ago, the eustatic level remained, more or less at the height which, despite some slight variations, it has maintained until now.

The Sub-boreal phase

The Atlantic phase of climatic optimum between 4,000 and 7,500 years ago (or to put it in the more normal terms of human history, between 5,500 and 2,000 B.C.), was followed in Europe by the *Sub-boreal phase*, characterized by a drier, colder climate, as we have seen in other continents. This lasted until the first years of our era, documented in the Alps and Scandinavia through pollen analysis and by data on the progress of the glaciers' fronts in the middle of the fifth century B.C. If the Atlantic phase coincides with the expansion of Neolithic cultures and the progressive extension of land cultivation, the Sub-boreal phase seems to have been accompanied by a renewal of forestry and a decrease in crop lands in middle Europe, as well as by important migratory movements to northern Europe and to the Euroasiatic steppes.

The Sub-Atlantic phase

The Sub-boreal phase was followed by the *Sub-Atlantic phase*, which takes us up to the present. As a whole, this phase is characterized by a more humid and generally colder climate than that of the Sub-boreal phase, although with great climatic fluctuations that eustatic variations document quite well. These were most probably linked to modifications of the zonal flow from west to east of masses of air in the lower atmosphere. Eustatic maxima corresponding to relative warm temperatures first appear between the fifth and seventh centuries A.D. and later at the end of the 9th century and beginning of the twelfth (though with a relative minimum around the year 1000), as well as more recently around 1600 and another around 1800, at the beginning and end respectively of what has been called the *Little Ice Age* of the seventeenth and eighteenth centuries. On the other hand, eustatic minima coinciding with cold episodes occurred around the years 100, 700, 1000, 1450, and 1700 A.D.

29 Deciduous woodlands, such as those of European oak, were probably established some 5,000 years ago, coinciding with the thermic maximum. The areas of deciduous and mixed woodland occupy a total of about 3 to 3.5 millions mi^2 (8–9 million km^2), although very often its structure has been altered by human action. In earlier times, these forested landscapes extended continuously from the Atlantic to the Urals. Deciduous woods grow in a climate which has a warm period of 4–6 months and a winter period, which is not very cold, of 3–4 months. *[Photo: Jane Gifford / Photothèque Stone International]*

3. The history of life

3.1 The phenomenon of life

Life and the blue planet

At present we have no evidence that life exists beyond the surface of our planet. Although it is true that complex organic molecules are found in interstellar space and also that some of the meteorites that fall to the Earth's surface contain them, the phenomena we associate with life (a capacity to control the internal medium and exchange energy and food with the outside, the multiplication and development of new organisms from structures specialized for the maintenance and transmission of genetic information, etc.) are not limited to the simple presence or juxtaposition of certain molecules. To a considerable extent, the properties of living matter, as we know it, are linked to physical and chemical characteristics that, at least in our solar system, are exclusive to our planet or are a result of its history. Thus, for example, we cannot imagine life without water; all living beings contain large amounts of water.

Nor can we imagine life without a cellular organization, in other words, without the existence of certain units we call cells, made up of an aqueous fluid surrounded by a semipermeable membrane. This membrane allows cells to isolate their own chemical reactions from the exterior and, at the same time, to control the entrance or exit of particular molecules. Inside this aqueous medium of the cells, there are organic molecules that can be used as a source of energy (such as adenosine triphosphate or ATP), as a support for the information necessary for reproduction (such as deoxyribonucleic acids or DNA), as a vehicle whereby this information can be translated into the synthesis of amino acids and proteins (such as ribonucleic acids or RNA), or as catalysts for specific reactions.

The diversification of living things of many different forms, both in terms of organization and of species, each one well adapted to precise environmental conditions and use of resources, is another characteristic trait of life on Earth today. The evolution of the biosphere and its particular situation at each moment in time is the result of successive events of diversification and extinction of living beings from previous periods. As in the history of humans, we cannot predict their future evolution, but we can explain what has affected them and what is continuing to affect them, by looking at past events, some of which are more certain than others.

The obscure beginning

How did life on Earth begin? And when did it begin? How were the first cells, the first organisms, able to evolve from their then lifeless chemical precursors? What happened before the formation, some 3,500 million years ago, of the first rocks containing fossil remains? We are still a long way from being able to give conclusive answers to these questions, although we do have enough information to be able to put forward some fairly credible hypotheses. We must remember that what differentiates living systems from inanimate ones is their capacity to record, store, and use information throughout long periods of time, while simultaneously being able to obtain replicas of this information and duplicate the series of molecules and structures that are determined by this information. In other words, living organisms are systems that are capable of ensuring their own preservation and identity.

Most researchers who have studied this question agree that life on Earth began much earlier than 3,500 million years ago, which is when our uninterrupted fossil record begins. The fact that the first known fossil remains are of organisms that are very similar, if not identical, to present-day bacteria seems to indicate that the emergence of life on Earth must date back much further, perhaps even to before the formation of the oldest known sedimentary rocks. The oldest fossil remains from the beginnings of prebiotic evolution might be traced back to the very origins of the planet Earth. Indeed, the abiotic synthesis of organic compounds (organic compounds derived from non-organic sources), which is thought to be a necessary condition for life to exist, can come about in very short periods of time.

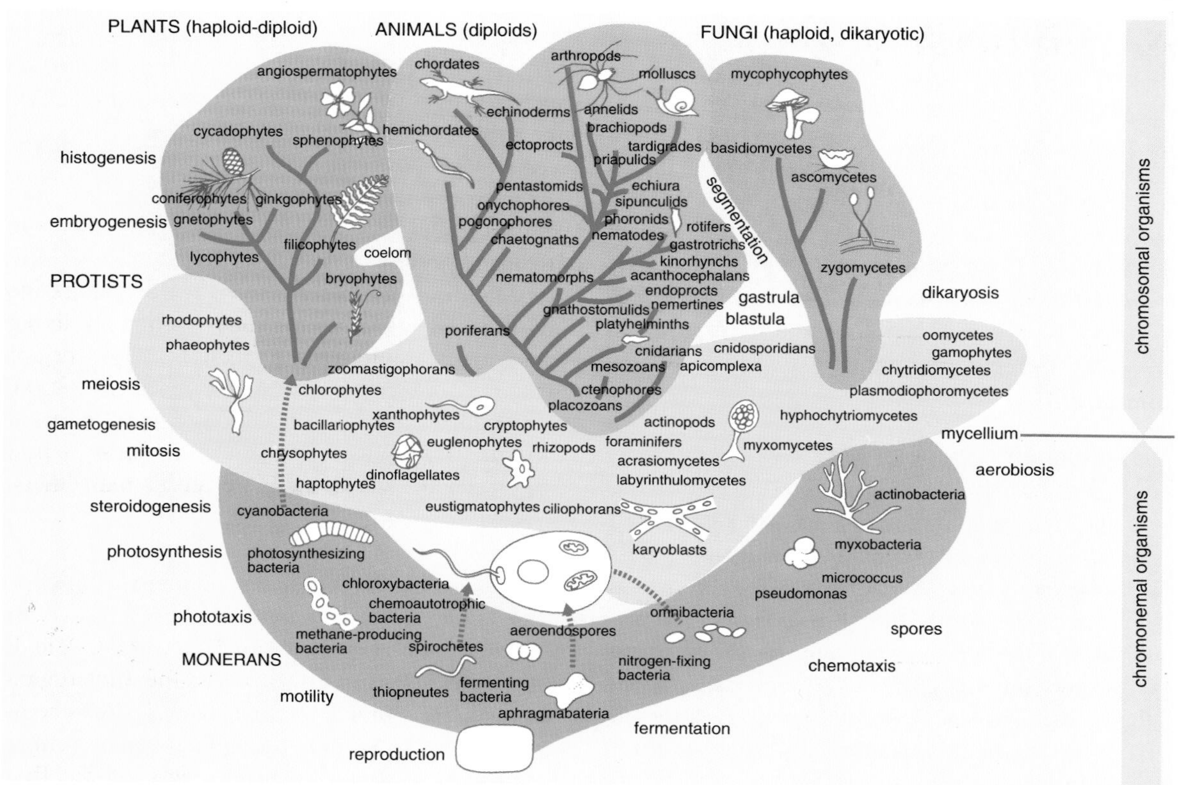

30 The classification of the organisms has suffered radical changes due to increased knowledge of the fine structure of cells and the various hypotheses that have been put forward regarding the origin of life as well as understanding of the eukaryotic cell. The division into two kingdoms, animal and plant, based on the capacity for movement and whether the organism obtained characteristics and food through other organisms or from minerals and sunlight, which have been attributed to the animal and plant kingdoms respectively, has become obsolete. It's now believed that the main differences between organisms are not based on motility or nutrition, but on whether the organisms are prokaryotes or eukaryotes—that is whether or not they have a cellular structure with a nucleus. The system of classification of organisms into five kingdoms proposed by R.H. Whittaker (1924-1980) in 1959 is now the most widely accepted. In this scheme, all the prokaryotic microorganisms, that is the bacteria and related organisms, belong to the kingdom Monera. The eukaryotes belong to the remaining four kingdoms: (1) the protists which include all the unicells, whether autotrophs or heterotrophs. Protists include many genera which were previously considered algae, protozoa, or fungi; (2) the photosynthesizing plants adapted to a terrestrial life; (3) the multicellular animals with internal digestion; (4) and the fungi. *[Diagram: Biopunt, from various sources]*

Biochemistry, the chemistry of living matter, is based on reduced carbon compounds, in other words on molecules formed essentially by carbon atoms surrounded by hydrogen atoms. The chemical flexibility of carbon chemistry is one of the basic secrets of life on Earth. No one now doubts that in the very unstable conditions of the first few hundred million years of the Archean Eon, carbon atoms could have easily combined with hydrogen, nitrogen, oxygen, phosphorus, and sulfur to generate a wide variety of substances. This combination of molecules with a high carbon content must have prevailed long enough to interact and evolve, whether in the primitive prebiotic "soup" suggested by the Russian biochemist Alexander I. Oparin (1894-1980), the British physiologist John B.S. Haldane (1892-1964), and many other authors, or, as has been suggested in more recent hypotheses, in the shallow pools or the hot, water-drenched surfaces of primitive Earth, where hydrogen-rich gases emanating from the Earth's interior reacted with carbon-rich gases in the atmosphere in an aqueous medium, where they could remain in solutions of sufficiently high concentration. It could also be that the submerged—or at least damp—surfaces of clay and crystals on Hadean earth favored the polymerization of small organic molecules into larger and more complex ones.

The supposition that the abiotic synthesis of organic compounds would not have required particularly long periods of time has been confirmed both by empirical data facilitated by extraterrestrial objects, such as comets and meteorites, and by laboratory data collected since 1953, when experiments simulating this synthesis were carried out for the first time. In these experiments they prepared a mixture of gases similar to the one which is thought to have existed in the Earth's primitive atmosphere (ammonia, water vapor, hydrogen, and methane). They subjected this mixture to electrical discharges for several days and obtained a group of organic compounds, among which they found two amino acids, alanine and glycine. Later, starting with mixtures of simple gases and using different energy sources (electrical discharges, ultraviolet radiation, or heat), more complex organic compounds, including amino acids and the base units of nucleic acids, were synthesized. There is no doubt, then, that these molecules could have existed on Hadean Earth. In some of the most recent experiments, even adenosine triphosphate (ATP) molecules have been formed, as well as other pre-nucleotide triphosphate molecules and the five nucleotides (adenine, cytosine, guanine, thymine, and uracil), which are components of nucleic acids. It is worth adding that, as could very well have happened in the Earth's primitive atmospheres, these laboratory-produced Hadean mixtures yielded other organic compounds unknown or nonexistent in living beings today. Their identity and possible function in primitive life still remain a mystery. However, it is not unlikely that they played some role in the structure or metabolism of some primitive micro-organisms that have since disappeared, although some authors do not discount the possibility that some of these products were toxic.

These considerations give rise to the theoretical possibility that life may have originated on Earth more than once and was extinguished every time except once. In any event, in practice, the great similarity between all known organisms in terms of their fundamental biochemical and genetic aspects seems to confirm a common origin for all of them.

The molecular bases of life

It is clear that in all living organisms today there are a certain number of molecule types without which it is impossible to conceive of the existence of life. Their universal presence in all cells would seem to indicate that they are molecules already present in the oldest common antecedents of all present-day living things, including ourselves. Furthermore, they are related to the basic characteristics common to all cells, and no organism would be able to survive without them. These molecules are adenosine triphosphate (ATP), nucleic acids, and phospholipids.

ATP

Every living cell contains adenosine triphosphate (ATP). Its presence is necessary for reactions requiring large amounts of energy, whether the main source of energy is sunlight or the assimilation of organic molecules through the ingestion of food. Even the simplest cells need food and energy to be able to grow and multiply. The energy obtained from ATP allows the cells to produce nucleic acids and proteins from precursors present in the environment. As we have seen, ATP can easily be obtained from hypothetical models of Archean atmospheres in the presence of phosphates, and its presence in organisms is universal. We cannot discount the possibility, therefore, that the first cells obtained their energy in the most direct way, using ATP as a food. Even more, it is possible that they used ATP together with other energy-rich molecules related to ATP, such as guanosine triphosphate (GTP) and uridine triphosphate (UTP). With the growth of the cell population, the rate of consumption of these substances must have easily outstripped the rate of spontaneous synthesis, and only those cells that developed their own internal ATP production mechanisms could survive. It is likely that one of the first of these mechanisms was fermentation. It is still the most common mechanism today, and we shall return to consider it later.

Nucleic acids

All cells also contain replication systems based on nucleic acids, without which neither reproduction nor growth would be possible.

The exact replication of deoxyribonucleic acid molecules (DNA) is essential for the reproduction of organisms and for the maintenance of a species' identity. Modifications that are introduced sporadically into this replication system represent the biochemical basis of evolution and explain the origin, from a limited number of cells formed more than 3,500 million years ago, of millions of species of plants, animals, fungi, protists, and monera in existence today, as well as those which existed in earlier times and are today extinct.

DNA molecules are polymers, long chains of similar units: the so-called *nucleotides*. Each nucleotide is formed by a phosphate group, a sugar molecule (deoxyribose) and a nitrogen-containing unit (base). Although the number of nucleotides can be very high, millions even, only four unique types of nitrogen-containing bases, either adenine, cytosine, guanine, or thymine, intervene in their composition.

Ribonucleic acid molecules are also nucleotide polymers, but in this case their sugar part is ribose; the nitrogen-containing bases can be adenosine, cytosine, guanine, or uracil and the chains themselves are generally much shorter.

Phospholipids

Finally, all cells possess phospholipid molecules, indispensable for the formation of membranes that make them individual and regulate their exchanges with the environment. Phospholipids contain fatty acid radicals and phosphate groups. They form chains with very different properties at their two extremes; one of them, the polar "head," has an electric charge and is hydrophilic (having an affinity with water), while the other, the nonpolar "tail," is hydrophobic and only interacts with organic solvents. In an aqueous medium, these molecules initially tend to group together in small spherical structures with the "tails" driven inwards and the hydrophilic "heads" on the outside, so long as the "tails" are flexible enough and not too long. If they are more rigid or longer they begin to gather together in a sheet which forms a double layer (bilayer) with the "tails" pointing towards each other and the "heads" facing out. This lipid bilayer formation can close in on itself and form a sphere, enclosing an aqueous medium in its interior that is thus sealed off from the rest of the solvent.

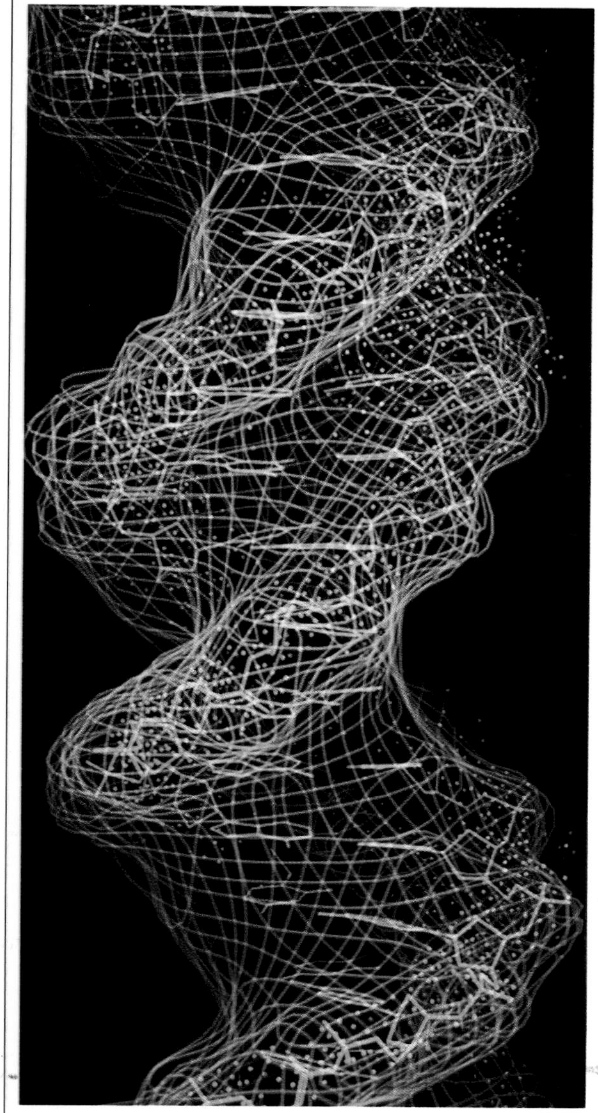

The biogenetic process

From what we have seen, we cannot rule out the hypothesis that today's life on Earth could have had ancestors with molecular characteristics different from those of today's organisms. Furthermore we can not overlook the fact that many forms of living matter may have become extinct before the ones that have persisted until today originated. If a life form based on chemical principles different from those which govern today's ever did exist, it has disappeared without trace. Today we can only go back as far as those ancestors with the same duplication and self-maintenance mechanisms that we find in all present-day organisms, from the most primitive bacteria to humans. Thes are mechanisms based on the chemistry of nucleic acids, the accumulation of energy in the bands of adenosine triphosphate, and the regulation of an internal medium through exchanges with the exterior across semipermeable membranes.

But what were these common ancestors like? From comparisons of gene sequences common to the three great evolutionary lines currently recognized [bacteria (eubacteria), archaebacteria and eukaryotes], we can deduce that there must have been an organism very similar to today's prokaryotes. It must have had a genome based on DNA and a transcription and transfer apparatus based on RNA and on the RNA polymerase enzyme. It also must have had a group of the most important enzymes for cellular metabolism, including some of those responsible for active transport through membranes and others involved in different metabolic pathways.

Going back even further means delving into more or less consistent, but always debatable, hypotheses. It is not implausible that that ancestor common to all present organisms had been preceded by a long series of more primitive organisms in which the synthesis of proteins, the genomes based on DNA, the biosynthesis of components of the membrane, and the energy transfer systems had appeared not as a result of prebiotic chemical processes but of biological processes of an evolutionary nature.

Prebiotic evolution

In the 1920s the Russian biochemist Alexander I. Oparin and the English geneticist J.B.S. Haldane had indicated that one of the indispensable requirements for the evolution of living matter from prebiotic organic molecules was the absence of free oxygen in the atmosphere; otherwise oxygen would have actively reacted with the compounds and they would have been short-lived. These first researchers, who presented hypotheses on the origin of life on Earth in their experimental plan, also postulated the existence of a primitive prebiotic "soup" at the heart of the Earth's oceans, still devoid of living beings. Because of the difficulty represented by the weak concentration of organic material that could have resulted from the dissolution at the heart of the great oceans of organic material synthesized at the heart of the atmosphere, many of today's authors support the hypothesis of an origin of life linked to shallow pools or coastal areas affected by the tide or beaten by waves.

Without free oxygen that could react with them and destroy them, amino acid molecules, nucleotides, and sugars were able to maintain themselves without alteration either in solution or, even better, in adsorption on some surface. In these conditions a molecule, such as that of ATP, could form from the union of adenine with ribose (basically a simple five-carbon sugar) and three phosphate groups.

31 Model of the structure of a DNA molecule. The nucleic acids (DNA and RNA) constitute the basis of the systems of replication that all living cells possess, and without which neither reproduction, nor growth would be possible. The universal presence of these molecules leads one to believe in a common origin for them. The molecules of DNA are large chains of identical units, the deoxyribose nucleotides. Each nucleotide is made up of a phosphate group, a sugar molecule (desoxyribose), and a nitrogenated organic base. But there are four kinds of nitrogenated bases (adenosine, guanine, cytosine and thymine) and for this reason there are four types of different deoxyribose nucleotides. The DNA molecule can become very large and contain millions of nucleotides.
[Photo: J.C. Révy / CNRI]

32 The Russian biochemist Aleksandr Ivanovich Oparin (Moscow, 1894-1980) and the Britain John Burdon Haldane (Oxford, 1892-Bhubaneshvar, 1964) were pioneers in the study of the formation of the first organic molecules. Studying inorganic compounds in an atmosphere without oxygen and under the effects of ultraviolet solar radiation they reached the conclusion that one of the necessary conditions for the evolution of life from non-living organic material was, in effect, that the atmosphere could not contain oxygen, since oxygen would have reacted with any organic compound. *[Photo: AGE Fotostock]*

Some molecules could have become catalysts, facilitating and accelerating the union or separation of other molecules without themselves being destroyed in the process of the reaction. These catalysts were—and still are—vitally important for living matter because they introduce order and organization in certain chemical processes that would only take place at random without them. Gradually these catalysts, and the reactions they facilitated, must have proliferated more than other combinations in the waters of primitive Earth. Even though they became more and more complex, they did not have to require any more energy for this. Today, some groups of molecules can auto-catalyze, either in an orderly or a cyclic manner. This process involves a whole series of surprisingly intricate reactions, in such a way that each change acts on another in the molecular chain. Some of these "inert" auto-catalytic reactions produce even more complex models; and this increasing complexity as time goes by reminds us of phenomena akin to living matter.

Hypercyclic self-organization

Both theoretical calculations and laboratory tests seem to suggest that the interaction of two or more self-catalytic cycles could have resulted in a "hypercycle." According to some researchers, though, if this had been the case, some such catalysts would have started "competing" for elements in their environment. This would have automatically limited their numbers. However, the basic idea of this hypercycle could be quite the opposite: far from mutually destroying each other in a chemical "struggle for existence," these self-organized compounds must have complemented each other to produce, through replication, structures similar to living matter. This type of cyclic process similarly formed the foundations, not only of the first "cells," but also of a whole group of subsequent structures based on cells and their products. Cyclic processes are very important for life: they allow living beings to preserve key elements of their past, despite the fluctuations and tendency towards disorder present in their broader environment. Moreover, this linking of processes permit the energy that is released in the exothermic (heat-releasing) reactions to be used to facilitate the realization of endothermic (heat-absorbing) reactions that would not otherwise be possible.

As organic molecules became better protected and more concentrated, so their activity was able to become more prolonged, complex, and self-reinforcing. Some were perhaps protected by a bubble or stuck to the surface of clays or crystals. In the more remote Archean times, nature's experiments with long chains of hydrocarbon must have managed to produce phospholipid-type molecules, capable of encapsulating a tiny drop of water that once surrounded them, together with whatever this contained, while still allowing for the movement of other molecules both inside and outside the enclosure that they formed. This is, in other words, the minimum expression of a semipermeable membrane surrounding a cell.

The appearance of membranes

There is no doubt that the formation of membranes must have played an essential role in the appearance of the first cells. In present-day organisms, membranes are made up of different types of lipids, proteins, and carbohydrates. Their functions are so complex and calibrated with such precision that we are still a long way from being able to understand them completely. Probably, though, the first membranes were much simpler, little more than a double layer of phospholipids that, differing from other possible encapsulating structures, man-

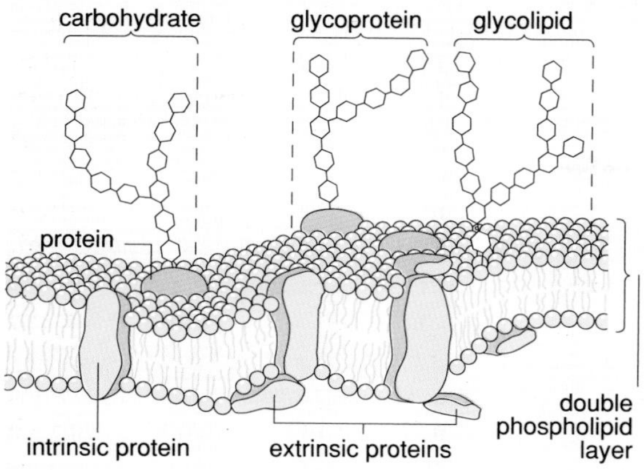

aged to concentrate a solution of other carbon compounds, thanks to their unique chemical properties. They were thus able to capture different substances from their immediate environment to be used as nutrients, which were able to interact on the inside, while at the same time preventing the water inside from escaping.

The appearance of the membrane opened up the way for the first discreet unit of the living world to be produced: the prokaryotic cell. Before, though, the majority of researchers think that proteins and lipids combined in translucent flakes of still non-living matter before the beginning of life proper. We know of no life form that does not have some form of membrane. It was probably not just once but on several occasions that amino acids, simple sugars, phosphates, and their derivatives, under the protection of a bubble of lipids, combined into complexes, using solar energy and absorbing ATP and other carbon and nitrogen compounds from the outside as "food." First of all, some of these lipid bubbles must have been able to divide simply from the force of surface tension without either half having to interrupt its own internal activity. Later, adequate catalyst molecules could have begun a more active maintenance of the lipidic membranes. Perhaps when the necessary components available in the limited niche that they occupied ran out, these protocells simply disappeared as others took shape in another pool left by the tide, each one with workings slightly different than another.

The tendency towards autopoiesis

A living being, to be properly qualified as such, has to be autopoietic, or able to maintain itself actively against aggressions from the outside. Life responds to disturbances by using material and energy to remain intact. An organism is constantly exchanging its parts and renewing its chemical components without losing its identity. Living organisms have the task of trying to maintain the conditions in which they arise and develop. This modulating, holistic phenomenon of autopoiesis, of active self-preservation, is the basis of all known life: all cells react against external disturbances in order to preserve, within their limits, key aspects of their identity.

A structure like that of these protocells, once capable of sustaining itself, has then to achieve the capacity to reproduce itself in order to remain alive. Protocellular systems were what the Russian-born Belgian Ilya Prigogine called "dissipative structures," in other words, objects or processes that are self-organizing and spontaneously change shape. With an injection of energy, dissipative structures can become more, rather than less, ordered.

From dissipative structures and hypercycles, chains of nucleotides, ribose, and phosphates emerged that could not only self-replicate but could also catalyze chemical reactions: RNA, the first expression of nature's language. Still not autopoietic but highly structured, primitive RNA, in small spheres surrounded by layers of lipids, must have accumulated in warm waters rich in organic material on a benign Earth. With no predators and with plenty of energy available, they continued to become more and more complex, giving rise to forms with delicate equilibrium and highly advanced interactions.

Even before the emergence of life proper on Hadean Earth, it is likely that two chemical tendencies appeared: self-reference and autocatalysis. These were cyclic reactions of chemical substances that produced version after version of themselves with a tendency to create a favorable atmosphere for the repetition of the original reactions. One step more and they must have been able to begin organizing themselves into autopoietic structures capable of using energy to maintain themselves actively and successfully against important external disturbances, and with ever more clearly distinguished limits. At some stage, more than 3,500 million years ago (and maybe even more than 3,900 million), one of these structures, sealed off with a lipidic membrane, and with proteins and RNA inside, began to multiply. This microscopic cluster of cells, similar to today's bacteria, were the first manifestation of what we today understand as life. Once autopoiesis assured their survival and reproduction guaranteed their expansion, evolution had taken its first tentative steps. The age of the prokaryotes had begun.

33 The membrane isolates the cell from the medium. Life, such as we know it, shares some basic features that we suppose already existed in the first living organisms—or at least in the first manifestations of life that did not become extinct: a) the accumulation of energy in bonds of ATP, b) replication by means of the nucleic acids, and c) regulation of the internal medium through exchanges with the exterior through semipermeable membranes. The formation of the membranes was linked to the very nature of the phospholipids, strongly polarized molecules that are hydrophilic at one end and hydrophobic at the other, and that in an aqueous medium tended to form small spherical groups with the hydrophobic tails to the interior and the hydrophilic heads to the outside. These molecules can enclose a drop of water and still permit a molecular exchange between the enclosed space inside and the outer space; this is the principle of the formation of semipermeable membranes, a mitone in the formation of the first cells.
[Diagram: Editrònica, from various sources]

Life, the Earth's heritage

Long before "flying saucers" and UFOs (Unidentified Flying Objects) fired the imagination of many people, some astronomers and thinkers had already asked themselves if there was life on other planets.

Copernicus's astrolabe
University of Cracow [E. Lessing / Zardoya]

From time immemorial, stargazers have wondered whether there might be life in outer space. Giordano Bruno, a heretic burned at the stake, believed the heavens to be filled with life. Plato, in a more philosophical vein, named the planets after animals. After Charles Darwin gathered overwhelming evidence for the theory of evolution, scientists speculated on the possible existence of extraterrestrial life in evolutionary terms. The so-called Green Bank equation of Frank Drake and Carl Sagan attempted to predict the likelihood of detecting such life beyond the Earth by multiplying variables to calculate the chance that a star has planets orbiting it, that life has arisen on such planets, and that such life is intelligent and technologically proficient enough to communicate by sending electromagnetic messages through the interstellar medium. Nonetheless such a quantitative approach does not really put speculations concerning the possibilities of life in outer space on a firmer basis: if any one of these variables is zero, then the chances of finding extraterrestrial life will be, according to the equation, zero.

THE MAN FROM VENUS
by PAUL

A scientific conception of life on earth's nearest neighbor. Science says Venus is a sister world and human forms of life are more possible than on any other planet.
(For further details see page 97)
Copyright, FANTASTIC ADVENTURES 1939

Impact of a meteorite [AGE Fotostock]

Advances in computer technology have allowed radioastronomers searching for extraterrestrial intelligence to examine several million radio frequencies simultaneously, especially on the relatively interference-free so-called hydrogen (1.4 GHz) and hydroxyl (1.7 GHz) lines, chosen as attractive bands for transmission partly because hydrogen is the most abundant element in the cosmos. No life has been yet detected in outer space. The evidence for life elsewhere remains nonexistent, and exobiology, the study of such life, remains the only science without a true subject matter to study.

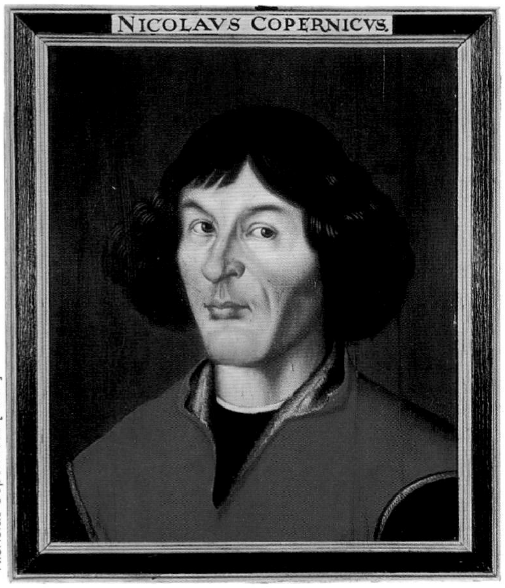

Nicholas Copernicus [AISA]

The debate between scientists on the possibility of life elsewhere has crystallized into two camps, those who speculate that the universe is rich with life, and those who argue that we are alone in the cosmos. One powerful argument in favor of extraterrestrial life is an essentially "Copernican" argument. Copernicus showed that the Earth is not the center of the universe, but a mere adjunct to the sun, itself a medium-sized star in the periphery of a typical spiral galaxy. In the same way, those who argue for life in outer space suggest that the belief in our own uniqueness is an anthropocentric conceit. The rise of modern science, they argue, has been accompanied by a series of blows to humanity's view of itself as a special, chosen, and divine species. As Copernicus showed the Earth not to be central, so Darwin showed humankind to be simply a natural result of animal evolution. It is a kind of human arrogance, this argument goes, to believe that our planet is the only one imbued with life.

All life on Earth is the result of energetic transformations of carbon, hydrogen, oxygen, phosphorus, nitrogen, and sulfur—elements common throughout the cosmos. Moreover, the gaseous giants—Jupiter, Saturn, Uranus, and Neptune, and their moons—of our own solar system contain chemical environments thought to be similar to those prevailing on the Earth during the time when life evolved from nonliving matter. Why should the universe, an immense 15,000 million light-years in space, not contain countless environments similar to the early Earth in some of which, at least, life, and perhaps intelligent life, has arisen? Opponents of this argument refer back to the absence of evidence and raise the question, put succinctly by physicist Enrico Fermi, "Where is everybody?"

Some have even speculated that civilizations even slightly more technically advanced than *Homo sapiens sapiens* would have constructed robotic machines capable of reproducing themselves. However, since no trace of these has been found, it seems logical to assume that there is no life elsewhere. Or perhaps, as some science fiction writers have suggested, we are being studiously avoided. There is also the pessimistic possibility that a technical intelligence, far from being evolutionarily adaptive, leads rapidly to overpopulation and nuclear destruction, thus cancelling itself out. According to this grim scenario, nobody is answering our call because all who could have contacted us already killed themselves off.

Perhaps the most sanguine area for scientific work on the question of extraterrestrial life deals not with the discovery of life similar to our own on other planets, but the spreading of the Earth's "biospheric" form of life into the solar system and beyond. A study of the evolution of life on Earth reveals that individuality in organisms has evolved in several distinct ways from symbiotic cellular aggregates. The first sort of life to evolve was bacteria, some of which evolved desiccation—and radiation—resistant resting forms, called spores. Symbiotic groupings of bacteria led to the origin of amoeba-like cells with nuclei, including the eukaryotic cells ancestral to all plants, animals, and fungi. Thus life on Earth, ultimately a growing chemical transformation of the energy of the sun, has in its prehistory achieved at least three distinct forms of identity: the bacterial cell (prokaryotes), the amoeboid cell (eukaryotes), and the larger organisms (multicellular eukaryotes such as individual plants and animals).

Detail of the Mayall telescope [P. Fuson - Magnum / Zardoya]

As human population pressure increases and creates pollution throughout the planet, we see the beginnings of yet another level of individuality or identity: human-constructed closed ecosystems that mirror the organization of the biosphere. The planetary biosphere shows autoregulatory traits similar to those of the physiological system of an animal. Closed ecosystems containing self-recycling assemblages of microbes, plants, and animals will be necessary for long space voyages or the settlement of other worlds. From a cosmic perspective of planetary evolution, human beings and our technical intelligence may be a prerequisite for the reproduction of the planetary system known as the biosphere. To survive such astronomic violence as the nuclear explosion of the Sun, life will require copies of itself at the biospheric level of organization. From this point of view life, on Earth is like a seed and is just beginning to glimpse, from the depths of its soil, the nurturing light of distant stars.

34 The landscape of Hveravellir, in the center of Iceland, is one of the few emerged areas in which the processes of formation of new terrestrial crust can be observed. It evokes, with its thermal springs, the kinds of landscapes that were common on the Earth at the end of the Hadean and beginning of the Archaean. During the Hadean era, between 4,500 and 3,900 years ago, there was no solid land, no oceans, and no lakes. The planet was a ball of molten lava, burning through the decomposition of the radioactive elements in its interior, from which emerged spouts of water through geysers water, so hot that it remained in the upper levels of the atmosphere as water vapor. The continuous volcanic activity, though gradually decreasing, filled the atmosphere with toxic gases which surrounded a lifeless Earth. None of the rocks which were formed survived that period of chaos. Later, about 3,900 million years ago, as the surface of the Earth cooled, the clouds of vapor which filled the atmosphere began to produce torrential rains and formed warm, not very deep oceans. Thus the Archaean era began, an era which saw the beginnings of life, and its spread over the Earth in the form of bacterial mats. *[Photo: Martyn Chillmaid / Oxford Scientific Films / Firo Foto]*

3.2 Evolution without oxygen

As we have already indicated, chemical evolution occurred before there was free oxygen in the Earth's atmosphere. The first bacteria lived in an anaerobic world. This represents a very important difference between the earliest bacteria and most of present-day ones for which gaseous oxygen is indispensable. For those first living beings, oxygen was a dangerous toxin. Earth, like its neighbors Mars or Venus, would still have nearly no free oxygen today if it had not been for the action of bacteria that produce oxygen as a product of their metabolism. Oxygen is not a usual component of volcanic gases, and only a small quantity of it is formed in the upper atmosphere through the action of ultraviolet rays causing the breakdown of water molecules. Given its chemical activity, oxygen tends to react, not just in the atmosphere on Earth, but also on that of other planets. Only its prodigious production by the first bacteria (and later by algae and plants) assures its planetary presence.

First biochemical strategies

It is very likely that the first organisms, were similar to the smallest ones we know today. The DNA of the tiniest cells is insufficient to be able to make all the amino acids, nucleotides, vitamins, and enzymes needed for self-maintenance and reproduction, and the earliest organisms also must have been similarly limited. Probably less than 0.5 micrometers in diameter, our DNA-containing bacterial ancestors themselves may have evolved from the RNA world, cells lacking both DNA and protein. We know that RNA molecules both catalyze (like protein) and replicate (like DNA). Such RNA cells probably were the first living beings on Earth. The majority of the smallest bacteria that have been studied are parasites that get what they need from the animal or plant within which they reside. In Hadean times, the conditions were equally severe. Without the barrier of the ozone layer and in the absence of oxygen, the first living cells freely fed from the organic chemicals accumulated in the environment by the action of solar radiation and electrical discharges on mixtures of carbon—and nitrogen—rich atmospheric gases. The earliest cells were probably heterotrophs, which feed on organic molecules of the same type as those from which they themselves were made: amino acids, sugars, short chain organic acids, and ATP.

However, the day came when the chemical feast ended. Those atmosphere-derived chemicals were rapidly depleted by microbes using them to grow and multiply in every space they occupied. Without doubt in the first few million years of life's implantation, each "famine," every survival crisis, every change in climate or pollution catastrophe, due to gases produced through the metabolism of the microbes, was the cause of death of some (and may be almost all) of patches of life then spreading over the Earth. Life must have fluctuated at rates depending on how fast sunlight triggered the synthesis of more nutrients. In fact, life would have totally disappeared in a very short space of time if it had not been for one vital and fundamental trait: DNA's capacity to self-replicate and to introduce, in certain copies, random changes that led to mutant cells.

Just as the replication of DNA is necessary for the continuity of life, so mutation, in the broad sense of hereditary change, is absolutely essential for the processes of evolution. Without mutation, there can be no "descent with modification" that Darwinian formulation of evolution requires. Thanks to their tiny size and enormous number, microbial populations respond quite readily to most major environmental changes. If supplied with food and energy, bacteria grow and reproduce without cessation. A rapidly reproducing bacterium would take only 20 minutes to grow enough to divide. In two days a single bacterium would produce 2^{144} offspring, a number greater than the total population of humans that have ever lived. In four days of unlimited growth, this bacterium would have produced 2^{288} offspring, much larger than the number of protons (roughly 2^{266}) or quarks that physicists have estimated to exist in the universe.

This biotic potential of reproduction is not realized in life on Earth, but it serves as a useful reminder to us of the power of exponential reproduction. About once in every million cell divisions, a bacterium appears that differs from its parent: it is a mutant. Most mutants die because the nature of their difference has a negative effect on their self-maintenance or reproduction. But some mutants do succeed and grow, reproducing rapidly in the medium in which they occur. All the environmental variables—temperature, quality and quantity of light, acidity, concentration of salts and organic compounds in the water—tend to diversify the microbe populations according to their location, selecting those mutants best adapted to the specific conditions found there.

Fermentation

One of the first metabolic innovations, selected for its adaptive value, probably enabled bacteria to use sugars to obtain and store energy, by means of the production of ATP molecules from ADP and phosphate. The compounds derived from sugar—alcohols and acids—were excreted as waste. This process, which takes place in the absence of free oxygen, we call *fermentation*: it still operates today in many organisms.

The fermentation process uses simple sugars like glucose, fructose, alcohols, organic acids, or even carbohydrates with long chains of sugars, like cellulose or starch. They can also start from simple compounds containing nitrogen, like amino acids. The final residue can be carbon dioxide and ethanol, as is the case with today's bacteria and yeasts, which ferment the juices of different fruits or grains to produce alcoholic drinks. The excretion products may be acetic acid or lactic acid, as in the fermentation of sugar to form vinegar (acetic acid) or of milk to form yogurt, or in the ripening of certain cheeses containing lactic acid.

Fermentation generally provides the fermenter with a few ATP molecules for each molecule of degraded sugar. It is not a very efficient process, since its products—acids and alcohols—still contain energy. The evolution of some fermentative bacteria led to selection pressure for the appearance of other bacteria that degraded their residues obtaining the carbon and energy left in them. These play a similar role to that of eukaryotic organisms feeding on animal feces, such as dung-beetles or the shaggy mane fungus. Microbial food chains of this type still exist on intertidal mud flats, lakes, and soils.

They also live in the guts of insects such as wood-eating cockroaches and termites, in stagnant water, and any place where there are carbohydrates to ferment and oxygen and light are in short supply. This ancestral fermentation capacity is used as a strategy by some more recent organisms, such as aerobic marine animals. Our own leg muscle cells, when, for example, we get tired by climbing stairs, momentarily bypass their aerobic metabolism and revert to the old type of fermentative metabolism, producing lactic acid. Even though it is less efficient as a way of deriving ATP, fermentative metabolism, a legacy of our past history, is still used in all animals, including humans.

Nitrogen from the air

Some extant fermenting bacteria that probably most resemble early bacteria are the Clostridia, some of which also survived by developing the ability to use nitrogen in the form of atmospheric gas as source of protein nitrogen. Using a battery of enzymes (easily destroyed by oxygen), they attack the bond in gaseous nitrogen (N_2) and "fix" the nitrogen into molecules of amino acids, nucleotides, and other organic compounds, thus making the huge source of atmospheric nitrogen available to the rest of the biosphere.

Nitrogen fixation requires a considerable quantity of energy (from 6 to 18 ATP molecules per nitrogen molecule). To do this on large scale, as, for example,in the industrial process which produces chemical fertilizers, requires high pressure (300 atmospheres) and temperature (932°F or 500°C). No plant, animal, protoctist, or fungus—and hardly any bacteria—is capable of nitrogen fixation at low temperature. All organisms depend on nitrogen-fixing bacteria for their survival. Without these, life would disappear from Earth through lack of nitrogen, even though this is the most abundant compound in the Earth's present atmosphere. Clostridia species, together with other bacteria that evolved later, such as *Azotobacter* and *Rhizobium* species, found on the roots of legumes, including some cyanobacteria, have supplied nitrogen compounds to the whole biosphere since Archean times.

Certainly the early populations of fermenters—even though some could also use carbon dioxide (CO_2) from the air—still required compounds produced in the environment for their nutrition. As prebiotically produced organic compounds became scarce, the selection pressures intensified. Life might not have continued if new strategies had not developed that enabled organisms to produce their own energy and nutrients from materials in the environment.

Sulfate reduction from the water

An early metabolic pathway that could be considered a step toward autotrophy arose in the lineage of the group of bacteria currently represented by the genus *Desulfovibrio*: they display a capacity to "breathe" sulfates, and to generate ATP from the conversion of sulfate into sulfide through the transfer of high energy electrons from one of the stages of fermentation to sulfate. *Desulfovibrio*,

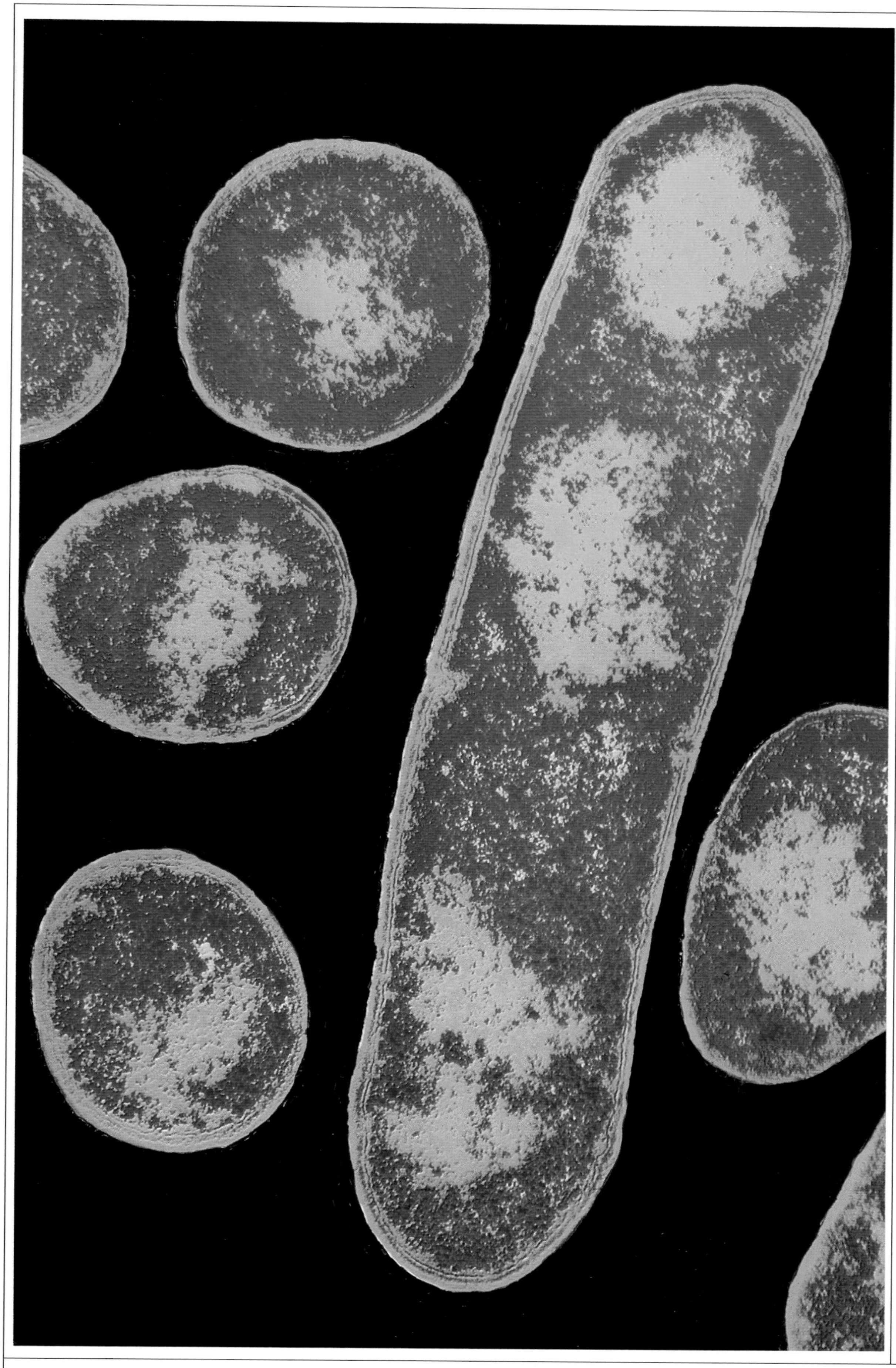

35 One of the present-day fermenters which most resembles the first primitive prokaryotes, (to which we owe probably the continuity of life on Earth, since they were able to produce nutrients themselves from simple and abundant molecules in the medium at a time when they began to become scarce), is *Clostridium*, which—with *Azotobacter*—has been identified in the sediments and waters of lakes. Of *Clostridium*, it is estimated that in natural waters it can fix between 0.07 mg and 7.2 mg of N per m^3 a day, making it potentially more important than the cyanobacteria in the fixation of nitrogen. Denitrification of fresh water has been intensified by human action, because it has increased the cyanophyceae. When N is lacking, as happens in very slightly mineralized water of rivers and boggy areas, or in water where there has been substantial denitrification in the hypolimnion, or in the sediment of lakes, or in contaminated rivers, the nitrogen becomes a necessary function of the organism, which confers a competitive advantage on those prokaryotes that have this capacity. Nitrogen fixation presupposes the existence of a reducing medium, but can coexist with photosynthesis in separate cells (heterocysts of cyanobacteria) and even in the cells themselves. Low concentrations of oxygen are not always necessary. Some riverbank trees also fix nitrogen, such as the alders (*Alnus*) and macrophytes associated with cyanobacteria such as *Azolla*. *[Photo: A.B. Bowsett-Science Photo Library / AGE Fotostock (x 50,000)]*

like other similar bacteria (*Desulfotomaculum*, *Desulfuromonas*, etc.) live in anaerobic sediments which contain organic matter and sulfate ions (SO_4^{2-}), in the mud at the bottom of the sea and in lakes. They can ferment organic compounds like lactic and pyruvic acid, producing acetic acid. However, they obtain more ATP if they simultaneously transform sulfate into sulfide (S^{2-}), which can be as released gases into the environment in the form of hydrogen sulfide (H_2S) or dimethyl sulfide (H_3CSCH_3), both noted for their strong odor, similar to rotten eggs or decomposing algae.

The reduction of sulfate requires protein molecules called porphyrins, which consist of four pyrrole rings linked by CH bridges with a heavy metal atom in the center. This porphyrin and metal complex is called a *heme* group. Such heme groups are also frequent in the protein complexes, called cytochromes, that sulfate-reducing bacteria require for "sulfate respiration." It is also present in the hemoglobin in animal blood, where it helps transport oxygen from the respiratory organs to all the cells.

Toward photosynthesis

Porphyrin and protein complexes like cytochromes must have been an early evolutionary acquisition, because they are nearly universally distributed. Only bacteria who generate ATP exclusively by fermentation lack the ability to synthesize heme proteins. Nevertheless, as many types of bacteria acquired the capacity to produce porphyrin rings, they also were able to develop an ability to use the most dependable and abundant of all energy sources: light from the Sun.

When a molecule receives light, its electrons are raised to a higher energy level. Normally this energy is simply dissipated in the form of light or heat, and the molecule returns to its initial state. But when these molecules are in contact with porphyrins attached to proteins and embedded in membranes, like those in the sulfate-reducers, the light energy can be retained and used in the form of chemical energy bound to ATP. ATP energy can then be used for movement and for processes of synthesis, such as the conversion of atmospheric CO_2 into food, and in the replication of nucleic acids necessary for self-maintenance and growth. This bacterial process of obtaining food through light and air, called photosynthesis, completely frees certain groups of microbes from dependence on preformed organic compounds.

All other photosynthetic organisms contain some form of *chlorophyll*, a group of green pigments based on a porphyrin ring in which the metal is a magnesium atom. Thus the appearance of photosynthesis, probably the single most important innovation in the evolution of life, was only possible thanks to the prior development of porphyrin synthesis.

36 The development of large populations of sulphur bacteria is characteristic of many aquatic systems of karstic origin. These microorganisms are able to use the hydrogen sulphide acid produced in the anaerobic sediments as donors of electrons, and are also able to fix carbon using their distinctive purple. The small pond of Can Cisó, in Banyoles (Catalonia), is dyed red because of large populations of purple bacteria which originate during the vertical mixing of the waters, when there is hydrogen sulphide acid in the entire hydric column.
[Photo: Ricard Guerrero]

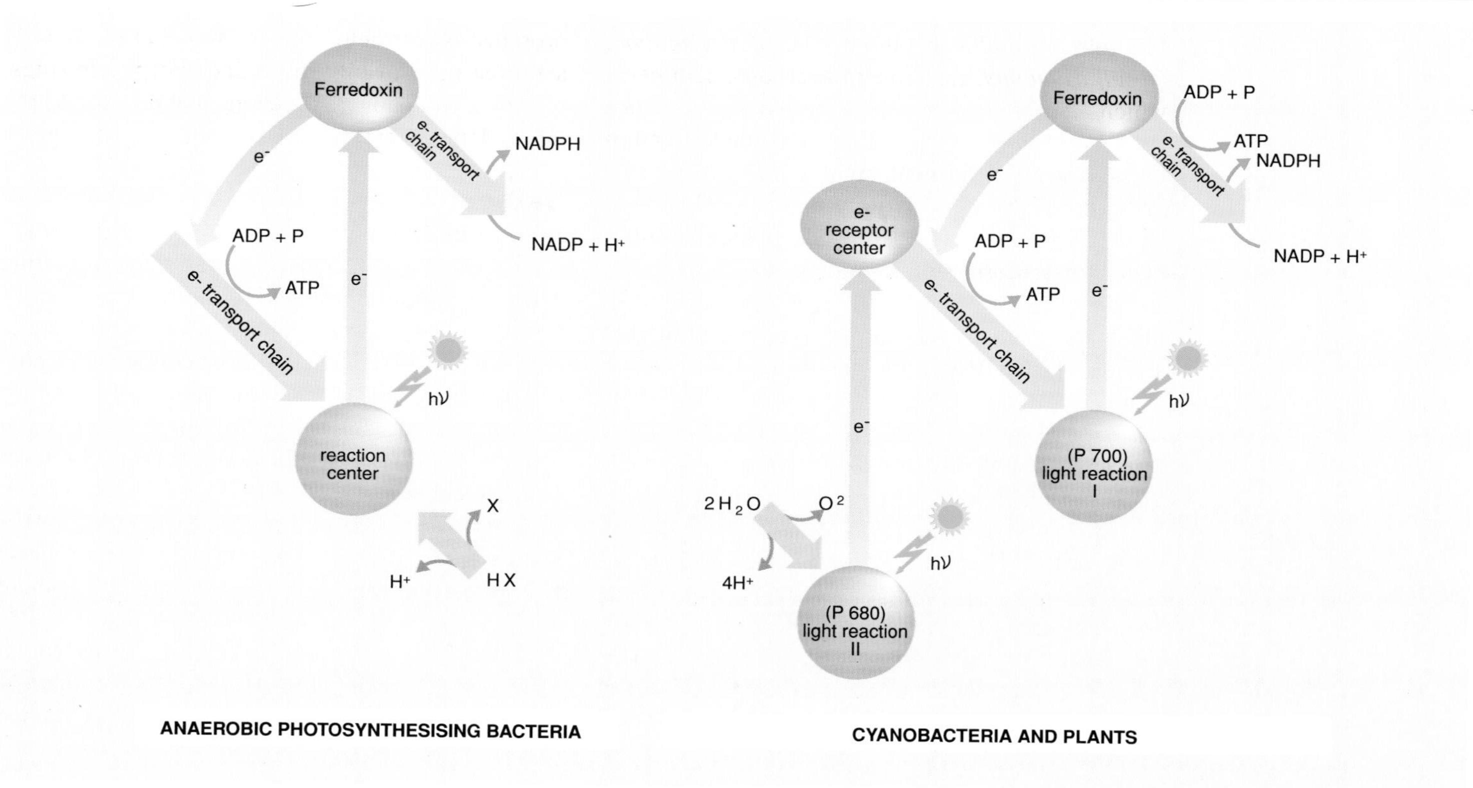

The earliest photosynthetic organisms were bacteria that used hydrogen gas or hydrogen sulfide to reduce carbon dioxide. They did not produce oxygen, but photosynthesized in the same way as the purple and green sulfur bacteria do today. From their present-day descendants, we can partially reconstruct the earliest evolution of photosynthesis. Different types of bacterial chlorophyll are known that are always supplemented by molecules called carotenoids—red and yellow pigments complementing chlorophylls by absorbing the wavelengths of light that chlorophylls can not make use of and then transferring the captured energy to them. The pigments and the proteins to which they are attached, with other lipids and proteins, form flattened membranous sacs called thylakoids.

The process of photosynthesis is divided in two phases, each one of which consists of a series of chemical reactions. The first phase (known as light reactions) is the chemiosmotic generation of ATP using sunlight. The electrons of chlorophyll molecules are raised to a higher energy level, and the excited chlorophyll molecule of a thylakoid transmits its energy to an adjacent molecule, then this to another, until it finally reaches a particular molecule present in each packaged unit of chlorophyll in the thylakoid. Known as the *reactive center*, this is where high energy electrons generate ATP. The final destiny of these electrons differ according to how much of their energy is used. If all their energy is used to generate ATP, they return to an oxidized chlorophyll molecule, but if their energy is just partially used in the generation of ATP and the electrons still conserve some energy, they will be transferred to a nicotinamide adenine dinucleotide phosphate (NADP), in which state the energy is used to reduce it, generating NADPH. This reduced organic compound serves as a source of energy and hydrogen atoms. In the second phase, independent of light (known as dark reactions), the newly generated ATP is used to drive the formation of organic compounds such as glucose from atmospheric carbon dioxide (CO_2), which cells can use to form their bodies or accumulate nutritional reserves for later use.

Detailed study of the sequences of nucleotides in the ribosomal RNA molecules of hundreds of bacteria show them to be assignable to two groups: archaebacteria and eubacteria. All photosynthetic bacteria are eubacteria. No archaebacterial group is photosynthetic, with one notable and probably ancient exception: the rhodopsin-bearing halobacteria. These orange and red-colored organisms use sunlight as source of energy to generate quantities of intracellular ATP, but they cannot use sunlight to make food. On the contrary, they use food, in the form of organic molecules, to make their non-chlorophyllous photosynthetic system.

37 Photosynthesis is the mechanism through which certain organisms utilize the energy given off by electrons excited by light. Certain present day bacteria (the red and green sulphur bacteria) are able to undertake anaerobic photosynthesis, a process that has been used in the past for millions of years. The use of sunlight as a source of energy was the culmination of a process of biochemical evolution initiated by anaerobic fermenting bacteria, such bacteria were followed by the appearance of anaerobic photosynthesis by bacteria endowed with photosystem I (which does not break down water and need hydrogen donors, which were abundant at that time); following them oxygenating prokaryotes appeared, they were endowed with photosystem II as well as I (able therefore to split water and give off oxygen); and finally aerobic bacteria appeared. This development to aerobic bacteria happened gradually, in line with the increase of oxygen in the atmosphere produced by the activity of cyanobacteria. *[Diagram: Biopunt]*

It is more than likely that the "famine" that threatened Archean fermenters was overcome thanks to the evolution of photosynthesis in these two kinds of bacteria. By accumulating nutrient reserves in their cells, they did not only feed themselves, but also provided food for many heterotrophs. Prosperous communities of photosynthetic microorganisms and heterotrophs that depended on them must have grown considerably during the Archean era. Proof of this is contained in the enormous quantities of rocks, primarily shales and flints, that are rich in carbon, at least 3,400 million years old, and were found in southern Africa. Some carbon seams of bacterial origin found in these rocks are just as rich as those formed from the forests of the Carboniferous period, 3,000 billion years later.

Photosynthesis cannot take place without light. For this reason, the ability to detect light and to move toward it was an advantageous adaptation for photosynthetic organisms and for others dependent on them. It is quite likely that before the appearance of the first photosynthetic bacteria, a certain ability to move, linked to the search for food, existed through some simple chemical detection. In the anaerobic muds of the Archean age, heterotrophic microorganisms capable of pursuing their own food must have had enormous advantages over their competitors. But after the evolution of photosynthesis, the presence of sunlight and slightly salty water began to signal the presence of food all over the surface of the Archaean planet.

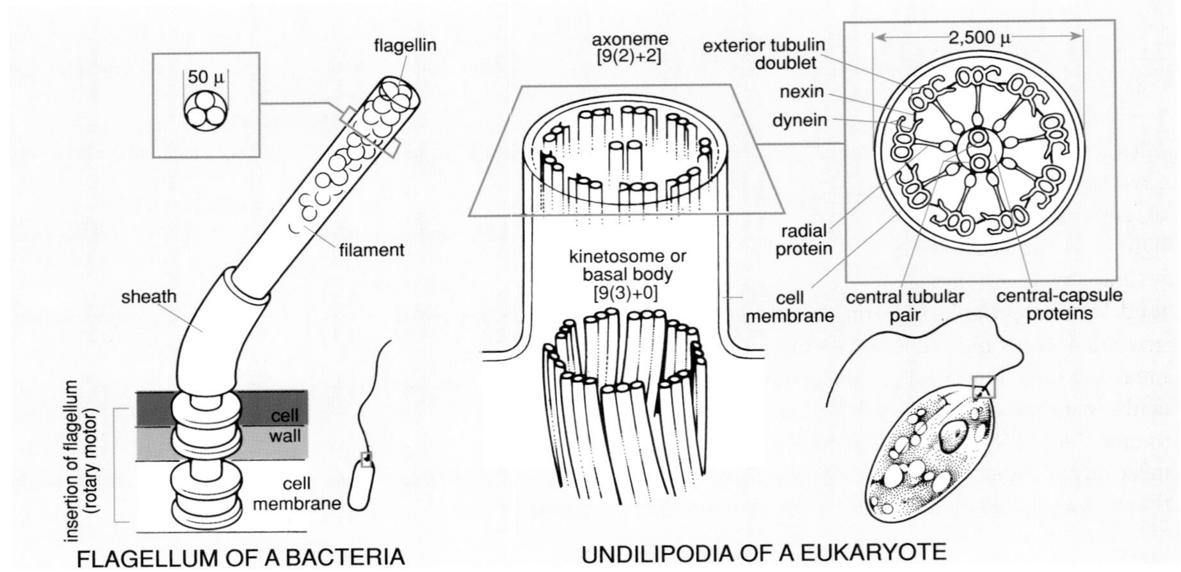

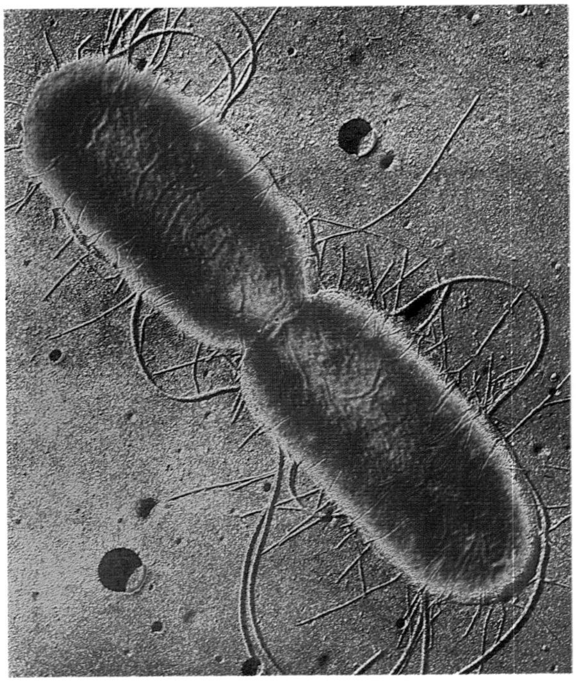

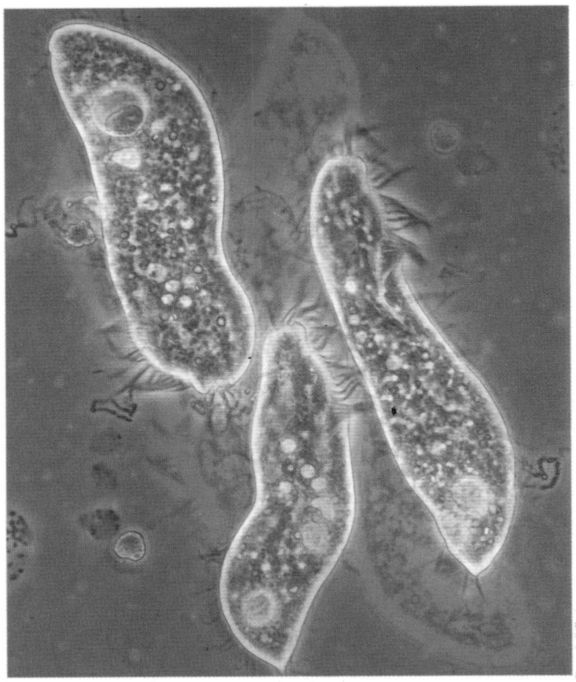

38 The undulipodia, that is the flagella and cilia of the eukaryotic cells, such as those of the ciliate *Cladotricha* (below, right), seem to have been derived from certain present day spirochaetes provided with bacterial flagella, such this *Leptospira* (bottom, left). The undulipodium of eukaryotic cells (above) consists of two differentiated parts: a basal body or kinetosome, and a body or axoneme. Viewed in section, the body of the undulipodium, some 250 m in diameter, shows a circle of microtubules arranged in pairs, surrounding a central pair [9 (2) + 2] and, in turn surrounded by the cell membrane. The kinetosome, on the other hand, have nine triplets of microtubules but without a central pair [9 (3) + 0]. Bacterial flagella are much smaller (some 15 nm in diameter) and are made up of a single filament fixed directly to the cell membrane and with a motile structure which gyrates at the base. This is the only motile structure, while in the undulipodia, the whole filaments move in an undulating manner. *[Diagram: Biopunt, from various sources; Photos: Institut Pasteur (x 5,000) / CNRI and Francesc Torrella (x420)]*

Mobility and protection against radiation

The origin of movement in bacteria seems to be connected to the development of a rotary device, nonexistent in eukaryotic cells. A simple whip-like strand called a flagellum (not to be confused with the wider undulipodium or cilium of eukaryotic cells far more complex in structure than the bacterial flagellum, but often called by the same name) attaches itself to a "flagellar motor" consisting of one or two disk-shaped plates, one of which is always embedded in the inner cell membrane. The disks turn by means of electrical charges, making the flagellum spin. Only in the case of spirochetes is the flagellum inserted beneath the outer membrane of the outer cell wall.

As noted, bacteria endowed with movement had an enormous advantage: easier access to different habitats and to usable nutrients. They were more exposed to foreign genetic material, to the chemical products of other organisms, and were therefore predisposed to develop complex symbiotic relations in a wide variety of environments. However, movement in search of light also implied danger. Solar radiation not only included what we now call visible light and was that used by phototrophic bacteria, but the stronger and more dangerous ultraviolet (UV) radiation that could break the chemical bonds of the proteins and nucleic acids, causing the death of the cell. Phototrophic microbes had to find different protective measures, and those that acquired them in their evolution had an additional selective advantage. One immediate protective measure was the discovery of some sort of light filter, for example through living in salt-rich solutions such as sodium nitrate, the sand, or other substances that permitted the penetration of visible light but blocked ultraviolet radiation. Some bacteria even evolved "tanning" mechanisms; they developed pigments that absorbed the dangerous radiation. Conditions were thus created to build colonies so vast as to visibly alter the landscape. On the watery earth, colonies of different kinds of microbes combined in common habitats. At first they were merely colored scums, purple and sienna patches or strange, stratified, dough-like masses. One outer layer of bacteria after another died from radiation exposure, but their remains protected the lower layers that accumulated clay, sand, and organic sediment to form a living mat. Microbial mats and muds dominated the shallow-water landscape of the Archean Earth. Structures of this type can still be found today along many warm seacoasts around the world, such as in the Persian Gulf and the northwest coast of Australia or in the great commercial salt flats of Baja California, in Mexico, or the Ebro Delta, in Catalonia. These rather insignificant mats of bacteria, long ignored, are living examples of an ancient world dominated entirely by bacteria.

Gene repair and sexuality

Besides protecting themselves from excessive radiation with filters, the bacteria also evolved mechanisms for repairing damage to their DNA.

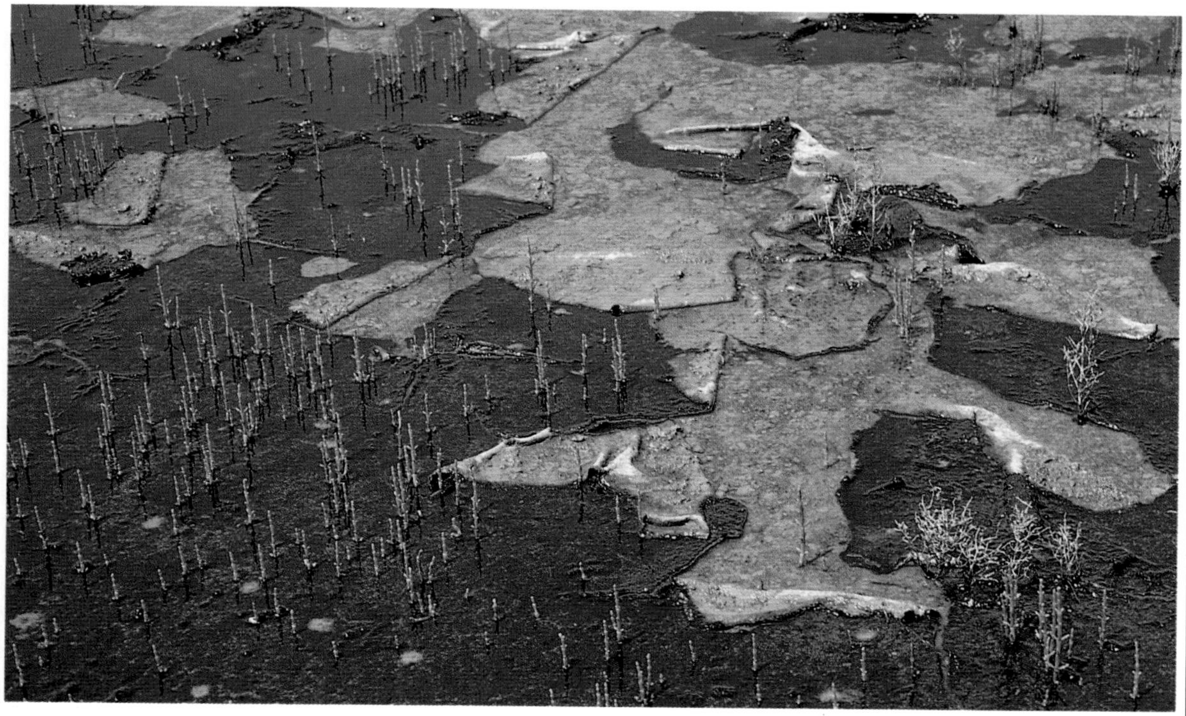

39 The formation of bacterial mats is a characteristic of shallow salty lakes, and it is believed that they are comparable to stromatolites. If a section is cut of these mats, one can easily see various differently colored layers. Throughout the world one can find bacterial mats wherever salty lakes exist, as in the marshes of the Ebro delta (photograph), as well as in the immense areas of California and Australia, in Mediterranean arid zones, or in the interior lake of Gallocanta in the Iberian cordillera (Iberian peninsula). *[Photo: Xavier Ferrer]*

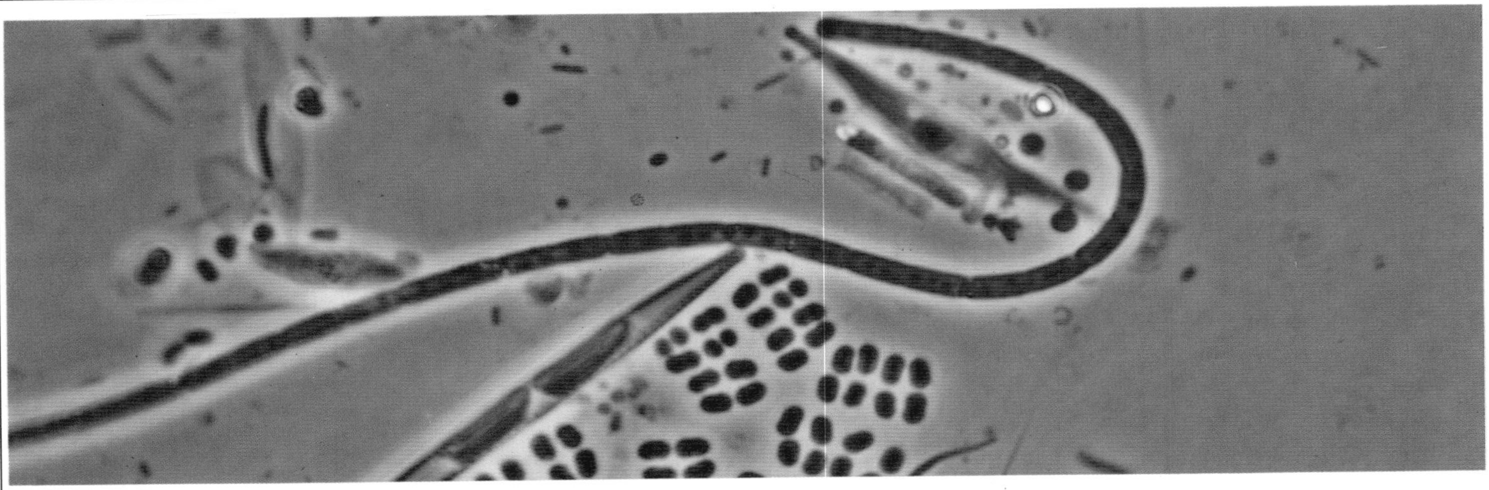

40 The filamentous cyanobacterium *Oscillatoria limnetica* is considered a living fossil in the sense that it exemplifies exactly what we believe the first Archaean cyanobacteria were like. It can live as an anaerobic photosynthesizing bacterium, using sulphuric acid as the principal source of hydrogen, but it is also capable, when there is sufficient water available, of using water, which is what most present day cyanobacteria do. The need to obtain hydrogen from an alternative source, in the face of the growing scarcity of free hydrogen in the Archaean atmosphere, led to the appearance of respiration, using water. It seems that the cyanobacteria—possibly mutants of sulphur bacteria—were the pioneers of this experiment. It is believed that in the biosphere before the Cambrian, this kind of organism was in the majority, but were later displaced by other organisms more able to undertake photosynthesis, and thus were restricted to certain media. The progressive enrichment of the atmosphere with oxygen was due to the vital contribution of these cyanobacteria. *[Photo: F. Torrella (x 1,500)]*

Replication errors in complementary DNA chains, for example, were caused by the formation of "thymine dimmers," one thymine paired with another instead of pairing with adenine, its complement. This kind of accident was mortal for any cell not equipped with repair enzymes to sort out the error. One type of repair enzyme, DNA polymerase, separates the badly copied part and makes a copy of a new DNA with the bases correctly paired. Most organisms today still have repair enzymes, even though the ozone layer has been protecting life from ultraviolet radiation for two billion years. In many bacteria, enzymes are activated in the presence of visible light to this day, just as if the secondary disadvantages of exposure to solar radiation, for which they were selected as a defense, still existed.

Elaborate protection against ultraviolet radiation helped bring about another important innovation: the interchange or fusion of genetic information between different cells, otherwise known as sex. Of course, bacterial sexuality differs greatly from sexuality as we know it in animals or plants of the same species and different sex. Bacterial sex does not imply reproduction, and while it requires two sources of genes, only one of which must be a living organism.

The other may be a virus or even a DNA fragment from a dead cell. On the early Earth, the first sex was just a mechanism whereby a bacterial cell whose genes were altered by ultraviolet radiation could get new ones from another source. In its origin bacterial sex does not lead to reproduction, but to the recombination of genes, a kind of trump card to keep bacteria in the game of evolution and to aid the survival of bacterial populations in whatever hostile environments occurred.

3.3 Oxygen, the first global pollutant

About 2,200 million years ago, during the early Proterozoic period, life had to face one of its first pollution crises: massive poisoning by oxygen. The Proterozoic Eon dates from the end of the Archean Eon (2,500 million years ago) to the beginning of our own period, the Phanerozoic (580 million years ago). The great majority of anaerobic organisms, until then all anaerobic, were displaced by emerging forms of aerobic organisms capable not only of living with oxygen, but of making it one of the bases of its metabolism, thanks to the process of respiration.

The origin of oxygen

The crisis most likely began because of the increasing scarcity of available free gases such as hydrogen (H_2) or hydrogen sulfide (H_2S). This shortage led to the evolution of photosynthesizing prokaryotes, capable of obtaining hydrogen from its richest source on Earth, water. They were the ancestors of what today are known as *cyanobacteria* (until recently, before we know they are unequivocally bacteria, they were called *blue-green algae* or *cyanophyceae*). They seem to have been mutant sulfur bacteria faced with a struggle to survive caused by the disappearance of the hydrogen and hydrogen sulfide on which they depended.

A discovery made in 1975 by a group of Israeli microbiologists at Solar Lake in the Sinai desert gives us an idea of what those early cyanobacteria may have been like. In this small, artificial lake, different from most other lakes in that the warmest waters are the deepest, they found a filamentous cyanobacterium that moves by gliding, named *Oscillatoria limnetica*. After studying its metabolism, they discovered it is an authentic living fossil, a lost link between anaerobic, photosynthesizing sulfur bacteria and modern cyanobacteria. When found in environments with high hydrogen sulfide and low oxygen concentrations, it functions anaerobically, using the hydrogen sulfide as its main source of hydrogen. In environments lacking hydrogen sulfide, though, it behaves like other cyanobacteria, using water as its main source of hydrogen.

Later many other cyanobacteria were discovered that can return to anaerobic photosynthesis were discovered when placed in the appropriate conditions. This kind of photosynthetic "joker" was probably very abundant prior of the Cambrian period, but later was replaced by specialists. Today they seem to occur only in certain extreme environments.

Oxidative processes

The growth of Archean cyanobacteria filled the seas and the atmosphere with surprising amounts of free oxygen. This oxygen was highly toxic because of its capacity to trap electrons and produce so-called free radicals, which are short-lived but highly reactive chemical substances that can break up organic compounds. The same photosynthetic cyanobacteria that produced oxygen were the most threatened by it—since they were closest to the source of "pollutant" gas.

At first the free oxygen reacted with many gases present in the Archean waters and atmosphere, such as hydrogen, methane, ammonia, carbon monoxide, or hydrogen sulfide. Or it combined—by oxidation—with many minerals present in the oceans, rivers, and lakes, such as iron, sulfur, uranium or manganese.

The very presence of oxides of iron, manganese, uranium, and other elements in rocks from the Proterozoic Eon that are 2,000 million years old confirms the presence of considerable amounts of oxygen in the atmosphere at that time. On the other hand, rocks from the Archean era (more than 2,600 years old), which generally contain iron, uranium, and sulfur minerals, tend to be poorer in oxygen.

An example of reading the atmospheric record from the rocks is the *great Minechapecoten iron formation*, near the Woman River, in Western Ontario, Canada. The rocks are over 2,500 million years old and very rich in iron.

Geologists found evidence of a great water mass, an ancient, anaerobic sea, where it is likely *Desulfovibrio* dominated the surface of the margins. Modern representatives of this group of bacteria cannot tolerate oxygen and, therefore, live below the surface. On the other hand, in this formation deposited at the end of the Archean, large sulfur deposits suggest the *Desulfovibrio* anaerobically reduced the sulfate from marine water to sulfides using cyanobacterial products of photosynthesis as fuel.

Banded iron formations

The transition from an anoxic atmosphere to an oxygenated atmosphere is recorded in the impressive record of the great banded iron formations (BIFs). Found in vast areas in Australia, North America, and Africa, these geological formations are most important, since nine of them represent the greater part of the Western world's mineable iron reserves. They mostly date from the late Archean and the early Proterozoic Eon (between 1,800-3,000 million years ago) and consist basically of a succession of layers of more oxidized iron (hematite) alternating with layers containing less oxidized iron (magnetite) contained in a chert matrix.

The thickness of each band varies, from some measuring only micrometers to others tens of feet thick. The alternation between ferrous iron (reduced) and ferric iron (oxidized) is interpreted as the result of transport and sedimentation of iron, marked by varying concentrations of oxygen resulting from the seasonal growth of oxygen-producing photosynthetic bacteria in the surface of huge shallow basins, large lakes, or even seas. Bursts of seasonal growth and of oxygen emission year after year for 500 million years probably caused these colorful oxidized bands.

Photosynthetic bacteria were not the only ones to participate in the formation of banded iron formations. Certain iron-oxidizing bacteria take oxygen from the environment and obtain energy in nutrient-poor waters by combining it with iron to form oxidized compounds, in other words, rust. The Archean ancestors of these organisms must have proliferated in areas of oxygen production, and year after year they must have "purified" the oxy-

41 The growing levels of oxygen in the first atmosphere of the Earth seems to remain reflected in the iron band formations, which are found in Australia (in the photograph, the most typical and the best formed), North America, and Africa. These formations (which contain a large part of the iron ore reserves of the world in alternating layers), date from the end of the Archaean and the beginning of the Proterozoic, that is between 3,000 and 2,800 million years ago. The alternating iron rich and poor layers are related to the intermittent photosynthesis of oxygenating microorganisms. *[Photo: Reg Morrison / Auscape International]*

gen added to the environment by precipitating it in the form of rust around colonies of cyanobacteria. Such iron-oxidizing bacteria may have taken part in the formation of enormous quantities of iron ore that today is extracted from the great banded iron formations in Africa, America, and Australia. The alternating bands of minerals might be a record of iron-oxidizing bacteria's ancient relationship with cyanobacterial communities. Hematites may have been produced in the summer, when cyanobacteria produced more oxygen and when iron oxidation was more active, whereas magnetite may have been made in winter, when photosynthetic oxygen production and iron oxidation were severely curtailed.

During the early Proterozoic, from 2,200 to 1,800 million years ago, there was an unprecedented burst of banded iron formation that has not since been equalled. Then suddenly they disappeared, to be substituted by the so-called "red beds." This is interpreted to mean that anoxic habitats were rapidly diminishing and that oxygen in the atmosphere at that time had already significantly approached today's levels.

Gold-bearing deposits

Gold-bearing deposits provide still another testimony to early aerobic activities, especially those of Witwatersrand in the Transvaal (South Africa). Gold is a heavy metal that is rare on the Earth's crust and originated in the deep mantle sometime in the Archean era. Only a limited number of Archean formations contain bands of gold-bearing sediments.

Gold miners going down in elevator shafts in the Transvaal, where 70% of the Western world's gold is produced, actually descend into a kind of time machine where the layers of volcanic ash and alluvium they see were left more than 2,500 million years ago by an Archean river on surfaces that were even older. To find new gold deposits, they follow a certain rock layer full of conglomerate—the so-called carbon leader—that contains a high level of organic carbon. These layers, trapped between limestone and shale, contain fine seams of pyrite, gold, and sometimes uranium ore. The carbon leader of Witwatersrand also contains microscopic, filamentous, and spherical structures that are inexplicable by mineralogy alone.

The most convincing explanation is that they are remains of filamentous, coccoid bacteria that trapped detrital flakes of gold. Since gold moves more fluidly in the absence of oxygen than in its presence, it would have been easily eroded from volcanic source rocks by rivers and streams and carried toward the sea. However, gold particles in the presence of high concentrations of oxygen and

42 Among the geochemical differences between the Archaean and the later Proterozoic rocks is the Archaean's greater richness in gold, these rocks constitute the world's main source, especially in the Archaean rocks of South Africa. Above is the entrance to the oldest goldmine in South Africa (in Kimberley), and below is a detail of the inside of a mine. The narrow bands of gold-bearing conglomerates are encrusted between other rocks and have remained covered by layers of younger rocks. As well as gold, they contain seams of other metallic minerals such as nickel, cobalt and platinum, and they also show some microscopic, spherical filamentous structures which are attributed to bacteria capable of capturing the flakes of the gold detritus. The concentration of these metals in the Archaean rocks relates the geochemistry of that period to that of the meteorites and the deep mantle of the Earth, and is another proof of the aerobic activity of the first living organisms. It is believed that the gold was extracted by the fluvial erosion of the ancient rocks of the mantle and transported to the sea. After having experimented with present day bacteria, which are capable of separating gold from accompanying minerals, it is now believed that flocculation of gold-bearing particles was favored by high concentrations of oxygen and organic carbon. Such concentrations have been linked to the existence of photosynthesizing bacteria. The particles of gold flocculated and were deposited at the bottom. *[Photos: Index and AGE Fotostock]*

organic carbon tend to precipitate and form lumps that deposit in riverbeds. With its production of oxygen and carbon-rich compounds, any colony of photosynthetic bacteria creates a situation favorable to gold *flocculation*, so that it could well have been such bacterial colonies that gave rise to the considerable quantities of gold precipitated as flocs along beds of the Archean waterways.

Certain modern bacteria, such as *Chromobacterium violaceum*, are capable of producing hydrogen cyanide, the same compound used to extract gold from the ore. Perhaps the ancestors of these microbes lived in the mineral-filled rivers of the Archean period, helping consolidate the flocculated gold from the particles in solution with the help of oxygen and organic material produced by cyanobacteria communities. The riverbed, along which the Witwatersrand gold was deposited 2,500 million years ago, was enormous, as much as five times greater than the Mississippi delta. Dried up and buried under miles of sediment and folded, this river bed was ignored until the 19th century, when Boer colonizers were attracted to the Transvaal by the speckles of gold in the dark, carbon-rich rocks that outcropped in the desert. Following the outcrop to the depths of the subsoil, they found the buried ancient river system that formed part of the carbon leader, leading them to the gold.

Information from stromatolites

Our hypotheses so far are based on theoretical and empirical data, on comparisons with extant forms of life retaining ancient evolutionary features, or with indirect evidence of life. But now new evidence adds to our knowledge of early life: fossils. The most ancient record of life comes from three sources: microfossils, ancient organic matter in rocks, and stromatolites.

Stromatolites are finely laminated rocks shaped like barrels or domes, built up over large periods of time as a result of the activity of cyanobacteria in shallow water. They vary in size and are generally composed of carbonate, although in some cases mainly of silica. They are the remains of layered communities of bacteria turned to stone. Today stromatolites are formed in many places in the world, making the identification of fossil structures with the same characteristics very easy. They come from fibrous bacterial mats made up mainly of cyanobacteria that trap accumulated sediment. As the sediment accumulates, the microorganisms either remain trapped and die, or move to the surface where they form a new layer on top of the old one. If the old layer has enough sediment and the evaporation rate is high enough, it hardens and mineralizes. The constant repetition of this process leads to the formation of different-sized structures, ranging from only a few square feet to several acres.

Although the structures are organic in origin and active formation is still taking place today, stromatolites have been interpreted in many ways, making them difficult to understand until recently. In the late 19th century, they were described by some paleontologists, especially by the North American Charles Wilcott (1850-1927), and named *Cryptozoa* (hidden animals), since they were thought to be the remains of animals. But it was not until the study of modern, mat-forming cyanobacteria and stromatolites in extreme environments, such as the sabkhas or other highly saline lakes in arid countries (such as western Australia, where large growing extant and fossil stromatolites have been studied), that stromatolites were interpreted as resulting from preservation of microbial mat communities from the activity of the ancestors of cyanobacteria and other bacteria.

Stromatolites occur in the fossil record dating from between 3,500 and 550 million years ago. They are rare in Archean rocks, perhaps because of the distribution of land and sea, which at that time did not allow for the existence of appropriate environments for their formation. Microfossils of bacteria, including cyanobacteria, were discovered in the late 1960s in flint rocks from Fig Tree, in the Barbeton mountain land, in Zimbabwe, and dated about 3,400 millions years ago. Evidence of microfossils from Archean rocks associated with stromatolites from the Warrawooma formation also has been found. It is thought that at least six different types of bacteria took part in the formation of these bacterial mats.

The formation of an oxidizing world

Throughout hundreds of millions of years, excess oxygen was absorbed by metallic compounds, reduced gases from oceans and the atmosphere, and even by living organisms, so that at first oxygen accumulated in the environment only locally and by fits and starts. It has been suggested that the active assimilation of CO_2 by many kinds of bacteria, including the first photosynthetic ones, may even have contributed to the first glacial era, for which there is geological evidence (sometime

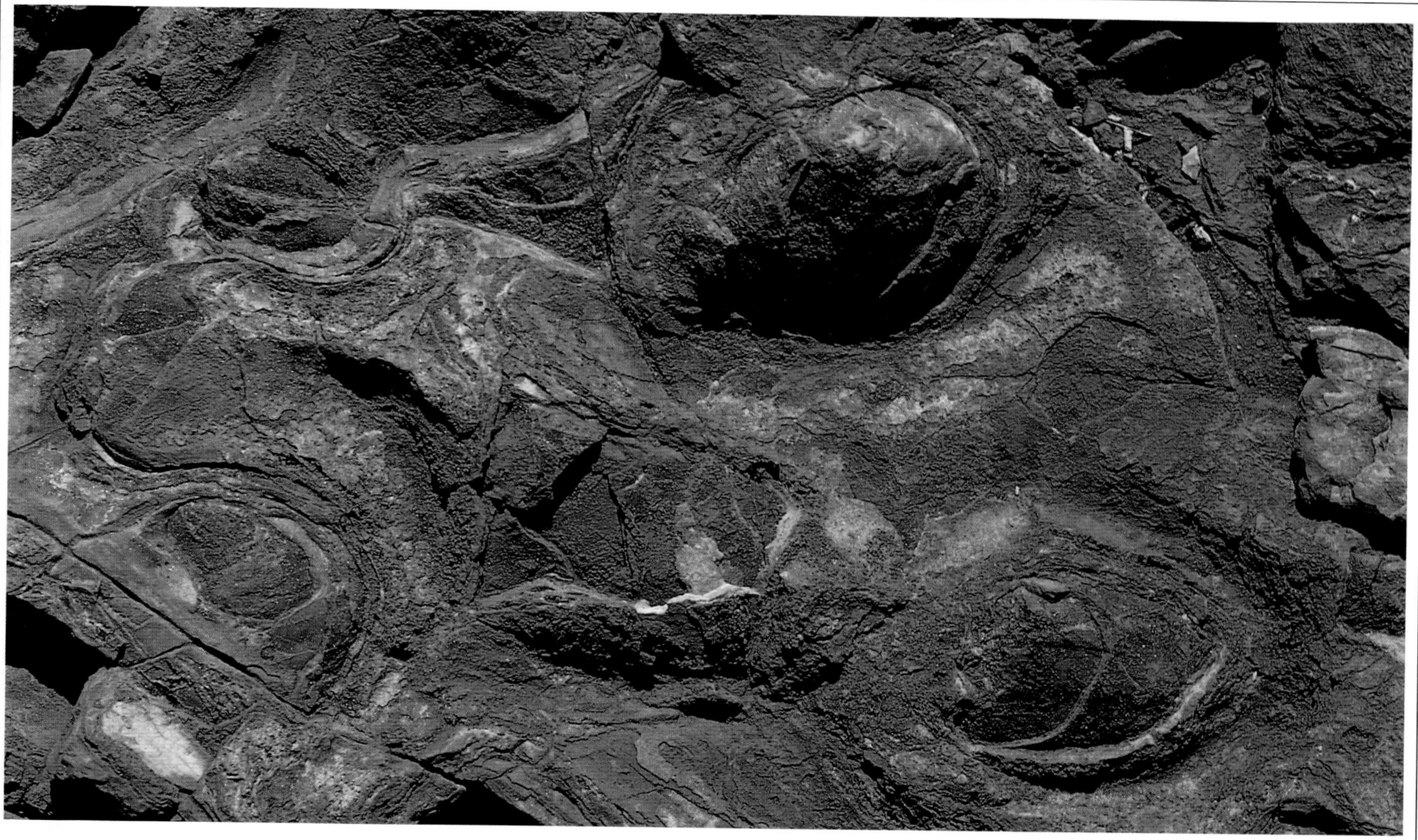

between 2,500 and 2,300 million years ago). The causes of the ice ages remain a mystery, but the removal of CO_2 may have eliminated or reduced the greenhouse effect in the atmosphere at a time when solar radiation was less intense than today.

In time the cyanobacteria, producing oxygen only when hydrogen or sulfide was limiting, gave rise to bright green bacteria that continually emitted oxygen. Thousands of oxygenizing photosynthesizing organisms, adapted to life on rock surfaces, in thermal waters, and in foam. Finally, over 2,000 million years ago, oxygen depleted the mineral and reduced gases with which it had been reacting and began to accumulate rapidly in the atmosphere, causing a catastrophe of global magnitude.

Many kinds of bacteria immediately disappeared, victims of oxygen and light that were even more lethal together than separately. Microbial life, then as now, had no other defense against that cataclysm except DNA replication and duplication, gene transfer, and mutation. At the price of high mortality, the intensified sexuality of bacteria when exposed to toxins managed to form a new totally reorganized microcosmos. The new, oxygen-resistant mutants multiplied and rapidly substituted those that were sensitive to surface conditions and exposed environments, while others survived by retreating into the anaerobic levels of mud and soil.

From the first time of the exposures to oxygen, different protective mechanisms developed. The information contained in and transmitted by the genes, so valuable to the new living conditions being created on Earth, were translated into new phenomena such as bioluminescence or the synthesis of vitamin E.

The appearance of aerobic respiration

The process of adaptation did not stop there; in one of the most decisive evolutionary advances of all time, certain cyanobacteria evolved a metabolic system in which a deadly poison, oxygen gas, became an indispensable element for sustaining life, aerobic respiration.

Aerobic respiration is a risky, but efficient, way of channelling and exploiting the reactivity of oxygen. It is essentially controlled combustion that breaks down organic molecules and produces carbon dioxide, water, and an important amount of energy. While fermentation produces two ATP molecules

43 The stromatolites, whose oldest examples are found in Western Australia, are rare in Archaean rocks, but dominate the fossil record from between 3,500 and 5,000 million years ago. The need to protect themselves from the ultraviolet solar radiation, is what appears to have induced microorganisms to live in materials such as water, which is rich in certain salts, or sand, through which visible light, but not radiation, can pass. Some bacteria, cyanobacteria to be precise, manage to form pigments that absorb harmful radiation, and are therefore able to form vast colonies on the mud. Under these conditions, real microbial communities are developed, forming an almost continuous layer over the inundated mires. These have been fossilized in the so-called *stromatolites,* which thus constitute the first known fossils of living organisms. *[Photo: Reg Morrison / Auscape International]*

44 The Krebs Cycle appeared in the evolutionary history of life as a significant step in its adaptation to an atmosphere that was rich in oxygen. In effect, adaptation to the presence of atmospheric oxygen consisted of inventing a metabolic system that did not just tolerate oxygen but made it indispensable. Aerobic respiration is a very clever and effective way of channelling and exploiting the reactivity of oxygen. It consists, essentially, of a controlled combustion that breaks up the organic molecules giving carbon dioxide, water, and a large amount of energy. While fermentation gives two molecules of ATP (adenosine triphosphate) for each molecule of sugar, respiration can give as many as 36.
[Diagram: Biopunt, from various sources]

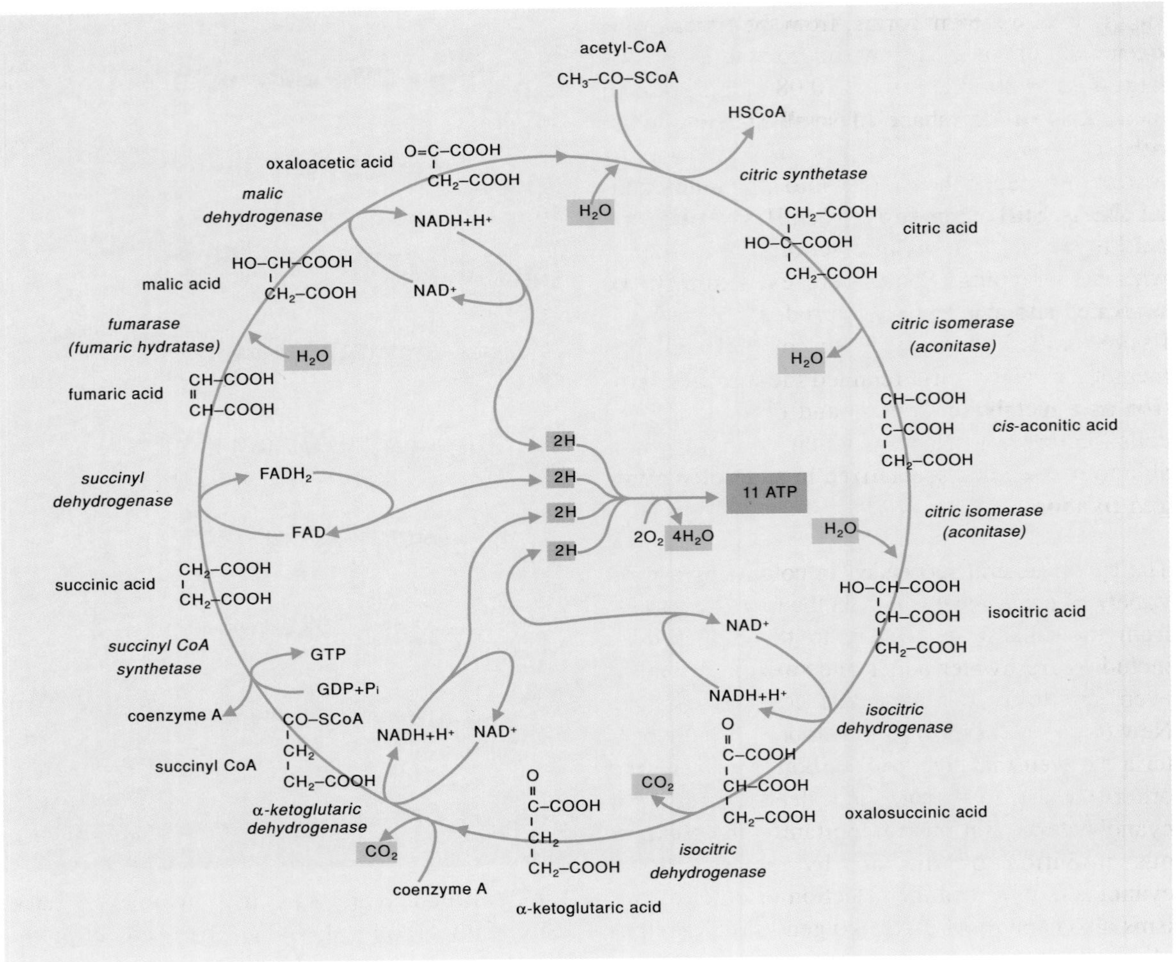

for each decomposed sugar molecule, respiration with oxygen can produce as many as 36.

In this case, ATP is generated in three stages. The first is identical to fermentation. A sugar molecule (for example, glucose) is transformed into pyruvic acid, and ATP is generated. The second stage consists of a cycle of reactions called the Krebs cycle, using products created by the first stage to make energy. (The Krebs cycle was named after its discoverer, Hans Adolf Krebs, awarded the Nobel Prize for medicine in 1953.) Part of the freed energy is used to produce more ATP, but most of it is transferred in high-energy electrons to transport molecules such as the flavin adenine dinucleotide (FAD) or the nicotinamide adenine dinucleotide (NAD), which change to their reduced forms (FADH and NADH respectively). These molecules, which contain most of the energy from the initial nourishment, transfer their high-energy electrons to the third stage of respiration, a chain of electron transport in which different kinds of electron acceptors participate, among them ferredoxins and cytochromes. Molecular oxygen plays the role of final acceptor. On receiving the electrons together with the corresponding hydrogen atoms, it is reduced to water. Most of the ATP resulting from aerobic respiration is produced in this stage.

The first cyanobacteria that used oxygen for respiration most likely used the same oxygen they produced. They had to do something with the copious quantities of waste their metabolism generated. Even today many cyanobacteria use the same electron transport chain for their respiratory processes that they do for photosynthesis. These respire only in the dark when photosynthesis cannot occur since they cannot use the electrons simultaneously for both processes.

The diversification of aerobic life

Photosynthesis and aerobic cyanobacteria had literally found their places in the sun. With only sunlight, a few salts always present in water, and the atmosphere's carbon dioxide, they were able to produce everything they needed: nucleic acids, proteins, vitamins, and the biochemical machinery for making all of this. Given the large quantities of oxygen to which they had access, it was not at all surprising that the cyanobacteria diversified into hundreds of different forms, from the tiniest, with diameters of only a few micrometers, to the largest up to 80 micrometers (0.08 mm). Some of them took on the shape of small spheres, while others enveloped themselves in a gelatinous matrix or grouped themselves into fine multicellular sheets. Still others formed bundles of filaments held together by an organic gel or simple threads with no wrapping. Some were even straight or branched and able to release products of multiple fissions called baeocyts. Both colonial and filamentous cyanobacteria retained the nitrogen fixation as a metabolic strategy and developed large cells—called heterocysts—which were impermeable to oxygen and specialized in anaerobic nitrogen fixation.

The cyanobacteria succeeded in colonizing a wide variety of environments—even the most extreme—from the coldest sea waters to thermal springs, including freshwater ponds and streams, humid or even dry soils, and rock surfaces and fissures. New trophic relationships developed as many bacteria evolved that lived off carbon, nitrogen, and other metabolites from the dead remains of cyanobacteria. But most importantly, the continuous pollution of the air by photosynthetic cyanobacteria forced the selection of other organisms also capable of using oxygen in their metabolism. Bacteria that tolerate the presence of oxygen first appeared, followed by ones that used it functionally. Finally, oxygen-dependent microorganisms came into existence.

The independent development of aerobic metabolism by different bacterial groups gave rise to waves of specialization, as well as the appearance of highly elaborate forms and life cycles. Some microbes began to reproduce mobile daughter cells, very different in appearance from the parent cells, by budding. These flagellate bacteria, budded from sessile parents, moved to more favorable locations, fastened onto solid surfaces, and reverted to the original form to continue developing. Other bacteria formed filament networks similar to fungus that curl up and penetrate between soil particles. Still others formed branched structures that released spores. All these organisms were multicellular, even though they were still prokaryotes.

Modern atmospheric conditions

Between 2,000 and 1,800 million years ago, the concentration of atmospheric oxygen and the density of the ozone shield may have had already risen to about half of their present-day levels. By

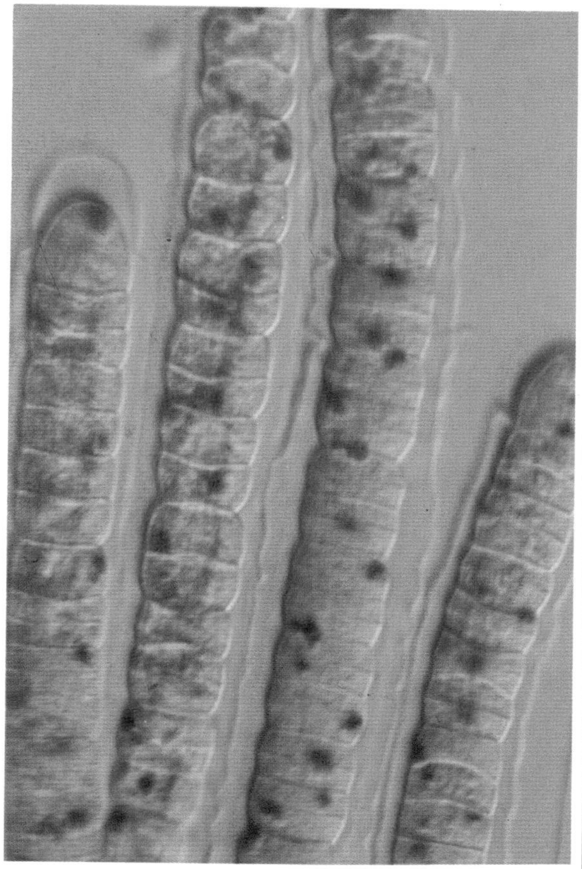

45 The great adaptive plasticity of the cyanobacteria assured their survival throughout the last 2,500 million years in many, frequently extreme, environments. They survive desiccation without harm, they do not have natural enemies because they are difficult to digest and are often toxic, they also can live in nutrient poor water because of their capacity to fix nitrogen and dissolved organic matter. Some cyanobacteria have sufficient physiological plasticity to allow them to respire only in the dark; since they apparently use the same molecular machinery for the chains of transport of electrons for respiration and for photosynthesis. Shared parts, however, are not used at the same time for the different pathways. The filamentous cyanobacterium in the photograph (*Tolypothryx distorta*) lives on rocks in streams; this example is from the barranco de Castellfollit, in the south of Catalonia. *[Photo: F. Torrella (x 1,400)]*

1,000 million years ago, they may even have reached the levels of today. There are different opinions on these points, but a consensus exists on the fact that atmospheric oxygen concentration has never much surpassed its present level of approximately 21%. If it had been higher, the fossil record would contain evidence of a widespread fire all over the Earth. The present concentration, which is high but not too high, seems to demonstrate a compromise between the threat of generalized spontaneous combustion and the advantages of aerobic metabolism.

The formation of the ozone shield put an end to the abiotic synthesis of organic compounds by impeding the ultraviolet rays from reaching the Earth's surface. By the middle of the Proterozoic, 1,600 million years ago, most biochemical evolution had taken place. The Earth's surface and atmosphere were fundamentally as they are today. What was still to come were the enormous evolutionary changes that would lead to the appearance of plants, animals, and fungi, but oxygen-generating cyanobacteria had already prepared the way. Animals, for example, would not have come into existence without their predecessors, green plants, primary producers of their own nourishment, and these in turn would not have evolved without oxygen.

Gaia: is the Earth alive?

Gaia was the name that the novelist and Nobel Prize winner William Golding suggested for the hypothesis of the Earth's organic behavior put forward by the British biologist, James Lovelock. According to the first Gaia definition, we could consider all the planet's living beings as a single living entity; a unit that is homeostatically regulated, capable of adapting the planet's atmosphere to suit its own global needs; an entity with faculties and powers far exceeding those of its constituent parts. In fact, Gaia has the power to regulate or modify, for example, the composition of the gases causing the greenhouse effect, the temperature, and the atmosphere's acidity. In the 18th century, James Hutton, recognized as the father of geology, already had a similar idea, when he spoke of the Earth as a superorganism that be studied according to physiological principles.

The goddess Gaia/Tellus (II century A.D.) [The Ancient Art & Architecture Collection]

Gaia was a divine figure in Greek mythology who rewarded those who respected the laws of nature and punished those who did not. She was the benevolent goddess of the Earth. A suggestive ecological figure, even before the term was conceived.

Hutton compared the movement of the elements in the Sun and the movement of oceanic waters toward the continents to the circulation of the blood through the body. The revolutionary Gaia hypothesis came about, according to Lovelock, through being able to look down on our blue planet from space for the first time, and through research into the atmospheres on other planets, such as Mars and Venus. In Lovelock's own words:

"The Gaia research project is an attempt to find the Earth's largest living creature. (...) If Gaia exists, we will then know that the many different living beings which inhabit this planet, including the human species, are the constituent parts of a vast entity which, when taken as a whole, has the power to maintain those conditions which make the Earth a suitable habitat for life."

Lovelock was commissioned by the National Aeronautics and Space Administration (NASA) in 1965 to devise various experiments to detect life on Mars. These were to be carried out by the space ship *Viking*. To the surprise of the NASA staff, Lovelock and his colleague, Dian Hitchcock, suggested that it was not actually necessary to go to Mars to determine whether there was life there or not. All they had to do was to look at the composition of its atmosphere, which had already been discovered using telescopes and infrared detectors. Lovelock wondered why the atmospheres on Venus and Mars were so different from the Earth's and why the Earth's atmosphere had such a constant composition of gases when these gases (oxygen, carbon dioxide, water vapor, and methane) are mutually very reactive.

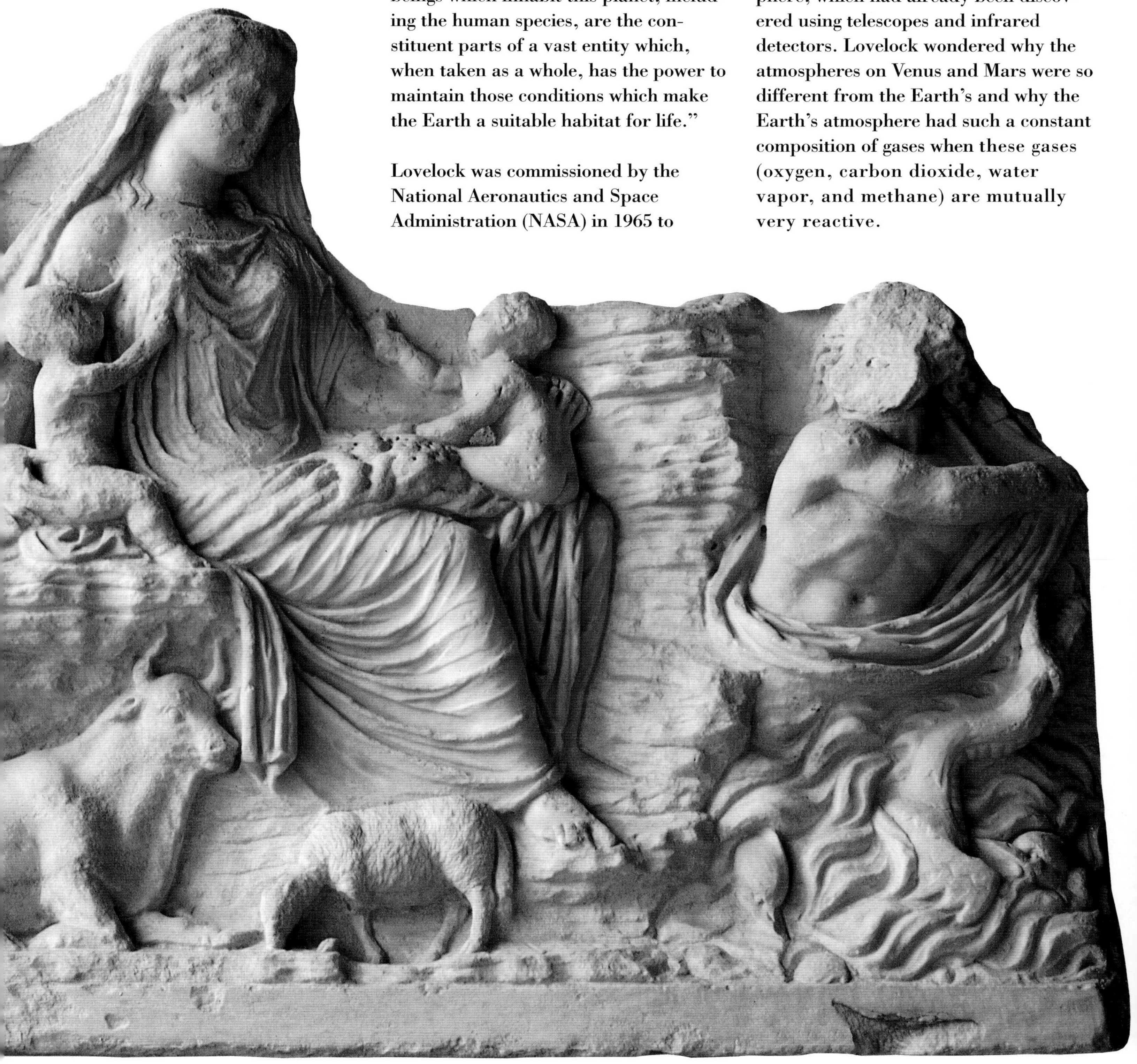

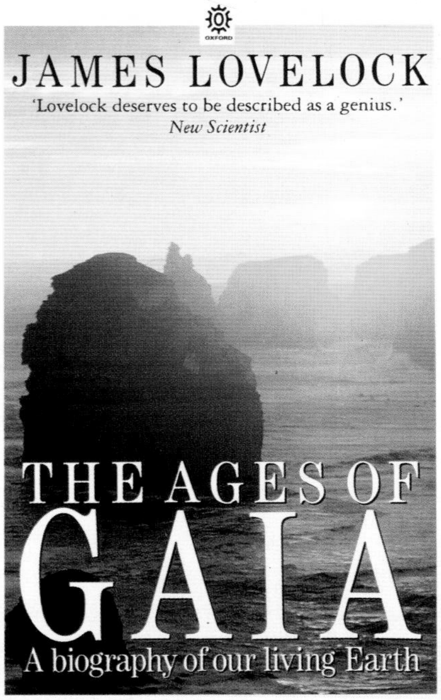

First edition of *Gaia*, by Lovelock [Jordi Vidal]

The atmosphere of the Earth has a high oxygen content, 21%, and 1.5 p.p.m. of methane. We know that when methane and oxygen are illuminated by sunlight, they react with each other. For both gases to be able to coexist in the atmosphere in their present state, there needs to be a constant supply of methane and oxygen. The only feasible explanation for this process—which is highly improbable according to the laws of chemistry—is that it is manipulated on a daily basis from the Earth's surface. No chemical reaction could free the enormous quantities of methane and oxygen necessary, and so we can conclude that the manipulating agent is life itself. The significant reduction of entropy alone is clear proof of biological activity. We could apply the same reasoning to explain the existence of ammonia and nitrous oxide in a state of chemical imbalance. Taking this idea to its logical conclusion, we could then also conclude that there is no life on Mars and Venus, where the gases are in a state of chemical balance. For Lovelock, the atmosphere is not a part of life's environment, but a part of life itself, an extension of the biota.

At a scientific conference on the origins of life on Earth held in Princeton, New Jersey in 1969, Lovelock presented his hypothesis. It was not well received, but Lynn Margulis, an American biologist, did show an interest in the idea. Lovelock used three basic facts to justify his hypothesis. The first is that since the appearance of life, some 3,500 million years ago, the climate has varied very little, with any climatic changes falling within relatively narrow margins; the great ice ages and periods of warming represented relatively small average global temperature changes. The second is the previously mentioned imbalance in the chemical composition of the Earth's atmosphere. The third is that throughout the long evolution of life, the Earth's chemistry and climatology always seem to have fallen within limits acceptable to life. Since then, both scientists have worked together on developing the Gaia hypothesis, looking for evidence and redefining it. The now-famous book *Gaia, a new look at life on Earth*, which came out ten years later (1979), presented the redefined version of the hypothesis. Gaia is a complex entity consisting of the Sun, the oceans, the atmosphere, and the land biota, which together make up a cybernetic system. This system adjusts itself through constant replenishment, maintaining an environment on the planet that is physically and chemically conducive to life. The hypothesis also introduced the term "homeostasis" to describe this maintenance of various conditions, which to a certain extent are relatively constant, through active control.

[AGE Fotostock]

The contrast between this hypothesis and the more traditional viewpoint, according to which life and the conditions on the planet follow two separate paths, the former adapting itself to the latter, is patent. This led to a direct confrontation, which has still not been resolved, with those in the scientific community who defend the traditional viewpoint, according to which life adapts itself to an environment that is only determined by physical and chemical conditions. This sector of the scien-

tific community has been especially critical of the determinism implicit in the hypothesis, which suggests that Gaia controls its own state more or less consciously. James Lovelock and Lynn Margulis, however, continue to build on their hypothesis with new facts and discoveries, which are gradually convincing more and more people. In response to the above criticism, they have stressed the fact that Gaia does not exercise a conscious control, but rather that the series of organisms on the Earth's biota act together to form certain cybernetic mechanisms that are capable of detecting environmental factors such as oxygen, light, temperature, pH, magnetic field, and so on, and then responding to them with different types of behavior, such as changing color, swimming away, hibernating, entering a different stage of the life cycle, or growing exponentially. Taken as a whole, the behavior, growth, and metabolism of the organisms tend to modify the environment on the Earth's surface. Only time will tell, though, which of the two hypotheses is nearer reality.

Despite everything, though, Gaia has already served to initiate a new way of thinking and of seeing life on Earth. The all-encompassing conception in this hypothesis goes beyond the purely scientific realm and enters the social and public spheres, transmitting a message of planetary unity, based on ecological foundations, which appears attractive to an ever-larger group of people.

3.4 From bacteria to protists

The appearance of the eukaryotes: the acritarchs

The increase of usable energy available to organisms because of aerobic metabolism led to the appearance of a new kind of cell: the eukaryotic. The defining features of the eukaryote is the presence of a nucleus, separated from the rest of the cell by a membrane and containing DNA that stores the genetic information.

The biological transition between the prokaryotic cell and the eukaryotic cell seemed so sudden that it is hard to explain it by gradual changes over time. The eukaryotic cell is generally much larger than the prokaryotic cell and, besides the nucleus, it contains complex organelles, elaborate membrane systems such as mitochondria, plastids (only in photosynthesizing organisms such as green plants), undulipodia, and Golgi apparatus. Mitochondria, plastids, and undulipods, on the other hand, contain their own DNA, or genes, and can reproduce themselves by division as if they were independent cells.

We cannot know for certain how the first eukaryotic cells, looked, nor when they appeared. The

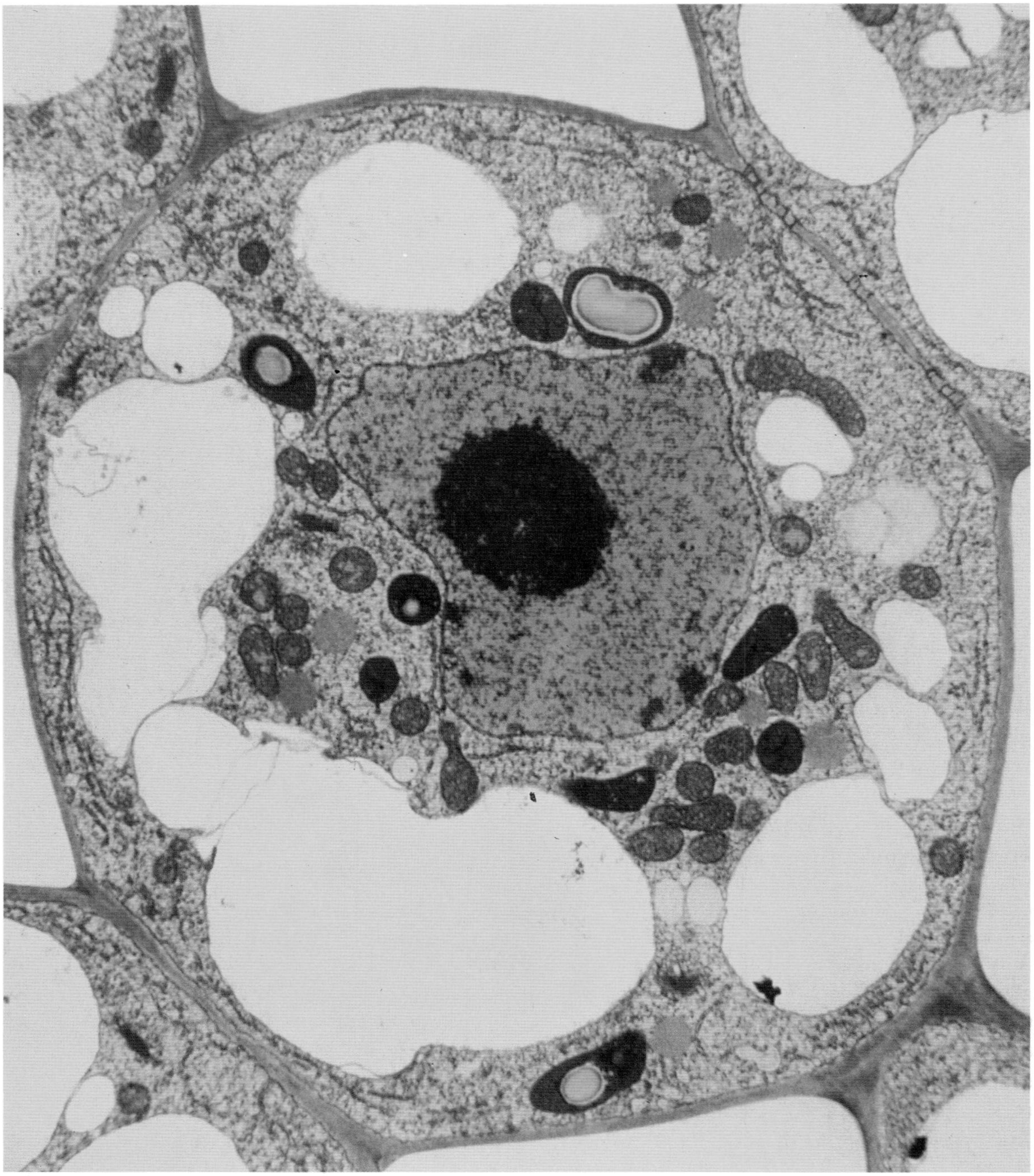

46 The eukaryotic cell has a more complex structure than that of the prokaryotes, and can, moreover, develop much more varied life strategies. The main difference is that, unlike the prokaryotic cell, which generally has only a circular DNA molecule and reproduces itself by direct cell division, the eukaryotic cell transports its genes in chromosomes that are grouped together within a membrane, and reproduces by means of a complex process involving two different sexes. All eukaryotic cells have a similar metabolism—leaving on one side their ability to photosynthesize—whose basic characteristics lie in their ability to respire aerobically. *[Photo: Biophoto Associates-Science Source / AGE Fotostock (x 14,000)]*

fossil record between 2,000 and 1,500 million years ago is very poor and only lately has been improving with the discovery of *Grypania* and other early eukaryotes. Most likely during that period of time, once the ozone layer had developed, evolution toward more complex, longer-lived organisms took place in the eukaryotic cells.

The first eukaryotes were probably anaerobic unicellular protists, aquatic organisms with variable patterns of cellular division and life cycle that varied from one species to another. Unfortunately, it is virtually impossible to follow the origin and first steps of protist evolution in the fossil record because, like most modern protists, they probably did not form hard parts, making their fossilization unlikely. Hypotheses about the characteristics of the first protists are based on the study of modern ones. Many characteristics of modern anaerobic mastigotes like the retortamonads or diplomonads (e.g. *Giardia*) back the hypothesis that the first eukaryotes were like some protists of today. For example, the peculiar reproduction traits of many of them seem to indicate that both mitosis as well as biparental sexuality evolved in the protists.

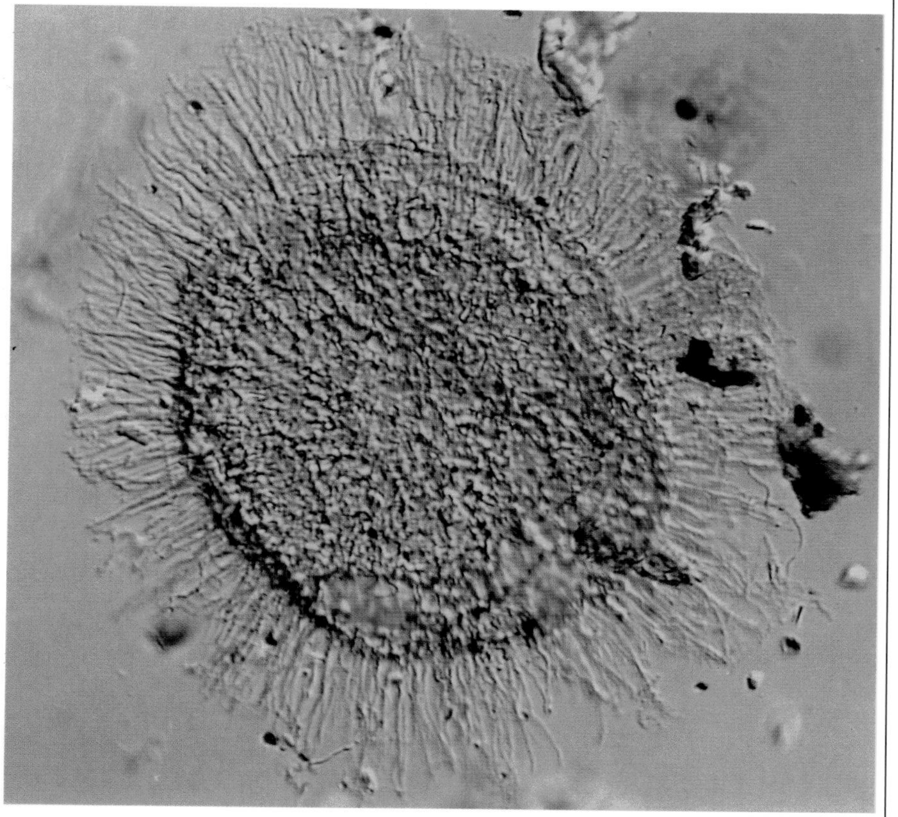

47 The first eukaryotes on Earth may have been the acritarchs (such as *Appendisphaera grandis*, a Neoproterozoic acritarch from the Siberian platform), since they are unicellular organisms with a thick wall around them. This led them to have a planktonic way of life for millennia. Abundant acritarch sediments are found in sediments deposited on shallow oceanic platforms of less than 570 million years in age, but they also seem to occur in Proterozoic rocks, a period in which they have a great palaeostratigraphic value. *[Photo: Moczydlowska, Vidal and Rudavskaia (x 600)].*

Acritarchs are probably the oldest group of eukaryotes that ever existed. They are spheric microfossils (or exceptionally, polyhedric, or star-shaped) with thick, complex organic walls. Because of their size and complexity, they appear to be of eukaryotic origin. They are probably cysts that correspond to a life cycle stage of a protoctist, perhaps an alga, resistant forms that would seem to be confirmed by the fact that some microphotographs of thin sections of rock with acritarchs show within them differentiated structures that could very well be nuclei. Acritarchs are very common in sediment deposits on shallow oceanic platforms (schists and carbonates) of 570 million years ago, but they are also found in older rocks. The discoveries by Baltic, Scandinavian, and North American paleontologists of much older fossils appearing to be acritarchs have moved back the origin of the organisms that produced them to the Proterozoic. Acritarchs from the southern Urals from between 1,650 and 1,400 million years ago have been described as similar to algae of the order Prasinophyceae or the family Chlorococcaceae, while thick-walled acritarchs, together with filamentous cyanobacteria and fine, spheroidal vesicles, have been also discovered in rocks from Montana, 1,400 million years old. These ancient microfossils may or may not be evidence of eukaryotic life, but what is certain is that rocks from Scandinavia and Arizona from the end of the Riphean, over 700 million years ago, contain fossil records of planktonic plants and animals, and that in Canada's *Dal formation*, macroscopic layered material dated about 1,000 million years ago has been found, which could be the remains of an alga similar to the present-day genus *Ulva*.

The origin of the eukaryotic cell

Different theories on the origin of eukaryotic cells have been suggested. Some biologists believe that cellular organelles were differentiated from the nucleus. According to this theory, the cells would first have had to develop internal membranes, some of which would have enveloped their DNA and RNA, thereby constituting the nucleus. In a second stage, some of the genes that made up the cellular DNA would have escaped from the nucleus and, when surrounded by other intracellular membranes, would have formed the other organelles of the eukaryotic cell. This hypothesis allows for a satisfactory explanation of the origin of different organelles, but it does not explain why organellar DNA is so different from that of the nucleus and much more similar to bacterial DNA. The eukaryotic cell more likely evolved from symbiotic mergers among different bacterial cells, which was accidental at first, then more stable, and finally permanent. With the passage of time and selection pressure, more and more integrated relationships between different organisms which were initially independent would have been favored until a new type of cell evolved. This theory of symbiogenesis for the eukaryotic cell, besides providing a satisfactory explanation for the differences between the DNA of the nucleus and the organelles—since they came from originally different prokaryotic cells, is based on a deeper understanding of the role of biological associations, following a line of biological thought that began with Russian and German naturalists late in the 19th century.

Cell symbiosis as the origin of nucleated cells

A partial interpretation of Darwin's theory of evolution has traditionally emphasized the importance of competition in the relationships between organisms and has undervalued relationships based on cooperation, or symbiosis. The idea of evolution as a bloody "struggle for life" leading to "the survival of the fittest," and understanding the fittest as being the strongest and most ruthless fighters, is not strictly speaking, Darwinian thought, but rather the work of philosopher and economist Herbert Spencer (1820-1903), one of the founders of the misnamed social Darwinism. For Darwin, fitness was not measured by muscular strength or predatory habits, but by reproductive efficiency. In the game of evolution, survival does not consist so much as in avoiding death (which is inevitable for all individuals), as in assuring the propagation of life, the continuity of the information in one's own genes. Besides, in this game the winner is never the isolated individual. No individual, in fact no species, can survive without many others.

In the specific case of microorganisms, symbiosis is frequent, especially in oxygen-poor atmospheres. Without oxygen, organic material degrades very slowly. The transformation of a dead bacterium into its final gaseous products such as ammonia, hydrogen sulfide, and methane often requires the action of another bacterium and even of bacteria from more than one species. *Methanobacillus omelianski*, for example, a supposed methane-producing soil bacterium, had been classified as a microorganism producing methane from ethanol and was believed to be a single bacterium. It was not until later that it was discovered that two different kinds of bacteria participated in the process. They were morphologically so similar that very few microbiologists were able to distinguish them, but they were metabolically very different. One type of bacterium ferments

48 The Earth's landscape between 1,300 and 800 million years ago would not have been very different from that depicted in the drawing. Towards the end of this period, there probably already existed organisms (indicated by the ovals) that were the ancestors of the plants and animals. These possessed cells that contained sacs of chlorophyll (plastids), which co-existed with the subunits capable of using oxygen for aerobic respiration (mitochondria). All these kinds of small intracellular bodies were able to split into two, despite forming part of a eukaryotic cell. Evolution led to these eukaryotes of some 800 million years ago, which had two ways of obtaining ATP, respiration and photosynthesis, and to them abandoning the water and colonizing the land. *[Drawing: Biopunt]*

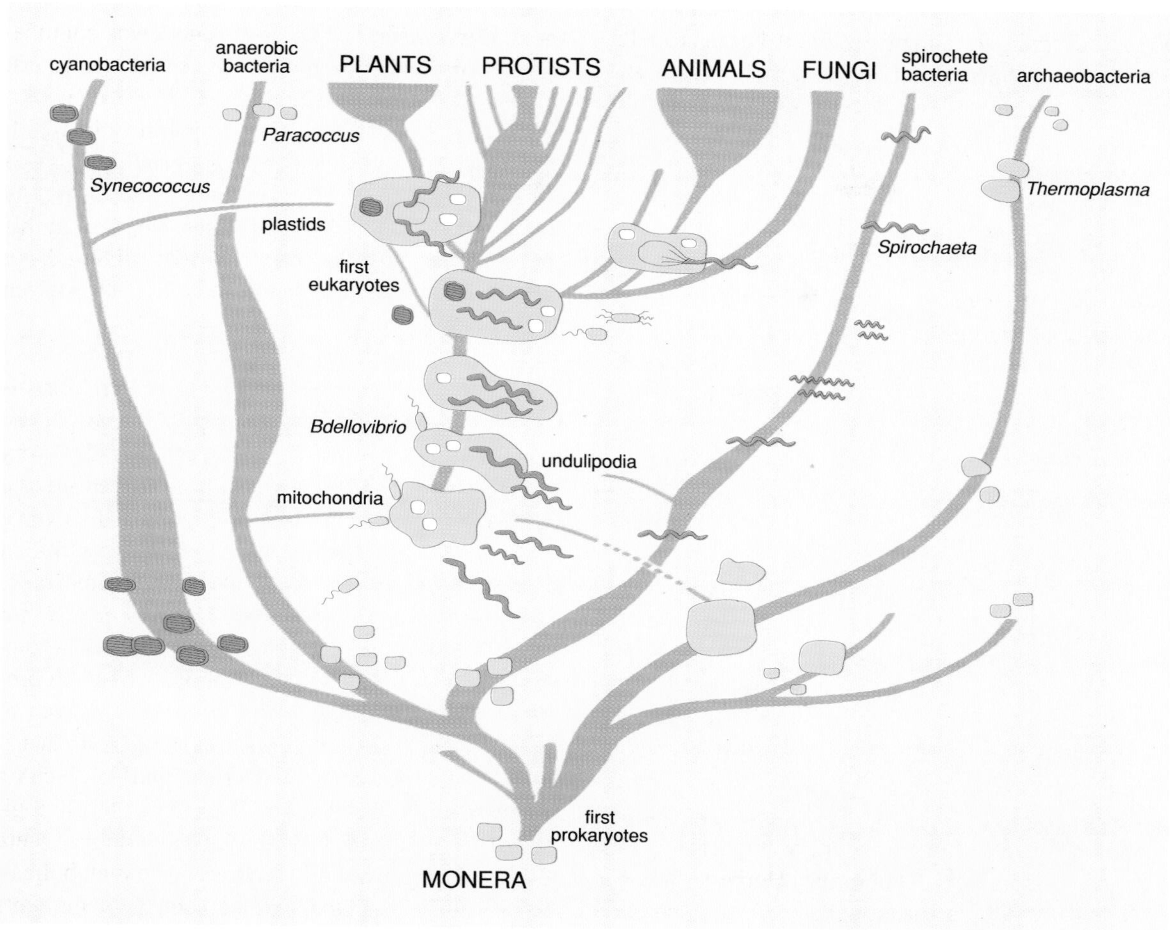

49 The hypothesis of the endosymbiotic origin of the eukaryote cell, which explains the different organelles that are found inside the cells, is based on the belief that symbiotic relationships occupied a much more important role than has been supposed until now, and applies to microorganisms in environments which are poor in oxygen. The idea derives from experiments with present day bacteria, in which it has been shown that many times they produce a symbiosis between different bacteria, which are very similar morphologically, but which complement each other in metabolic terms. *[Diagram: Biopunt, from various sources]*

the ethanol, while the second uses the products from the degradation of the former and transforms them into methane. It has been proven that together these bacteria grow much more quickly than separately.

The bacterial ancestors of mitochondria

The bacterial origin of mitochondria is well established by new molecular biology. *Mitochondria* are small membrane-bounded bodies found as inclusions in the cytoplasm, either oval or elongated in shape. They measure about 1.5 µm in diameter and can be up to 10 µm long. They contain all of the cell's respiratory enzymes, providing all the energy necessary for metabolic processes. Thanks to the presence of mitochondria, all eukaryotic cells, including human ones, have remarkably similar metabolism. Leaving aside the capacity of plants and algae for oxygen photosynthesis, analogous to that of cyanobacteria, the fundamental characteristics of eukaryotic metabolism are the same for all animals, plants, and fungi: those of aerobic respiration. This greatly contrasts with bacteria, which, as we have said, have display great variation in their respiratory metabolism, including aerobic respiration. The metabolism of all eukaryotic cells starts with fermentation in the cytoplasm of food molecules, until pyruvic acid is produced and this is transformed into acetyl coenzyme A, which penetrates the mitochondria and feeds the Krebs cycle. We have already referred to the basic characteristics of this cycle, which is essential to respiratory metabolism and electron transport chains, with oxygen as the final acceptor, and which constitute the basic source of ATP formation, the supplier of energy for cell processes.

Mitochondria contain a complex system of membranes with the enzymes that catalyze the respiratory processes on the inner layers. Not only do they produce energy, but they also contain the enzymes required for the synthesis of complex organic molecules, such as steroids (four-ring lipid molecules including numerous hormones), provitamins, and other cellular compounds. On the other hand, a clear sign of the remote origin of mitochondria as independent bacteria is the fact that they contain their own genetic and protein synthesizing systems, including DNA, messenger RNA, transfer RNA, and ribosomes. It is a bacterial-type genetic complex without chromosomes and with ribosomes sen-

50 The ability of cells to tolerate oxygen was due to the evolution of certain enzymes, such as catalases, peroxidases, and superoxide-dismutase which reacted with the toxic radicals produced by the oxygen and converted it into innocuous organic compounds and water. The microbes soon found a solution for dealing with this oxygen, which not only protected them from a potentially toxic gas, but provided them with another way of transforming energy through their capacity to consume the oxygen produced by photosynthesis. With this new method, the production of cellular ATP increased, since it was much more efficient than anaerobic respiration in the oxidation of molecules. *[Diagram: Biopunt, from various sources]*

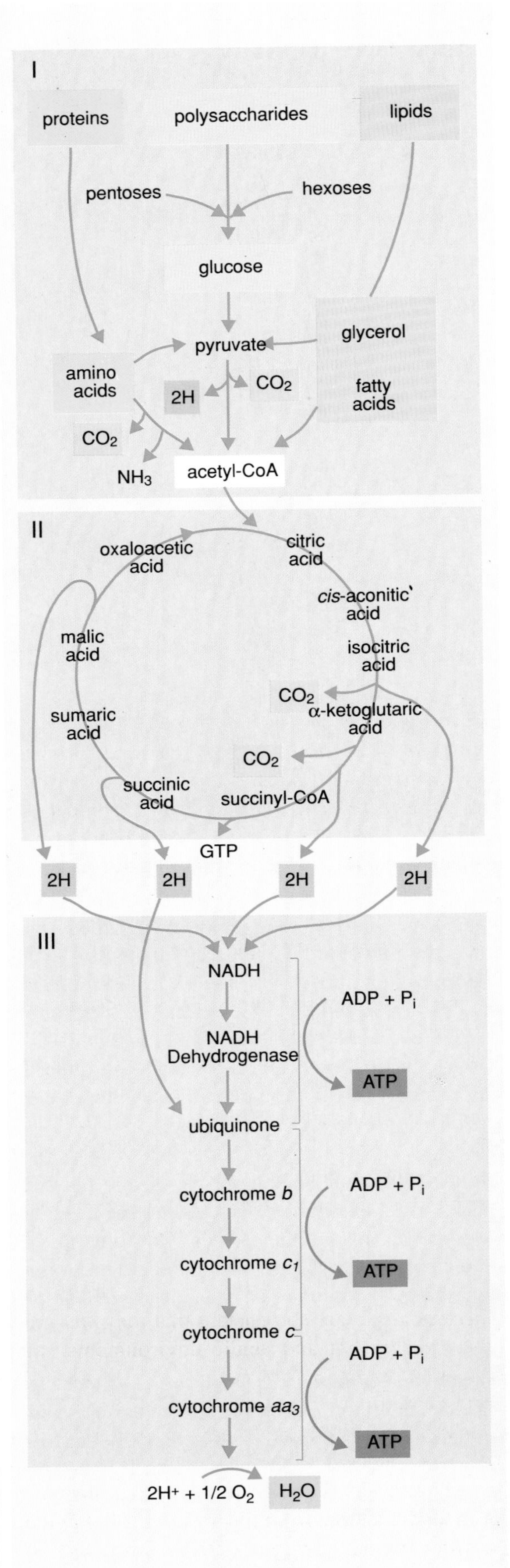

51 The small present day aerobic bacterium *Bdellovibrio* (on the right) is classed as a predator because it fixes on to the cell wall of other bacteria and penetrates into them with spiral movements (like a drill) and once inside is able to utilize the genetic material of the host for its own reproduction, and the proteins to feed it until the host ends up dying. It is believed that a bacterium of this type, which lived inside one of the bacteria precursors of cellular cytoplasm, could have given rise to mitochondria. *[Photo: H. Stolp (x 350,000)]*

sitive to antibiotics, such as streptomycin, just like aerobic bacteria.

The bacterial ancestors of mitochondria were probably similar to aerobic, predatory bacteria such as modern *Bdellovibrio* or *Daptobacter*. *Bdellovibrio* are small, aerobic bacteria that attach themselves to the cell walls of other bacteria, penetrate them with a drill-like whirling and multiply, using the genetic material and proteins of their victims. When they have taken all they can, they burst open the empty bag of what was a bacterium and the freed bdelovibrios look for a new host to repeat the cycle. *Daptobacter* has been found to be an active predator of photosynthetic bacteria, such as *Chromatium*, in samples from the ponds of Cisó, near Porqueres at the Pla de l'Estany (in northeastern Catalonia). It was found to multiply in its host both in aerobic and anaerobic conditions. The ancestors of mitochondria were most likely bacteria similar to *Daptobacter*, which attempted to feed on bacteria that were ancestral to the nucleocytoplasmic portion of the eukaryotic cell.

At the beginning, perhaps 2,000 million years ago, the infected organisms died, followed by the death of most of their predators—if the predators could not find a new host in time and the environment was hostile. But some host cells must have developed a tolerance for their predators, allowing them to live on for prolonged periods of time in the nutrient-rich environment of their own cytoplasm. Meanwhile, they benefited from the capacity of mitochondrial

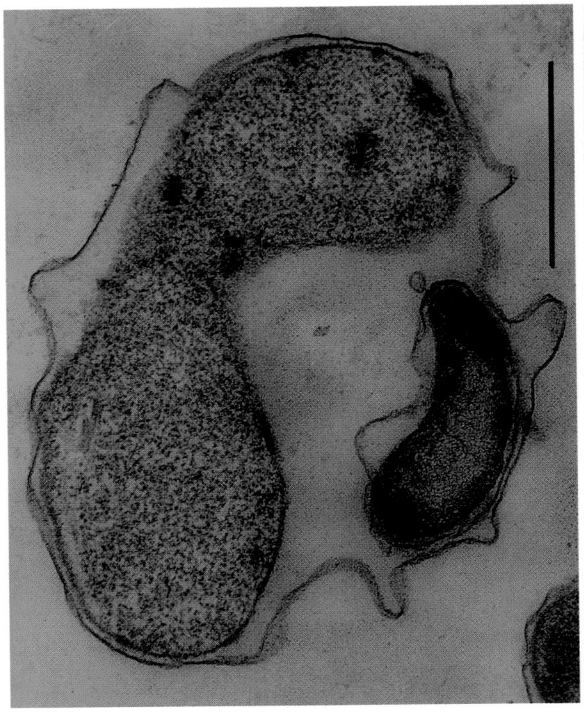

ancestors to breathe oxygen, not so much for the advantages directly obtained from respiratory metabolism from the energetic point of view, as from the fact that this freed them to some extent from the toxic dangers increasingly present in the outside world. The formation of the nuclear membrane may have been a necessary condition for establishing this symbiosis to protect the DNA from the increase in oxygen, not only in the environment outside the cell, but in the cytoplasm as well, because of the mitochondria's function.

For the precursors of mitochondria, delaying or even avoiding the host cell's death was advantageous in that it assured their own descendents, especially in highly adverse external environments (high temperatures, extremely acidic or saline conditions, etc.). The conflict between predator and prey, when both survived, slowly became an advantageous interchange that did not exclude occasional returns to the harmful virulence of the past, with disadvantages for both. Some researchers believe that certain forms of cancer are an atavistic return by mitochondria to the antagonistic relationship with the cell that they stop recognizing as their own, a kind of mitochondrial rebellion against the established symbiotic relationship.

The bacterial ancestors of cytoplasm

The host bacteria that contributed cytoplasm and primary genetic material to the symbiosis described above were probably similar to modern *Thermoplasma*, inhabitants of extremely hostile environments and also able to tolerate small quantities of oxygen. *Thermoplasma* are very peculiar bacteria. Although they belong to the bacteria group called *Aphragmabacteria*, characterized by their inability to synthesize the polysaccharides making up the rigid cell wall of all other bacteria, diagnosis of their RNA and lipids shows they are Archaebacteria (like halobacteria and methane-producers). Their lack of a rigid cell wall surrounding their cells does not make them more vulnerable, despite their very small size (the diameter of some species in this group is not even 0.2 μm), precisely because this makes them immune to the effects of penicillin and other antibiotics which inhibit the growth of the cell wall. The membrane surrounding them is made up of three layers formed by lipids and hydrocarbons that dissolve only in organic solvents.

Thermoplasma are so resistant that they can grow in extremely hot and acidic environments, with temperatures of almost 140°F (60°C)—they die from cold at temperatures below 104°F, or 40°C , which makes studying them enormously difficult—and a pH of 1 or 2 (the acidity of concentrated sulfuric acid). The only samples that have been studied come from the surface of hot cinders or from the hot springs of Yellowstone National

52 The living organisms that are considered to be the precursors of the cytoplasm of the eukaryotic cell are bacteria of the genus *Thermoplasma*, which are capable of living under extreme conditions of temperature 140°F (60°C) and acidity (1 or 2 pH) in thermal springs in the Yellowstone National Park, in the USA. These organisms show some properties that are unique in bacteria, such as the lack of a cell wall and, above all, the possession of a DNA covering made up of proteins very similar to the typical histones of the eukaryotic cell. This, and the need to associate with other bacteria to obtain the steroids needed for its membrane, makes one think that it would have been associated with the bacteria that were precursors of the mitochondria, which it is presumed had the ability to synthesize them. *[Photo: TPS / Index]*

53 It is thought that the plastids, which allowed some bacteria to be autotrophic in the early stages of evolution, began as green photosynthesizing endosymbionts of host cells and that later, through loss or reduction of their digestive organs the organisms capable of using oxygen were transformed into intracellular organelles. *[Photo: AGE Fotostock (x 10,000)]*

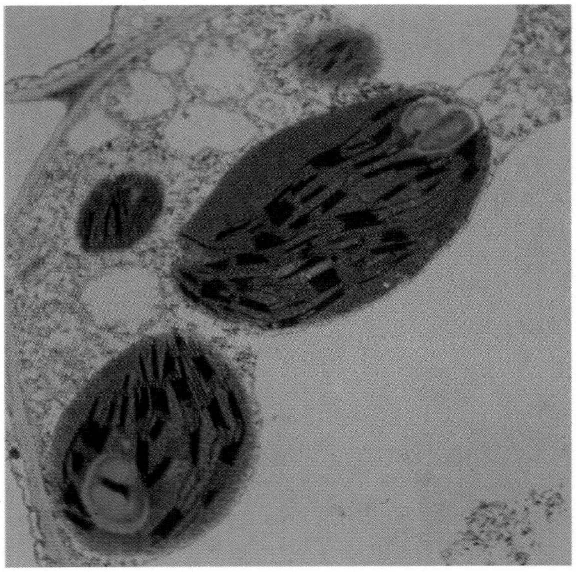

Park in the United States. But what makes them the best candidate for the ancestors of the nucleocytoplasmic portion of the eukaryotic cell is the fact that they are the only prokaryote whose DNA is wrapped in proteins similar to the histones which form the same function in chromosomal DNA of plants and animals.

To reinforce their membrane and make it more flexible, most Aphragmabacteria need steroids, although practically none synthesize them, and they have to get them from their surroundings, often from the animal or plant they parasitize. It is precisely the capacity of mitochondria's ancestral bacteria to synthesize steroids that would have helped establish the symbiosis that created the eukaryotic cell. The membranes of the Aphragmabacteria are more similar to those of eukaryotes than to cell walls of other prokaryotes. To make their membranes flexible, eukaryotes pack them with steroids, molecules needing mitochondria metabolism for synthesis, although the first stages of steroid synthesis take place in the cytoplasm. Perhaps at first, steroid synthesis was only the contribution of the ancestors of mitochondria to life in conjunction with the genetic material of its host cell, in order to save it from contact with the dangerous oxygen used in their metabolism. But later the availability of steroids became advantageous to the formation of flexible membranes, easy to break and fuse and capable of forming vesicles to wrap and protect the mitochondria itself or its nucleus and organelles, as well as forming other cell structures.

The bacterial ancestors of plastids

Perhaps hundreds of millions of years after mitochondria had become established as cell organelles, a new type of organism joined them in certain cells: the ancestors of plastids. Nearly a hundred years ago, the symbiogenetic origin of plastids had already been recognized, but it was not until the mid-1990s that this was generally acknowledged. Plastids, like mitochondria, are small organelles wrapped in a double membrane suspended in cytoplasm. Their shape is generally oval or discoid and their size varies from 3 to 10 µm. Plastids normally contain the pigments required for photosynthesis in strange layered membranous structures, although in some cases they can lose these structures and then generally function as storage houses for reserve substances.

Unlike mitochondria, the precursors of plastids were not incorporated by infection, but by ingestion. Certain protists probably ingested some cyanobacteria or other photosynthetic bacteria, among many other sources of nutrition. But some of them must have developed the capacity to resisted being digested, allowing them to keep their valuable light energy-capturing pigments active within the cytoplasm of their hosts.

In fact, there is a living organism, *Prochloron*, which behaves exactly as plastid ancestors must have, although not with cells that were eukaryote precursors, but with the tissues of the cloacal (a waste chamber) walls of different tropical Pacific tunicate species. In the late 1960s Ralph Lewin, a marine biologist of the Scripps Institute of Oceanography in California, discovered that several supposed green algae that lived in symbiosis with colonial ascidians (tunicates) of the tropical Pacific were really photosynthetic bacteria. They differed from a chloroplast only in that they had a typically prokaryotic cell wall. These organisms, which were named *Prochloron*, are the missing link in the evolutionary history of symbiosis that led to the algae and plants. They successfully combine the physiology of a plant chloroplast with the structure of a bacterium. Like the cyanobacteria, Prochloron can fix nitrogen within the tissues of the host. Unlike cyanobacteria, which are also photosynthesizers but only have chlorophyll *a* and bluish-green pigments, *Prochloron*, like green algae and plants, has chlorophyll *a* and chlorophyll *b*. It is not at all unlikely that the undigested bacteria that were ancestral to chloroplasts were also the ancestors of *Prochloron*.

The ancestors of the chloroplasts of the red algae must have been coccoid cyanobacteria. Their characteristic colors result from their possession

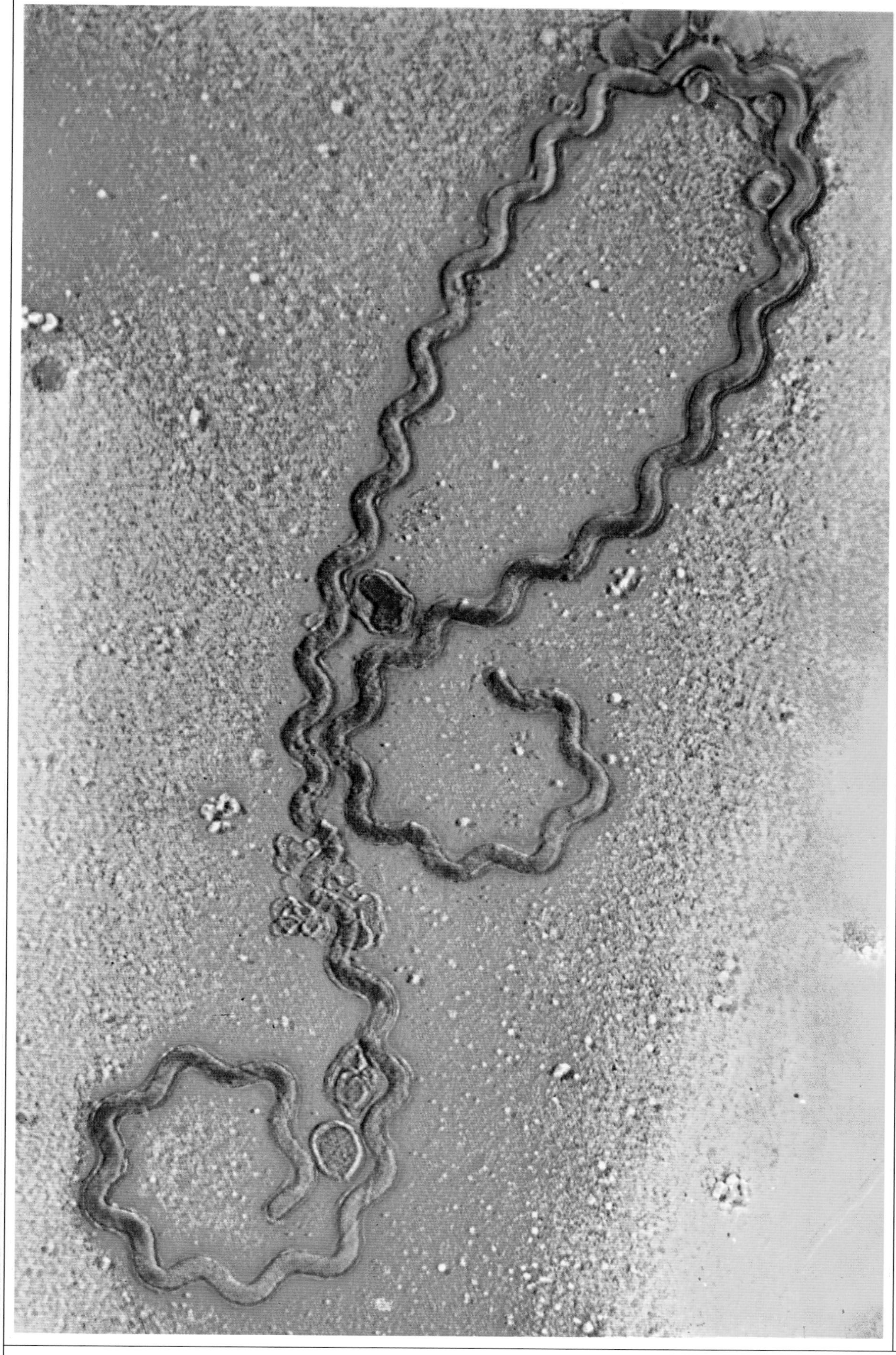

54 It is believed that the spirochaetes had a lot to do with the explanation of the origin of the undulipodia—that is of the cilia and flagella that are present in all kinds of eukaryote cells—since it is known that many of the present day ones help the eukaryotic cells on top of which they are fixed to move. The photograph (transmission electron micrograph in false color) shows a spirochaete of the genus *Leptospira* (in red) which forms a very fine spiral (20 x 0.1 micrometres thick). To this genus *Leptospira* belong the agents of many illnesses of humans and animals such as leptospirosis, known also as Weill's disease, which affects the liver or the membranes of the brain (meningitis), whose cause is *L. icterohaemorrhagiae.* *[Photo: CNRI / Science Photo Library / AGE Fotostock (x 50,000)]*

of the same pigments, phycobilins, which are responsible for the colors of the cyanobacteria. The sequences of nucleotides in the ribosomal RNA of plastids have been compared with those of the cytoplasm of the *Porphyridium*, and it was observed that they were very different (with no more than 15% in common). It was then noticed, however, that the RNA of plastids is much more similar to the sequences of the ribosomal RNA in the chloroplastids of a photosynthetic protist such as *Euglena* or those of a cyanobacteria such as *Synechococcus* (with similarities are 33 and 42% respectively).

The ancestors of cilia and flagella

Undulipodia, that is the cilia and so-called flagella of many plant and animal sperm and eukaryotic cells, might also have had a symbiotic origin, although biologists are not yet as willing to agree on this as they do on the symbiotic theories for the origin of mitochondria and plastids.

First of all, the structure of undulipodia is exactly the same in all cells containing them, whether or not they are ciliate infusoria, like those of mammal sperm, the cells of the human trachea, or the zoospores of water molds: nine pairs of microtubules, each tubule about 24 nanometers in diameter, arranged in a circle surrounding two more single microtubules in its core, an arrangement referred to as the 9 + 2 structure, comprise the undulipodium axis. It is derived from a basal body called the kinetosome made up of nine triplets of short microtubules. The walls of the microtubules are made up of specific proteins called tubulins, along with several hundred other less well-known proteins. Until 1989 only ribonucleic acids were known and that was not sufficient proof of the symbiotic origin of undulipodia, but later DNA has been discovered in the kinetosomes of *Chlamydomonas*, a photosynthetic protist with two undulipodia.

Microtubules similar to those of undulipodia have been known to exist in spirochetes since the mid-1960s. Spirochetes (or similar bacterial precursors) are seen as the most appropriate candidates for the symbionts responsible for introducing motility to the eukaryotic cell. The best known spirochetes, such as *Treponema pallidum*, the causal agent of syphilis, have the reputation of being dangerous pathogenic microbes, but many others live freely in stagnant waters or in microbial mats. Still other spirochetes live as symbionts in animal intestines. Some spirochetes confer motility to the protists to which they are attached. This is the case of the spirochetes that live on the surface of *Mixotricha paradoxa*, a protist living in the gut of the Australian termite *Mastotermes darwiniensis*. The treponema-like spirochetes allow the protist to move because of their coordinated movement. It is probable that an association between an archaebacterium similar to *Thermoplasma* and surface spirochetes preceded the origin of eukaryotes through symbiogenesis by the precursors of mitochondria. In the anoxic muds of the early Proterozoic eon, such protists were attacked by mitochondria's precursors to form the basis for all subsequent life.

3.5 The evolution of the first eukaryotes

The rise of sexual reproduction

The first eukaryotic organisms must have been unicellular protists (to the extent that we can consider an organism resulting from symbiogenesis unicellular) that reproduced by simple division, like bacteria. But another trait that radically distinguished the new eukaryotic life from prokaryotic life was the emergence of a new form of reproduction: sexual reproduction. All prokaryotes reproduce asexually by dividing or, more rarely, by budding. In both cases, the offspring receive all of its genes from one parent. Examples of sexuality, formation of a new being with genes from more than a single parent (normally but not necessarily two), exist in some prokaryotes, but in these cases sex is not part of reproduction. Rather, it involves the acquisition of one or a few genes from the environment or from another cell or virus. On the other hand, all animals and plants and most fungi reproduce sexually with an equal genetic contribution from each of two parents to the offspring.

Humans tend to think of sex and reproduction as inseparable. It helps restore perspective to remember that the three components of sexual reproduction that are now associated were once separate: halving of the number of chromosomes, fusion of nuclei from two sources, and the cyclical sequence of these processes are actually at least three distinct processes.

Mitosis and microtubules

Sexual reproduction as we know it entails two different kinds of cellular division: mitosis and meiosis. Both evolved in protists.

The first, *mitosis*, "the dance of chromosomes," also occurs in unicellular eukaryotes that repro-

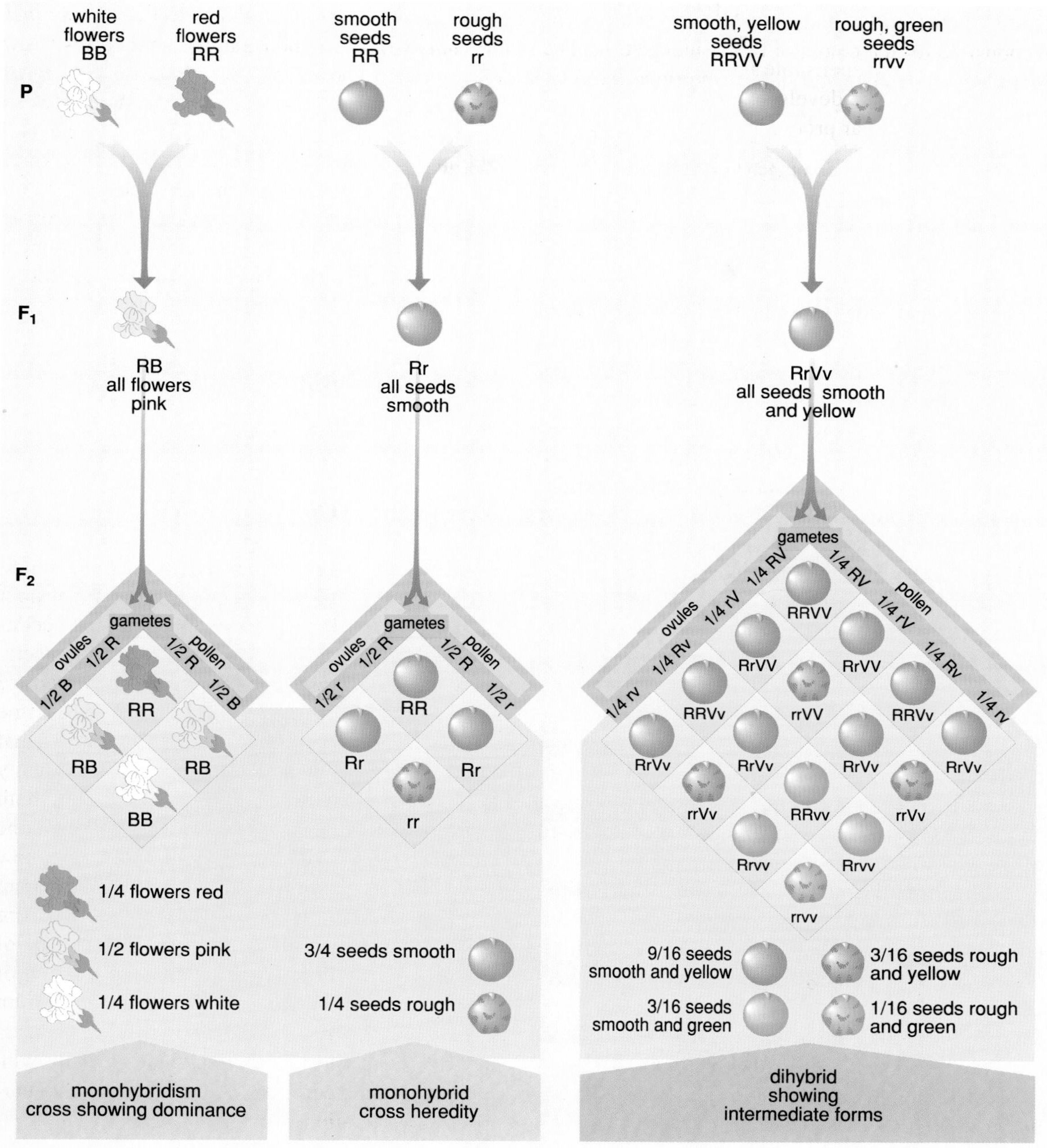

55 The laws of Mendel explain the segregation and the independence of the hereditary characteristics. In the three cases one can observe the uniformity of the first filial generation: in the first case (left), the phenotypes of the individuals of the F_1 are intermediate; in the second case (center) one characteristic (smooth seeds) is dominant over the other (wrinkled seeds); in the third case (right), the inheritance of two characteristics is shown: smooth yellow seeds versus green wrinkled seeds. *[Diagram: Biopunt, from various sources]*

duce asexually by division. The nuclei of most animal and plant cells contain two full, homologous but not identical, sets of chromosomes with 104 to 106 genes per set. Cells whose nuclei contain two sets of chromosomes are diploid; cells whose nuclei have a single set are haploid. In mitotic division, each offspring cell receives a copy of all the parent cell's genetic material. This genetic material is found condensed in chromosomes, small bodies made up mainly of long spirally arranged DNA molecules covered in different kinds of protein molecules, usually histones, also containing RNA. The chromosomes of the parent cell duplicate, and their two halves divide and move to opposite poles of the cell. In each half the DNA of chromosomes uncurls, a nuclear membrane forms around each one, and finally, separation of the two daughter cells is achieved. Mitosis requires a close coordination of two cell systems: one doubles the quantity of the chromosomal DNA by synthesis, and the other forms the mitotic spindle that moves chromosomes to the opposite sides of the dividing cell.

Almost certainly the evolutionary origin of mitosis occurred during protist diversification. In the cells of animals, plants, and fungi, it is a perfectly normal process, but there are no precedents

56 Mitosis of a cell with a haploid number of chromosomes. The cell divides to form two cells that are genetically identical to the original one, through a continuous process in which; however, different phases can be distinguished. The division begins with the prophase (1), after some time the interphase, in which the genetic material has doubled. Later, in the metaphase, the chromatin condenses, allowing one to see the chromosomes (2). During the anaphase, the fibers of the achromatic spindle, which hold the chromosomes to the centromere, pull and separate—each of the halves towards the poles of the cell—so that when a new membrane is formed, the initial cell becomes two (6). When mitosis is complete, the genetic material again decontracts itself so that it can be read according to the function and needs of the cell. *[Diagram: Biopunt, from various sources]*

among prokaryotes and, except for some spirochetes and *Azotobacter*, prokaryotes lack microtubules that are indispensable for the formation of mitotic spindles. The development of mitosis cannot be seen as a linear process, but one that moved forward by trial and error and through all sorts of variations, successes, and dead ends: these resulted in the origin and evolution of approximately 250,000 species of protists.

Some amoebae, for example, with no sex differentiation, have DNA complexes with proteins that never form chromosomes. In some dinoflagellates the chromosomes are anomalous, the DNA has large quantities of hidroxyuracil—an unusual base—and the chromosomes never unspiral. They remain densely packed even when mitosis is not taking place. They lack histones. In other dinoflagellates, the chromosomes adhere directly to the nuclear membrane in a way that resembles prokaryotic cells. In Euglena chromosomes move toward their respective poles at different times.

But the presence of microtubules in the cell spindle that allow for and direct the movement of chromosomes suggests a common origin for these structures and undulipodia. If we imagine that some of the spirochetes participating in the symbiogenesis of a eukaryotic cell had passed into the interior of the host cell and were the origin of the microtubules of the mitotic spindle and the centrioles, this might explain why some unicellular eukaryotic organisms with well-developed mitotic systems, such as amoebae or Rhodophyceae, have no undulipodia for motility, while others, such as amoebomastigotes, that do have them, lose them during mitotic processes.

Meiotic reduction

But mitosis alone does not achieve sexual reproduction. There must also be a process for reducing the number of chromosomes by half, at least in the reproductive cells or gametes, a process called meiosis. Meiosis distributes the chromosomes so that each offspring cell has exactly one member of each of the homologous chromosome pairs originally present in the parent cell. Thus, cells produced by the meiosis of a diploid cell are always haploid. In fertilization, the fusion of two haploid cells reestablishes diploidy. Meiosis may or may not include crossing-over, that is, the exchange of DNA between homologous chromosomes. In any event, meiosis and fertilization lead to new assortments of chromosomes.

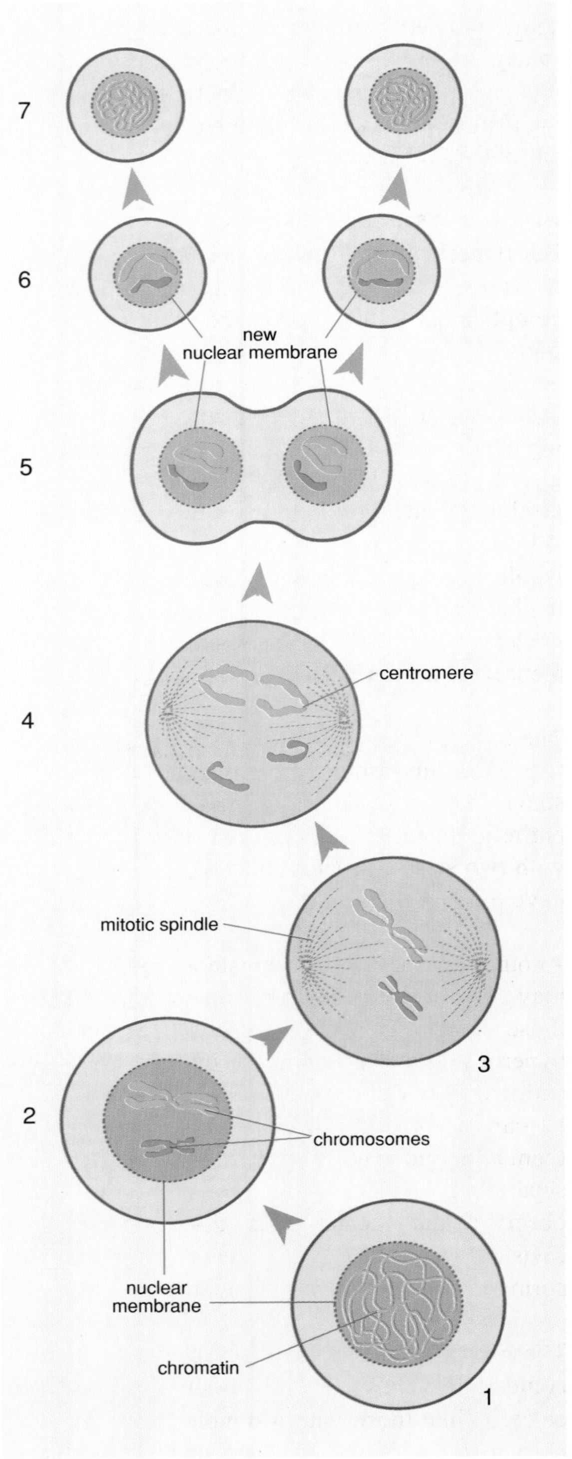

The details of mitosis and meiosis vary considerably, especially in protists. Their functions, however, do not vary: mitosis ensures equal distribution of genetic material to offspring (any variation of mitosis that leads to imprecise segregation of chromosomes or loss of genetic material is selected against immediately), and meiosis produces haploid cells from diploid ones. Fertilization, the fusion process that reestablishes diploid chromosome numbers, must intervene between meioses in any stable life cycle. Mitotic organisms may be recognized by their typical genetic patterns, called mendelian, whether or not direct observations of chromosome behavior exists.

The riddle of sexual reproduction

But there is a riddle in all this. Sexual reproduction appears to be a superfluous and unnecessary complication. It has none of the virtues of the free transfer of genetic material of bacterial sexuality and its "cost" (producing a special kind of sexual cell with half the number of chromosomes, finding mates, etc.), in the economic terms that biologists have used to describe it, seems out of proportion to any possible advantage it possesses. Why must two halves come together to make a whole only to become two halves again? Probably the halving of the number of chromosomes in the nuclei of some cells was prompted by that ancient menace of life on Earth, starvation.

The threat of starvation could have led some protists to cannibalism on more than one occasion. In some instances, the prey may not have been entirely digested, leaving our hungry cannibal with two sets of genetic material, that is, it would have become a diploid.

Another possible way to create a diploid nucleus may have been an anomaly in mitosis, such as those studied in different protists, especially in hypermastigotes, living in the intestines of wood-eating cockroaches and termites. These anomalies in chromosome division, after doubling, cause them all to move to one pole in the cell, instead of separating. But in other protists, it has been observed that nuclear division—but not cellular division—has taken place, and that the two offspring nuclei have fused together.

These processes, which were accidental at first, could have been selected by evolution, since larger cells (like those with a double set of identical chromosomes, diploids), were more favorable in adverse circumstances. They could have returned to their original state, having a single set (haploid), if there were another change in the environmental conditions favoring smaller cells again.

The success of sex

The irregular behavior of many unicellular protists in reproduction is fairly common. A sequence that had included the formation of a diploid cell, the pairing of the homologous chromosomes of

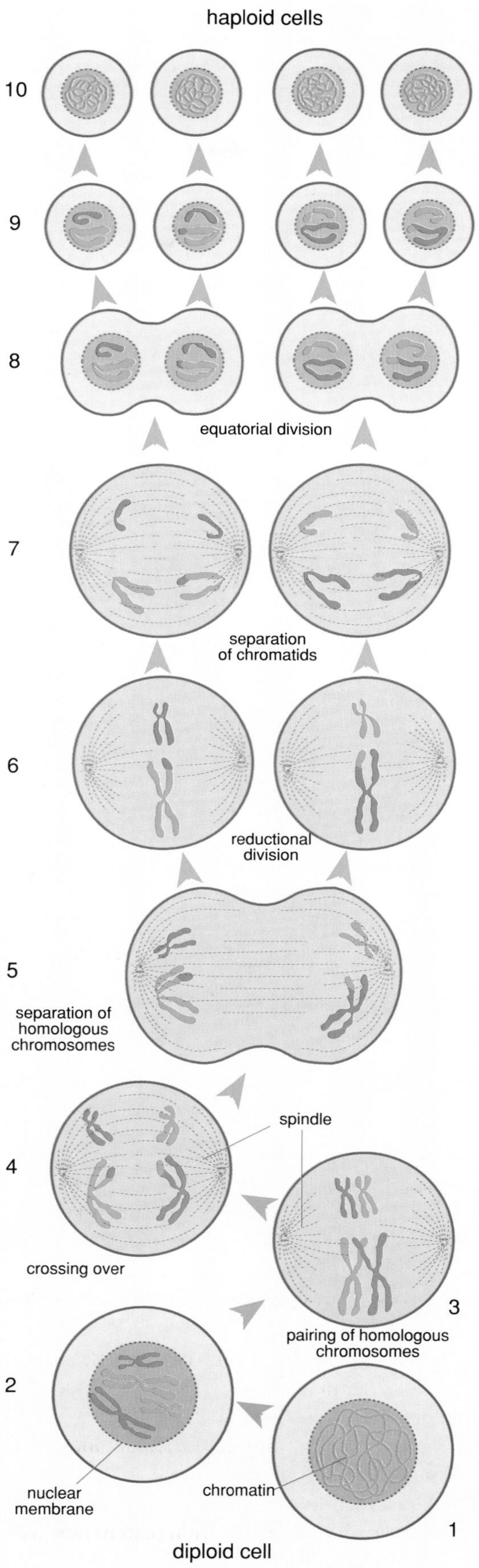

57 Meiosis is the mechanism by which a diploid cell divides into four haploid cells. As in mitosis, each chromosome is condensed after doubling. The two identical halves are united at a narrow point called the kinetochore; but there are still two similar, homologous chromosomes of each type, coming from each parent (phase 2). The homologous chromosomes are situated symmetrically on either side of the equatorial plane of the cell. Before cell division separates them, they may exchange sections of DNA. In continuation, the first cell division (phases 5 and 6) gives rise to two cells, each one with half the number of chromosomes of the original cell. The second cell division (phases 8 and 9) is similar to that of mitosis, since it simply separates the double chromosomes by the kinetochores. The final result is four cells, each with a different genetic composition. *[Diagram: Biopunt, from various sources]*

58 The evolutionary pathway that led to the association of reproduction with the exchange of genetic information between two progenitors, or, to sexuality, was complex and full of variations of which no record remains. In the case of conjugate filamentous algae or conjugatophytes, such as those of the genus *Spirogyra*, which is shown in the photograph, sexual reproduction means total fusion (conjugation) of the two cells of two different filaments, or of the same filament (one of which leaves its cell wall and penetrates the other through a conjugation tube which facilitates the union of the two cells) in a zygospore which develops a thicker cell wall and remains in a resting state for a more or less prolonged period before dividing and giving rise to haploid daughter cells, each of which will generate new filaments by asexual reproduction.
[Photo: AGE Fotostock]

this cell, and the failure of these chromosome pairs to divide so that each double chromosome moved to one of the cell's poles, seems to be an indispensable condition for the establishment of meiosis. A combination of cannibalism, nuclear fusion, irregularities in the division of chromosomes, and cyclical environments alternately favoring diploidy and then haploidy, could lead to death (which certainly must have happened many times). However, some of these organisms successfully negotiated these hazards and established the new form of reproduction.

As in other evolutionary events, sexually reproducing organisms began to proliferate with gathering momentum as they began to interact with their environment and evolved together. Had there not been environmental changes and if climatic conditions and geological phenomena had always been regular and predictable, sex might not have evolved. There are, in fact, organisms, such as sponges or fungi, that live in very stable environments and alternate sexual and asexual reproduction, but most of the world's environments are variable to some extent, and animals and plants, which are intrinsically sexual, evolved to cope with them.

Cellular specialization

In any case, in the late Proterozoic, about 700 million years ago, the most important genetic mechanisms assuring variation by means of sexual reproduction had already developed, as we can see from the oldest known multicellular animal fossils. They had probably already developed, even if only partially, about 2,000 million years ago. The development of certain structures (*chromosomes*), that allowed for the efficient packaging of considerable quantities of genetic information, the appearance of an efficient process for transmitting this information to the descendant cells (mitosis), and of a way of quickly and efficiently recombining the genetic information from more than one parent (sexual reproduction), opened the way for the appearance of multicellular eukaryotic organisms in the Late Proterozoic that were ever larger, with more complex and diversified structures, and altogether more specialized. All that was needed was for a cell from a flagellated protist to join with another and propel it along, so that it no longer needed to use its flagella and could put its microtubules to other uses. This was the beginning of the evolutionary line that led to animals. It was the beginning of cell specialization, of which animals have become masters. Some cells swam, others retained their capacity for meiosis, and others applied their spirochete apparatus to detecting signs from the outside world.

There is, however, a practical limitation to the size of a cell and, therefore, to a unicellular organism. Cells need to interact with the environment in order to absorb materials and expel waste products. Many of the cell's vital reactions take place in its external membranes, so from this aspect a small cell is more efficient than a large one. A unicellular organism that greatly increases in size has to deal with a decrease in its surface to volume ratio. Some organisms have compensated for this inconvenience by modifying their shape, for example, by repeatedly folding their membranes, which allows them to increase their surface in relation to volume within limits. The only definitive solution open to unicellular organisms to increase in size beyond this limitation was to become multicellular.

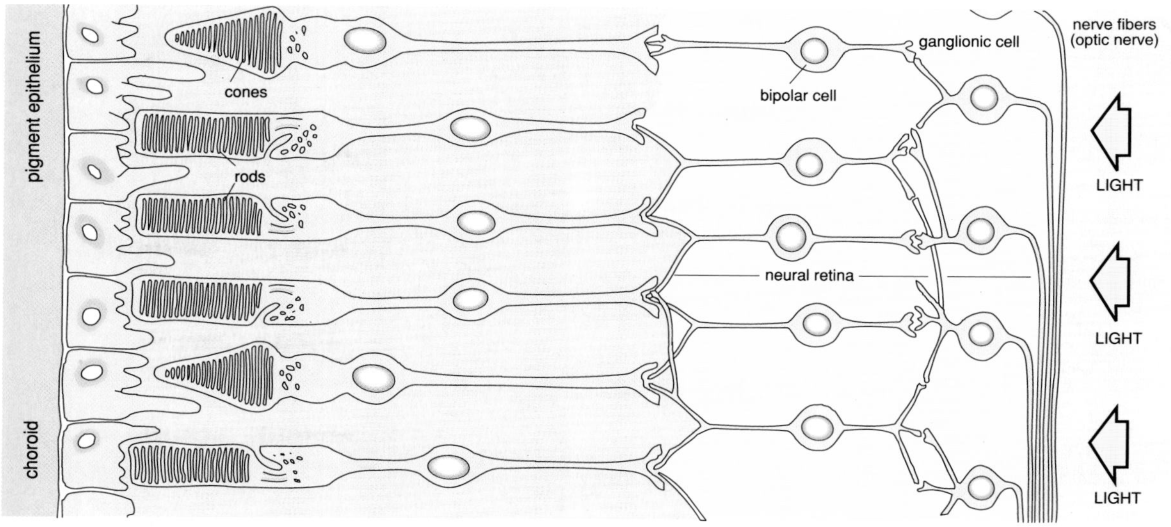

59 Cellular specialization has reached extraordinary levels of diversity and complexity in animals; a good example is the specialization of the light sensitive cells of the retina. In animals, visual perception ranges from the simple ability to distinguish light from dark, as in the case of planarians, to the formation of images with high definition, as in some mammals. *[Diagram: Biopunt, from various sources]*

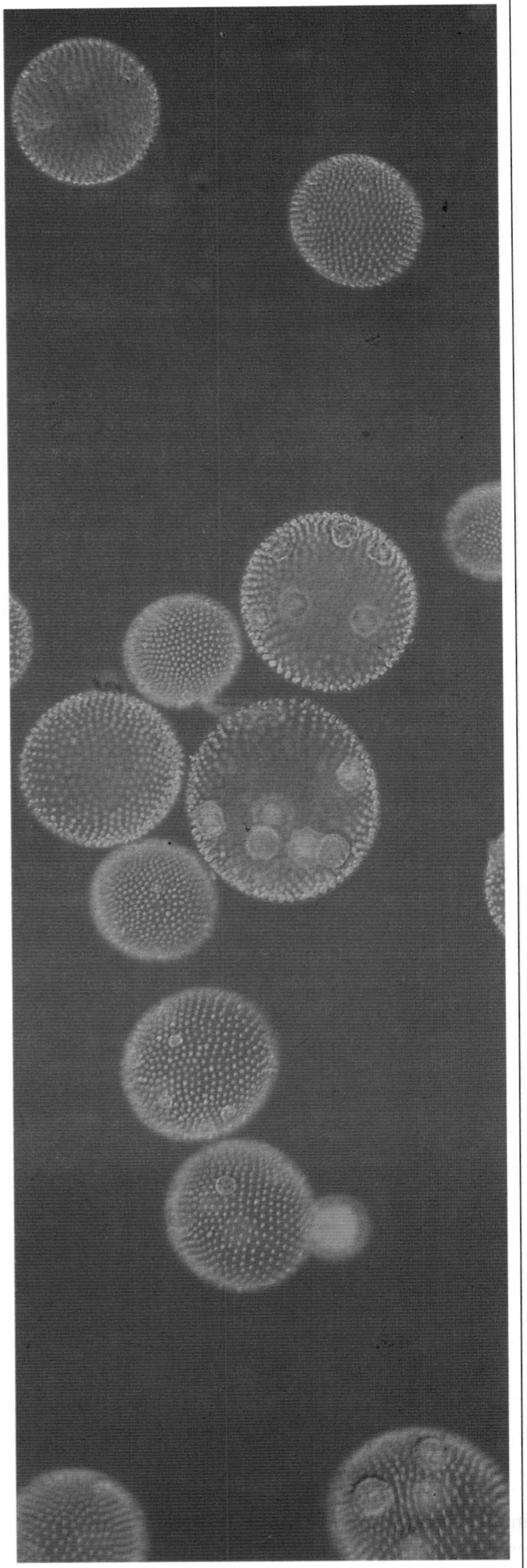

60 It is thought that the first algal ancestors of plants were simple chains or colonies of cells provided with chloroplasts, such as this colony of algae of the genus *Volvox*. Each of their cells, has flagella, an eye spot, and a chloroplast, and may be similar to the protoctist *Chlamydomonas*, a swimming unicell which lives in fresh water. We can follow the probable evolutionary steps of plant cells from these algal ancestors of the Volvocales. Four volvocine cells joined in a gelatinous disk form what we know as *Gonium sociale*; each one is able to separate from the colony to form a new one. In *Pandorina* one finds a special arrangement of the cells in one part of the colony; were members larger eye spots. In *Volvox* the cells are arranged so as to form a hollow sphere in which both poles are distinguished; the reproductive function is restricted to some cells situated at posterior pole. The last example can be interpreted as step very similar to the multicellular state, since the cells which are only joined by gelatine cannot do without the others. *[Photo: AGE Fotostock]*

The appearance of multicellular organisms

Multicellularity of one kind or another has appeared many times in many kinds of organisms. Some groups of procaryotes (such as myxobacteria, cyanobacteria [Nostocales] and actinobacteria) are all multicellular. It is not, therefore, a characteristic that is exclusive to fungi, plants, and animals, although we tend to associate it with them.

Multicellular protists

Cell differentiation, and links and communication between cells are very rare in multicellular protists. The Volvocales, a group of colonial green algae, are a good example of the development of situations, from the simple apposition of cells to organisms made up of numerous and interdependent cells. The individual cells of the Volvocales are very similar to those of the unicellular green alga *Chlamydomonas*, which we referred to earlier: each has two flagella, an eyespot sensitive to light, and a chloroplast.

Gonium, the simplest of colonial Volvocales, has a gelatinous disk that holds together four, eight, 16, or 32 of these cells with their flagella all on the same side of the disk. Each of these cells can divide and start to form a new colony identical to that of the mother cell. *Pandorina*, another genus, is made up of an oval pile of 16 or 32 cells in a gelatinous bag with their flagella and eyespots facing outwards and with a differentiation of the eyespots at one extreme of the colony, which are bigger than the rest, a fact that indicates the direction of the movement of the colony. Any of their cells can produce an offspring colony by division.

But those of the *Volvox* species are much more complex. They consist of a hollow sphere composed of 500 to 60,000 cells with anterior and posterior ends. The colony moves around its axis as it swims forward, propelled by its flagella in the direction of the anterior end. A gelatinous matrix holds the cells together, and only those near the posterior end can reproduce. They do this by freeing offspring cells that actively divide and bulge inward, into the hollow interior. When they have made a colony that is big enough, they release an enzyme that dissolves the gelatin binding them to the parent colony. Some species, however, can reproduce sexually, sometimes with both sexes present in all the colonies and other times with a separation of sexual roles from one colony to another. They therefore represent a border between coenobial life and true multicellularity. The moment in which the cells can no longer live independently and when there is "division of labor," as in the more differentiated *Volvox* species, is when the reproductive cells no longer have flagella and are, therefore, immobile.

The first multicellular animals

In the case of animals, *Trichoplax adhaerens*, the simplest of all known animals, is an example of what the most primitive multicellular animals must have been like. First discovered by Franz Eilhard Schulze in a marine aquarium at the Karl-Franzens Universität Graz in Austria in 1883, it was mistakenly classified as a coelenterate larva. The true nature of *Trichoplax* was not discovered until 1965.

The only thing that distinguishes it from a multicellular amoeba is that it undergoes embryonic development, from the fertilization of an egg by sperm to the formation of a blastula. The adult animal looks like a blastula with a few thousand cells, whose dorsal side is formed by flat cells and a small number of whips and whose ventral side is formed by columnar cells and a greater number of whips that allow them to crawl. Between the two cell layers there is an intermediate layer containing a fluid with few cells. It is clearly a multicellular organism with heterotrophic nutrition and, therefore, an animal, but it has no differentiated tissues, and its functional specialization is minimal. But if *Trichoplax*, as seems to be the case, is really an example of a descendant of one of the first differentiated animals, it is obvious that we cannot expect to find fossils of it because of its lack of hard parts.

The oldest fossil records of animal life were found in 1947 in the hills of Ediacara on the Flinders Range, about 280 mi (450 km) north of Adelaide in Southern Australia. They were found in Proterozoic sediments nearly 700 million years old and include very different kinds of animals. More recently, animal fossils, similar in age (between 600 and 570 million years old) and in other characteristics, have been found in Canada, Russia, Great Britain, and Scandinavia. It could be the case that all later animal phyla evolved from animals of the Ediacaran fauna (which include sponges, cnidaria, annelids, and arthropods). Some authors, however, interpret Ediacaran fauna as a failed evolutionary experiment, which led to certain kinds of animals that were completely extinct by the end of the Ediacaran era, about 570

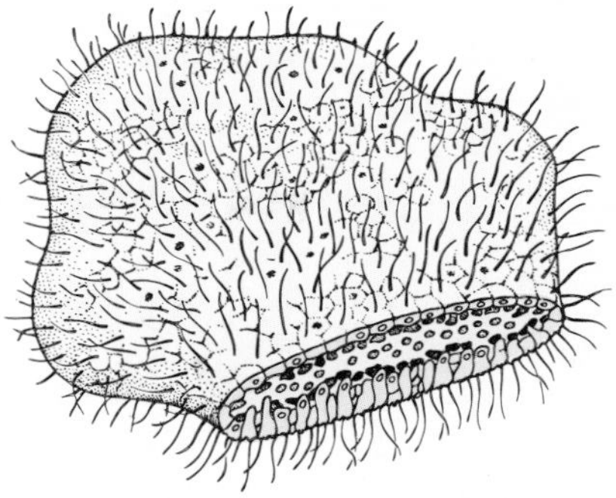

61 The simplest animal in terms of organization that we know is *Trichoplax adhaerens*, which is nothing more than a sac of flat and ciliate cells without any tissue formation and with a minimum of specialization of functions. A marine dweller, it is capable of moving in any direction and lacks polar differentiation. *[Diagram: Biopunt, from L. Margulis, 1985]*

million years ago (also the end of the Proterozoic or the early Phanerozoic). Ediacaran fauna mark a fundamental limit in the history of life and the Earth. Up until 1930 they were an indication of the boundary between the first Cambrian fossiliferous strata and the Precambrian strata, from which no fossil records were known until then.

The most important evolutionary advantage of multicellularity can be found in the possibility of separating functions and differentiating cell groups, organized into tissues and organs, each with a different function. But this also requires different kinds of connections between the cells of a multicellular organism, allowing them to coordinate their functions in activities such as embryonic growth, cell differentiation, growth, and metabolism. These connections are very simple in fungi, become more complex in plants, and very much more highly complex in animals.

Another innovation that multicellular organisms must have developed was the acquisition of physical

62 The trilobulate (*Tribrachidium*) is a fossil some 600 to 570 million years old, found in Ediacara, to the West of the Flinders Range (Australia). The first multicellular animals that have survived in the fossil record lived at the end of the Proterozoic, some 670-555 million years ago, a period which has been called the Ediacarian after the place where they were first found. Fossils of the Ediacarian fauna have been found in all continents except South America and Antarctica. *[Photo: R. Morrison/Auscape International]*

EVOLUTIONARY TREE OF INCREASING DIVERSITY

EVOLUTIONARY TREE OF DECIMATION AND DIVERSIFICATION

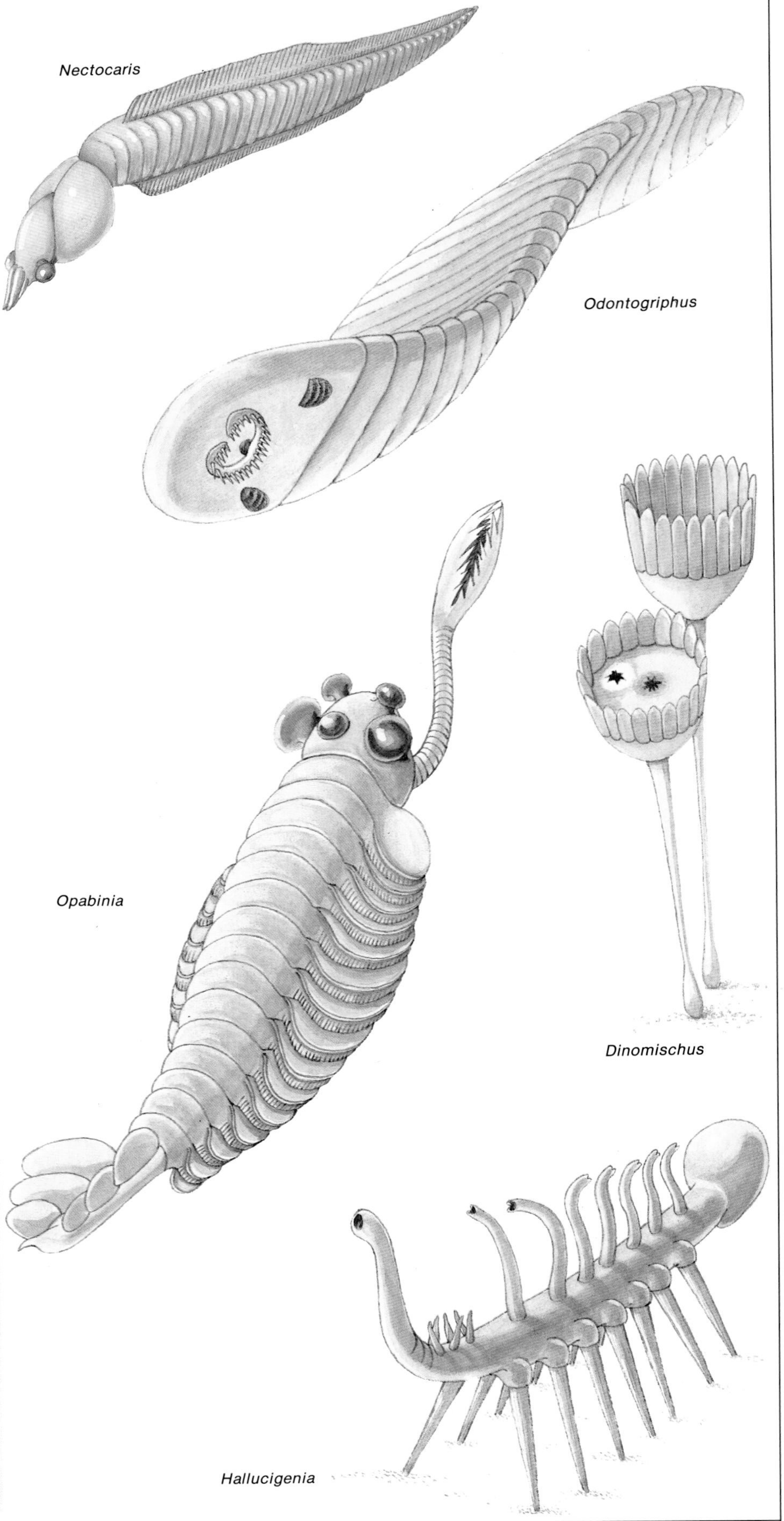

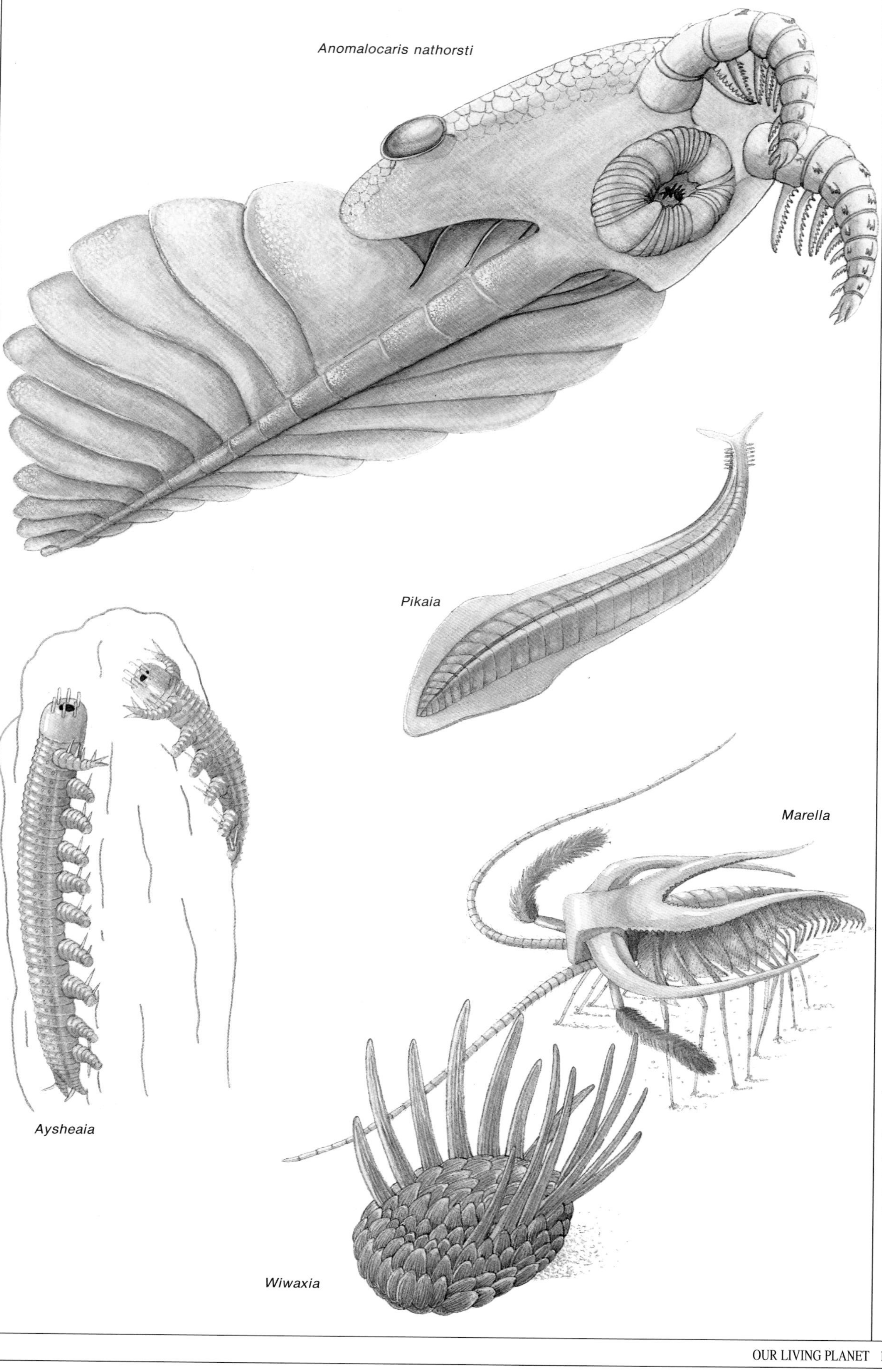

63 The great diversity of faunistic models of the Cambrian—the majority of which were evolutionarily unsuccessful—inclines one to think that the evolutionary tree based on the persistence of the majority of the main stems that appeared and the extinction of virtually nothing more than the unsuitable collateral forms is incorrect. In practice, all the large groups or phyla found by C.D. Walcott in 1909 in the Canadian Cambrian deposits of the Burgess Shale, dating from 530 million years ago, were interpreted in the 1980s by H. Whittington's group; an example of most of them being shown in the figure (the colors are speculative). Today only three of them persist: that of the arthropods and of the onychophorans, represented by *Marrella* and *Aysheaia*, respectively; and that of the chordates, represented by *Pikaia*. *Pikaia*, the strange phyla to which *Nectocaris*, *Odontogriphus*, *Dinomischus*, *Opabinia*, *Wiwaxia*, *Hallucigenia* or *Anomalocaris nathorsti* belong, have disappeared in a manner that is as disconcerting as was the suddenness of their appearance in the fossil record. This leads one to consider, as S.J. Gould has suggested, a different kind of evolutionary tree. One in which many of the basic trunks die out, not necessarily because they were unsuitable, but because some environmental catastrophe wiped out the population. According to this interpretation, the existence of present day humans has not depended on a long process of evolutionary complexification of the animal kingdom (the classical and, more or less, teleological interpretation), but on the "good luck" experienced by *Pikaia*, our oldest known ancestor.

[Drawings: Jordi Corbera (left) and Carles Puche, from originals by Mariannne Collins, taken from Gould, 1989 (right)]

supports to insure the maintenance of their own structure. As today (with the exception of *Thermoplasma* and the example of *Mycoplasma* already mentioned), most prokaryotic cells had a protective cell wall. But the capacity of multicellular organisms to secrete nonliving material for the protection and support of both individual cells and the organism as a whole has become extraordinarily varied and sophisticated, within the general framework common to each group. For example, in animal cells, their membranes normally seem to consist of a complex of proteins and polysaccharides that holds the cells together. Plants have rigid cell walls of cellulose; the walls of fungi are made of chitin. The exoskeletons of invertebrates are also chitinous; the bones of vertebrates combine a protein (collagen) with mineral salts such as calcium and magnesium carbonates and phosphates. The wood of woody plants' principal component is lignin, an organic polymer which is a derivate of phenylpropane; cutin, the external protection of most land plants, minimizes water loss.

The Cambrian event

The early Phanerozoic is marked by the appearance of the first multicellular animals with mineralized support structures, exoskeletons of calcium carbonates or phosphates, that were better preserved than their soft-bodied, Proterozoic ancestors. This is what is known as the *Cambrian event*: the apparently sudden appearance of a large number of different animals (almost the totality of existing phyla and some extinct ones) that left considerable amounts of fossils. All of them were aquatic, and they included representatives of the two animal phyla that would later have the greatest evolutionary success: arthropods and chordates.

When referring to a "sudden" appearance, we are, of course, speaking in terms of geological history. In fact, two periods can be distinguished in the Cambrian event. In the first period, the Tommotian, first described from a locality in Yakutia in Eastern Siberia but present in many other places in the world, the first fauna with hard parts must have appeared (the so-called "small shell fauna") made up of small organisms (a maximum of only about an inch) except for some sponges and the so-called archeocyathids, a kind of organism similar to sponges that became extinct along with the rest of Tommotian fauna about 560 million years ago. Tommotian organisms include the undoubted precursors of some modern phyla (sponges, molluscs, etc.), but there are also fossils of uncertain affinities that probably correspond to extinct phyla.

In the second period, the Atdabanian, also initially described from a locality in Eastern Siberia but equally represented in many other parts of the world such as North America, Greenland, Australia, and China, the true Cambrian event appears. At this time, a great number of fossil animals with both soft and hard parts in countless new forms appear, including all of today's phyla and some extinct ones. At the famous quarry in Burgess Shale near Field in British Columbia, nearly 20 organisms of unique morphology that could correspond to other extinct phyla have been described, as well as numerous representatives of better-known types, corresponding to both modern phyla and extinct ones such as trilobites.

3.6 The conquest of the land

Some time would pass before life was to colonize the continents, or surfaces of emerged lands, which were as hostile to most Proterozoic organisms as the surface of the moon is for humans. However, it does seem that some cyanobacteria colonized the wet surfaces of some emerged lands at some stage during the Proterozoic. The road to the invasion of terra firma was probably prepared by the geological phenomena of transgression and regression that brought about the periodic drying of certain areas.

Life on terra firma had considerable attractions. On the one hand there was much more oxygen, and the living space was unlimited, but there were also serious obstacles. Having left the protection of the buoyant medium of water, the organisms would collapse under their own weight if they did not have stronger muscles and more solid skeletal structures. Appropriate breathing equipment was also necessary, since they had to move from an environment in which oxygen was present in only a few parts per million, to one in which its concentration was thousands of times higher. Therefore, surface coatings such as skin, cuticles, and shells were indispensable as protection against the intense sunlight that shone on land without water as a filter. But the most serious threat was desiccation. Only those organisms capable of retaining and conserving water could survive on land.

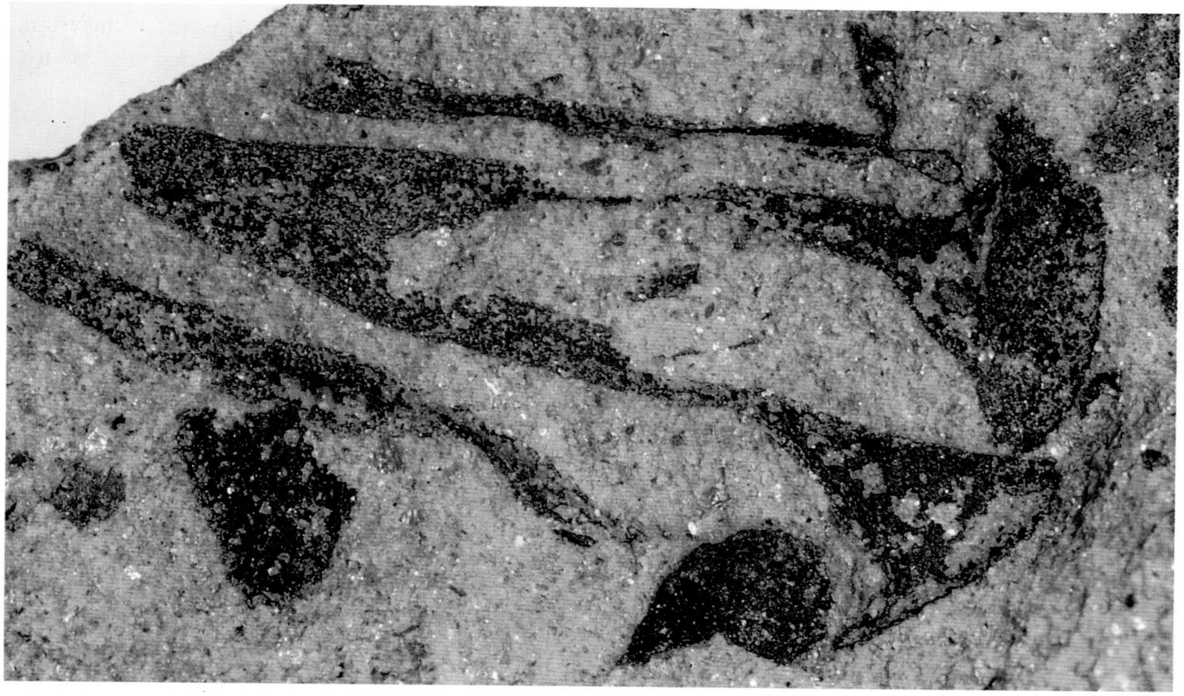

64 The first terrestrial plants known to us, found in rocks from the end of the Silurian in Wales and Australia, are *Cooksonia*. They were small plants, of a few centimeters; we do not know if they were vascular plants. It is believed that the first plants, with leaves or stems, were similar to today's mosses and liverworts. What distinguishes them from the algae was the fact that the spermatozoids swam towards the ovules and the fertilized eggs developed within special coverings of parental tissue. The need to protect the gelatinous tissues from drying up caused the development of a lignified cell wall which, combined with cellulose, gave the structures strength and flexibility. From this stems the possibility of developing a vascular system capable of transporting water from the roots. The fossils of the genus *Rhynia*, at the end of the Silurian or beginning of the Devonian, on the other hand, are considered with much more certainty to be vascular plants, with a true xylem that allowed them to grow much taller than previous plants. The most recent hypotheses regarding the origin of plants involve a symbiosis between algae and fungi, in the opposite sense to the lichens, since it was the algae which were dominant. Many of today's plants cannot do without their fungal association in the roots (mycorrhizae). *[Photo: Dianne Edwards]*

The first terrestrial plants

Terrestrial plants perhaps emerged from symbioses between algae and fungi, similar to lichens, but with a difference; the algal component was dominant. It is probably no coincidence that 95% of today's land plants have symbiotic fungi in their roots, called *mycorrhiza*. The algal component of the first plants that began to colonize the shores of terra firma allowed them to exploit atmospheric oxygen and retain water in structures that were at first gelatinous, like the ones described when referring to *Volvox*, which were later surrounded by a lignin wall. The fungal component allowed them to alter the surface of the rocks they were colonizing more quickly and to extract mineral elements directly, as well as to retain water and survive droughts more successfully.

The result was probably the appearance of plants similar to today's hepatics and mosses, whose sperms still need water to reach the female gamete, the ovocellula. In any case, the oldest land plants to leave fossil records are *Cooksonia* from the Upper Silurian in Wales and Australia (about 420 million years ago). It is not certain whether they were vascular plants or not. They were only about an inch tall and had a smooth stem with no leaves, dichotomically branched and with spherical sporangia at the end of the terminal branches. Small capillary bundles can be observed that may be incipient xylem, but could also be simply vessels similar to those in the setae of the sporangia of today's mosses. In some examples, stomata have been observed that would indicate the presence of a protective cuticle. However, this was probably not the first land plant, because in sediments from the Late Ordovician (about 450 million years ago), spores with triletes in a triradiate aperture have been found, which are considered to be characteristic of vascular plants or at least of land plants. The real conquest of land by plants took place in the Devonian and, especially in the Carboniferous Period, by new vascular plants, some of which reached the structure and size of trees.

The first terrestrial animals

Animals took longer to emerge from water to terra firma, among other reasons because before they could colonize the swamplands, shores, and plains that could be flooded by plants, the animals that could have survived the difficulties and inconveniences of an aerial existence would not have found anything to eat. The fact is that few representatives from the animal kingdom succeeded in adapting fully to life on land. Not a single phylum of animals is made up exclusively of terrestrial organisms. All animals today that complete their life cycle on land belong to three or four phyla that are predominantly aquatic: some arthropods (mainly insects and spiders), very few molluscs (land snails and slugs), some annelids (land worms), and some members of our phylum (the

65 About 500 million years ago, animals developed hard parts in their organization starting with deposits of cellular waste. The presence of fossil spores in the Middle Ordovician and Silurian sediments, more than 500 years ago suggests that the flora of those times also comprised organisms which were like bryophytes in appearance, similar to our mosses and liverworts. About 400 million years ago, at the end of the Silurian, when the first fish with jaws and the first wingless insects already existed, vascular plants were already progressing. The challenge posed by the scarcity of water on terra firma was faced with the development of seeds, which allowed the embryo to postpone its growth until a favorable time. Fertilization and the development of the seeds inside moist parental tissues allowed them to survive despite the irregularity of the rains.
[Diagram: Biopunt]

chordates). In the remaining animal phyla, not a single species in the whole of evolutionary history succeeded in adapting to life on land.

In practice all the animal species that have succeeded in adapting to life on land did so by bringing their former environment with them. No animal has totally abandoned water. The blastula and embryo of reptiles, birds, and mammals still develop in a liquid-filled cavity (the embryonic sac). The concentration of salts in blood is practically identical to that of sea water. The proportions of sodium, potassium, and chlorine in our tissues are also surprisingly similar to that of oceans.

A crucial factor in animals' migration to land was the metabolism of calcium. The concentration of calcium in the cytoplasm of a eukaryotic cell is of the order of one part per 10 million, while in sea water it is about one part per 10,000 or even higher. Calcium tends to enter cells, and the cells have to rid themselves of it continually. However, calcium plays a central role in the metabolism of nucleated cells. It is indispensable to amoeboid cell movement, cell secretion, microtubule formation, tissue cohesion, the transmission of nerve impulses, and muscle contractions. Once used, however, excess calcium must be eliminated or accumulated outside of the cell cytoplasm. This is why since Cambrian times organisms have been storing their calcium reserves as phosphates by making teeth and bones, or as carbonates in the form of shells. These structures, which initially appeared in aquatic animals, were later to serve as support for the animals on land, to protect them from sunlight or predators and to act as individual "aquaria" protecting them against the dangers of desiccation.

In any case, leaving aside hypothetical traces of Myriapoda in the Ordovician Period, more than 450 million years old, the oldest known land animal fossils are from the Late Devonian in Scotland (Rhynie Chert) and Germany (Alken-an-der-Mosel) from about 400 million years ago. During the Devonian Period the Rhynie Chert was covered by a peat bog occasionally flooded by waters from nearby geysers or thermal springs rich in silica. The silica precipitated in form of cryptocrystalline quartz or chert, which is where the name of the deposits comes from. Plant material fossilized in it, along with some small arthropods (mites and Collembola in particular) that lived off plants and some bigger predatory arthropods (millipedes and spiders) that must have fed off smaller ones. At Alken-an-der-Mosel, near Koblenz in the Rheinland, there was a small Devonian lake to which some clearly terrestrial organisms must have been dragged. These organisms included spiders and a 4 in (10 cm) long millipede (*Eoarthropleura*), the largest Devonian land animal known. Other animals that must have been amphibious and that perhaps fed on land but lived preferably in water, such as the 3 ft (1 m) long scorpions and Eurypterida (an extinct group related to scorpions), both with gills that had ventral protections allowing them to raid the land in search of food, were also found there.

Some vertebrates also managed to survive on land during the Devonian Period. Chordates seem to have originated during the Cambrian from *Pikaia*, one of the strange, soft-bodied organisms discovered in the famous Burgess Shale in British Columbia, or from a similar organism. But the first vertebrates are undoubtedly agnathous fish, which began to appear in the Ordovician Period, of which *Astraspis*, discovered in clay at Harding, Colorado, is the best preserved. Today, however, it is thought that conodonts were the first invertebrates. They are organisms from which only some supposed buccal pieces are known. (The oldest conodonts date back to the middle Cambrian, about 520 million years ago.) Four prints exist, not yet completely studied, which were found between 1983 and 1986 near Edinburgh, in Scotland, and which could be Agnatha or some intermediate form between Cephalochordata and Agnatha.

In any case, at the beginning of the Devonian, about 400 million years ago, fish had already diversified into all the modern groups and some that are already extinct. From one of these groups, Sarcopterygians, from which four of today's genera have survived—the coelacanths (*Latimeria*), living in the Indian Ocean and in the seas of the South-East of Asia, and the three genera of pulmonate fish, each one living in a different southern continent (*Lepidosiren paradoxa* in South America, *Neoceratodus forsteri* in Australia, and *Protopterus*, the only one represented today by more than one species in Africa)—the lineage of the Rhipidistians emerged, the first amphibious fishes from which terrestrial tetrapods evolved.

Rhipidistians were long, thin fish with strong muscles and powerful fan-shaped fins and tails, making them excellent swimmers. They had long snouts, especially the larger ones, and perhaps this was why they developed a cranial articulation that allowed them to separate their two mandibles at the same

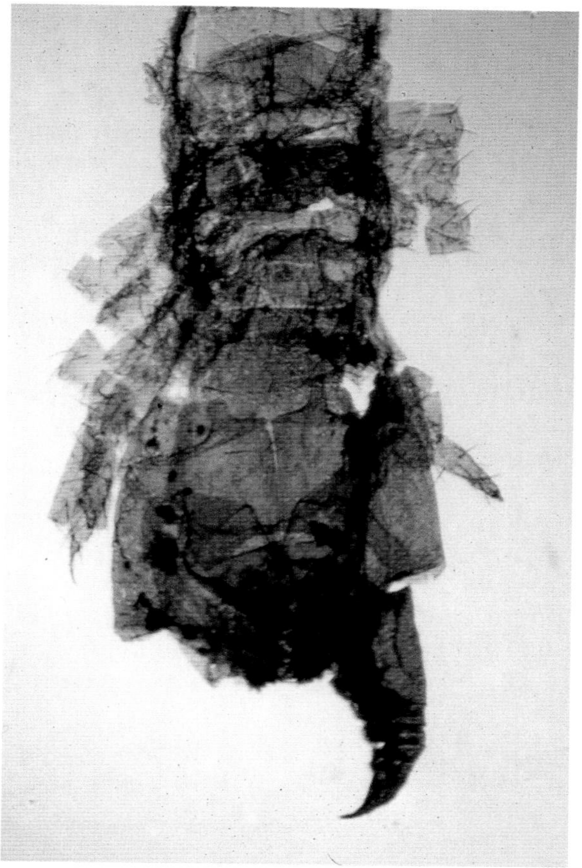

66 The oldest known myriapod (*Devonobius delta*), and the type of a new order of myriapods, was identified in the rocks of the middle Devonian (about 375 million years ago) near Gilboa in the State of New York (United States). It appears that the arthropods were the most suitable marine animals to live on terra firma: their body already had a protective covering and a musculature capable of moving them and sustaining their own weight. *[Photo: William Shear (x 3.5)]*

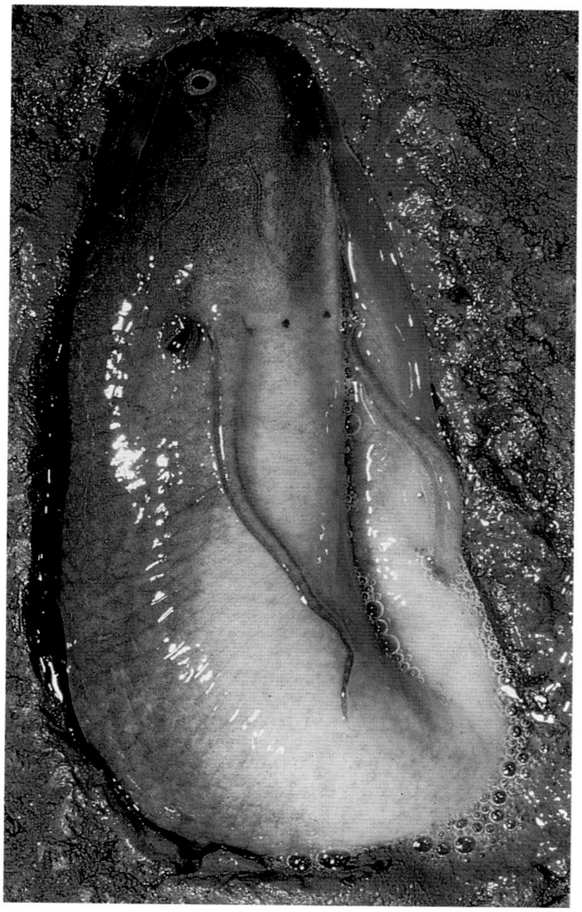

67 The Dipnoids or lungfish form a small group of species which are found in the Australian, African, and South American continents. *Protopterus* (in the photograph) can reach 79 in (2 m), and lives in marshy zones which dry out periodically between August and December; as long as the drought lasts it buries itself in the mud and makes a nest up to 19.5 in (50 cm) deep—according to its size—where it spends the dry period curved in the shape of a U. *[Photo: Alan Root / Survival Anglia]*

time, or separately, the upper or lower one alone. This fact had two important effects, both related to life in shallow waters. In the first place, the movement of the snout allowed them to modify the volume of their mouths and keep a considerable amount of water ready to pump towards the gills even when their bodies were partially emerged. In the second place, they could capture prey in shallow water with a quick movement of the snout, as crocodiles do today, without lowering the lower mandible. These traits and their powerful ventral gills allowed them to hunt prey through the swamplands and over the small barriers of sand banks or mud that could get in their way.

Towards the Late Devonian, about 370 million years ago, true amphibians finally appear. The oldest known ones are *Ichthyostega*, discovered in the 1930s in southeastern Greenland, and *Tulerpeton*, discovered in 1984 at Tula, south of Moscow, in Russia.

The case of the fungi

Although we have focused on the evolution of plants and animals to land environments, we must not forget the fungi. Along with plants and animals, fungi represent a third organizational plan in the great evolutionary strategy of multicellular eukaryotic life.

Fungi develop from spores and grow in the shape of slender tubes called hyphae, divided by transversal walls called septa. A feature of their particular organization is the fact that fungal cells can have many nuclei, and their cytoplasm can flow more or less freely from one cell to another through the septa. Unlike plants, they do not get their nourishment from photosynthesis, but through digestion and absorption of the products of photosynthesis. But unlike animals, this digestion takes place outside their bodies. With thick, consistent chitinous cell walls, fungi are able to resist drying out. They are highly adaptable organisms, perfect candidates for life on land as confirmed by the fact that most of the approximately 100,000 known species still grow on land.

We have already spoken of the probable symbiotic role of fungi in the establishment of plant life on land. Even so, the oldest known fossil records, found in fact in fossils of plant tissues, date back only to the Carboniferous, about 300 million years ago.

3.7 The emergence of a landscape dominated by life

The appearance of fungi, plants, and both vertebrate and invertebrate animals on terra firma marks, perhaps, the beginning of the modern era of the biosphere, when the complex relationships between organisms of the different terrestrial biomes that we know of today began to take shape. In these more recent stages, evolution has not been free of jolts. Mass extinction episodes, such as those of Ediacaran, Tommotian, and Atdabanian fauna, for example, were repeated between the end of the Permian Period and the beginning of the Triassic, 245 million years ago, with the disappearance of 52% of the known families of the Permian Period, and at the end of the Cretaceous Period, 65 million years ago, with the disappearance of only 11% of families, but which included all the dinosaurs and many families of mammals.

The concept of evolution as a process of continual advancement toward progress, measurable in terms of the growing diversity of organisms or of the emergence of progressively more complex organisms, must be revised. Rather, the history of evolution is that of a succession of episodes of diversification followed by phases of mass extinction. The cycle is then repeated, using the surviving forms. Like a phoenix rising up out of its own ashes, DNA has renewed itself in new forms and has overcome successive phases of mass extinction. We humans can trace our own history and the history of the organisms with which we share today's biosphere, but we must remember that neither ours nor theirs is more necessary than the others because life will survive the next mass extinction, which we might well be capable of causing ourselves.

The Devonian swamps

During the Devonian Period, when terrestrial animals other than the arthropods, mentioned earlier, were still absent, the majority of the plants that had begun to conquer the newly emerged land were living in tropical swamps, where they found the necessary seasonal fluctuations in light, temperature, or humidity. There were small differences in floral composition between the vegetation communities living in the brackish delta and estuary regions and those living on the banks of waterways or lake margins. The border between the Devonian and the Carboniferous Periods, 360 million years ago, turns out to be an extremely convincing border, because it is in this last

68 The Carboniferous covers the period between 360 and 268 million years ago. This period was decisive in the history of the Earth, since during it the Hercynian orogeny took place, the diversity of the terrestrial flora increased, and the first lung-breathing animals (amphibia) appeared. It is the epoch of the great cephalopods and of the brachiopods which coexisted with the arthropods on dry land. They are favored by the warm climate and the exuberant vegetation. In parallel, the microbes also moved to a terrestrial way of life, transported inside the intestine of terrestrial animals. *[Diagram: Biopunt]*

period that the terrestrial plant world underwent, almost as suddenly as marine fauna in the Cambrian Period, an unprecedented explosion of diversity that was accompanied by a similar explosion of animal life. Toward the middle of the Devonian Period, some 380 million years ago, there were many fern-type plants, called progymnosperms, with well-developed leaves and lignified stems that were covered with bark. They looked like trees, and could reach up to 30 ft (10 m) in height. It even seems that some of these progymnosperms were the first plants to develop structures similar to seeds, but this happened during the Carboniferous Period.

Carboniferous and Permian forests

The first landscapes on emerged land that can, to a certain extent, be compared with our present ideas of them are the Permian ones. They were the first landscapes with more or less conventional, plant-like vegetation, inhabited by animals of all types, including tetrapods. But during the Carboniferous, this landscape must have evolved in a spectacular way.

The appearance of the seed and the expansion of vascular plants

During the Carboniferous Period, the appearance of the seed in vascular plants was a transcendental event that had considerable repercussions on the landscape. The appearance of seeds on vascular plants reflected an escape from the need for water, whereby the male gametes reached the ovule. It was a decisive evolutionary innovation that enabled plants to become established in ever drier environments. On the other hand, we must not discount the fact that the growing success of terrestrial plants in swamps led to an enormous increase in dead organic material in a state of decomposition. This considerably reduced the amount of oxygen in stagnant waters and led to some arthropods and fish taking the step toward aerial respiration. This same fact would explain the excellent preservation of plant fossils of the end of the Devonian and throughout the Carboniferous Periods, which in fact gets its name from the large deposits of carbon resulting from this accumulation of organic material. It indicates that the forests of arborescent lycopods and progymnosperms were the dominant terrestrial biome throughout this period.

The first Carboniferous fauna

These Carboniferous forests, still without vertebrates, were ruled by arthropods, both herbivores and predators, which established and shaped the wide variety of ecological niches today's tropical rain forests still have. With the proliferation of tree species, on the other hand, aerial life took on a whole new meaning

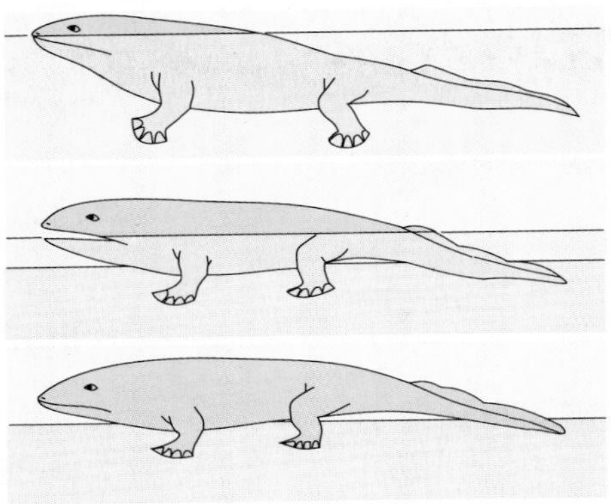

69 The oldest amphibian known, from about 370 million years ago, *Icthyostega*, was found in rocks of the Upper Devonian in Greenland. At the beginning of the Devonian, about 400 million years ago, fish had begun to diversify into all the groups known today; and some groups had even become extinct. In the Upper Devonian, some 370 million years ago, the true amphibia appeared. Their general features were similar to many of those of the upper Devonian Rhypidistians, but they differed from them by their longer and stronger, unlobed feet, and by their rib cage; characteristics which are interpreted as adaptations for walking in the open air. Judging from their dentition, it seems that they caught large fish rather than small prey. It is believed that the first amphibians were more similar to present day reptiles than to the frogs that we know; thus we can imagine them as like a large crocodile, both in appearance and life style. *[Diagram: Biopunt]*

70 The pteridosperms are the oldest plants we know of that possessed seeds. Seeds protected their ovules with teguments which surrounded them and kept them from drying up. In the photograph can be seen a leaf of the genus *Sphenopteris*, from the Carboniferous deposits of Erillcastell, in the Alta Ribagorça, on the southern slopes of the Central Pyrenees, showing the membranes protecting the ovules. *[Photo: Jordi Vidal / MGB]*

for animals. They were no longer limited to the two-dimensionality of the surface soil but occupied the whole three-dimensional volume of the arboreal mass. This was accompanied by some insects making their first attempts at flight. It was in this type of forest, at its edge or in a clearing, that the first amphibians, like *Ichthyostega*, began to walk. The diversity they rapidly achieved, itself proof of their evolutionary success, reflects the fact that they were the first large animals exploiting both the medium from which they came, in other words the shallow waters of lake sides and swamps, and a new medium, the now totally emerged land appearing near the swamps.

Most amphibians of the Carboniferous period were carnivores; the smallest ate insects and the largest consumed other arthropods (we must remember that arthropods of a considerable size roamed through some Carboniferous forests, including millipedes of up to 11.5 ft [3.5 m] long, and the air was inhabited by equally fearsome insects, like dragonflies with a wingspan of up to 24 in [60 cm]), fish, small amphibians, and, whenever they arose, small reptiles. Centipedes and dragonflies were also carnivores that fed off smaller arthropods, while the smaller arthropods and the larger millipedes, which fed off wood, were herbivores.

The appearance of the amniotic egg and the Permian expansion of reptiles

However, the amphibians never managed to free themselves totally from the water. Present-day amphibians still need to fertilize their eggs and produce their larvae in fresh water. It was a new group of tetrapods, reptiles, which finally broke free from this dependence on an aquatic medium, and they did it through a particularly successful evolutionary innovation: the amniotic egg, a structure which was capable of maintaining an enclosed aqueous medium around the fertilized egg and growing embryo until the embryo reached a state of development where it no longer needed it. This adaptation, comparable to what a seed means for progymnosperms, was very probably produced in some species of small amphibians of the anthrocosaura group. These were perhaps similar to some present-day tree-dwelling salamanders of the South American jungles. They began to adapt themselves to a form of life as active predators of insects, spiders, and other arthropods in the canopies of large trees in carboniferous forests. Another highly significant innovation, linked to the vertebrates' move from aquatic life to aerial life, is the synthesis of keratin, one of the rare

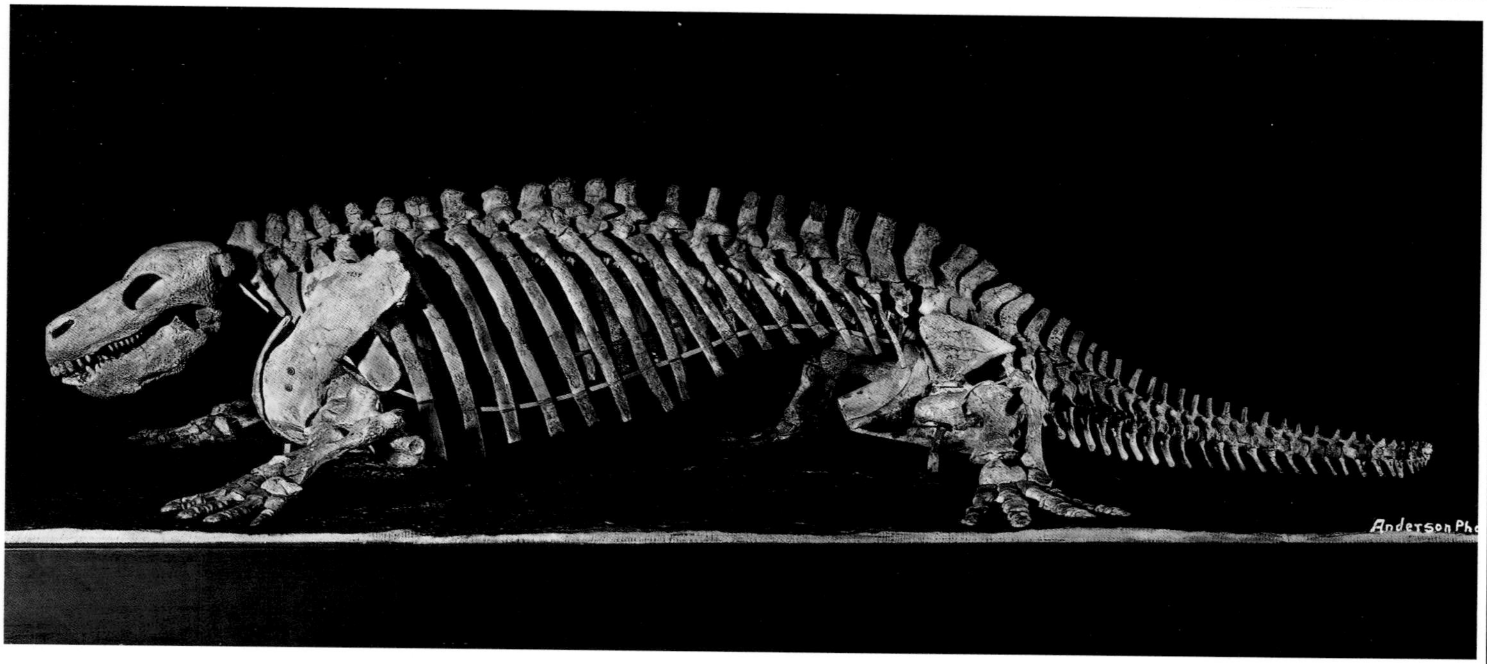

metabolic innovations in the world of the prokaryotes. Keratin is the characteristic protein present in the scales of reptiles' skin, of birds' feathers, and of the skin and horns of mammals, and it is this that prevents terrestrial vertebrates from drying out after they leave the egg. It is for this reason that their ability to produce this keratin was decisive.

All the first terrestrial vertebrates were carnivores. Most plant material is difficult to digest because it contains a large quantity of cellulose. Vertebrates are not able to digest it if they do not chew the plant very well. They also have to find a way to attract and support a population of bacteria and protista capable of fermenting cellulose, hosting them symbiotically in their digestive tract, as do ruminants today in their stomach. Only some plant products, especially the constituents of the reproductive organs, are rich enough in proteins and sugars in relation to their cellulose content for it not to be necessary to chew and digest a large volume of plants to satisfy the needs of an animal. In practice, this leads to two different adaptive paths in the herbivore. One was the selection of small, intensely active, and specialized food products of plant origin (nectar, pollen, plant juices, fruit, seeds); this is the case today of many small mammals and birds. The other was to co-evolve with symbiotic bacteria populations capable of digesting cellulose as it passes through specific sections of the digestive tract, accompanied by the ability to move about in search of new pastures or leaves, an ability which is often associated with larger animals. Some amphibians and reptiles from the Late Carboniferous Period and the Late Permian Period became herbivores after vascular plants had colonized land of a certain height. Similarly, they exploited the environments around the edges of the lush Carboniferous forests of swamps and water-soaked soils. An idea of the importance of this bushy or grassy vegetation, which was very similar to a savanna or a savanna woodland, is given by animals like the amphibian *Diadectes*, one of the oldest herbivore tetrapods, which measured up to 13 ft (4 m) in length, and whose feeding needs demanded wide areas of suitable vegetation.

The first fossil remains of reptiles correspond to small animals associated with plant fossils of giant arborescent lycopods preserved in an upright position, just as they lived some 310 million years ago, in strata corresponding to lower Pennsylvanian in Nova Scotia, in southeastern Canada. Since they have been found inside tree trunks, it could be the case that, as Richard Cowen of the University of California in Davis believes, these older reptiles lived in holes in tree trunks just like some insectivore mammals do today in the tropical rain forests, and that they lived in the same way as these do.

The evolutionary success of reptiles was considerable throughout the Permian Period (between 290 and 245 million years ago). Through spectacular adaptive diversification they totally displaced amphibians from the greater part of terrestrial habitats and, during the Triassic Period, even from many aquatic habitats, to which some reptiles had become secondarily adopted.

71 A skeleton of the amphibious herbivore *Diadectes*, about 13 ft (4 m) long, which lived in the late Carboniferous, at the beginning of the Permian of Euramerica. The expansion of animal life to dry land must have happened in tune with a gradual development of the trophic relationships, which the adaptation of plants to aerial life made possible. This amphibian developed at the same time as the great changes that were taking place in the plants which replaced the Carboniferous woods. In any event, it is believed that the food chains included both terrestrial as well as aquatic animals. *[Photo: A.E. Anderson, by courtesy of the Department of Library Services, American Museum of Natural History]*

Coal, oil, and natural gas

Fossil fuels (coal, oil, and natural gas) currently account for 88% of the world's energy consumption. It is true that other forms of energy are used, and that there have been varying degrees of success regarding research into alternative energy, but, at present, organic fuels are still our principal source of energy. Where does this fossilized energy come from?

The conservation of organic material, even though it has undergone transformation, is one of nature's great marvels. Under normal conditions, and in the presence of oxygen, organic remains are progressively transformed into inorganic material by decomposing organisms. During this reduction process almost all the energy incorporated into the chemical bonds of a living organism's molecular structure is lost or dissipated. A good part of the material will be reused, and the cycle is closed: in the words of Paul Valéry, "tout va sous terre et rentre dans le tour." The cycle is only broken under exceptional conditions of anoxia and sedimentation. These conditions have occurred at particular moments throughout the history of life on Earth, moments that may be separated by hundreds of millions of years. It is at these times that immense amounts of dead organic material fossilized into coal and oil.

Oil well in Kuwait (April 1991) [A. Tannenbaum - Sygma / Contifoto]

Engraving from the *Daily Graphic* (1870) [AGE Fotostock]

Although processes of coal formation were set in motion on numerous occasions, they only occurred in abundance during two geological periods. One of these periods lasted for a large part of the Carboniferous Period up until the Permian Period. The other began during the Cretaceous Period and lasted until the beginning of the Tertiary. Coal appears cyclically, interspersed with layers of clay and other sedimentary rocks. The thickness of the coal layers varies from a thin film to 100 ft (30 m) or more, although the layers which are usually exploited are 3-15 ft (1-5 m) thick.

As numerous studies have been carried out on coal layers, a great deal is known about the flora that created them, and attempts have even been made to reconstruct the plant communities from which they derived. The equatorial flora that existed in the watery environments of the Carboniferous Period, for example, included Pteridosperms (*Pecopteris*, *Neuropteris*, etc.) with their broad, serrated leaves like those of ferns, but capable of producing seeds. Other trees found among the flora of that time were those of the Lepidodendrales order (*Lepidodendron*, etc.). These were huge trees that could reach heights of up to 130 ft (40 m) and had straight, cylindrical trunks, surmounted by a parasol-shaped crown. The *Sigillaria* were trees related to the Lepidodendrids and had bark that was regularly marked (hence the name) and an enormous tuft of pointed leaves. Certain giant horsetails, of the genus *Calamites*, which reached heights of up to 33 ft (10 m) and which had huge stems, were abundant in that tall forest, together with treelike Cordaitaceae (*Cordaites*), which had long leaves and a similar shape to that of the araucarias, and ferns (*Sphenophyllum*, etc.), perhaps the best-known plants among the flora of that time. The ferns, which could reach heights of up to 33 ft (10 m), were veritable trees, though with weak, unbranched stems onto which the broad, divided leaves were directly inserted. There were also giant lycopods (*Lepidodendron*, *Sigillaria*, etc.), which reached up to 100 ft (30 m) in height and often had hollow trunks, as is the case in many present-day tropical trees. Giant plants and shallow roots made up the luxurious vegetation of those times, growing in the unstable soils of extensive coastal, fluvial, or lake marshes, were frequently subjected to storms and floods. Leaves, roots, spores, and immense trunks would then collect in the mud. Whole forests could be swallowed up in the mire. If the environment did not allow for complete decomposition, then the vegetable matter would eventually be transformed into coal.

Fossil fern (*Alethopteris pennsylvanica*) [Jordi Vidal / ECSA]

The world's principal coal deposits are generally found in the northern hemisphere (above all in the United States, the former Soviet Union, and China). These deposits, which supplied the energy base for the industrial revolutions of both Europe and North America, could still provide sufficient resources for a number of decades, if other fossil fuels become exhausted or alternative energy sources prove incapable of meeting demands.

Oil wells in Libya [Peter Turner / Image Bank]

The origins of oil and natural gas are completely different. Although their origin has always been a cause of disagreement and the source of numerous theories, current thinking tends towards the idea that they were formed from planktonic organic matter that built up on the sea bottom along coastal platforms, or in the relatively shallow basins of lakes and lagoons. Those remains, mixed together with the rich muds of interstitial water, made up *sapropel.* Bacterial action, in the absence of oxygen, would produce kerosine, a compound that, after a process of thermal maturation, is converted into oil. Pressure would force the oil from the original stratum (the parent rock), towards more porous and permeable neighboring rock, and from there it would continue moving toward the surface, where it would oxidize to produce asphalts. If, on its journey to the surface, its path was blocked by impermeable rocks (covered by an anticlinal, by an angular discordance, etc.), it would remain trapped and impregnate the porous rock (reservoir rock).

Finally, the oil layers so far discovered almost always consist of three layers of fluid, distributed in a density gradient: salt water, oil and, on top, a pocket of natural gas (normally methane).

Ease of transport and storage, and the fact that their combustion is easily controlled, are some of the reasons why fossil fuels are so popular and why they are consumed all over the world. While coal is generally consumed in the country of production, most oil and natural gas is exported, either in oil tankers or via pipeline networks. Fossil fuels are not evenly distributed. Furthermore, their control is in the hands of only a few companies. That explains why, for example, firewood—or "coal which has not yet formed"—provides 90% of the energy used in poor countries.

Behind the bustle of a city's cars, the vast combustion of a power station, or a fast-flying airplane, lies the solar energy of remote times, built up over thousands of centuries by the organisms of species that no longer exist. In addition to the fact that the current rate of consumption is much greater than the rate of formation (which means that the exhaustion of resources is relatively imminent), the consumption of fossil fuels poses other problems, such as the emission of enormous quantities of carbon dioxide into the atmosphere. It is also worrying to think that the consumption of non-renewable resources, which took millions of years to build up, has taken place in a matter of a few decades.

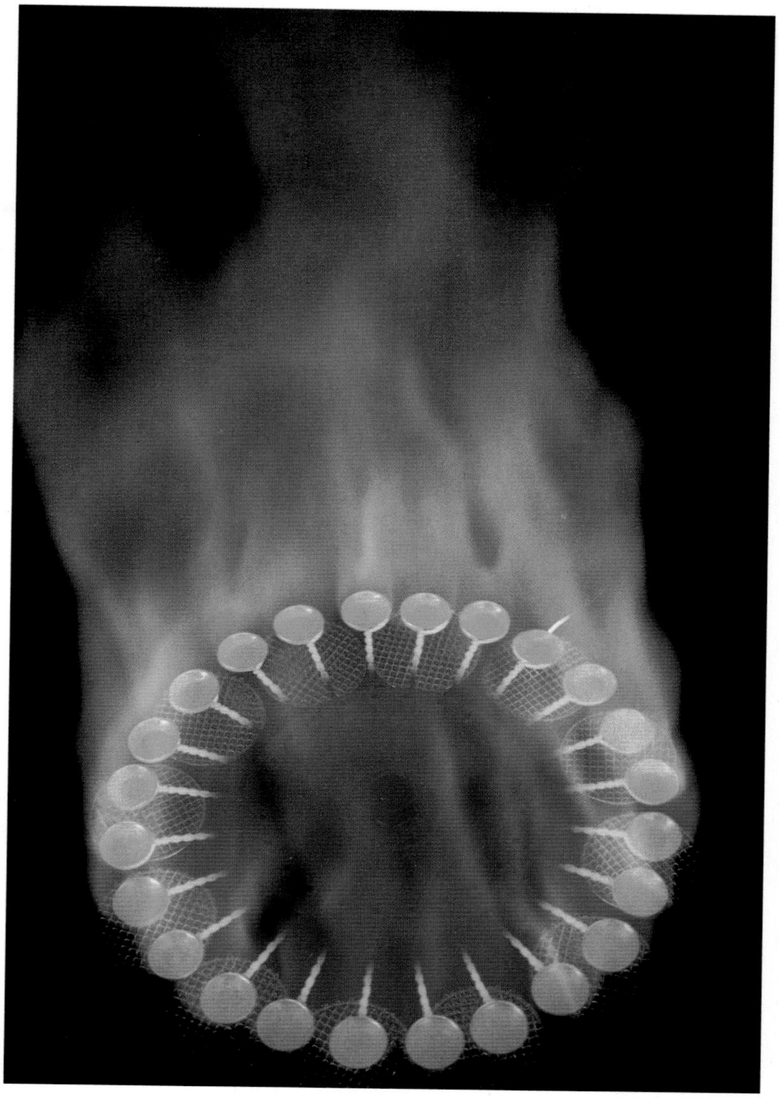

Gas burner [AGE Fotostock]

72 The flower of the buttercup (*Ranunculus*) with its elongate floral axis and perianth parts cyclically arranged, and the gynoecium of many free carpels, is considered a good example for understanding the structure of the first flowers. Again, the success achieved by a new way of life, seems to have been due largely to cooperation between different groups of organisms. Thus the success of the first flowering plants, at a time when the Earth was dominated by arthropods, was based on the change from wind pollination to insect pollination, and the improved systems of seed dispersal, thanks also to the development of birds and mammals.
[Photo: Jordi Vidal / ECSA]

Mesozoic landscapes

The tectonic events of the end of the Permian Period put an end to the humid equatorial climates that had favored the complex system of lakes, deltas, marshes, and estuaries all along the southern coast of the Euro-North American continent (Euramerica), where the Carboniferous forests and their fauna had developed.

From gymnosperms to angiosperms

The climate of the new northern continent of Laurasia, shifted to the north by its collision with the southern continent of Gondwana, became drier; its flora reflected this change. Paleophytic flora, dominated by lycopods and progymnosperms, gave way to mesophytic flora, which would cover practically all of terra firma during the Triassic Period, dominated by gymnosperms, mainly conifers, ginkgos, and cycads. These, and especially the conifers, were better adapted to living in drier environments.

Throughout the Cretaceous Period, the angiosperms, which appear in the fossil register from the Early Cretaceous Period some 100 million years ago, became widespread, until the beginning of the Cretaceous Period, the flora of the Mesozoic had been dominated by gymnosperms which, during the Jurassic Period, came to represent 80% of the vegetation preserved in the fossil register. During the Cretaceous Period, however, angiosperms underwent a rapid expansion, starting at low latitudes, until towards the end of the Cretaceous, when they soon became the dominant plants all over the planet, as they still are today. The phylogenetic origin of angiosperms is not known for certain, even though there are reasons for thinking that they came from forms related to the pteridosperms and that they originated a long time before the oldest fossil remains known. What is certain is that one of the keys to the angiosperms' success was the step from an anemophilous to an entomophilous pollination, which led to a co-evolution of plants and insects, as well as an increase in the efficiency of dispersal of seeds for considerable distances. This often relied on the participation of animals, and became more common with the appearance and expansion of birds and mammals.

Reptilian splendor

Throughout the Permian Period, the fauna, as we have said, became poor in amphibians and rich in reptiles, now released from their dependence on water for reproduction and, for that very reason, better equipped than the former to colonize drier, less stable environments than the humid forests of the Carboniferous Period. The diversity of environments that they colonized also favored the diversification of the reptiles themselves. Groups as important as dinosaurs (extinct at the end of the Triassic Period), birds, and mammals, among others, are descendants of the reptiles which appeared in the Permian Period. Carnivorous and herbivorous reptiles appeared, as well as terrestrial and aquatic ones, some of which developed different ways of gliding and flying. They invaded all the continents and all environments. The Mesozoic Era, even up to the end of the Cretaceous Period (some 66 million years ago) was the era of the reptiles, even though some reptile groups had already developed to become the first birds (during the Jurassic Period), and the first mammals (during the Cretaceous Period), whose role was still fairly negligible in the majority of the ecosystems of the Mesozoic Era.

The appearance of birds and mammals

The evolutionary origin of birds still remains a mystery, above all because of the scarcity of fossil remains. The lightness and fragility of birds' bones, their generally modest dimensions, and the habitats that these animals have generally occupied, all mean that they are bad candidates for fossilization. *Archaeopteryx*, the oldest of the birds which has left fossils, appears rather suddenly in the fossil record of

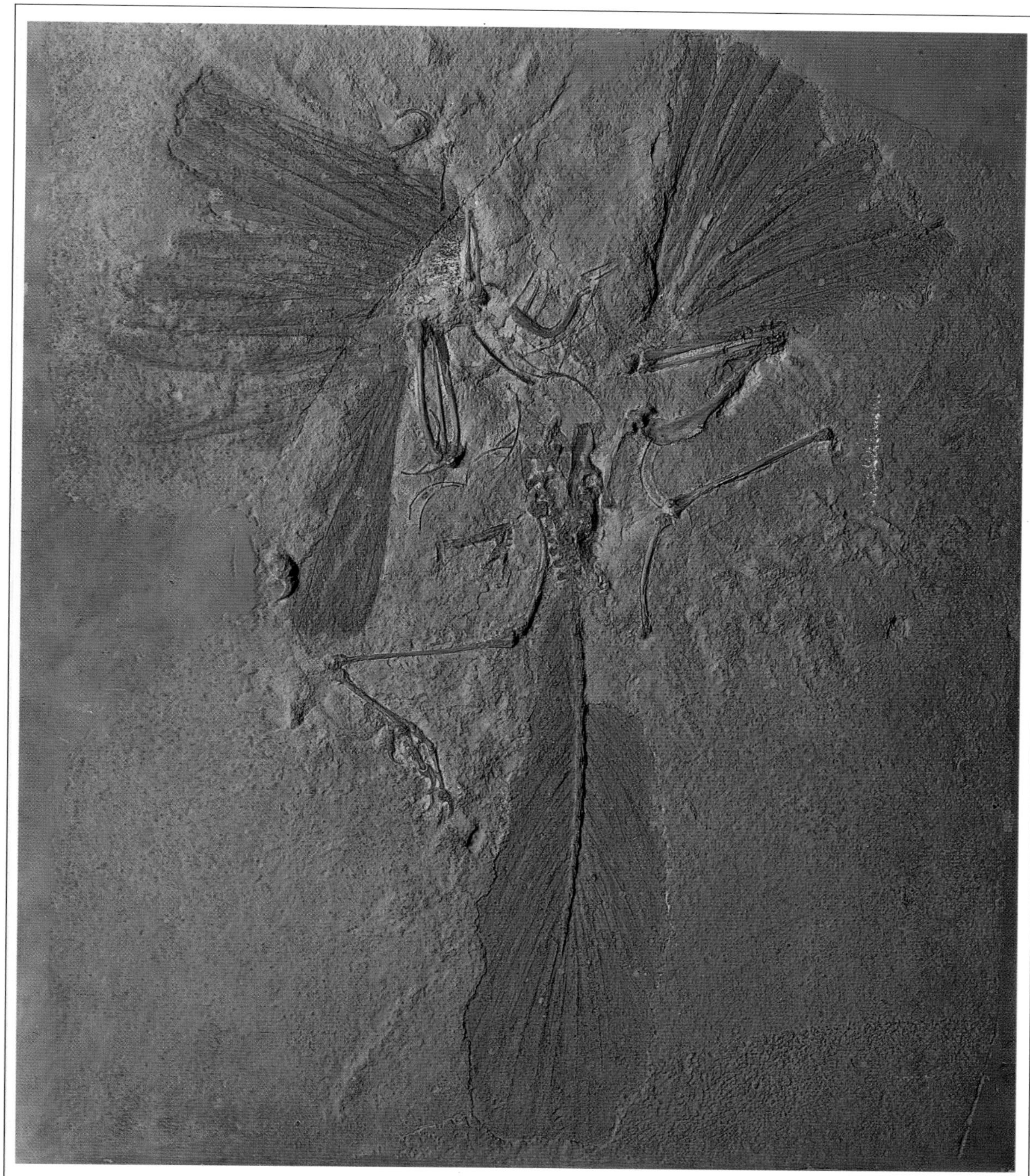

73 ***Archaeopteryx* in the Muséum National Histoire Naturelle, Paris**. This bird, 18 in (46 cm) long, is the oldest and most primitive one known (mid Jurassic), and is probably the common ancestor of all birds, or at least the nearest to their ancestral forms. Six specimens have been found in limestone from the Upper Jurassic near Eichstatt (Germany), three of which are nearly complete skeletons, two are partial skeletons, and the other is an isolated feather. The limestone is fine-grained so that even the impression of the feathers is conserved. The fossil consists, in fact, of an object made up of reptilian features (the teeth and the rear claws) and of avian features (the wings with feathers and fork). It is not certain that the bird could fly, despite its feathers, since the bony parts in which the strong muscles would be inserted to allow it to fly have not been found in the skeleton.
[Photo: R. de Seynes / Firo Foto]

the late Jurassic, between 140 and 170 million years ago. It was found in the well-known Solnhofen limestone quarry in Bavaria in 1861, already with some of the characteristics (feathers, presence of a clavicle, shape of the cranium and of the anterior extremities) of a modern bird, even though it shares many more characteristics with pteropod dinosaurs (jaws with conical teeth, skeleton of the tail and the pelvis, etc.). More recently, in mid-Triassic rocks in Catalonia some 240 million years old and in Late Triassic rocks in Texas some 220 million years old, older fossils have been found that may correspond to the ancestors of birds. These are related to small two-legged reptiles with sharp teeth and a long tail, but are already equipped with a clavicle and fairly long anterior extremities in which small bumps can be observed, perhaps identifiable as feather insertions. However, after *Archaeopteryx*, the evolution of birds is much better documented and seems to have been rapid and diversified from the Early Cretaceous Period.

The cynodonts, the reptilian branch from which mammals were to develop, appeared in the Late Permian Period, between 260 and 245 million years ago. As in the case of amphibian line that developed into reptiles, and reptiles that developed into birds,

Warm-blooded reptiles?

It has been traditional, although at the same time simplistic and mistaken, to attribute the characteristics of present-day reptiles to the great reptiles of the Mesozoic Era. We have, therefore, always thought of the dinosaurs of that time as being relatively inactive, slow-moving, and incapable of regulating their own body temperatures. They were also thought to have only a very limited mental capacity, and they ended up being portrayed as dim, sluggish giants. Today, however, they are seen in a different light.

The attribution of a fossil to one particular group does not mean that it has to agree with modern members of that group in all its characteristics. The dinosaurs, then, with their enormous bodies and distinctive morphological and anatomical features, were different from today's reptiles (legs underneath the body, horns and external armor plating in some cases). They are now no longer automatically presumed to have been cold-blooded, like present-day lizards, nor did they necessarily walk on all fours or drag their tails along the ground. Although it can now be shown that certain dinosaurs were bipeds, the question of whether or not they could control their body temperatures remains open. Indeed, if we knew something of their circulatory and respiratory systems, we would have the key to understanding their metabolisms, and accordingly the degree of homeothermy (warm-bloodedness). However, as this is not the case, we have to approach the subject indirectly.

In 1964 an important discovery was made near the town of Bridger, Montana, in the United States. The fossilized remains of a reptile, which came to be called *Deinonychus*, were found. This was a relatively small, carnivorous dinosaur (with a weight of only 175 lbs, or 80 kg) that moved with its tail raised and bore its weight only on its rear extremities. The presence of a fearful claw on the side of its foot and its overall anatomical structure suggests a highly active predator, well-adapted for rapid movement, and with a balance and agility which are unthinkable in present-day reptiles. All this, in short, suggests a high metabolic rate. For that reason it was suggested that *Deinonychus* was not endothermic like the birds and mammals of today, but that it was homeothermic, in other words that it was capable of regulating its body temperature either internally or externally. Some paleontologists believe that if this characteristic was extended to the whole group, then it would be easier to explain not only the success of the dinosaurs over a period of tens of millions of years, but also their extinction. On the other hand, according to Robert Bakker, the small ratio of carnivorous dinosaur remains in comparison to the herbivores would make them "necessarily" endothermic, because otherwise the proportion of cold-blooded carnivores to the herbivores on which they fed would be much greater. It is clear, however, that this line of reasoning does not take into account the irregularities and chance factors playing a large part in creating the fossil record, nor the possibility that the predator lived on small prey, of which there might no longer be any trace. The differences between ectotherms and endotherms diminish as size increases, because of the simple fact that a body with a large mass maintains a very constant temperature. In the case of the dinosaurs, it should be borne in mind that even the smallest would be bigger than 80% of present-day mammals, among which only 2% weigh more than two tons. It is estimated that over half the dinosaurs would have exceeded that weight. Such a large body mass would have prevented any great variation in body temperature between day and night. On the other hand, they would probably have had to avoid extremes of temperature. All this, in short, allows us to think that the large dinosaurs might have had stable body temperatures, which were still perhaps lower than ours (9-18°F, or 5-10°C less). To put it another way, a delicate homeothermy could have been maintained alongside a weak endothermy (internal energy expenditure). In the case of large herbivores that inhabited areas with extreme seasonal variations, the problems of food shortage and falls in temperatures could have been overcome by making migrations of hundreds of miles. Another find points to the existence of some form of homeothermy. The skeleton of the *Stegosaurus* has highly vascularized, pentagonal dorsal plates that might have acted to dissipate heat. This is an indication that, at least on occasions, it was necessary for them to be able to cool their blood. Moreover, relatively recent finds of dinosaur remains (mainly footprints) in polar layers complicate even more the arguments about thermal regulation. The dinosaurs of those areas, relatively small in comparison with those of lower latitudes, would have lived, at least during the Cretaceous Period, within the Arctic and Antarctic circles. Nevertheless,

Iguanodon bernissartensis, reconstruction.
[Drawing by Jordi Corbera]

although we can be sure of their existence, we cannot be absolutely sure that they had to endure the same degree of cold that presently prevails in those regions.

The diversity found among the dinosaurs of the Mesozoic Era has often been compared with that of mammals during the Cenozoic Era. Clearly there must have been a great deal of variety among those animals, from small, fast, carnivorous bipeds, to slow-moving, vegetarian quadrupeds: after all they existed for well over a hundred million years. The information we have is no doubt scant. As regards temperature, there would not have been a simple regulatory mechanism common to all groups. Rather, we must imagine diverse groups with differ-

Dinosaurs at the Crystal Palace, Sydenham [Mary Evans Picture Library]

ent temperature control mechanisms and, therefore, different body temperatures. The fauna of the Jurassic and of the Cretaceous Periods, to look no further, are completely different.

The investigation of the dinosaurs' locomotion has been based on their skeletal remains and on the depth of their footprints and the distance between them. The preserved footprints of the large dinosaurs seem to indicate that they only moved by walking, whereas many of the footprints of the smaller dinosaurs suggest that they could run. The most rapid footprints belong to a biped found in Texas, which weighed a little over half a ton, and which, when it made the footprints, was running at about 40 feet (12 m) per second (more than 25 miles per hour). McNeill, on the other hand, has dismissed the long-held belief that the huge sauropod *Diplodocus*, with its highly graceful skeleton, would have been confined to floating in the water, and was incapable, or so it was believed, of moving on the ground. The investigation also suggests that the imposing *Apatosaurus*, popularly known as the brontosaurus, would have had the same agility as an elephant, able to run slowly, though not capable of galloping or jumping.

The dinosaurs were, then, agile creatures, either carnivorous or herbivorous, in particular cases, and the possessing of thermoregulatory mechanisms. They were an evolutionary success that suddenly disappeared, along with many other forms of life, for reasons which are still not clear today.

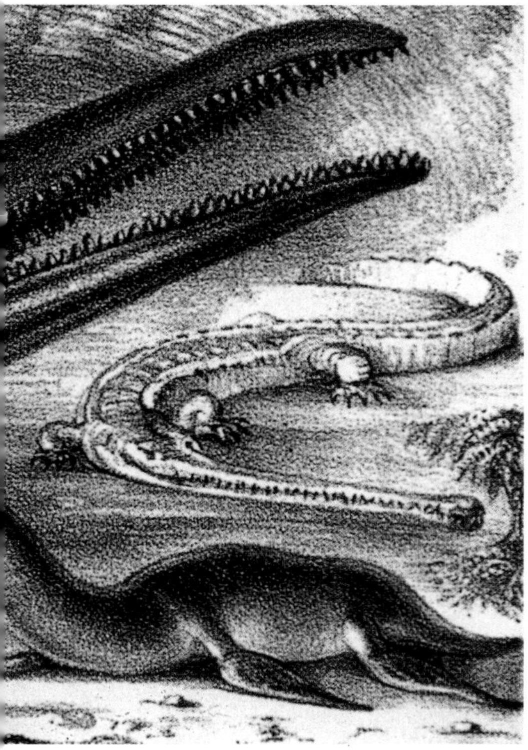

Ichthyosaur and plesiosaurs [Sheila Terry - Science Photo Library / AGE Fotostock]

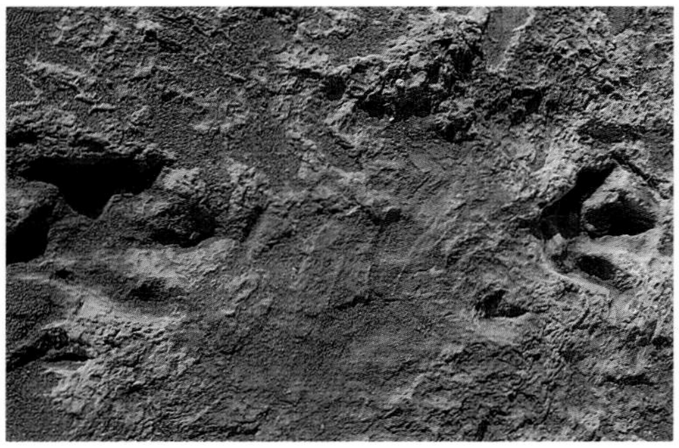

74 About 200 million years ago, at the beginning of the Mesozoic, when the reptiles occupied the seas and the skies, the first mammals developed. The biggest differences between the reptiles and the mammals are found not only in the skeleton but also other features. As regards reproduction, the reptiles laid large eggs, which contained great amounts of reserve materials to feed the chicks; the mammals had small offspring; thus, the new born depended on the care of their parents.
[Diagram: Biopunt]

we are dealing with small animals, roughly the size of today's hedgehogs, which lived especially on the southern continent of Gondwana, where seasonal changes were particularly marked. They were particularly abundant and diversified during the Triassic Period. During this period, at least six groups of cinodonts, both carnivores and herbivores, developed mammalian characteristics, although it seems that it was a group of small carnivores which, at the end of the Triassic Period, some 215 million years ago, gave rise to the first true mammals.

The first mammals were small (some were hardly 4 inches, or 4 in [10 cm], long from the end of their noses to the base of their tails), and their fossils are rare and difficult to find unless enormous quantities of sediments are washed and sifted. They must have been similar to today's small insectivores and, like them, they must have been nocturnal, the most effective way for small animals capable of regulating their temperature to compete with larger, cold-blooded, and, subsequently, less nocturnally active animals. Even though there may have been warm-blooded reptiles, in general the low temperature and the fresh night air inhibited the activity of reptiles. Alert and active in the dark of night, with penetrating and dilated eyes, the first mammals escaped from dependence on the sun's heat and spread throughout the world. As they moved further away from the heat of the tropics and from the reptiles that lived there, they gradually perfected their means of isolation by keeping their internal temperature constant. Perhaps some developed bird-like feathers, but the majority developed skins, a new use of keratin as protection against low temperatures. In their development from cynodonts, the female mammals gradually stopped placing their eggs in holes in the ground; instead, they began to feed them inside their bodies, warmed by a specialized organ that, in the most developed species, evolved into the womb. After birth, the hungry offspring could suck the secretions from glands on their mother's bellies. This secretion, initially only sweat enriched with calcium, became the richest of organic liquids: milk.

From their beginnings some 200 million years ago, both birds and mammals differed from their reptilian ancestors and the majority of other reptiles, except perhaps for some dinosaurs, by the special attention and care which they devoted to their offspring. The majority of reptiles have abundant offspring, which they abandon after egg-laying or, at most, as soon as they have come out of the egg. Birds and mammals, on the other hand, feed and bring up their less numerous and more vulnerable offspring, which need this level of care if they are to survive into adulthood.

In the Early Cretaceous Period, the first placental mammals appear, in other words those with a structure linking the growing embryo with the mother's womb and through which nutritious substances and oxygen are passed from the mother to the embryo. This structure also permits the excretion of materials and carbon dioxide from the embryo to the mother. The development of the placenta has allowed placental mammals, in contrast with marsupials, to have longer gestation periods in which the offspring reach a more advanced state of development and a shorter lactation period before becoming independent of their mother for their food. Despite the advantages which now seem evident to us, during the Cretaceous Period, mammals, even the placental ones, maintained a discrete presence in certain ecosystems in which the dominant animals were dinosaurs. The latter, which appeared during the Jurassic some 215 million years ago, underwent, throughout the Cretaceous Period, an expansion and diversification without precedent in any other group of animals. This expansion led them to colonize all environments, both terrestrial and aquatic, to try flying and even viviparity, and to reach dimensions that have never been equalled by any other animal. At the same time, there were also other dinosaurs not very different in size from the first birds or mammals we have described. Simultaneously, other groups of reptiles, like the ancestors of all those alive today, also achieved a favorable phase of diversification and speciation.

Cenozoic biomes

The end of the Cretaceous and beginning of the Cenozoic Period, some 66 million years ago, is marked by a massive extinction event in which dinosaurs and other forms of life, like many planktonic groups, ammonites, and many families of plants, totally disappeared.

Convulsions during a rather unclear break

It seems that the cause of these extinctions was due to the collision of a planetoid with the Earth. Possible evidence for this is the strange abundance of iridium, an extremely rare metal on Earth but abundant in meteorites, in the sediments laid down between the Cretaceous and Cenozoic Periods. This was first discovered in Gubbio, Umbria, in the center of the Italian Peninsula, but it has later been confirmed at more than a dozen other points, from the sediments at the bottom of the Pacific Ocean to several points in Europe and North America; at the same time, an impoverishment of the fossil plankton and the proportion of pollen grains that appear in sediments has also been observed. It would seem that the collision could have produced a meteoric dust cloud caused by a prolonged darkening of the whole (or if not of a large part) of the Earth's surface (the mere eruption of the volcano Tambora in 1815 deprived large areas around it of a summer climate the following year). This would have led to a significant fall in the temperature of the Earth's surface and a spectacular decrease in photosynthetic activity both at sea and on land. The dead bodies of bacteria, photosynthetic protista, and plants would have accumulated, and their deaths would have caused famine for all those organisms depending on these producers for their food, leading to the extinction of a large part of them.

Recently, from studies carried out on the lava outflow of the Deccan Mountains in India, a new hypothesis has been put forward, according to which a series of generalized eruptions could also explain the increase in iridium, as well as other chemical anomalies in sediments from the border of the Cretaceous Period and the Cenozoic Era. These volcanic deposits, though, would have required a deposition period of 10,000 years, a very high figure compared with the months estimated for the asteroid hypothesis. The poor resolution of present dating systems (above 1.1‰) means that we cannot rule out either possibility. Whatever the case, widespread extinctions, which, at first sight seem disastrous, could have played a decisive part in the evolution of complex life. The extinction of the dinosaurs, seen from the perspective of these hypotheses, rather than being a question of genetics, could have been simply a stroke of bad luck. In fact, dinosaurs and ammonites, which were abundant for tens of thousands of years, disappeared forever, along with foraminifera, belemnites, rudist bivalves, and other entire groups. Life on earth embarked on new pathways. Among the surviving groups were the mammals, which began a explosive phase of evolution. These apocalyptical images are perhaps a little exaggerated. Most terrestrial plants do not seem to have been affected by the happenings that occurred at the border between the Cretaceous and Cenozoic Era, as can be seen from fossil records both before and after this date. To sum up, it is a fact that the impact did actually take place and that it did cause important changes in temperature, light, the mechanisms controlling atmospheric conditions, sea level, and many other factors that could have caused the destruction of a large part (though certainly not all) of the communities of organisms and, in any case, caused the extinction of those species that had the most difficulty in adapting to sudden change.

Cenozoic flora and fauna

The plants that were most tolerant to seasonal changes and the fauna associated with them, on the other hand, managed to survive quite well. Thus, with the

75 About 50 million years ago, an important expansion of the flora and fauna of the planet took place. The animals that expanded most were the mammals and the birds. The birds colonized the aerial environment, while the mammals also colonized other media: aquatic, aerial and terrestrial, and in the terrestrial environments occupied all ecological niches. *[Diagram: Biopunt]*

advent of the Cenozoic Era, a flora which has not changed substantially since, apart from changes in area motivated by climatic changes and the tectonic movements that have taken place in the last 65 million years, became established over the whole of the planet. With the disappearance of the dinosaurs, the way was open for birds and mammals to expand and diversify in an explosive manner. During this process, the success of mammals was so great that they increased from eight to 70 families in 10 million years, between the beginning of the Cenozoic Era or Tertiary Period to the end of the Palaeocene.

Finally, it should be mentioned that coinciding with the cold stages at the end of the Oligocene and beginning of the Miocene Epochs, some new forms of vegetation began to develop, rich in herbaceous species and above all grasses in tropical latitudes (savannahs) and temperate ones (prairies and steppes). These offered food resources greater than those previously available to new forms of mammals, both herbivores and carnivores. From this a new evolutionary explosion took place that mainly affected mammals.

The appearance of the primates

Among these families of particular interest that appeared at the beginning of the Cenozoic Era, some 65 million years ago, are those of our direct predecessors and closest relatives: the primitive primates. The early primates were small, wily insectivores who lived in trees. They could jump and escape from predators quickly. Some even held onto branches with modified claws, which in humans have become the fingers and toes. Leaping from branch to branch in the middle of the night favored the selection of acuteness and precision of vision in their descendants, and slowly their eyes must have moved from a lateral position to a frontal, central position. This made stereoscopic vision possible, something that was indispensable for the appreciation of distances as they moved through the tree tops. They must have come to resemble today's prosimians, which only survived in Madagascar and in some parts of southeast Asia. Primates survived the next episode of mass extinction, the abrupt break between the Eocene and Oligocene, 38 million years ago, during which many families of mammals became extinct, in particular in North America, and also many planktonic organisms, because of a new cooling of the climate. During the Oligocene, 30 million years ago, primates split into different branches (one of which would lead to the hominids), which included all the present anthropoids,humans with their extinct predecessors, and other related primates. The evolution of this group, in which we are particularly interested, firstly because it is the one to which we ourselves belong, but also because it has become a new and highly active agent in the biosphere's modification, will be the subject of the third part of this volume.

2
Matter, energy, and organization: the workings of the biosphere

1. The blue planet

1.1 One in a million

When contemplating the immensity of the universe, we are bound to experience a certain feeling of loneliness. Nowhere within our reach can we see a world comparable to ours: so many specifications were needed to create a model like the Earth that this has only come about in this universe with a certain reluctance. But we know intuitively that if life does exist in another place as it does here, then it must have some characteristics of organization and evolution in which we can recognize ourselves. This is what one would hope for from the material unity of the universe and from the reliability of what we hardly dare call laws, because perhaps they only take the form of very measured and discrete prohibitions. Despite the fact that the laws of organization are the same everywhere, the existence of another world similar to our own seems rather unlikely to us: the Earth is unique. The more we study and familiarize ourselves with the heavens, the more we realize that the chances of there being other worlds the same as or similar to ours are very low.

The complexity of singular things

The most repeatable things on Earth, are, strangely, also the most complex—namely organisms, because to handle a great deal of information, we must work with reproducible components, however paradoxical this may seem. Computers are much more similar to each other and more reproducible, within an external mold, than were the old artifacts of craftsmanship. The inevitable repetition of elemental components and the copying of more complicated components appear as regular occurrences throughout the universe.

Thanks to very effective normalization and control mechanisms, life does not break up into an infinity of divergent forms. At the level of life, there are regularities which, if we think carefully, are not so obvious: why does life appear in discontinuous units, belonging to a limited number of classes?

The solar system is no longer the immense clock marking an eternal rhythm. The solar system has a history, and we can assign a probable age to our universe that science estimates now to be approximately 14 thousand million years. In the first moments of its history, many things happened; the concentration of events was very great. After the first few minutes of creation were over, we had a universe in which the present state of affairs could almost be recognized. Is this mere illusion or fantasy?

But these speculations are in keeping with the style of material change that we live through every day. One just has to think of the relative slowness that the adventure of biological evolution was to adopt later on. It is as if the wealth of information had to mature in time, something worth bearing in mind at the start of a text dedicated to ecological matters. Individual life and succession in an ecosystem show an intensity of change which, seen from the outside, appears greater in the first moments, while novelties appear in never ending succession. This same style of differentiation can be seen the whole world over: no two geological structures are identical, despite the fact that the similarities we can observe with mechanisms and processes by which they were formed, and there has been no period in the Earth's history that is even an approximate replica of another.

If the science of evolution has brought us, generally, to accept the genetic unity of humans with living nature, ecological theory brings us to accept our functional unity. Because of our nature, we generally tend to accept this dependence and the limitations it implies, although we try to avoid many of the implications. We do not respect nature and we hardly respect our peers. We always want to be different, both as individuals and as groups. We have now become accustomed to reflecting, perhaps more freely, on our destiny. When a hypothesis on the animal origin of humans was put forward, it traumatized some people who thought our origins were rather more distinguished. But the truth is that to confess the acceptance of deep and direct biological roots with the rest of the world was more of a polemic diversion than the expression of a profound intellectual conviction.

At a human level, biological (genetic) evolution has been practically replaced by cultural (imitative) evolution. This has come about because it allows us

76 The Earth is the only planet in the solar system that combines all the conditions that make life possible. Neither the moon, nor the nearby planets, such as Mars or Venus, nor the more distant ones offer the living beings of the blue planet any expectations that they might be habitable. In the whole of space so far known by humans, no heavenly body has been found with conditions similar to those of the Earth. As humans, we are not always sufficiently aware of our isolation in the immensity of the universe, nor of the imperative need to maintain our planet in a habitable condition, an inescapable requirement for the survival of our species.
[Photo: Index / Stock International Inc.]

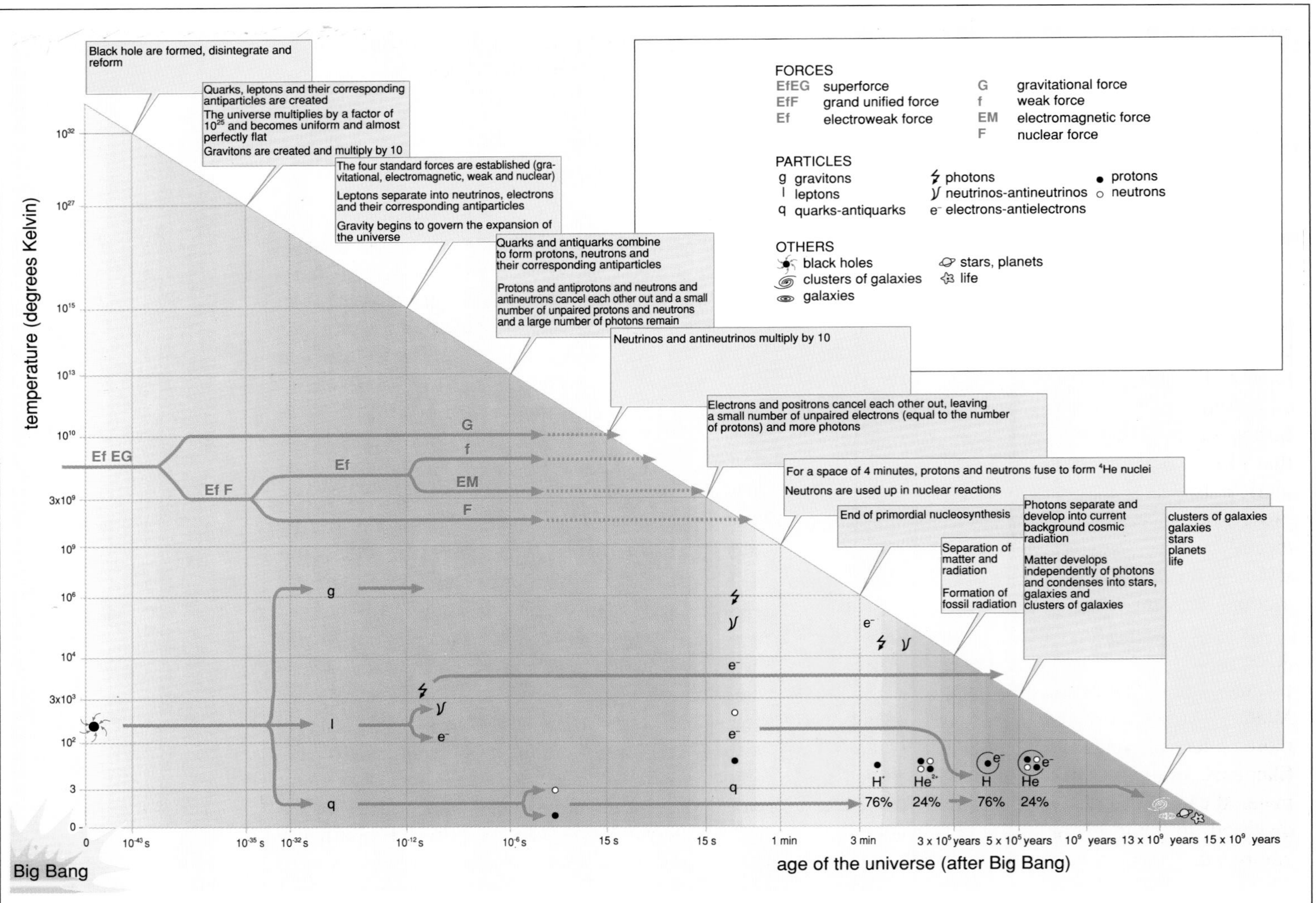
Black hole are formed, disintegrate and reform
Quarks, leptons and their corresponding antiparticles are created
The universe multiplies by a factor of 10^25 and becomes uniform and almost perfectly flat
Gravitons are created and multiply by 10
The four standard forces are established (gravitational, electromagnetic, weak and nuclear)
Leptons separate into neutrinos, electrons and their corresponding antiparticles
Gravity begins to govern the expansion of the universe
Quarks and antiquarks combine to form protons, neutrons and their corresponding antiparticles
Protons and antiprotons and neutrons and antineutrons cancel each other out and a small number of unpaired protons and neutrons and a large number of photons remain
Neutrinos and antineutrinos multiply by 10
Electrons and positrons cancel each other out, leaving a small number of unpaired electrons (equal to the number of protons) and more photons
For a space of 4 minutes, protons and neutrons fuse to form 4He nuclei
Neutrons are used up in nuclear reactions
End of primordial nucleosynthesis
Separation of matter and radiation
Formation of fossil radiation
Photons separate and develop into current background cosmic radiation
Matter develops independently of photons and condenses into stars, galaxies and clusters of galaxies
clusters of galaxies
galaxies
stars
planets
life
FORCES
EfEG superforce
EfF grand unified force
Ef electroweak force
G gravitational force
f weak force
EM electromagnetic force
F nuclear force
PARTICLES
g gravitons
l leptons
q quarks-antiquarks
photons
neutrinos-antineutrinos
e⁻ electrons-antielectrons
protons
neutrons
OTHERS
black holes
clusters of galaxies
galaxies
stars, planets
life
temperature (degrees Kelvin)
10^32
10^27
10^15
10^13
10^10
3x10^9
10^9
10^6
10^4
3x10^3
10^2
3
0
Ef EG
Ef F
Ef
G
f
EM
F
g
l
q
e⁻
H+
He2+
H
He
76%
24%
0
10^-43 s
10^-35 s
10^-32 s
10^-12 s
10^-6 s
15 s
15 s
1 min
3 min
3 x 10^5 years
5 x 10^5 years
10^9 years
13 x 10^9 years
15 x 10^9 years
Big Bang
age of the universe (after Big Bang)

77 The history of the universe, since the so-called Planck time (10^{-43} seconds after the Big Bang)—the limit beyond which the known laws of physics cannot be extrapolated—is a story of expansion, cooling, and growing complexity of an extremely dense mass of material. Material originally concentrated in a volume of a hundredth of a millimeter in diameter with a temperature of 10^{12} degrees. As happens in other temporal phenomena, the period after the Big Bang was not uniform, but the most significant events took place during the initial moments, and afterwards the changes took place over a longer period of time. Concentrated in the first three minutes of the life of the universe occurred its greatest number of significant events. *[Diagram: Biopunt, from various sources]*

to go faster and not because it makes us happier. The fact is that cultural evolution began on the basis of an old genetic substrate that potentially contains an inclination towards the use of violence, which seemingly cannot be eradicated. Here lies our destiny's grandeur and challenge. More directly related to the subject of these pages, humanity's successful manipulation of external or exosomatic energy shows us just how far some of humanity's less attractive characteristics can go when it controls too much power; it is as if it could not renounce this power to manipulate exosomatic energy. With the invention of money, humans created a mechanism to stabilize inequalities in society as effectively as territorial instinct had been in many other animals. The difference is that money has been created in such a way that humans are perfectly capable of seeing its wickedness.

Those who are more interested in distant problems than those closer to home would like, in answer to the present uncertainties or simply by way of consolation, to discover some indication in the universe of systems entities similar to our own, with which we could communicate in a real and profound way.

Life in the universe

The materials that make up the universe, and the laws or constants that apparently govern it, are uniform. Life can be interpreted as a cosmic phenomenon, based, as it is, on properties that can be found in any material system. We could even believe that developing reflexive subjects is an essential property of any universe, leading us to believe that organic evolution is perhaps not only fatal but also has to be rapid. This is the same as saying that in biological evolution, like in ecological succession, the roughest job is finished first, like a sculptor rough-hewing his block of marble when he starts work, while the final details are added at a much more leisurely rate; if need is no longer a constraint, the finished work will be a highly intricate object. Thus, the value that we can give to physical time, as a container of events and experiences, does not turn out to be uniform.

Let us dwell for a moment on the characteristics that an environment must have to favor the existence of life as we know it on our planet, and let us try and discover the probability of discovering similar planets throughout the universe. The most simplistic solution is to say that life appears in 11% of the solar system's planets. If there are a number of stars similar to the Sun and if we can attribute a certain number of planets to each star, we could estimate the probability that in the visible universe there is a large number of planets similar to ours, planets, therefore, which may possibly support life. According to these probabilites, you can rapidly arrive at figures that appear very high in absolute terms. It would appear very probable that life, as a cosmic phenomenon, exists in other worlds. But at the same time, it is clear that the probability of establishing contact with one of these living colonies is low. Time and space constitute an efficient quarantine that is opposed to mutual communication.

According to today's cosmologists, the distribution of matter and stars in the universe is not uniform. Matter is more concentrated in spaces that are found more or less in continuity, in the shape of reticula, filaments, or veils. Other volumes of less dense material can be rounded in shape and perhaps more disposed to emit energy. The above-mentioned combination corresponds to a construction model that nature uses on several scales and which we can find in bread and Emmenthal cheese.

Our Sun

The Sun is a star with a surface temperature of 9,572°F (5,300°C). Its properties have been subjected to historical changes. A fairly lengthy period of time, during which the Sun has hardly changed, allowed for a marvellous evolution of life on Earth. Stars are subject to slow processes of development and to more traumatic and rapid changes that take place on a smaller time scale. We know of explosions of new stars, but this only happens from time to time, and probably we will still enjoy the Sun for a long time to come. Our Sun forms part of the Galaxy, with a capital G, one of the visible conglomerations recognizable in the universe, and is 30,000 light-years (or 30,000 x 9,460,800,000,000 km) from the center of the same system, around which it revolves. It is thought that the furthest planet, Pluto, is more than an average of 3.6 billion mi (5.9 billion km) away from the Sun and that the star nearest to the Sun, Proxima Centauri, is some 6,800 times further away than that. Thus we can beginning to understand the idea of quarantine mentioned earlier.

The Sun's radius is 432,000 mi (696,000 km), 109 times the radius of the Earth, and its volume is just

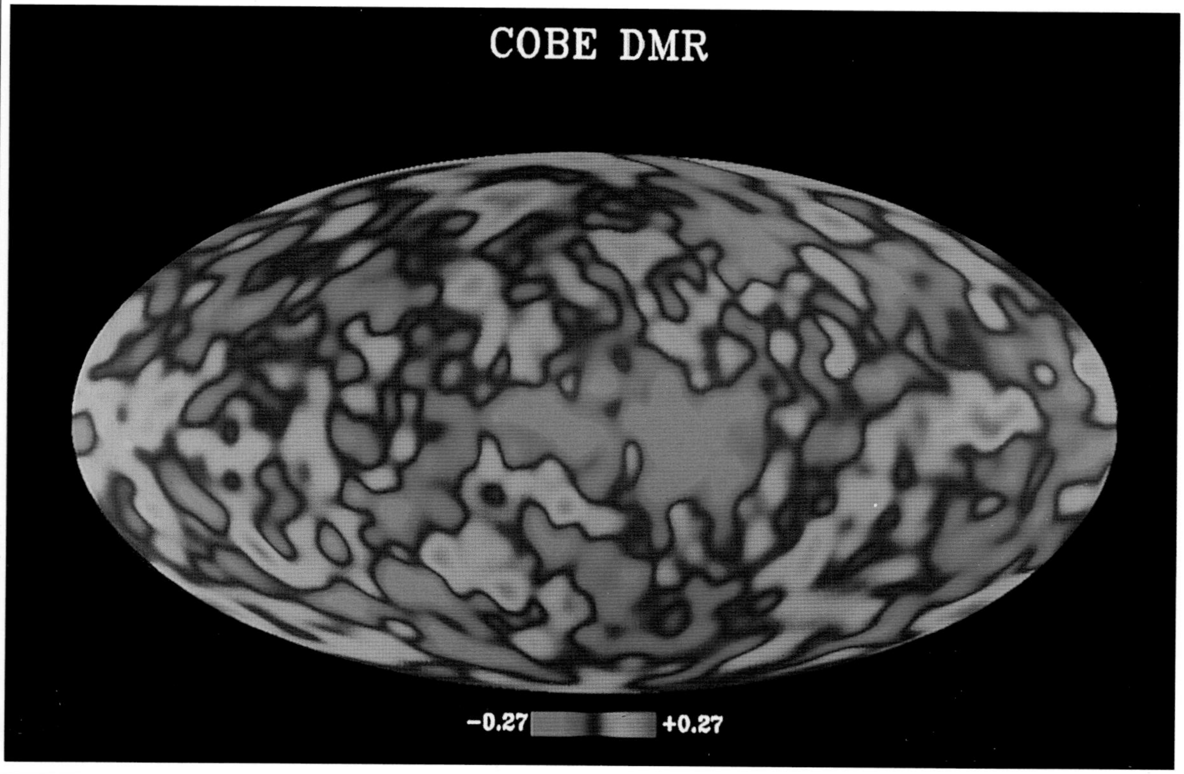

78 From data obtained since 1989 by the COBE (Cosmic Background Explorer), an image, in false color, corresponding to a map of microwave background radiation, was prepared. Areas in pink or red are hotter than average, while those represented by various shades of blue are cooler. The analysis of the image has confirmed the existence of dark matter (missing mass), which cannot be observed, and seems to confirm the hypothesis that an initial Big Bang preceded the expansion of the universe. This image is the closest to the origin of the universe that has ever been obtained, and it corresponds to the state of the universe about 15 thousand million years ago. *[Photo: NASA GSFC - Science Photo Library / AGE Fotostock]*

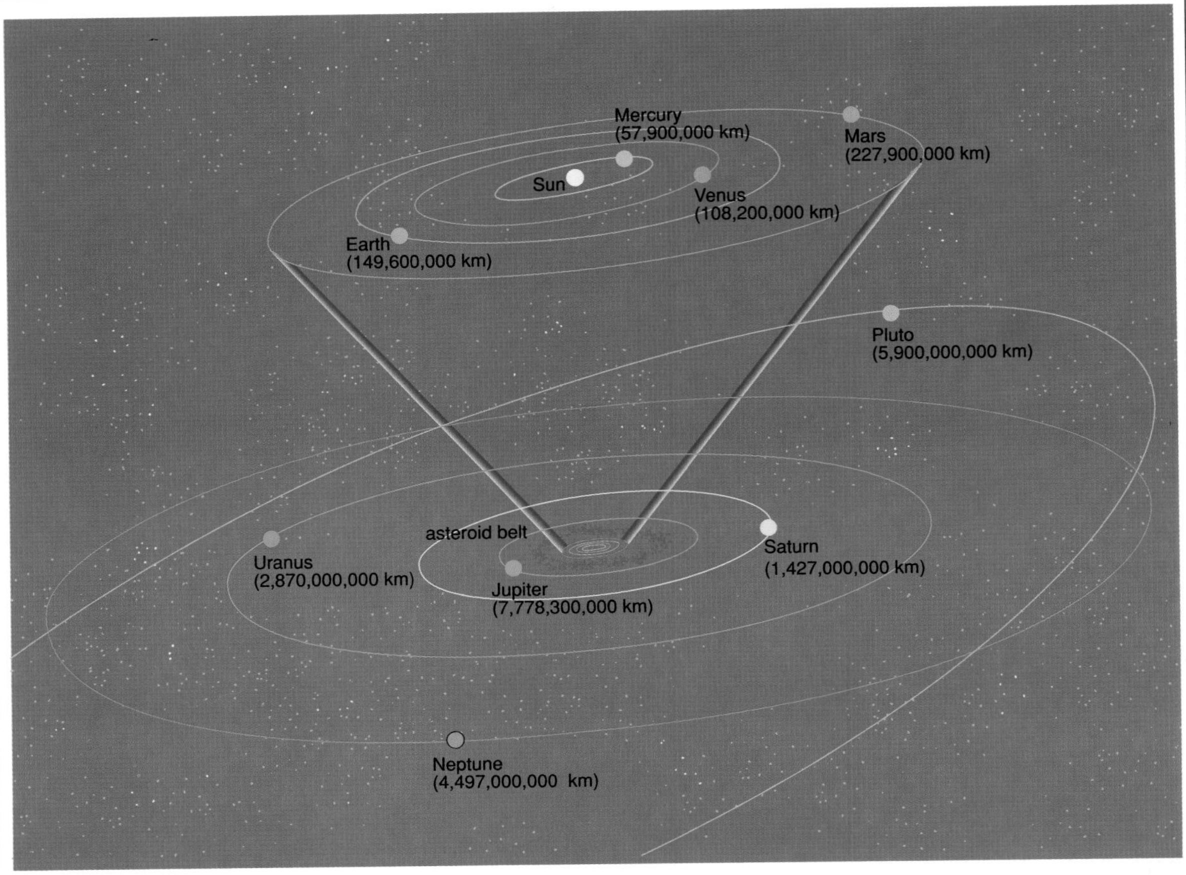

79 The solar system can be divided into two groups of planets separated by the asteroid belt: the earth's planets and the gaseous giants, to which can be added Pluto and its satellite Charon, strange astronomical objects still not well known, and the hypothetical planet not yet discovered, which orbits the sun beyond the orbit of Pluto. The Earth's planets have in common the fact that they are solid bodies with a metallic nucleus, surrounded by a siliceous core, which is also solid but broken up into pieces that maintain a certain degree of mobility on an intermediate fluid and plastic mantle. But only the Earth has a surface temperature that allows water to remain in a liquid state. Mercury has practically no atmosphere, and what it does have is mostly made up of sodium and helium. The high temperatures on its surface, which can reach 806ºF (430ºC), ensures that any water that may be there is held in gaseous state, although recently it has been found that some ice is preserved in the bottom of craters that the Sun's rays do not reach. Venus has a very dense atmosphere of carbon dioxide, with thick clouds of sulphuric acid, and due to the greenhouse effect the surface temperatures are even higher than those of Mercury. Due to its slow (retrograde) rotation (from W to E, the opposite of other planets) the day on Venus is longer than the year (243 as opposed to 225). Mars is an immense desert with temperatures around -58ºF (-50ºC). The great planets with their orbits furthest from the Sun, also have dense centers that are metallic in nature, but externally are immense balls of relatively light gases. Their temperatures are lower than those of Mars, due to their increasing distance from the Sun. Although temperatures are not as low as might be expected judging from the radiation they receive. Pluto, the furthest distant, is basically a ball of methane and water, frozen at a temperature of -382ºF (-230ºC). *[Diagram: Editrònica]*

over a million times that of our planet, with an average density of 1.4 g/cu. cm. The Sun is the seat of a self-supporting nuclear fusion reaction, in which hydrogen is converted into helium and losing a portion of matter (around 0.7%), which is converted into energy according to Einstein's famous $E=mc^2$ equation. This reaction takes place within the Sun's mass, in a peculiar state of matter called plasma. It is an internal process, and at the end of some trajectories, photons leave through the Sun's surface. The surface temperature is much lower than the interior temperature, between 7,200ºF (4,000ºC)—on the Sun spots—and around 11,000ºF (6,000ºC), and the characteristics of the spectrum of solar radiation adjust themselves to this emission temperature.

Quantitatively, the solar energy that arrives on Earth, at the outer level of the atmosphere, is 136.8 mW/sq. cm, which is equivalent to 2 cal g/sq. cm/mim. This value is known as the solar constant, but it is not constant and varies both according to the Sun's state, the quantity of sunspots, etc., and to the distance between the Sun and the Earth. More important for the climate and for its variation is the inclination of the Earth's axis (~23.5º), which is also subjected to a fairly regular radiation. Later, in section 2.3, we will go into more detail about the solar radiation that reaches our planet.

The planets and life

Perhaps it is not necessary to make such a rigorous distinction between planets and satellites; they are not very different in their constitution, although they do differ in the way the radiation that they receive fluctuates. The Earth's mass is much smaller when compared to the total mass of the bodies that revolve around the Sun: a small fraction of 1%. The distance from the Sun fixes the corresponding value of the solar constant. The solar constant of Venus is about double that of the Earth's, and that of Mars is about half of it.

Many properties, both internal and peripheral, depend on the planet's size. The Earth is of average size and has a solid, complex crust with lighter and relatively rigid plates that slide over more plastic strata. The movement of these plates has greatly stimulated evolution, and geographers and biogeographers take great delight in tracing them. Other smaller planets and satellites have a more continuous or more rigid cover or shell, and the largest ones are fluid and conserve more internal heat. As happens in overweight animals, they increase their internal temperature fatally because of their size. There is a thermic regulation based on the balance between the radiation that comes from the Sun and its own long wave emission. Such a regulation allows water in a suitable state of aggrega-

	VENUS	EARTH	MARS
Mean distance to the Sun (x18^8 km)	1.082	1.496	2.279
Inclination of axis (degrees)	177	23.45	23.98
Sidereal period or year (days)	224.701	365.256	686.980
Rotational period (hours)	5,832.24(retr)	23.9345	24.6229
Solar day (days)	117	1	1.02872
Mass (x10^{24} kg)	4.870	5.976	0.6421
Radius (equatorial, km)	6,051.5	6,357-6,378	3,398
Gravity on surface (m sec^{-2})	8.60	9.78	3.72
Mean density (kg m^{-3})	5.24	5.52	3.97
Solar constant (kW m^{-2})	2.62	1.38	0.594
Net entry of heat to the exposed surface of the planet (kW m^{-2})	0.367	0.842	0.499
Mean surface temperature (K)	730	288	220
Atmosphere, surface pressure (Nm^{-2})	92	1	0.007
Atmospheric composition (%, N_2:O_2:CO_2)	3.5:0:96	77:21:0.03	2.7:0.1:95

80 Some of the relevant characteristics of the Earth and its neighboring planets. *[Source: Data prepared by the author]*

81 The differences among the bodies of the solar system become more evident as they are studied in more depth. It is becoming clearer that there are no general characteristics that can be applied to all the planets, to all the satellites, nor even to those of a single planet. In the image produced based on data from the probe *Voyager 1* in the first days of March 1979, one can see the four satellites of Jupiter, and the planet itself. Each of the satellites of Jupiter has its own "personality:" in the foreground, on the right, a fragment of Callisto, one of the satellites with the lowest albedos (reflective power) in the solar system. On its right (in the image), Ganymede can be seen. Almost in the center—nearest to Jupiter—is Europa, which to the contrary of Callisto has the highest albedos in the solar system and a relatively low density; which leads one to suppose that water, either in liquid or solid state, must be an important component of it. Above, on the left, can be seen Io, the fourth of the Galilean satellites of Jupiter, with a very high density. *[Photo: ST-TCL / Index]*

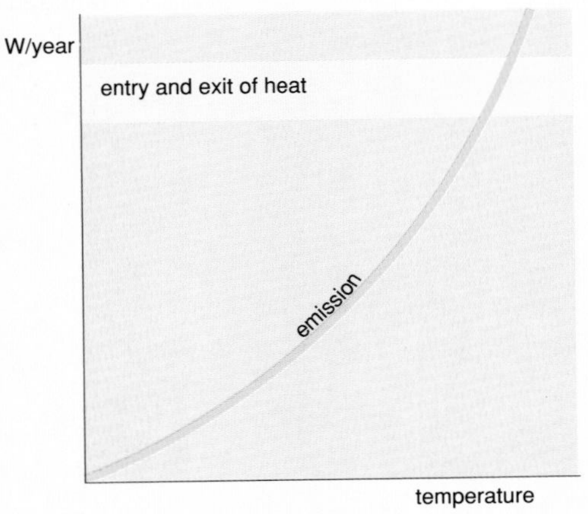

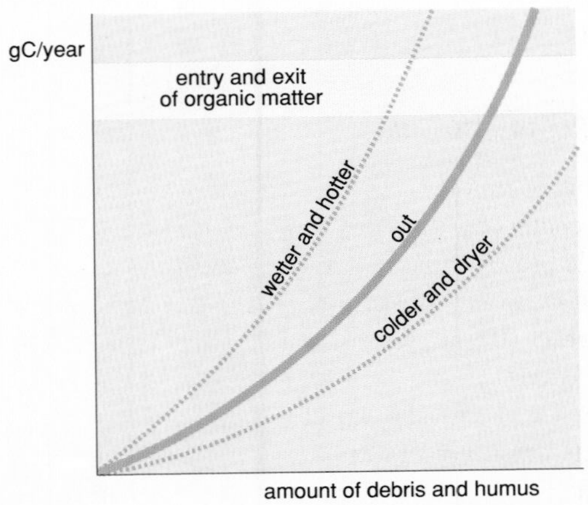

82 The temperature of the Earth, like other variables, obeys very roughly a general regulatory mechanism, which can be expressed in terms of a balance between inputs and outputs. In the case of terrestrial temperature (left hand graphic), the inputs depend on the distance (which varies throughout the year) and the state of the Sun (presence or absence of Sun spots, etc). The outputs are a function of the fourth power of the temperature, but this varies from one place to another on the Earth's surface. On average, it is as if the Earth gave out a temperature of -0,7°F (-18,2°C), which is the temperature that is actually found at 19,685 ft (6,000 m) altitude in the atmosphere. In another example of regulation, such as the accumulation of leaf litter and humus in the soil (right hand diagram), the inputs of materials depend on the primary production of the ecosystem, and the outputs, on the rate of breakdown which depends on temperature and humidity. *[Diagram: Biopunt, based on author's original]*

tion to persist on the Earth's surface, as well as allowing for the many kinds of chemical solutions, which largely go to make up the chemistry of life. Evidently, the availability of water and carbon can both be caused by the conserving properties of the planet itself, with a generous initial store, and by possible external contributions, like comets, for example. Exploration of the solar system since the 1970s has contributed enormously to detailing many interesting properties of the bodies that form it, some of which are seen as possible candidates for supporting life.

The planet's rotation period, which defines the periods of light and dark, is of great importance to living things, who use and depend on solar energy, as it defines the essential characteristics of organisms (for example, their size and metabolic regulation), which allow them to accumulate sufficient reserves to survive during the periods of darkness. The meteorologist and marine biologist can not forget the Coriolis effect or force, which is the result of the combination of the Earth's rotation with any trajectory applied to its spherical surface area. The varying obliqueness of the surface area in relation to the Sun's rays and the annual variation of this obliqueness due to the inclination of the Earth's axis in relation to the ecliptic, leads to a gradient in the intensity of our planet's atmospheric fluctuations and of the changes in biological production.

1.2 Lands, seas and the atmosphere

Structure and organization

Both in living and non-living systems, we can recognize a hierarchical structure in which larger entities are made up of smaller components. However, the essential thing about the concept of hierarchy is that not all possible relationships between the parts are equal, nor do they have the same intensity. And it is in the always partial contact or friction between the component elements where the work is done and where its results are most evident. Discontinuity begins with elemental particles and atoms and spreads throughout all levels, from atoms to stars. It is worth asking ourselves why there are stars but not a uniform gas filling space. One of the reasons is that in the hypothesis of a uniform gas there would be no one to consider the question.

In systems which are very energetic or young, or which have a high temperature, the diversity of elements is very minimal. In many regions of the cosmos, almost everything is hydrogen and helium. Later, in the interior of the stars, the nuclei of various elements from our periodic table are "cooked." If we now observe the frequencies of these elements across the Earth and in its different parts, the much greater diversity in their distribution occurs. It seems that there is a relationship between the passing of time and the possible acquisition of a higher degree of structuring or differentiation between the component elements.

The gradients of complexity and the variations in scale can clearly be seen in the Earth's organization. In it and in other planets, the dense and fluid central part, subject to high levels of pressure and temperature, is more homogenous than the peripheral or surface rocks. The rocks represent juxtapositions of minerals defined by restrictions of a chemical nature, often depending on historical circumstances. The relatively simple composition of many types of iron and other elements contrasts with the complexity of the rocks that form the greater part of the crust. Here the capacity to make silicon and silicate compounds almost anticipates the capacity to make different compounds from carbon molecules.

Lithospheric plates

Both the radius of an atom and the distance between the centers of atoms that form part of the same molecule are of the order of one angstrom (a ten thousand millionth of a meter). The diameter of our planet, about 10^6 m, represents then a leap of 10^{16}, leaving enough room to fit a great deal of structure in between. The solid part of the Earth is characterized by its heterogeneity on several levels. Basically it is made up of enormous plates or scales, with a surface area of tens of millions of square miles. There are, however, smaller plates or splintered fragments near the most important friction zones. These plates have behaved in a relatively independent way as regards their mutual dynamics. Throughout the Earth's history they have collided with one another, their edges scraping against each other. They have frequently been dragged down to the bottom in the so-called subduction zones. There are many signs of their vicissitudes, at least since some 100 million years ago. Before that, the dynamics of the Earth's surface could have been a little different.

Several scientists guessed at the movements of lithospheric plates, but most significant was the meteorologist, Alfred Wegener (1880-1930), to whom nobody paid much attention during his time. The acceptance and development of his basic ideas, supported by numerous recent research projects, has created a reasonable and quite detailed model that explains many things about the Earth's history and the history of life. It is also partly applicable to other planets and satellites whose surface structure and constitution are comparable to that of the Earth's. Just as in any mechanism made up of separate parts, whether they be cogwheels or levers, the effect that a planet's internal forces cause is most visible principally at the contact points between the plates. The main plates, and even the secondary ones, have been mapped, and we have considerable data about their changes of position throughout geological times. There has been a rearrangement of the external part of the Earth's crust, which has never come to a complete standstill. The discontinuity of the plates and their interaction offer us a very elegant way of understanding and describing a considerable part of the generation of the Earth's relief. Successive mountain ranges, the great plains, the corresponding composition of intrusive rocks and of sediments, lines of volcanic islands, these are all phenomena that fit into a rational model. The detail of land distribution, according to height and the development or present disposition of hydrographic networks, are both of great importance when trying to understand the distribution of climatic factors and many of the characteristics of the soils.

Interaction between the lithospheric plates occurs at a slower rate than in the fluid masses of the sea and the atmosphere, which interact at a rate thatcorresponds to that of climatic and atmospheric weather features. They appear to be phenomena having nothing to do with each other because of their difference in scale in terms of fluidity and time. Temporal ratios are of the order of 10^8 to 10^9. We still do not directly know the constitution of the Earth's interior. Only by performing exper-

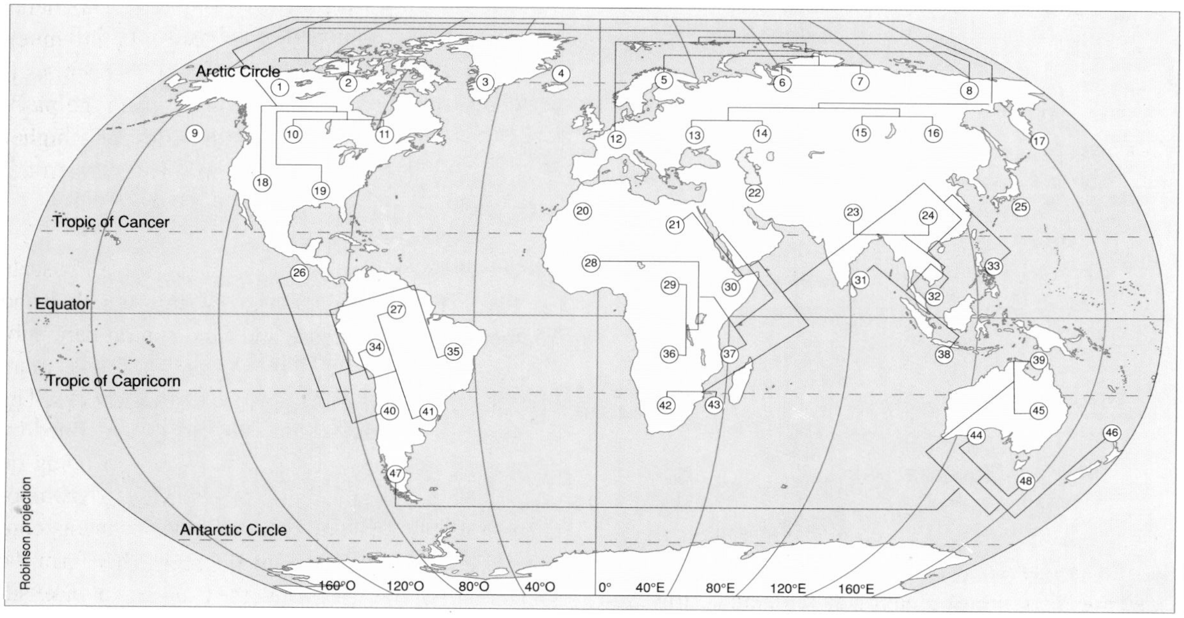

83 The relationships between the fish fauna of the different hydrographic basins of the world (indicated by the numbers) reflects ancient connections between continents and lands which are now far apart, such as South America and Australia, or Africa and India. The lack of agreement between distances and relationships are a historical consequence of the movements of the lithospheric plates. The length of the branches of the dendrogram do not reflect degrees of relationship but rather indicate hierarchical structure. *[Diagram: Editrònica, from Del Castillo, 1988]*

iments with pressure waves and seismic waves, and by making indirect calculations based on the Earth's density and certain analogies with other bodies, have we been able to establish a still-hypothetical model of what the central part of our planet might be like.

The Earth has two important characteristics from the point of view of the development of life: the abundance of water, the only mineral that is a liquid at ordinary temperature (except for mercury, which is found in the form of droplets in very small quantities between minerals of the same metal), and the differentiation of plates on the solid crust. These peripheral materials form two different classes: the continental plates are made of less dense materials (~2.8-3 kg/cu. dm), between which quartz and feldspar predominate, and while others, the oceanic plates, are denser (~3-4 kg/cu. dm) and are more basaltic in nature.

The planet's fluid coverings

Water is the universal solvent and contains a wide variety of materials in solution. The majority of the water present on the planet today, and even that in the atmosphere, must have separated from the solid part, because very little could be left from a hypothetical primitive gaseous atmosphere. The atmosphere has been profoundly modified through the action of living organisms. These have taken out carbon dioxide and have added oxygen and nitrogen. This is sufficient to explain the difference in atmospheric composition between the Earth and its neighboring lifeless planets. From an electrochemical point of view, this change has implied a centripetal movement of electrons in the Earth's periphery, in such a way that the atmosphere is oxidized, and the biosphere is composed of chemically reduced materials.

84 The molecular structure of water gives rise to a set of properties that have made it the fundamental substrate of life. Depending on the temperature, the water molecules form more or less compact multimolecular groups. Ice is more loosely packed than liquid water, and for this reason it is less dense and floats. The diagram represents the structure of water at a temperature of 68°F (20°C) and a pressure of one atmosphere, with the multimolecular packages in blue and the free molecules in green. *[Diagram: Editrònica, from various sources]*

HEIGHT ABOVE SEA LEVEL (m)	PRESSURE (mbar)	DENSITY ($g\ dm^{-3}$)	TEMPERATURE IN FREE ATMOSPHERE (°C)
0	1,013.2	1.226	15.0
500	983.5	1.197	11.7
1,000	898.6	1.112	8.5
3,000	700.9	0.910	-4.5
10,000	264.1	0.413	-50.0

85 Variation in the properties of the atmosphere at mid-latitudes. *[Source: data prepared by the author]*

The thermal conditions of the Earth are a result of the reception and re-emission of the Sun's electromagnetic radiation. The fluid layers that envelope the planet constitute a sort of beneficial greenhouse. These days we tend only to speak about this greenhouse in connection with possible undesirable consequences of our civilization's influence on the atmosphere: the so-called greenhouse effect. The word greenhouse has unjustly taken on a negative connotation in our social media, even though it is a greenhouse effect that maintains the Earth's present thermal conditions. The residual effects of the Earth's initial and central heat, now internal, on the globe's temperature are less important and show themselves in a discontinuous manner, in the form of volcanoes and other comparable phenomena. The transport of heat has been measured in depth. The places with a more intense energy flow are potential sources of usable energy, so-called geothermic energy; this internal heat also includes the one due to the radioactivity of the crust materials.

The planet's fluid coverings, the oceans and the atmosphere, constitute a penetrable matrix in the heart of which life is developed. Both oceans and atmosphere display common and analogous features, both between them and with the solid part of the earth too, principally because the whole is always broken down into discontinuous masses, at whose borders (limits between plates, marine fronts, and atmospheric fronts), the physical work that leads to the maintenance of life and to the discontinuities of its distribution takes place.

The atmosphere

The atmosphere is made up of oxygen (21% volume), nitrogen (78%) and other gases (1% argon, carbon dioxide, water vapor, and others), and in its quality as a compressible gas shows a gradual decrease in its density as we move further away from the Earth's surface.

The atmosphere also contains water vapor. In normal conditions the pressure of this vapor depends to a large degree on the temperature. The saturation of the atmosphere with water in turn depends on this pres-

	EXTENSION (millions of km^2)	PRECIPITATION (thousands of km^2)	EVAPORATION	DIFFERENCE
Oceans	361	385	425	−40
Continents	149	111	71	+40
All the Earth	510	496	496 (a)	

86 Distribution of water involved in the global exchange between oceans and continents, expressed as thousands of cubic km per annum [(a) equivalent to 973 mm per annum].
[Source: data supplied by the author]

sure: example, for saturation values of 2.16 g/cu. m at 14ºF (-10ºC) and 30.37 g/cu. m at 86ºF (30ºC). As the pressure changes, so the air temperature changes, thus affecting the amount of water that it can retain. This mechanism means that the transport of water through the atmosphere is not a simple thing, and that the separation of water takes place when there is a cooling or an upward movement. In short, the absorption and release of humidity are not symmetrical processes. Condensation is first seen in the formation of clouds, which are also important for regulating the albedo, in other words the reflection of incident solar radiation.

The evaporation of 38 in (973 mm) of water at 68ºF (20ºC) would require 57,700 cal/cm^2/year (7.658 mW per m^2), which is just over a fifth part of the energy received from the Sun. We can thus understand the

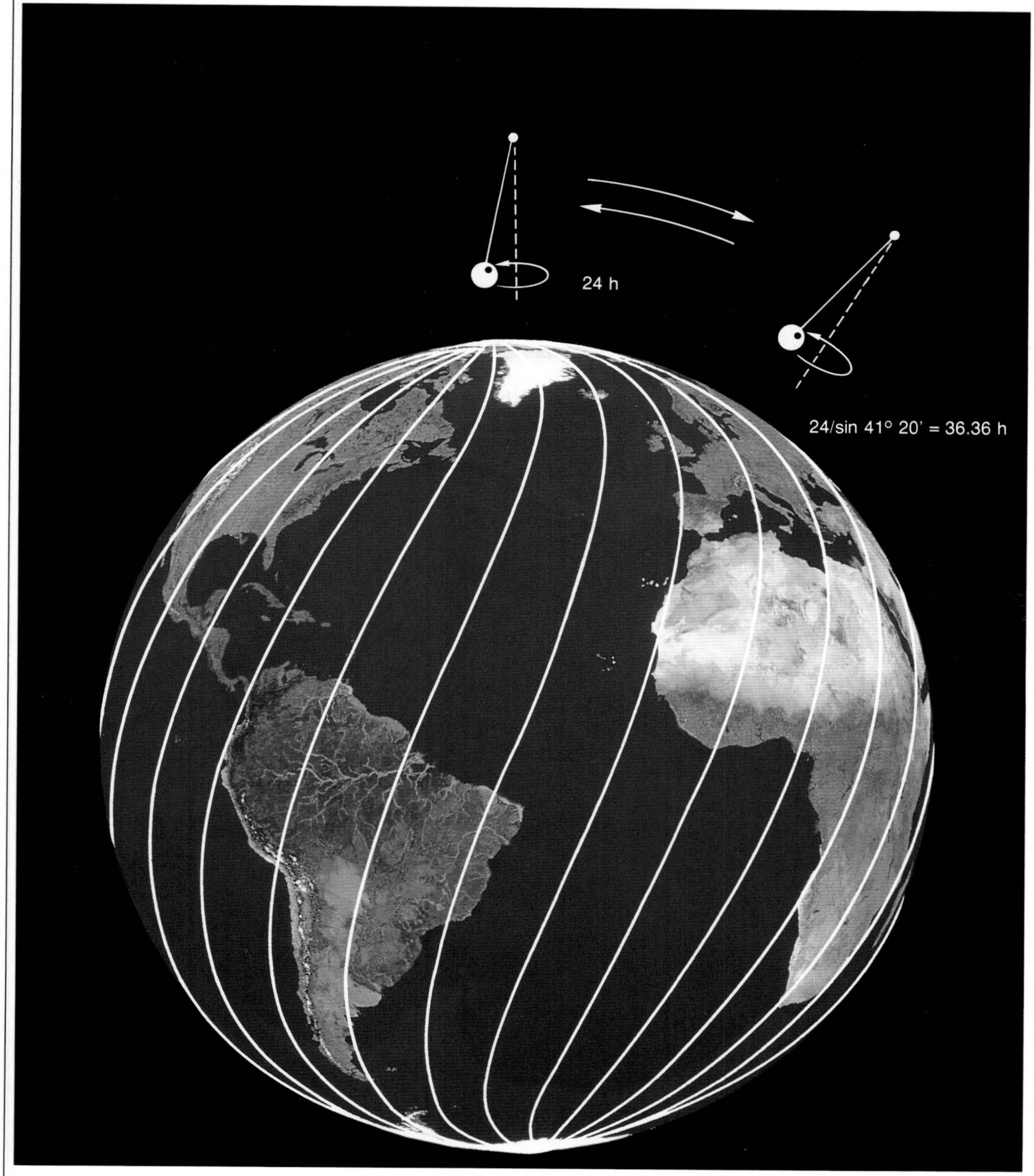

87 The Coriolis force is one of the consequences of the rotation of the Earth and consists of an apparent (but fictitious) acceleration shown by any moving object as experienced by an observer at a fixed point in relation to a rotating system (such as the surface of the Earth). This effect is very apparent in the orbits described by satellites in polar orbit, such as LANDSAT or SPOT. Although the real orbits described by these satellites remain in a constant plane in relation to the axis and solar orbit of the Earth, their apparent orbits deviate. The modification of the plane of oscillation of Foucault's pendulum also obeys this effect, as does the vorticity of the eddies of a liquid. Scarcely noticeable at the equator, the velocity grows with latitude until it reaches its maximum at the poles; and in each hemisphere the apparent trajectories change in opposite directions: they are clockwise in the northern hemisphere and anti-clockwise in the southern hemisphere.
[Photo: AGE Fotostock]

importance that water has for transporting heat and for contributing to the reduction of the temperature differences on the Earth's surface. We can imagine that the air heats up at the equator, picks up humidity there, and then moves towards higher latitudes, where it would leave its heat and water. But this component of circulation is combined with the Earth's rotation (*Coriolis force*), and the result is the breakdown of the globe's atmospheric movement into three circulation cylinders in each hemisphere, the axes of which are approximately parallel to each other, despite certain irregularities and fluctuations (see vol. 10, pages 25-26). One can understand that in larger planets that have an atmosphere, such as Jupiter, the number of "cylinders" has to be greater.

This fundamental circulation scheme results in very rainy areas, where upward movements predominate, and dry regions, where downward movements predominate. The location of these regions, though, is not fixed and has notably changed over time. Another characteristic of the weather are the irregularities that originate in the form of asymmetrical waves between adjacent regions and which in the end produce the atmospheric fronts that so characterise the state of the weather, principally in mid-latitudes in the northern hemisphere, where they have a revitalizing role. The contrast between sudden change and a slower progression, which can be forecast, is characteristic not only of the weather in the temperate zone, but also of most natural changes of ecological interest.

The hydrosphere: seas and oceans

The oceans are connected with the atmosphere through various momentum and heat exchange mechanisms. This exchange takes place on the water's surface, where there are waves and other forms of dragging the denser and more energy-conserving fluid. The wind's force is integrated and regulated. In the transmission of the wind's force to the water, we can observe the effects of the Coriolis force, with the result that in the northern hemisphere the marine current is deflected to the right of the direction of the wind, whereas in the southern hemisphere it is driven to the left. This same diversion is found at increasing depths, with water flowing in directions more to the right until it reaches a depth, known as the Ekman depth, where it moves in a direction that is exactly opposite to that of the wind. This phenomenon, called Ekman's spiral, is vital to the understanding of marine dynamics.

Large scale marine circulation combines the circulation resulting from the distribution of the winds with the effects of changes in density produced by local thermal changes, evaporation, or dilution from rivers or rain. In this way the stratification of the oceans is regulated and varies at a local level according to the density of the water. Extra energy is needed to mix the water vertically and break the established stratification. The tensions resulting from the distribution of masses of water with different densities in the gravitational field automatically adjust themselves to the moments of inertia of the same water in movement. On scales of 60-600 mi (100-1,000 km), both the sea water's characteristics and its movements can be subject to seasonal fluctuations. In accordance with what we said before, the anti-clockwise cyclonic circulation that is caused in the northern hemisphere, and the clockwise in the southern, tend to create whirlpools that divide the surface water in a centrifugal sense and make the deep and generally more nutrient-rich water rise in the center. On the other hand, the anti-cyclonic circuits that rotate clockwise in the northern hemisphere and in the opposite direction in the southern, have the effect of moving the water to the center of the circuit, where a downward movement is produced.

Large scale marine circulation reflects the distribution of the winds, with the modifications just indicated and

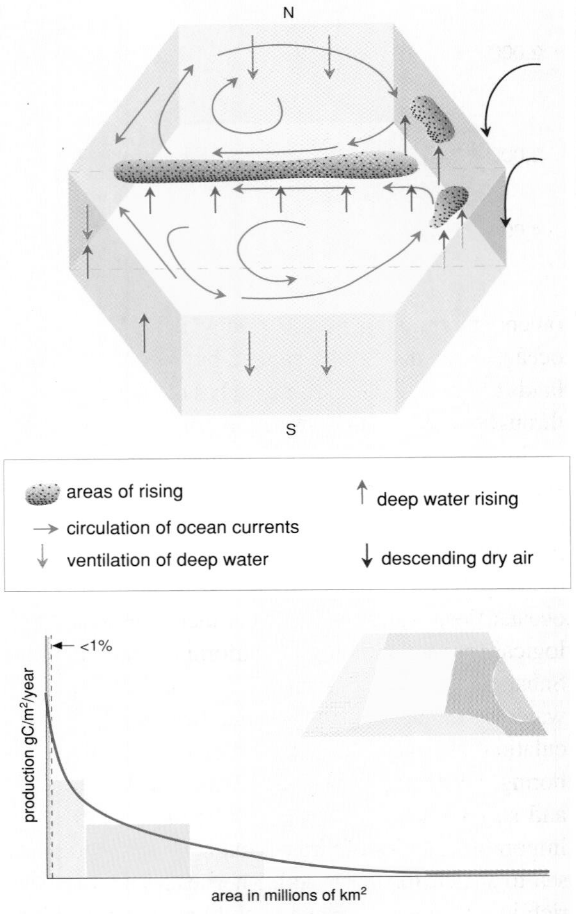

88 The circulation of the waters and the primary production of the oceans basically follows this model. In each hemisphere an anticyclonic circuit, which leaves a mass of not very productive descending water at its center, can be detected. Locally, at different places, due to the particular way in which land and water is distributed, ascending or descending movements occur. The cooling of the waters as one gets nearer polar latitudes leads to a descending circulation that ventilates the deep waters. In the equatorial zone, on the high seas, there is an upwelling. Beside the western edges of the continents of each hemisphere, in areas which represent scarcely 1% of the oceans' surface, the phenomenon of upwelling of deep waters rich in nutrients occurs; the greater part of primary production depends on this. The lower diagram shows the unequal levels of production by the different areas of ocean, and these are shown in schematic form on the right. *[Diagram: Editrònica]*

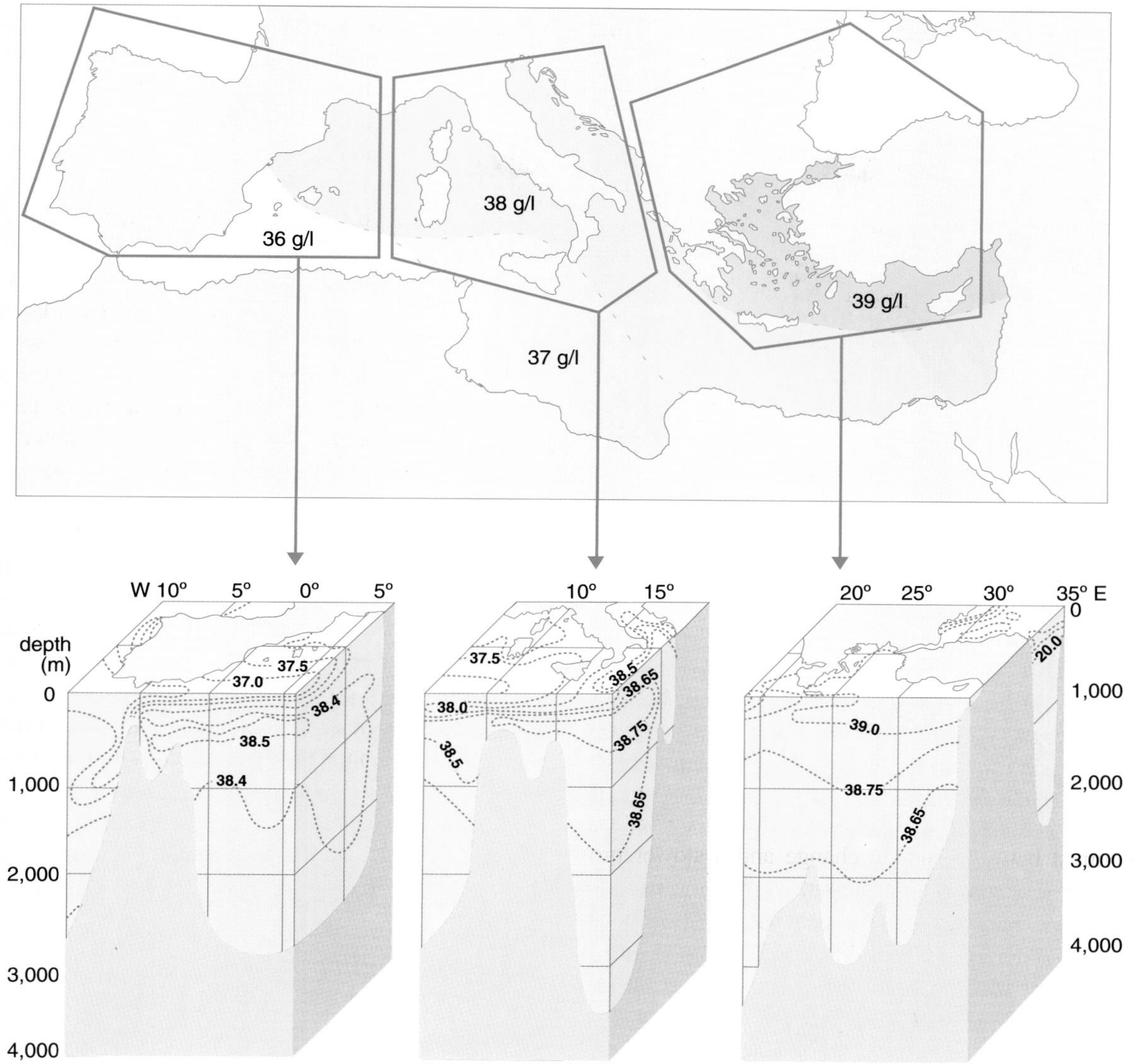

89 In the Mediterranean sea, the quantity of water lost by evaporation is higher than the amount coming from rainfall or rivers. It functions therefore like an inverted estuary. Through the Strait of Gibraltar, shallow Atlantic water comes in and dense deeper water, relatively rich in phosphorus and other nutrients, flows out. The further east, the higher the salinity as shown in these diagrams.
[Diagams: Biopunt, from various sources]

others imposed by the continuity and shape of the ocean limits that are determined by the distribution of lands and seas. This distribution has continually varied throughout the Earth's history. Normally a basic anticyclonic type of circuit is recognized in each hemisphere, which means that the water at the center of the oceans is moving downward and is biologically rather poor. There is also an asymmetry between the east and the west: this means that on the eastern side of the large oceans, deep waters surface near their coasts, and biological production is high (California, Peru, Namibia, Sahara). The rise of deep and relatively cold ocean water in these places means that the atmospheric circulation is for the most part downward on the neighboring coasts: they are areas where it rains very little and so the land is not very fertile; they are home to important colonies of birds, though, which head out to sea to search for their food. Their excrement (guano, rich in nutritious elements, mainly phosphorus, nitrogen, and silicon) deposited on the land slows down somewhat the local marine biological productivity. Between the two hemispheres on the open sea, in the equatorial zone, there is also a rise to the surface because, due to the Coriolis effect, the surface water has a tendency to move toward the respective poles, creating a relatively empty space that is filled by the deeper and more nutritious water moving upward.

As the layout of the continental masses has gradually changed in the course of geological times, the configuration of the oceans and their dynamic properties has been considerably modified as regards anything relating to the proximity of land. All this serves as a very active background for an uninterrupted process of biological evolution.

Ocean water contains a considerable quantity of salts in solution, normally between 34 and 37 g per kg of

90 The processes of formation and destruction of the thermocline in seas and lakes provides a good example of the contrast between slow changes (in this case associated with the formation of the thermocline, which can last several weeks or months) and rapid changes (in this case its destruction, which can be a matter of days or hours).
[Diagram: Biopunt, from data prepared by the author]

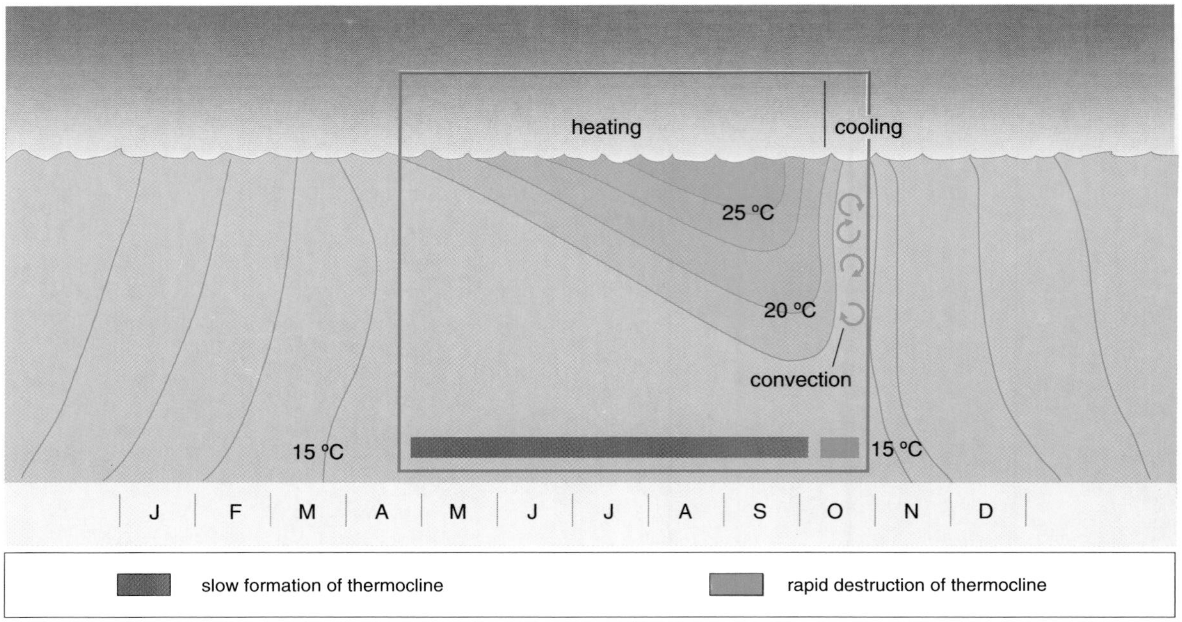

water, or, roughly, per liter or quart. (The density of sea water also varies according to temperature and is around 1.027.) Stability of the water masses demands an increasing density towards the bottom and can vary locally according to the evaporation or dilution conditions. The most important salt is sodium chloride, which accounts for more than 86% of the total, but one can find nearly all the elements in the periodic table, in smaller proportions, in sea water. The dilution and concentration phenomena on a local level can go much further: some five million years ago, the Mediterranean practically dried up, after having been closed off and subjected to an extremely intense net evaporation, which has since remained at chronic levels. Today, if it were not for the water that enters through the Straits of Gibraltar, the sea level of the Mediterranean would drop at a rate of nearly 3 ft (1 m) every year.

Organisms are the most important causes of the partial segregation of particular elements: they assimilate phosphorus, nitrogen, and silicon in the better lit areas of water (roughly in a band stretching from the surface to 300 ft [100 m] below) and then release them at lower levels. This downward movement is continuous and slow, while the return tends to be linked to more sudden and discontinuous upward movements, which are generally uncertain both in time and space.

A similar contrast between slow and sudden change can be found in the thermal regime of seas and lakes. In temperate and polar regions, water heats up slowly from the surface downward, under the Sun's heat. Generally the process stops at a level where the agitation transmitted from the surface does not have enough strength to continue mixing the water against a perceptible thermal gradient, which is also a gradient of density. This level, which becomes persistent, is the thermocline. But when cooling begins in autumn, the water near the surface, whose temperature has gone down and whose density has been increased, moves rapidly downward. This convection movement destroys the thermocline in a much shorter space of time than the one needed for it to form.

1.3 The climate

Climatic elements

Solar radiation that reaches soil level, over the year, reaches a maximum in the eastern Sahara of 920 kJ/cm^2 and a minimum, naturally, at the two poles, of 50 kJ/cm^2. Rainfall distribution is the result of a complex interaction between the average location of the disturbances' trajectories, together with a possible oceanic influence and numerous local circumstances such as height, dominant winds, and so on. Climates are not easily defined: not all the combinations which are in principle possible occur, and proposed classifications, such as the one proposed by the German meteorologist and climatologist, Vladimir P. Köppen (1846-1940), which was very popular, have always been based more on a naturalist's approach and on craftmanship than on a rigorous approach to the subject. Climates are characterized by temperatures, rainfall, and their daily and seasonal fluctuations. The number of combinations that occur is less than the total possible and this explains the empirical nature of these classifications.

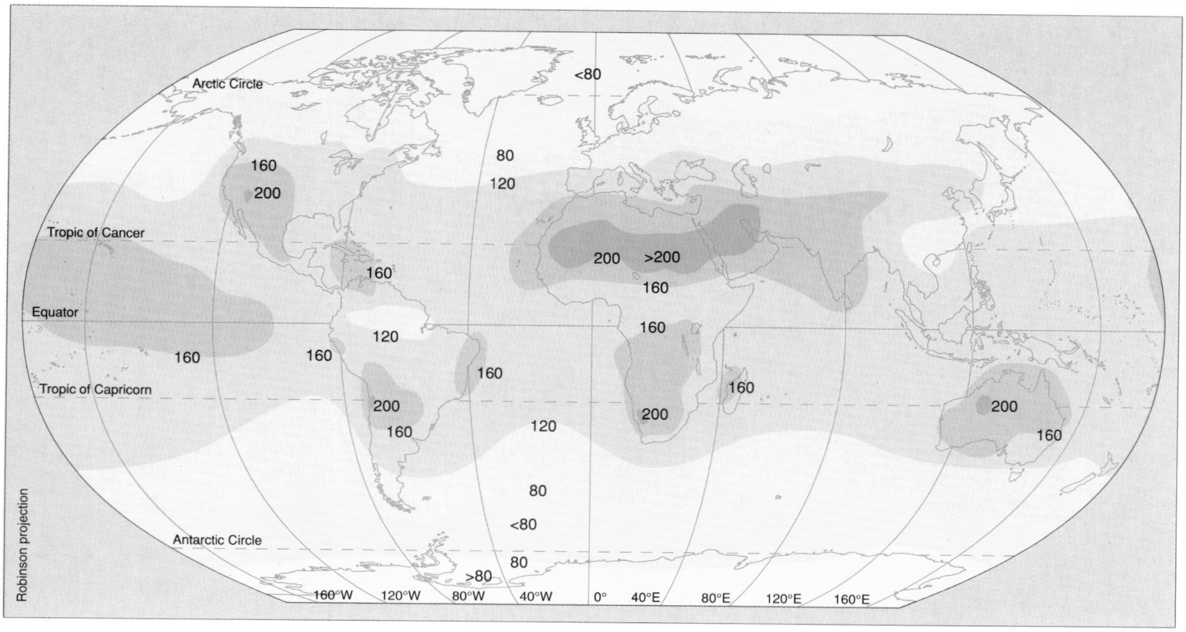

91 World distribution of the intensity of solar radiation at sea level, expressed in kilocalories per square centimeter (1 kc=0.24 kJ). *[Diagram: Editrònica, from various sources]*

The climate changes continually. One could say that the today's climate dates from only 11,000 years ago, the end of the ice ages. Today we have many indications of how the climate has changed progressively at all levels. This has been deduced from the distribution of past organisms, their remains and, recently, often from the relative proportions between the frequencies of isotopes of certain elements (oxygen, carbon). The explanation of these changes is, in part, based on astronomy: the inclination of the Earth's axis, in relation to the axis of the ecliptic, fluctuates roughly 21.8-24.4º in some 40,000 years. These changes have been related to the ice ages. The slight variation in the distance between the Earth and the Sun is less important; the nearest point to the Sun (the perihelion) is reached in January and the furthest (the ephelion) at the beginning of July. The difference is about 7%, and in about 10,000 years the relationships will have been inverted, a circular orbit having been completed. It is against this canvas of changes that an attempt has been made to interpret the signs in the descriptions of present and past climates. But these astronomical causes do not seem to be sufficient, and it is necessary to consider intrinsic regulation mechanisms on the Earth, such as the changes with extent and distribution of land and sea, the effects of life on the atmosphere, and yet more. We are at present wondering if the recent changes can be seen as a simple continuation of the changes of the past or whether they reflect the results of the various human influences or actions (the greenhouse effect among others).

From the point of view of biological production, the fundamental elements of continental climate are the availability of water, which is also the way that elements are brought from the soil, and, if necessary, the number of days that this water cannot be used because of its solid state. We must also include the average temperature and the thermal regime.

The atmosphere does not only allow an important fraction of incoming electromagnetic radiation to pass, but it also filters it, an effect which has been dramatized in the recent stories about the hole in the ozone layer above the Antarctic. The atmosphere selectively absorbs radiation of determined wavelengths according to a known physical interaction. For example, oxygen absorbs radiation below a wavelength of 210 nm. The absorption of these photons makes the formation of ozone molecules (O_3) more probable. These molecules in turn absorb photons in the neighboring area with a longer wavelength, up to 300 nm. This eliminates a large part of short wave radiation that is very energetic, and this is a possible cause of chemical alterations eventually manifesting themselves as mutations, or skin cancers. The absorption of radiation as ozone forms explains the heating of the atmosphere at a height of around 30 mi (50 km) (the *stratopause*), with temperatures around 14°F (-10ºC), contrasting with the *stratosphere*, 6-25 mi (10-40 km) where the temperature drops to below -58°F (-50ºC). In the polar night, new ozone does not form, and part of what was left there continues decomposing through reaction with reactive radicals and molecules, which come from lower latitudes and spread out horizontally in the upper atmosphere. This transportation process is favored by the existing atmospheric circulation, which is more effective at the South Pole. The atmosphere interacts intensely and directly with life, principally on the sur-

92 The variations in temperature and air density with altitude, and in particular their inflection points, determines the division of the atmosphere into regions. The absorption of the shortest wave length radiation by oxygen, which produces ozone molecules, explains the heating of the atmosphere in the upper limit of the stratosphere, around 31 mi (50 km) high, in the so-called stratopause. The most active and dense part of the atmosphere is the troposphere, the lowest level, which is the part in which most of the weather occurs, and that most affects living beings. The upper limit of the troposphere, the tropopause, varies according to latitude (it is highest over the equator where it is found at an altitude of some 11 mi [17 km], and is least over the poles, at 5-6 mi [8-10 km] above the Earth's surface).
[Diagram: Biopunt, from various sources]

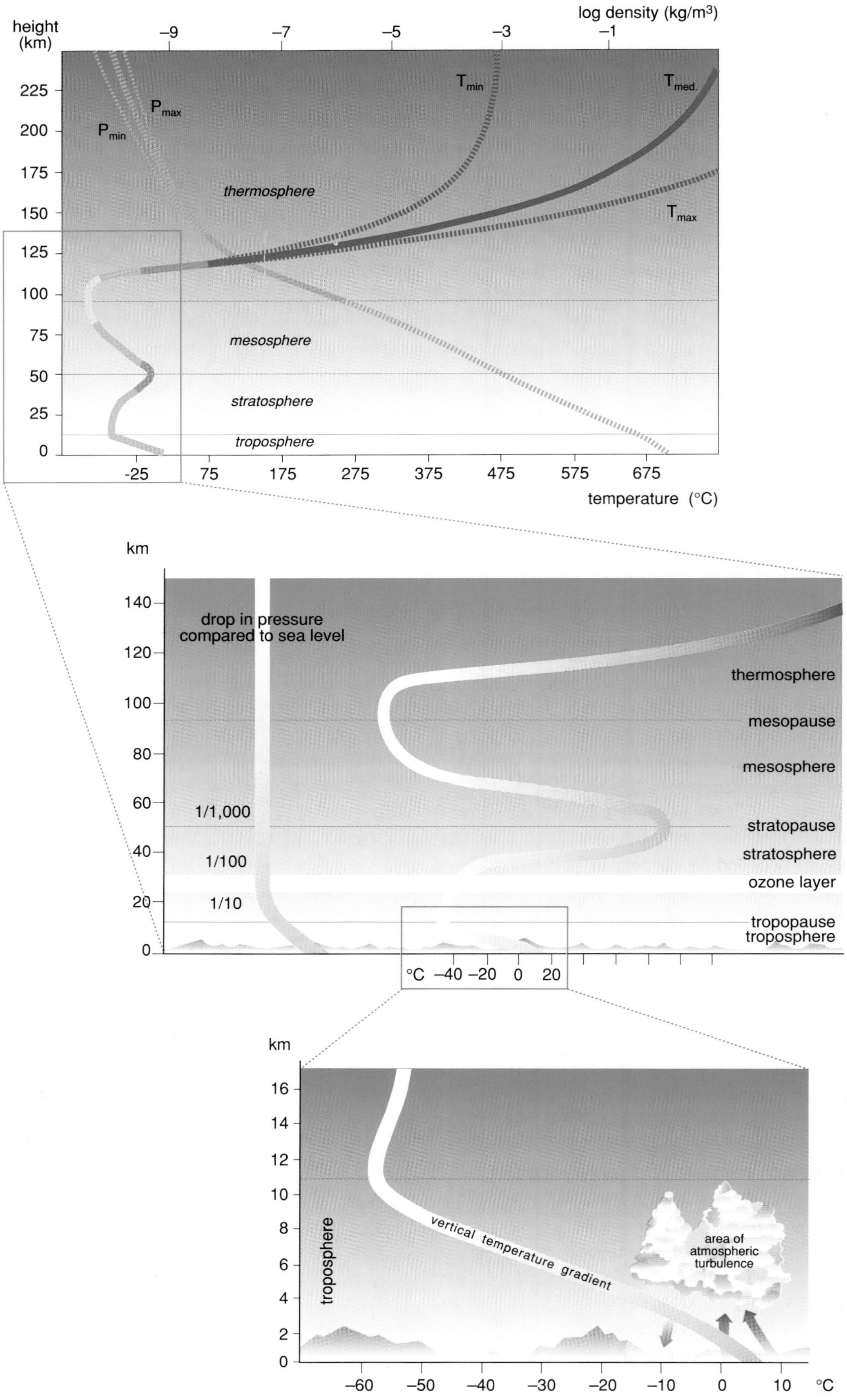

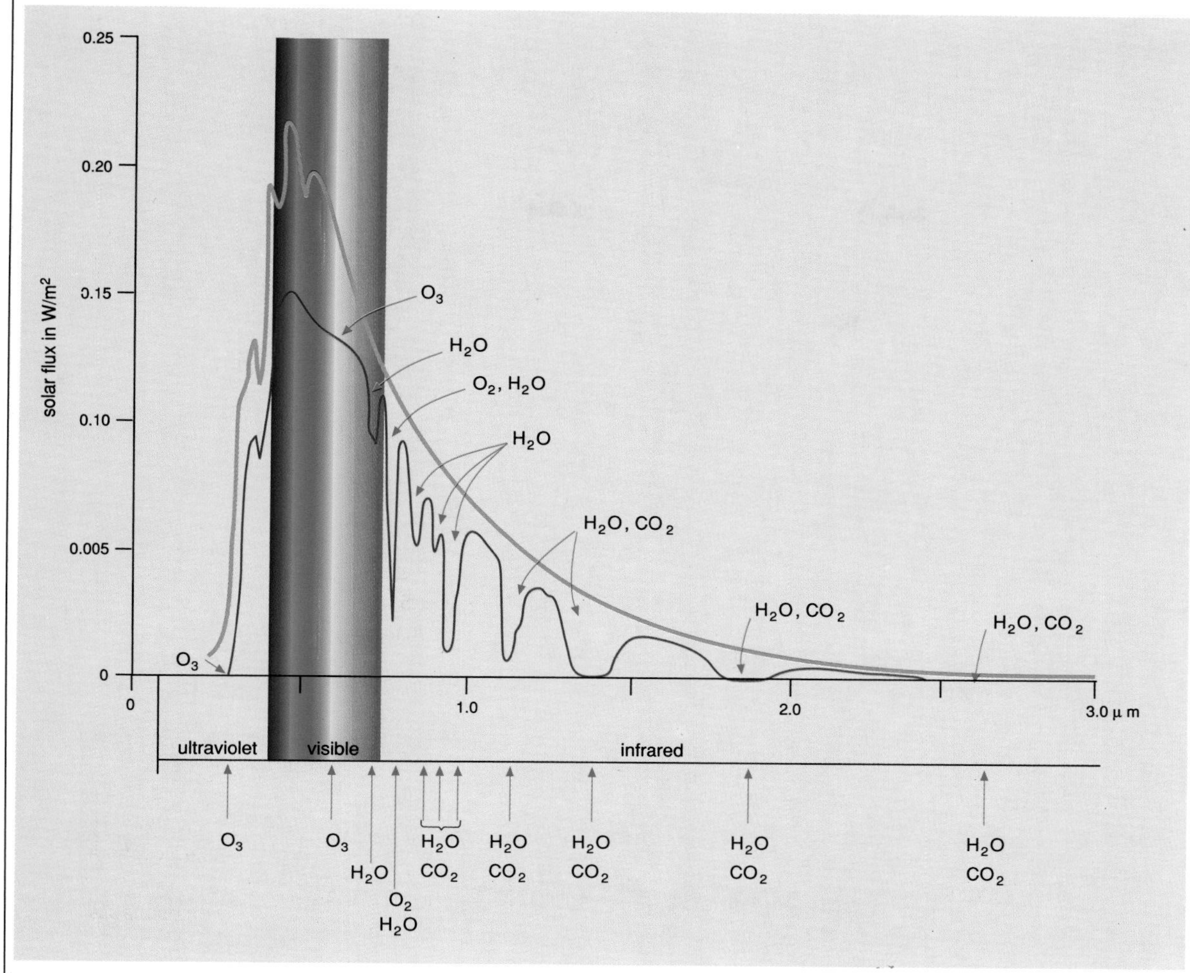

93 The spectrum of solar radiation that reaches the surface of the Earth at sea level (violet) is not the same as that of the radiation which reaches the limit of the atmosphere (red). As shown in the diagram, different atmospheric gases absorb specifically the radiation of certain wavelengths; and thus; filter a part of them. Other gases which are their more by chance, such as methane (CH_4), contribute to the absorption at specific wavelengths.
[Diagram: Editrònica, from various sources]

face of the continents. To see this we only have to contemplate a tree with its branches and leaves stirred by the wind; the exchange of gases at leaf level is thus intensified, and the changes in orientation of the leaves allows the photosynthesis mechanism to operate in an integrated manner. For many organisms, the atmosphere is a busy thoroughfare, and at the same time the setting for extraordinary events of life. Both accidental collisions with airplanes and direct observation from the highest mountain ranges have shown that some large birds often travel at a height of over 26,200 ft (8,000 m): the specialized and intensive respiratory system of birds makes this possible.

Atmospheric weather and forecasting

The desire to forecast the weather has been a constant stimulus for the development of science, and it is encouraging to observe how weather forecasting has advanced. This could be based on a series of observations made at a single location and in which we could recognize, perhaps, a certain periodicity in relation to other natural clocks (the year, lunar phases). We can also find locally characteristic sequences of weather conditions: these phenomena, which are repeated irregularly (such as those associated with the passing over of fronts), although they still cannot be predicted, do occur on a more or less regular basis. It is also possible to get an approximate idea of the frequency with which the fronts come according to the seasons and the speed with which they move from west to east.

The second method of weather forecasting is synoptical and requires the creation of a network of observations and the possibility of being able to transmit the information quickly. This basically allows us to recognize fields of atmospheric pressure, with which we can associate gradient winds, revolving, in the northern hemisphere, around centers of high pressure in a clockwise direction (anticyclones) or around centers of low pressure in an anticlockwise direction, with the reverse happening in the southern hemisphere. Weather conditions move, maintaining certain relationships between their parts, and there are structures more resistant to displacement than others. Thus, for example, there are very persistent areas of high pressure and masses of cold air above large continental land masses.

94 Meteorological satellites have accustomed us to observe directly (when speeded up) changes in the weather and the movement of atmospheric disturbances over large areas of the Earth's surface, as in this sequence of six images taken by the METEOSAT satellite above the Western Mediterranean basin at 11:55 GMT on October 16, 1988. *[Photo: European Space Agency (ESA)]*

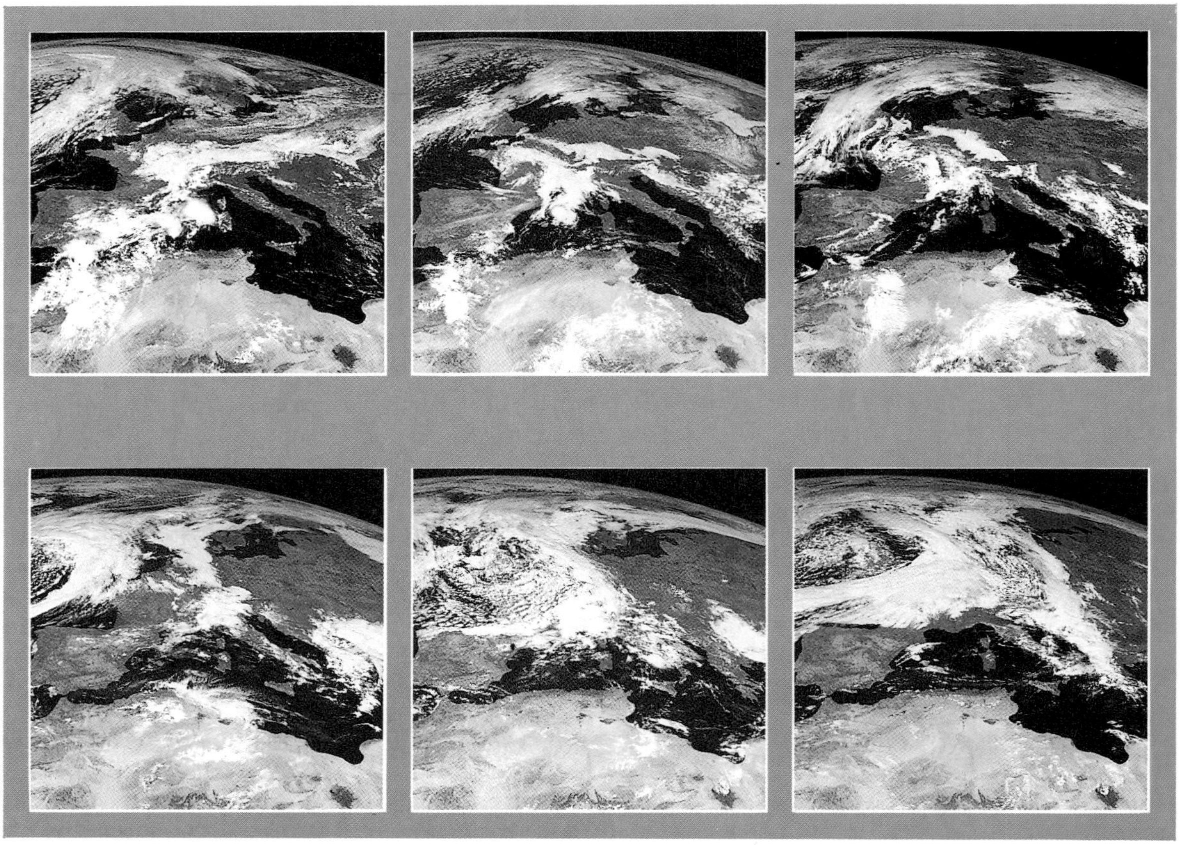

In the past, the fluctuations that a local observer noticed came to be seen as integral parts of more regular systems following particular paths. For example, over the Iberian Peninsula, weather conditions observed in the extreme west can be found again after about 20 hours on the Mediterranean coast, even though they markedly changed or evolved. On the other hand, when the weather (the wind) comes from the east, through some local disturbance, prediction becomes more difficult (and even more so because of our current lack of knowledge on the matter). This form of forecasting never managed to analyze sufficiently deeply the tendency of weather conditions to "curl up" on themselves as they move along. The word is appropriate because it refers to vorticity, measure of the circular motion of air relative to the Earth's axis. As there are many satellites that are spinning around the Earth, this effect is easier to understand: all one has to do is to project the trajectories of a satellite turning on a meridian plane onto a classroom globe or map.

Today it seems that it is not even necessary to make so many calculations. Clouds are the great indicators of atmospheric dynamics, almost in the same way that little bubbles show the trajectories of ionizing particles in a vapor or hydrogen chamber. The atmospheric images that satellites constantly supply us with allow us to follow faithfully the global evolution of weather conditions. If we have a sequence of weather charts at hand, we can treat them like images taken in slow motion and project them between 1,000 and 10,000 times faster than real time. In these conditions, one can clearly see on the screen the dynamics of the disturbances: we can see how the temperate Nordic region enjoys pretty regular fronts, which act as a stimulus at all levels of the biosphere. This contrasts with less marked, and perhaps more irregular, changes of short duration in the southern hemisphere and the tropics.

It is even more revealing to do the same projection the other way round. Starting with disturbances that are well formed, or are dying out in rain, we go back in time until we can locate the origin of the disturbances that, in favorable conditions, can be seen as a small dot. It has become a cliché to say that a butterfly flapping its wings at a low latitude could have generated a tropical cyclone, to indicate that a whole host of unpredictable consequences can derive from an extremely small cause, and there are even mathematical arguments to back this up. This refers to a chaotic dynamic combined with vorticity, which would amplify small disturbances. Maybe it is true that, despite all efforts, one cannot forecast the weather in detail. The unpredictability of the weather is, perhaps, simply due to one aspect of nature's inscrutability. It makes it difficult to imagine a system of equations, no matter how many variables it may contain (four or eight, it does not matter), which would give a determinist solution. There could be an element of mathematical chaos that introduces unforeseen factors. However, it is some consolation that meteorologists feel justified doing a job that involves a bit of wizardry. The positive part of the difficulty has to be seen as a sign that the world is not closed and that it can surprise us at any time with beautiful things. The scientific desire to rationalize it, though, will never die out.

1.4 The very fine and torn film of life

The biosphere

There is a very direct connection among the natural peripheral coverings of the Earth, known as the atmosphere, hydrosphere, and lithosphere, and that subtle spider's web that grows there in contact with them, which we call the biosphere, and which is the central theme of this work. The meaning of most words changes more or less with use. Thus the man who coined the term biosphere in 1875, the Austrian geologist Eduard Suess (1831-1914), was probably simply looking for a "consonant" in a classification of the "spheres" of the Earth's surface. Everything that begins by being a classification can end up being the origin of a rational science. If we give primacy to life in general, and especially to humans, without losing sight of the links with other aspects of the Earth, we come closer to a concept of the biosphere in the sense that Vladimir I. Vernadsky (1863-1945) understood the word, closer to the way it is generally used today. The concept of the biosphere has been renewed and has acquired a new vitality that has made the word very much more common in the media.

The biosphere has operated chemically in a simple and unequivocal manner: it has oxidized upward and reduced downward, and this is especially apparent when we observe the accumulation of dead organic material in the lower part. The expected atmosphere on a planet like Earth would have to contain more CO_2 and be more reducing than the present one in a chemical sense. There is evidence that it was like this in the beginning, but there are also signs that it started oxidizing relatively early, when abundant iron oxide was deposited on the Earth's surface. This oxidation of the atmosphere is the result of the activity of life that takes CO_2 and possibly ammonia and releases molecular nitrogen and oxygen. The activity of organisms can be seen on the surface of rocks: it is evident in the chemistry of the solid crust and is also reflected more indirectly in the composition of sea water. Both the reaction of silicates with water and carbon dioxide and the global cycle of transformations in which carbonates take part, remain under the influence of life. Both silicates and carbonates work as buffers to maintain the pH of natural waters within a relatively narrow scope of variation, about 8.3 in the oceans, and generally a little lower in soil water and fresh water. There are, then, reasons for believing that the continuous reaction of living

95 The Russian chemist and mineralogist Vladimir Ivanovich Vernadski (1863-1945) was the first to develop the concept of the *biosphere*, which he defined as that special region of the Earth's crust in which life is found. The latter being considered an indivisible assemblage bound to the biosphere. The photograph was taken in Paris in 1925 when he was preparing the manuscript of the first edition of *Biosphere* (1926), his principal work.
[Photo: University of Moscow]

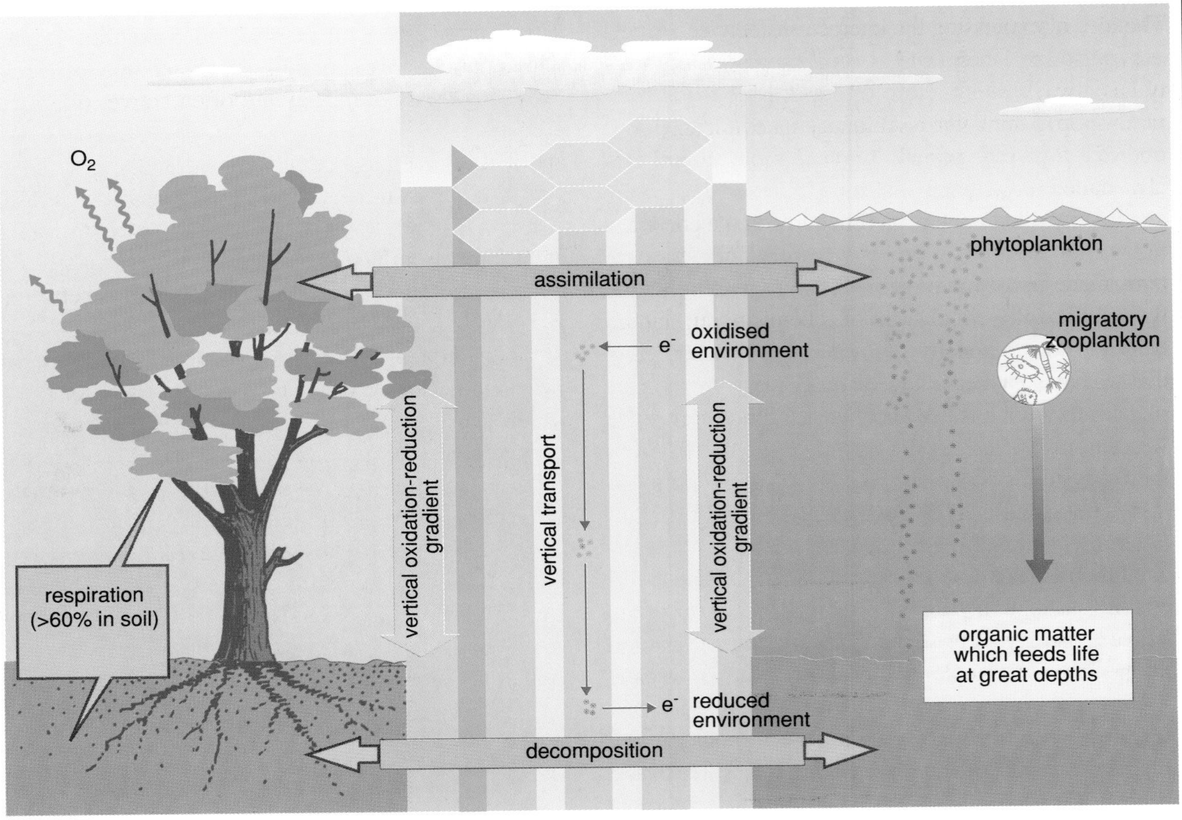

96 In aquatic as in terrestrial ecosystems, each column that can be delimited behaves as a more functionally integrated unit than it, or any of its parts, is with the entities that surround it laterally. There is always an upper level (canopy in forests, herbaceous layer in meadows, phytoplankton in water) with oxidized surroundings in which assimilation predominates; vertical transport (by the vessels in vascular plants, by sedimentation of the phytoplankton in aquatic environments) of the products of assimilation. There is also always lower level (the soil in terrestrial ecosystems, sediment in aquatic ecosystems) in a reduced environment, in which decomposition predominates. Lateral exchanges are limited, practically, to the movements of animals—from zooplankton to large herbivores and carnivores. *[Diagram: Biopunt, from various sources]*

beings with their environment has forced some of the environment's characteristics to converge toward values that vary relatively little.

Why has life created species and individuals? We might contemplate the hypothesis of a continuous layer of life, not necessarily divided up into organisms, covering the whole Earth as a continuous and completely active membrane. But if there has been some attempt to adopt this model of life, the truth is that there is no evidence of this, and we have found remains of now extinct organisms dating back more than 3,000 million years. Perhaps this is because those now-extinct organisms allowed a more rapid evolution and made better use of solar energy. The Earth would not have been the same without life, nor would life have been able to originate on a planet with characteristics far removed from those our planet initially had.

Ecosystems

The word *ecosystem*, along with the word biosphere, is now part of our everyday speech. We can think of an ecosystem as a subdivision of the biosphere that can be studied as a functional unit and defined by its distribution, physiognomy, particular climatic conditions, and its properties of biomass and production. Ecosystem is a unit that is practically equivalent to others, like community, biocenosis, biome, and so on, that have been proposed. Some of these represent concepts that geographers already use in their study of landscapes. Both the enormous variation in the composition of natural communities, and the difficulty in tracing the limits between one type and another, can be seen in not very constructive disagreements towards the end of the first quarter of the 20th century. A British ecologist, Arthur G. Tansley (1871-1955), proposed the word *ecosystem* to refer to a certain level of organization. An ecosystem consists of many individuals of different species who live together in a common physical environment in which their functions are complementary to a variable degree. The word ecosystem was well received because it includes a reference to system, a concept that was beginning to be fashionable. It is appropriate that each science can indicate the structural or organizational level of the phenomena it studies. In this sense, ecosystem gives an appropriate idea of where the interest of ecology is focused.

The composition of the biosphere and that of ecosystems are subject to endless historical changes. Evolution has progressively enriched the biosphere with more species with new properties. Other species have become extinct. But it is very likely that the way in which ecosystems have been grouped together and the forces that operate on them have not changed greatly.

The idea of expressing the interactions between different species and their state of equilibrium quantitatively has always been a great dream of ecologists. They rarely stop to think that a stationary state probably does not exist for a long period of time, what was traditionally called *ecological equilibrium*. Nowadays, the availability of computers has encouraged the construction of models to explore and simulate how ecosystems made up of many species function, or to model the predictable circulation of chemical substances between conventionally defined compartments. Now that we have reached a stage where we have very complicated expressions, we are always falling short, since we can only include in our models a small fraction of the ecosystem's observable complexity. But this exercise is not completely useless, even though the predictions rarely prove to be accurate. We have not managed to grasp the essence of these ecological phenomena: it is as though we were looking at the order of the heavens as they were seen in Ptolemy's time, waiting all the time for a Kepler or a Newton to appear to clarify our confusion, a confusion that arises from the multiplicity of points of view that are possible. Perhaps the biosphere is intrinsically very complex, even to the point of being confusing for us to understand. In any case, we must wait until more substantial constants are found than those we have today.

Ecotones

The old problem of defining biocenoses, communities, or types of ecosystems has not disappeared: it persists at least in such practical tasks as making maps, which are indispensable when making decisions in applied ecology. They are also necessary to locate and simplify in an appropriate manner all the data that come to us from remote sensors installed in planes or in space satellites. The needs that derive from this lead us to use only boundaries on the surface of the Earth, to separate some segments of the biosphere from others. Certainly there are also vertical differences in the biosphere, which are especially evident in the oceans, but it should be recognized from now on that every ecosystem column behaves more as a functionally integrated unit within itself than in relation to entities adjoining it.

Differences in the horizontal plane lead to the tracing of frontiers or limits, lines that join points in which the gradients are at their maximum and, precisely, perpendicular to the frontier at that particular place. These are known as *ecotones*. Natural space is receptive to a kind of organization that is as rich or more so than that of the old district of a city. There are boundaries that have a tendency to be well marked, often rectilinear, and with a fair degree of contrast, corresponding to places under high pressure. They are often active: one part exploits that situated on the other side of the boundary. This is the case of the boundary between taiga and tundra; some height boundaries, like those between high mountains and snow; those which separate forest from open land, especially on the edge of tropical rain forests; and, naturally, the limits between land and water in rivers, lakes and seas. They also occur, in human affairs, in the borders guarded by police and customs officials. More sinuous frontiers, which vanish and become lost in a confused intersection of gradients, characterize old landscapes between similar ecosystems, which represent small nuances of adaptation to only slightly differing environmental situations. The natural evolution of nature leads, in the majority of cases, to a blurring of boundaries and to the transformation of straight lines into more sinuous lines, all of which reduces tension. Any violent action, and especially the actions of humans, favors the return to straighter frontiers.

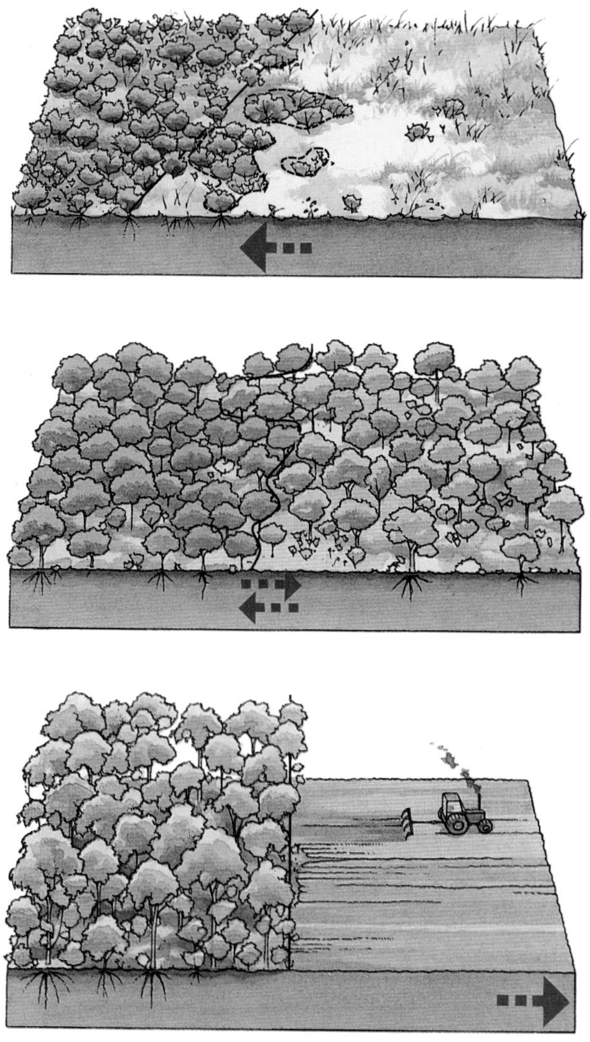

97 The three frontiers or ecotones in the diagram represent three different situations. Above, a well-marked boundary as there might be between a wood and a clearing or an abandoned field; the tendency of the more mature ecosystem to exploit the less developed one involves the progressive colonization of the latter by species from the former, and the change to a wavy boundary, which reduces tensions. The second example (in the middle) is that of two distinct ecosystems with articulated and wavy boundaries, between which the exchanges are in equilibrium. The third example (below), is one of a straight-edged boundary maintained forcibly by human exploitation; which prevents any colonization by species from surrounding ecosystems, and which exports all the production to more or less distant urban centers.
[Diagram: Biopunt, from data prepared by the author]

2. The material of live

2.1 The elements of life

The chemical components of life

Life is based on material structures and stubbornly increases in complexity. Living systems have achieved a considerable improvement, gaining organization in exchange for the expenditure of energy that cannot be recovered. The great wealth of ever-changing structures, characteristic of life, would not necessarily have to be linked to a very precise material nature. But in fact, chemical elements began the process. Certain classes of atoms enter more easily than others in a process of material complexity. As we do not know of life beyond Earth, we do not know, and perhaps never will, if another point of departure could have been taken using more or less different materials.

Six elements (carbon, hydrogen, nitrogen, oxygen, phosphorus, and sulfur) account for more than 99% of the weight of living cells. The predominant atoms are those with a low atomic number and weight.

The material substrate in which vital phenomena take place contains a lot of water and carbon. In its liquid state, water is an excellent support. Its molecular structure is extraordinary, as it is made from polar molecules that give it some important properties, among which is that of being able to convert water into a very effective solvent. Furthermore, water forms groups of molecules, in such a way that, unexpectedly, it is a liquid with a relatively high density. The water molecule measures just over 2 angstroms [1 angstrom (Å)=0.1 nm=10^{-10} m]; this measurement helps to give an idea of the degree of miniaturization in the constitution of life.

ELEMENT	ATOMIC WEIGHT	% OF WEIGHT OF HUMAN BODY
Oxygen (O)	16	640
Carbon (C)	12	185
Hydrogen (H)	1	99
Nitrogen (N)	14	26
Calcium (Ca)	40	25
Phosphorous (P)	31	11
Chlorine (Cl)	35	1.6
Sulphur (S)	32	1.4
Sodium (Na)	23	1
Potassium (K)	39	1
Magnesium (Mg)	24	0.7
Iron (Fe)	56	0.1

98 Main chemical components of the human body. The list—to which one has to add small quantities of aluminium, arsenic, boron, bromine, copper, fluoride, iodine, manganese, silicon and zinc—gives the weight in parts per thousand of the elements that make up the human body. The example has been chosen as representative of living matter; the atomic weights are those of the commonest isotopes of each element. *[Source: the author]*

Around three quarters of all living matter is made up of water. The approximate proportion of carbon, nitrogen, and phosphorous proposed by the American biologist Alfred C. Redfield (1890-1983) applies to the rest, though it referred initially to the average composition of marine plankton, which, in terms of atoms, is 106C:16N:1P. Bearing in mind the respective atomic weights (12, 14, 31) of the elements concerned, the recalculated proportions in weight are nearer 41:2.6:1. This relationship is only for guidance, but is worth remembering and useful when trying to see if the environment's composition is favorable to life or where the supply could fail. When there are deviations, it is generally an excess quantity of carbon that tends to occur in land vegetation, where wood contains a great deal of carbon and a lot less nitrogen and phosphorous.

Carbon

An estimate of the total amount of carbon in the biosphere could come out at between half a kilogram and one kilogram (1-2 lbs) of carbon per cubic meter (35 cu ft), not counting humus or dead organic matter (the necrosphere), but including materials that it is not easy to decide if they are alive or not. It is comparable to the reserve of atmospheric carbon in the form of CO_2, which is also around 1 kg/m^2. (Remember that by multiplying atmospheric pressure [10^4 bars] by the CO_2 concentration [in volume] by the factor to convert carbon from volume to weight [the same as 10,197 x 0.00035 x 12/44] we get 2.1 pounds, or 0.97 kg.)

Carbon atoms join to form highly varied molecular frameworks, generally in the form of chains or rings. Recently, other unpublished variants have been discovered in the laboratory that add even more structural possibilities: like footballs or tubes of indeterminate length. The distance between the center of each consecutive atom is of the order of 0.1 nm. Around a tenth part of the total weight and roughly 40% of the weight of dry matter of organisms is carbon. The chains or rings made from carbon atoms, which are both stable and constant, have free valences, which join up with other atoms and groups of atoms with very different functions. Plastics, which are now so widely used, are based on the properties of the molecules that have a carbon skeleton. Life has taken even more advantage of this than human technology: abundant water and carbon, and a temperature that means most of the biosphere's water is in liquid form, together with a suitable climate of electromagnetic radiation, constituted the Earth's best offer as a possible scenario for life.

Water

About three-quarters of the mass of all living things (the biomass) is made up of water. This quantity includes water in whatever state, whether liquid or semisolid water, which strongly binds to the molecules of living matter, and also the water that is equivalent to the oxygen and hydrogen forming parts of organic molecules.

Nitrogen

Other chemical elements have become acceptable to life systems and contribute to them with the peculiar properties of their atoms. Nitrogen is notable for the variety of states of oxidation-reduction (nitrate and nitric acid, nitrite, ammonia, and elemental nitrogen in gaseous form or dinitrogen). Nitrogen is abundant on Earth and is somewhat volatile. At present the atmosphere contains four-fifths nitrogen gases. Of the two elements that generally limit the growth of organisms, nitrogen is recycled principally between the biosphere and the atmosphere, while phosphorus is recycled more significantly between the biosphere and the solid part of the Earth. These two elements are traditionally found in fertilizer mixtures.

Nitrogen, together with carbon and the components of water, make up the molecules of the so-called amino acids, because the duality of their functions facilitates their union in chains. Some amino acids also contain sulfur. With a special profusion, life uses a little over two dozen forms of amino acids which, individually, are relatively stable. These amino acids can easily join together with each other with relatively mobile bonds. In the same way that a limited number of letters, roughly the same number as amino acids, are used to spell an infinite number of words, so we can build almost an infinite number of proteins from common amino acids. The analogy goes even further, because proteins have more in common with words; they are like the words of life, the carriers of an almost limitless amount of information, based on a very effective alphabet. Proteins perform a wide variety of tasks, and they are excellent catalysts, in other words, enzymes. The great variety of three dimensional shapes they allow, especially those with a high molecular weight (consisting of hundreds of amino acids), gives them the capacity to organize particular surroundings, and to situate various functional groups in a opportune way, which predisposes them to function as enzymes. There are also many proteins that have a structural function, and all follow the plan of modular construction that we find on so many levels in nature.

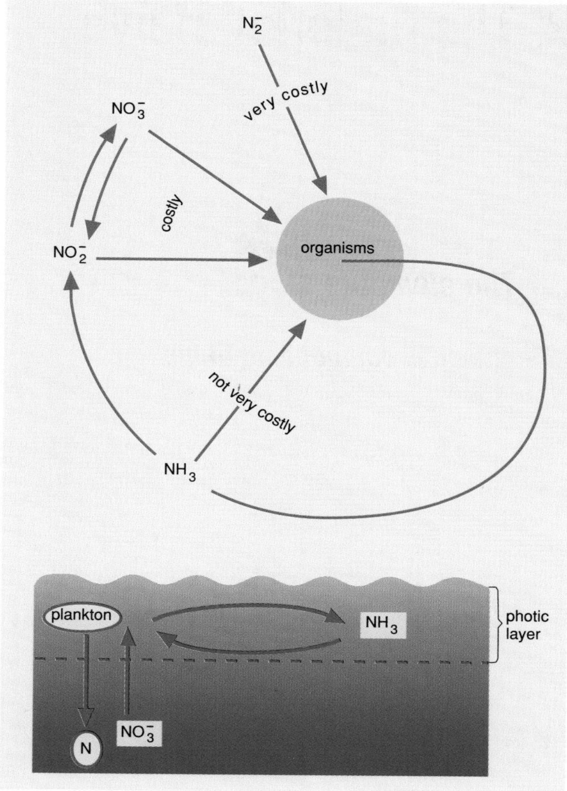

99 The entry of nitrogen into organisms has a different energetic cost depending on the form in which it occurs. When this is in the form of ammonia (NH_3) it is less costly than if it were in the form of nitrite (NO_2^-) or nitrate (NO_3^-). The most expensive form in energetic terms is that of gaseous atmospheric nitrogen (N_2). The recycling of nitrogen (which takes place, for example in the upper layers of the oceans) is largely in the form of ammonia.
[Diagram: Editrònica, based on data supplied by the author]

Phosphorus

Phosphorus is another element that is essential for life. In organisms, it is found in its oxidized form as phosphoric acid and phosphates and has important functions: it can be the essential component of very effective molecules for storing energy in relatively flexible bonds that act as accumulators and transporters of energy. The best known ones are the adenosine phosphates (AMP, ADP, ATP, adenosine monophosphate, diphosphate, and triphosphate respectively; the second and third are important intercellular accumulators). Phosphate associated with sugars and nitrogenous bases are the main component of nucleotides, molecules carrying information essential for life.

While nitrogen is volatile, as it has more affinity for the atmosphere and its compounds are soluble in water, phosphorus easily forms very insoluble compounds. Among them there are the combinations with

100 The phosphorus and nitrogen cycles behave in a different way in an oligotrophic lake than in a eutrophic one. In an oligotrophic lake, while in the nitrogen cycle, the passage from air to water predominates. In the phosphorus cycle, the passage from sediment to water predominates. If the lake receives a large dose of nutrients and becomes eutrophic, the nitrogen cycle tends to move upwards, with a net loss of nitrogen, while the phosphorus cycle tends to move downwards with a net loss of phosphorus, which joins the sediment. *[Diagram: Editrònica, from data supplied by the author]*

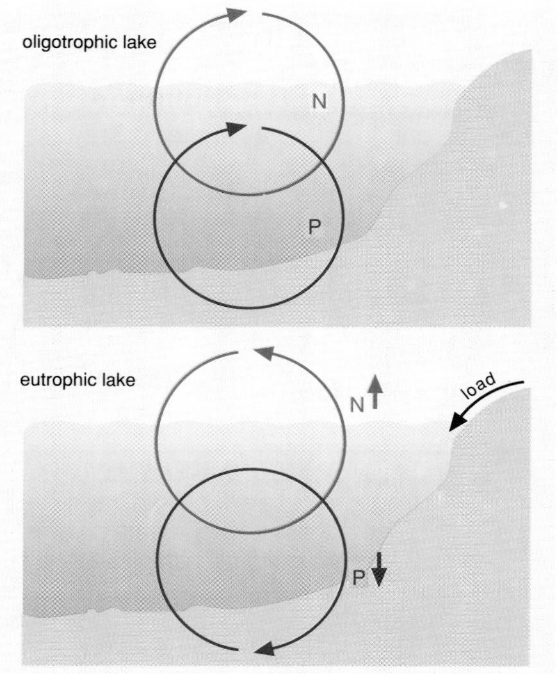

calcium (apatite), which become even more insoluble when fluorine is added. For example, in tooth enamel, the effects of a lack of fluorine increase the likelihood that they will dissolve under the combined metabolic action of microorganisms causing dental plaque. Phosphorus prefers to move between the liquid and solid medium, in sediments and soils. It has become absolutely necessary for life.

Minor elements

Since life began, and throughout its evolution, other chemical elements have been recruited. Sulfur is an important and essential element; it is present in several amino acids. Other frequent elements (sodium, potassium, chlorine, calcium) are part of the basic mechanisms of the acid-base balance and of transport systems. Others, like silicon and calcium itself, together with magnesium and strontium, make rigid skeletons, among other functions. Metals like iron, which easily change their chemical valency, can exchange electrons with considerable ease. It is as if various available chemical elements have been locating themselves within the mechanism of life: performers finding their places in the orchestra.

These and other elements can appear accidentally, in an erratic way, without performing a specific or necessary function. They actually could be toxic if they found means of becoming concentrated in certain surroundings from which they pass into organisms, as is presently happening with many industrial products. This contamination is not new, nor exclusive to the present day. One could view the chemical aspect of evolution as a fairly opportunist adventure, an uninterrupted process of trial and error in appropriating certain chemical elements and adding them to certain functions that have always been oriented toward enriching their information capacity.

The architecture of living molecules

Living molecular complexes have certain common traits in their structure and behavior. For example, they have a marked tendency to maintain their structure, and they obey certain proportions between structural complexity and their size.

Molecules and persistence

Some of the organic molecules formed and managed by life become extraordinarily persistent. This is the case of deoxyribonucleic acids (DNA): we have all heard something about fossil DNA. It is just one aspect of a more general and very important question. *Biomass* refers to the matter of living organisms. We could speak of *necromass* to refer to materials synthesized through life processes, but are now dead and can remain in that state for a very long time.

There are many molecules that spend more time dead than alive. One example of this is the components of wood. Wood contains cellulose, which is made up of sugar molecules linked in such a way that they form a semicrystalline structure that is very difficult to decompose through the action of common enzymes in the environment in which living organisms are found. Wood also contains lignin, whose ring-shaped molecules are chemically very resistant and contain nitrogen and other elements. Wood is a good example of the transition between matter devoid of active life and living material, a transition that can be observed around the region of the cambium, the area of the trunk where the wood grows inward and the bark outward. In petroleum, there are persistent chains of hydrocarbons that were produced by organisms tens to hundreds of million years ago, and which continue to conserve, in their interatomic bonds, the Sun's energy from that time. It is this energy that we break down today for the multiple uses that our civilization makes of petroleum.

Dimension and structure

The fixed dimensions of atoms and molecules define the scale of construction of organisms. All cellular functions need clearly defined dimensions to manifest themselves. The cellular nucleus has a minimal size defined by the quantity of DNA and by the accessory systems that are necessary for its workings. Analogous limitations are found in the structure of the cell membrane (in which the intervention of lipids

101 The wood of tree trunks, especially of tropical ones, and combustible fossil fuels, share the common character of organic molecules that are no longer living but possess very strong and energy-rich bonds. They form part of the *necromass*, which conserves in its bonds energy captured from the sun in the past (the near past in the case of wood, the remote past in the case of petroleum) by living organisms. This is no longer living matter but nonetheless durable.
[Photos: Abbas-Magnum / Zardoya and Bruno Barbey-Magnum / Zardoya]

is important, and which contains special passages or transport channels), in muscular fibers, etc.

Viruses do not have the necessary mechanism to replicate themselves, but they do conserve reproducible material: they measure a fraction of a micromillimeter (0.05-0.2 μm) and are the smallest living structures. There are always free viruses in all ecosystems, and they are found in very high concentrations, as recent systematic analyses carried out in fresh and sea water have shown. Our knowledge of them is much more limited when it comes to soils.

Apart from exceptionally long cells, such as neurons and some others, cellular dimensions generally fall between 5 and 50 μm, and the upper limit to the size of organisms is also limited, for other reasons that will later become clear. The blue whale (*Balaemoptera musculus*), which weighs up to 150 tons, is the largest known animal from either the past or present. The degree of quantification of life is more important than one would suppose for the understanding of how the biosphere works. It defines, for example, the type of coupling between material fluxes and population dynamics. Transfers of material between different parts of ecosystems can be compared more to a dripping tap than to a steady flow. This contributes toward preventing equilibrium in partial systems between which an exchange is established (organisms or groups of organisms).

2.2 Nutrient paths: closed circuit, open circuit

Deposits and flows

In any material appreciation of the biosphere, we can distinguish between deposits and flows. Some time ago an attempt was made to evaluate them on a global or planetary scale, but for several reasons this can never really be exact. Perhaps there is more urgency now because of concern over the probable increase in the concentration of CO_2 in the atmosphere; however, it is worth pointing out that it is speculation rather than accurate study that has been more frequent. Water and its components are important, but as limiting components they come in second place. We can estimate the quantity of carbon in several parts of the Earth's periphery. The quantities of other important elements related to life (nitrogen, phosphorus) are even more difficult to estimate accurately.

The biosphere's organization can be conceptualized by constructing a model made of boxes, each one of which represents an important or definable reservoir or container, like the upper layers of the sea, the soil, and so on. The flows between one reservoir and another can be symbolized with arrows, and attempts are made to quantify and express them in units of time. With these data, and if a stationary state were acceptable, we could assign an average length of permanence to the material in each recipient. In reality, the contents fluctuate, and the flows between the containers speed up and slow down. Even though several elements can migrate in a parallel way from some reservoirs to others, we must not expect them to do so at the same speed. The phosphorus in the nucleus of a cell is more persistent than the much more changeable phosphorus related to the ATP $\rightarrow$ADPT system. The standard rate of turnover of a large part of the elements is higher in the liver than in the brain, or higher in leaves rather than in wood. The respective differences between the parts of ecosystems can be equally large.

	AMOUNT OF CARBON (billions of tons)
Atmosphere	728
Hydrosphere	
Organic carbon	1,400
Inorganic carbon	35,000
Living carbon	3
Sediments (coal and petroleum)	10,000
Continental biosphere	
Organic carbon (includes a large part of what could be called the necromass, *pro parte*)	1,200
Living carbon	550

102 The approximate distribution of carbon, expressed in thousands of millions of tons (petagrams), in the different compartments into which the Earth's periphery can be divided, is shown in this diagram.
[Source: data prepared by the author]

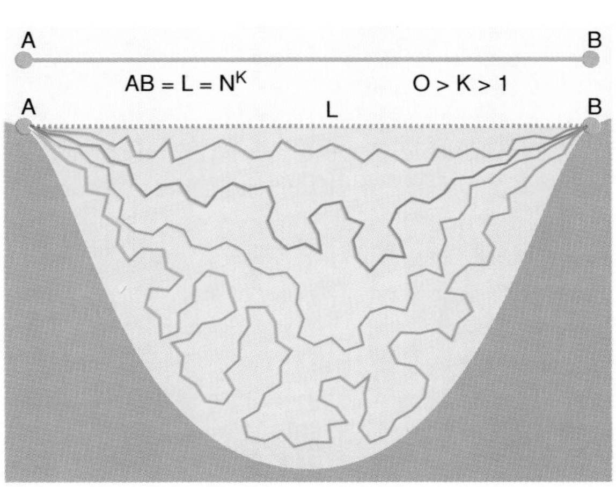

103 Between the two extreme points of a limited space (a lake), there are as many trajectories as values that *k* can assume in the expression $L=N^k$. In practice most cases the values of *k* is near 1/2 and varies depending on whether the drop of water, or the organism of the phytoplankton that we are considering circulates near the surface (value nearest to 1, shortest route) or at a greater depth (value nearer to 0, twisting path).
[Diagram: Biopunt]

The difficulty of combining speeds and trajectories is easier to understand if we try to imagine how water moves in a lake or a reservoir. Some water molecules will travel in an almost straight line, taking the minimum amount of time from the inflow to the outlet; others, on the other hand, will take their time tracing a long, sinuous, and irregular trajectory that might take them through the lake's deeper levels.

The simplest model is to establish the relationship in distance (L) between two extreme positions, measured in units of steps, and the number of these steps needed (N) to travel this distance. The equation will be

$$L = N^k, \text{ where } 0 < k < 1.$$

We can suppose that the distribution of the flow of a river that crosses a reservoir gives a distribution of k values, corresponding to a fairly broad spectrum, representing difference in velocities, just like the one that is found within organisms and in the fabric of ecosystems. If we use progressively shorter steps, complications of another type arise that bring us to the concept of fractal quantities and to the paradoxes mentioned in popular books, when they deal with the length of the frontiers between countries and the conflicts in which surveyors can be found. The ecologist is faced with very similar problems, whether as a student of energy flows, in making maps, or analyzing ecosystem boundaries.

We must bear these and other complications in mind when interpreting measures of production, judging the composition of a complicated system, or making and reading the graphs and diagrams that illustrate the majority of ecology books. We have to bear them in mind because small changes in speed can rapidly

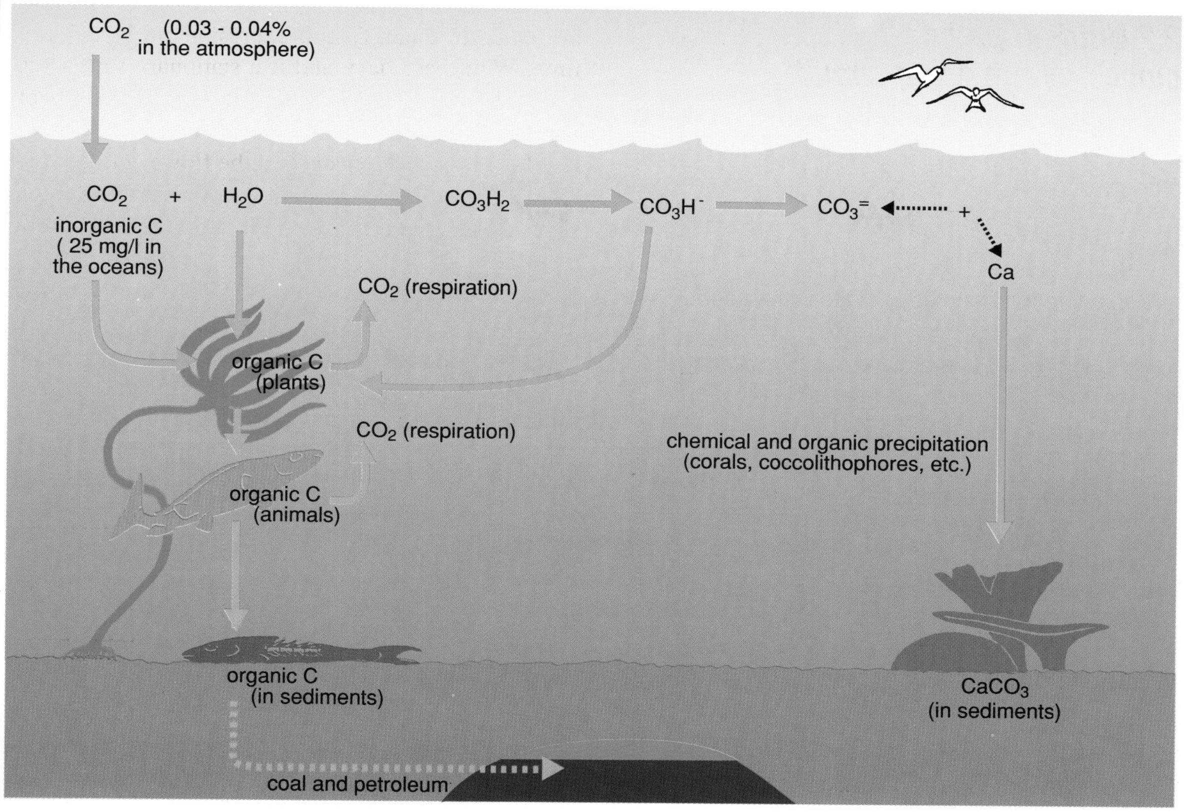

104 The circulation of carbon on a global scale is a good example of the mutual influence of global cycles of the different elements (in this case calcium) present in the medium, and of the intervention of the different types of organism in each of them. A part of the carbon present in the atmosphere in the form of carbon dioxide can combine with calcium and precipitate as different persistent organic structures, such as the matrix of corals, the exoskeletons of coccoliths, etc., or get lost in the sediments. Another part, after having passed as organic carbon through the trophic chains, can also end up in the sediments, but in the form of organic carbon of the necromass.
[Diagram: Biopunt, from data prepared by the author]

lead to very different distributions, and the difficulty of measuring that speed of flow, as well as the intrinsic variability of the flows themselves, mean that we should be sceptical about a fair number of the predictions that are made in the area of global ecology.

The recirculation of carbon on a global scale is a good example. Plants use CO_2, which they take directly from the atmosphere, where it is found in a proportion just over 0.3 parts per thousand in volume, or from what is dissolved in water in the form of gas or as dissociated carbonic acid ($CO_2 + H_2O \rightarrow CO_3H_2 \rightarrow H^+ + CO_3H^- \rightarrow H^+ + CO_3^=$). Part of this carbon assimilated by plants is respired by the plants themselves, and another fraction is consumed and respired by heterotrophs ($C_{organic} + O_2 \rightarrow CO_2$). Heterotrophs depend on autotrophs (plants) and fall into two categories: those that absorb organic substances in solution, or *osmotrophs*, like bacteria, fungi, and parasites (plants or animals), and those which ingest and digest nutrients as solid particles or *phagotrophs*. In relation with all the important elements, it is useful to recognize the limitations that are bound to affect global cycles and cycles within other cycles.

Circulation and recycling

In oceanography it is common to distinguish between new primary production and a recycled production, referring to the upper layers of the sea, in other words, the depth of water some 300 ft (100 m), which receives enough light. There, new living material is synthesized, which is in part respired or eaten by animals and which returns to the water in the form of CO_2 and the corresponding oxidized (or reduced in the case of ammonia products) compounds of other essential nutrients. Phosphorus always circulates in the form of phosphates, and phosphatases tend to be ubiquitous enzymes. This material can be re-assimilated by algae in such a way that the availability of light determines an almost closed circle in the upper layers, the same as happens in a culture in a laboratory flask or in a drop of water between slides and cover glasses well sealed and ready for observation under a microscope. Some years ago ecospheres became fashionable; systems with water, nutrients, and some organisms enclosed in a spherical glass recipient. The intensity of life in these ecospheres depended on the light and temperature to which they were subjected.

In the sea, a part of the material becomes sediment, either directly or through the effect of the animals eating near the surface and then moving to deeper levels, where they leave the residue. In fact, recycling in the upper layers, where materials become renewable, normally accounts for between 60 and 90% of the total. To maintain stable conditions of

105 In the seas and oceans, "new" (i.e. the synthesis of living material) and "recycled" primary production can be distinguished in the first 328 ft (100 m) of water. The ratio between "new" and "recycled" production normally varies between 10 and 50%. *[Diagram: Biopunt, based on data prepared by the author]*

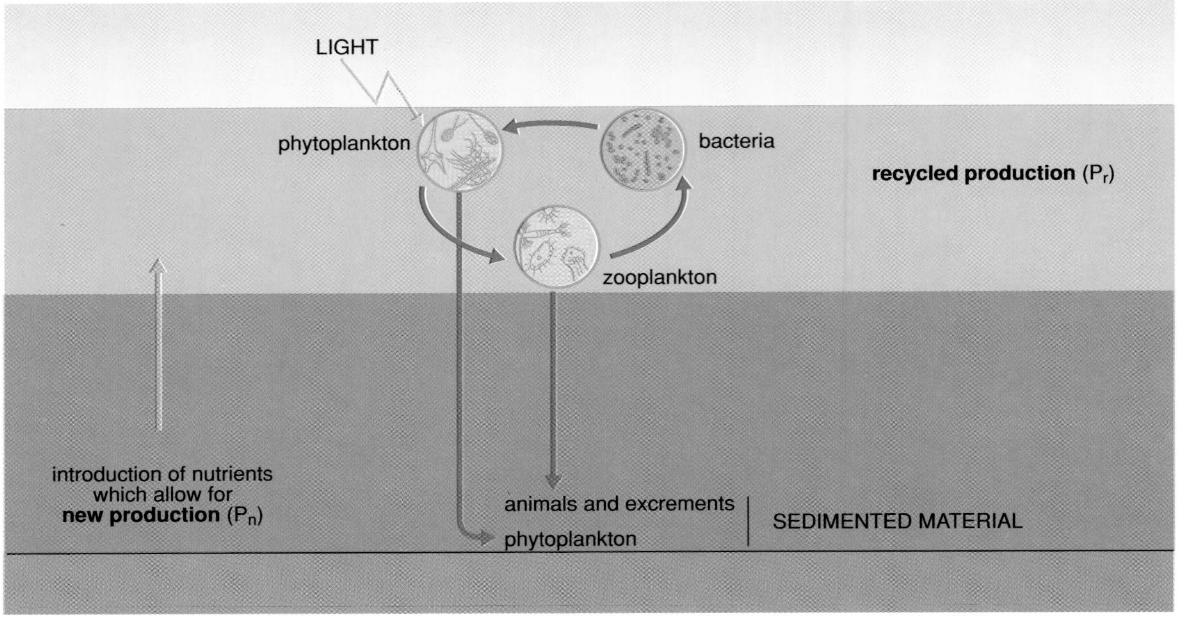

production, the rest has to come from outside the compartment formed by the sea's upper layer, and it normally arrives there with the upflow of deeper waters. Maintaining a uniform level of life means that the inflow of nutrients is equivalent to the part of the primary production that is sedimented. There is a kind of accessory current extending and circulating from top to bottom. Indeed, the delay that this secondary circulation gains in a deep ocean is a cause of the lower general productivity of oceans when compared to the continental surface.

Primary producers, plants, on the one hand assimilate CO_2 (in daylight) and on the other hand produce CO_2 in respiration (at all times). If CO_2 is limited, evolution has found a way to recycle the CO_2 that results from respiration, in other words, to take measures to reassimilate it, which implies maintaining it temporarily within the plant in another cycle involving certain non-volatile acids. There are many land plants that have achieved this internal recycling, particularly plants adapted to high temperatures and often those that grow in the clearings of tropical forests. They are plants that grow rapidly and respire a lot, such as maize, sugar cane, and bamboo. In evolutionary terms, this would seem to be a recent acquisition, as it has been achieved in several functionally convergent ways, and could have evolved in adaptation to a decrease in the atmospheric concentration of CO_2 in geologically recent times. In the case of aquatic plants, this need has not been so acute, and is even less in those living in waters with a high alkaline reserves, that is, waters retaining a great deal of carbon available in the form of bicarbonate.

Ecosystem strategies

Nature is very flexible and accommodating. If, in a suspension of algae, in plankton, there is a shortage of the elements necessary for cellular multiplication (phosphorus, nitrogen), but there is carbon and light, some algae often continue the synthesis. However, this synthesis is accompanied by the production of a gelatinous mucilage that can progressively envelop the cells, and which represents a precautionary measure against desiccation in coastal algae. A comparable relative slowing is found in tropical rain forests growing on plains: the bulk of essential nutrients have become incorporated within the living organisms, and these limit their growth to the replacement of damaged parts. At the same time, in terms of evolution, they have managed to reduce to the minimum the external phosphorus and nitrogen cycle. Under these conditions, the skeleton of any vertebrate is a distinct advantage; perhaps it is for this reason that there are not many vertebrates and hardly any snails in these forests. Only when we get nearer the mountains and rivers and have access to new materials do we find a higher rate of growth and renovation.

The interpretation of the polarity of ecosystems leads us to imagine them as systems integrated by vertical columns or fibers. Lateral transport is indeed an important criterion for analysis. Complete recycling along the local vertical is characteristic of a more closed system: the Amazon, for example, would come closer to this model, but also many other ecosystems where the frontiers that can be drawn on the soil's surface are not areas of the net horizontal flow of nutrients. These systems are emi-

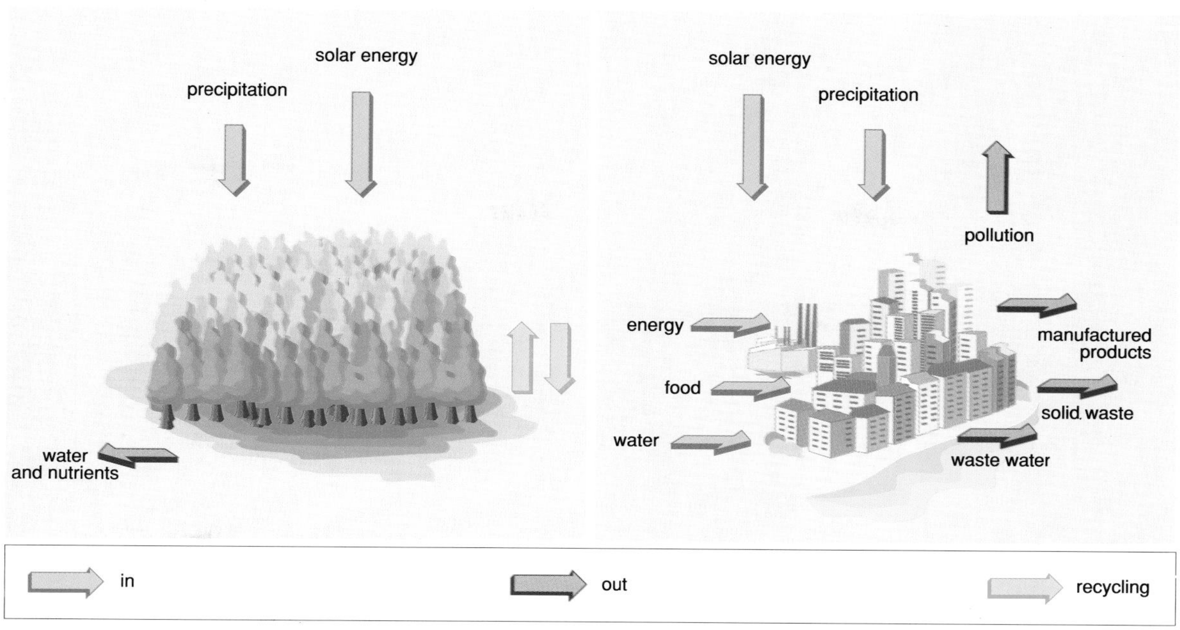

106 The forest and the city are extreme examples of the role of horizontal transport in ecosystems. The wood exemplifies those ecosystems where the horizontal flow of nutrients is minimal; and in practice can be perfectly divided into vertical columns that are functionally identical. The city, on the other hand, exemplifies those ecosystems that cannot survive without active lateral exchanges of essential materials or resources. Such ecosystems are organized internally in such a way that horizontal transport is at least, if not more, important than vertical transport.
[Diagram: Editrònica, based on data prepared by the author]

nently divisible. There are, in contrast, ecosystems that exchange essential materials with other laterally situated ecosystems, as the plain depends on the mountain or as the arable fields and cities appear horizontally connected. The special significance of the vertical dimension can be visualized through a very simple experiment. We could set up two aquariums with similar conditions and populations. In one, the contents are divided in adjacent columns by means of vertically placed partitions, or pieces of plastic tubing open at both ends with a vertical axis. In the other aquarium, the partitions are arranged horizontally. In the first one, the different parts continue to be very similar to how they were before and do not need horizontal transport to remain in their initial state, unless there is one very large fish that has been confined in one of the spaces. The second experiment has interfered with the ecosystems'

107 The fish-fattening cages, such as this one for the fattening of sea bass, installed in the gulf of Rosas on the coast of Catalonia, acts as an incompletely compartmented aquarium. In this case, a column of sea is compartmented both horizontally and vertically, leaving voracious fish inside. By regulating the supply of food and periodically removing fish that have reached the desired size, and by incorporating new resources fished in the open seas, equilibrium is artificially maintained. The names aquaculture or mariculture applied to these techniques suggest their similarity to agriculture.
[Photo: Lluís Ferrés]

108 Many species of ants use the sugar secreted by aphids (honeydews) as a source of food. This secretion is an adaptation to avoid the excessive assimilation of sugars relative to proteins, associated with the high concentration of sugars produced in the sap on which they feed. This honeydew is an energy-rich food source, especially valuable for animals such as ants that are very active and that have an energy expenditure greatly in excess of that of the aphids. *[Photo: Antoni Agelet]*

basic vertical organization and has created new conditions: there is contact with the atmosphere above but not below. Furthermore, in the lower part there is some sediment made up of materials from a previous stage of the ecosystem's activity.

The same has happened in soils, and agriculture has decapitated old ecosystems, substituting their upper part and conserving the lower part as arable soil. Similar ideas help to interpret forms of cultivation, fertilizing, etc. Basically, humans tend to "open" up all systems; for this reason one task of conservation has to be that of restricting the extraordinary transport functions that humanity has imposed on them.

Organism strategies

Some animal populations renew themselves more quickly than others. Some are successful because they reproduce rapidly even though they lose many individuals. Other species are better defended, and the individuals live longer and leave fewer descendants. All this is related to feeding as well, and it is the basis of curious biological relationships.

Plant juices are very dilute, with the exception of sugars. Sedentary insects that exploit plants, like aphids and cicadas, insert a type of beak into the sap vessels, from which they extract food, but often they get too much sugar and they excrete it in an almost direct way, using a type of filter attached to the digestive tube. This filter withdraws the sugar or manna from many small hemiptera, or the foam from cicadas. All of these notoriously inactive animals have a greater need for growth than for energy for movement. On the other hand there are the ants, insects with a more active life that expend a lot of energy on movement and use the sugar left over by the aphids. As for humming birds, it is clear that they need protein, as they cannot live just on syrup, but because they are such small and extremely active creatures, they use a large quantity of sugar that they obtain from the nectar of flowers.

Interaction between production factors

Students are always told to shake their test tube vigorously when they do their first chemical experiments. The shaking is necessary to speed up the reaction. Otherwise substances could be left without reacting because they are separated, for example, in different levels of the reactor vessel if the system is becoming more structured or if we are dealing with a colloidal material that is compartmentalized. The whole biosphere has a very rich structure and can easily keep components separate that would otherwise be able to react. The whole beauty of the world lies in the fact that space is a great isolator that keeps potential reactants apart. We could thus express real production as the result of multiplying external energy by the degree of superposition in the distribution of different production factors.

It is clear that production factors can be water, light, nutritient elements, and the microscopic algae of plankton. If all this is found together, the miracle of the increase of life takes place and continues reproducing until one of the necessary elements begins to run out. It is like a process of construction or assembly that is interrupted when one of the necessary parts, no matter which one, is no longer in supply.

Often these essential elements are not totally lost, but they remain held for a time in some particular or reservoir space. For example, the confinement of phosphate to deep waters and the uncertainty that conditions will come about that favor its return to the light are the principal cause of low production in aquatic systems, especially in central and subtropical regions of the great oceans. This could be expressed by writing the previous equation in a way that allows for an external loop (in fact often a whole hierarchy of external loops): persistent biomass in the locality + exports (sedimentation in aquatic systems) = imports + (external energy x covariance in the distribution of the different production factors).

Transport mechanisms

The distinction between renewable resources and non-renewable resources refers to the quality of recycling and the space in which it takes place. It is clear that, in our universe, everything is potentially recyclable, but if our civilization imports from one place materials coming from different places, and, after combining them and using them in some way, does not return each of these materials to its original place, it is erecting a barrier in space and making return slower. This is one of the most important risks of contamination, when seen as a transport sickness. This sickness consists in the refusal to pay for the return of these materials, entrusting it to natural transport mechanisms that in this case can be excessively slow for the speed at which our civilization is advancing. It is understood that an ecosystem can reactivate itself by supplying the deficient component from outside. This is the basis for the use of fertilizers and manure. This supply could be considered an external subsidy that often compromises the system's future.

Earlier, we compared natural transport paths to a type of random walk. This model offers many possibilities, such as that of understanding the difference that exists between the speed of water on a river bed and that which circulates by percolation in the sediments of the same river. The diversity of natural transport mechanisms is extraordinary, and the way they combine and become integrated or mutually influence each other generates interest and admiration.

The Mediterranean is enriched by the modest vertical mixture that is produced when the thermocline is broken in the autumn, by the contribution of the rivers, and by the upward movement that the rivers themselves create with the mixing of salt with fresh water. To this, it is necessary to add episodes of coastal outcropping that are produced by favorable winds. We also have to count on the upwelling of deep waters in suitable places along more or less persistent hydrographic fronts, without forgetting the interaction of marine currents with islands, islets, and even sudden changes in depth. And each marine space will contain a different combination of similar mechanisms, which define the total average production. Thus the different mechanisms become integrated in a different way in the classical Mediterranean and in the American Mediterranean, or the Caribbean Sea; in the latter, the situation is such that it gives a slightly higher total or average production. On the other hand, it is worth noting that, at times, these secondary seas are better at integrating than the principal oceans. This is so simply because the position of the different hydrographic structures that are significant in production end up geographically more fixed and easier to study in a relatively small sea rather than in a larger one.

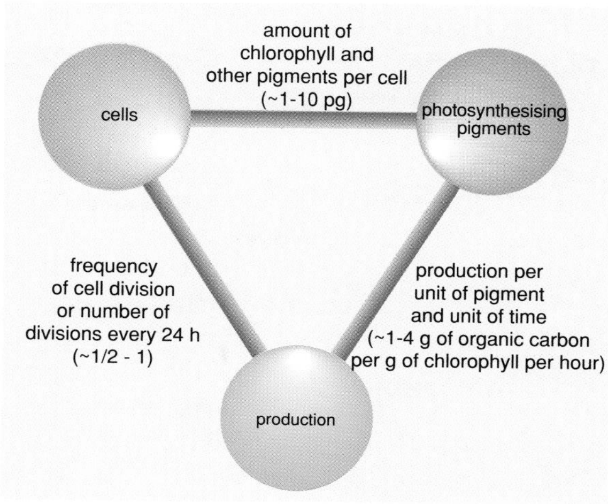

109 Normally, in a study of phytoplankton, the characteristics that are usually studied are the number of cells, the pigment content (measured chemically), and productivity (ability to produce O_2 or to fix carbon 14 [^{14}C]). However the relationships among these values, all of which can be considered intensive features, are of equal if not more importance. In the diagram, the most common values of these relationships are given in parentheses. *[Diagram: Biopunt, based on an original by Margalef]*

2.3 Terrestrial and aquatic environments

The evolution of life can be seen as a much-branched genealogical tree on whose branches we can see the general potentialities of life manifested, in part at least, and in different directions. There are various regularities or general principles that range from the simple to the complex, as the obstacles to survival erected by the environment are overcome. This environment makes well-defined demands, derived basically from the conditions offered by the Earth, which in turn define life's main directions of adaptation and its evolution. The conditions of the physical world operate in the first place on the primary producers, plants, which, although relying on certain common biochemical mechanisms to capture solar energy, adopt very diverse forms and structures, according to whether they grow in the air (land- or continent-based plants) or in water. Whether the that water is freshwater or salt water is of secondary importance. Because animals depend on plants (or better, are mutually dependent on each other), they also show adaptive characters that can be divergent—but perhaps not to the same degree as in plants.

Forests and plankton

A good approach to the initial dilemma is to compare a forest with plankton. Plant plankton or phytoplankton, which live in suspension in sea water and in fresh or epicontinental water, are very small, unicellular organisms, between 1 and 100 μm. If conditions are favorable enough, they multiply very rapidly by cell division and manage to double their mass in a time that varies between half a day and a week. Often the cells resulting from these rapid divisions remain linked to each other, making chains, fans, or other shapes.

The speed with which unicellular plankton multiply has led us to think that they would be useful for making cultures to obtain proteins or other materials for human use. Doubling biomass in a day is not possible for terrestrial vegetation, which requires months to produce an acceptable harvest. Biologically the comparison is misleading, because in reality the greater mass of terrestrial plants, consists of a support and transport structure made from highly resistant, barely alive, and even dead material. This is the case with wood, which forms a very considerable proportion of terrestrial vegetation. The same applies to the spermatophytes, which have returned to the aquatic medium from which they supposedly came.

What can be seen as an individual plant belongs, like all living things, to a species. The ultimate form of a plant depends on the general structure of the stem, which affects the tendency to develop a particular kind of branching. But no two plants from the same species are identical in form. Having a consistent form greatly favors perennial plants, whose vegetative activity tends to be limited to a favorable season because, through maintaining a structure, which at the same time acts as a gene bank, they are able to stay in the same place, ready to send out their leaves and flowers (and sometimes the flowers before the leaves) as soon as the favorable season arrives.

The exact significance of the differences in structure between the forest and the plankton has much to do with the physical nature of the environment and with the mechanisms that make the recycling of materials possible. Phytoplankton live suspended in water: some of its organisms, such as diatoms and many Chlorophyceae and Desmidiaceae, are passive and generally have a slightly higher density than water, so that they have a natural tendency to sediment, at a rate of several inches to feet per day. Other planktonic organisms, such as Dinophyceae, Euglenoidia, many Chrysophyceae, Coccolithophorida, and several groups of flagellates can swim, and if they do so vertically and upward they manage to maintain their level. Other organisms are so small (1-2.5 μm) that they are slaves of the water, trapped by the forces of viscosity and scarcely able to escape from their servitude.

Phytoplankton multiply in the lighter levels of the surface layer (generally no more than 330 ft, or 100 m, down and often much less), where they consume the scarcest and necessary elements to build their bodies. Generally phosphorous and nitrogen are the decisive elements. If the net movement of algae is downward, these materials circulate and become part of their body at lower levels. The tiny animals of plankton also contribute to it because they generally have the habit of eating near the surface at night and moving to deeper waters during the day, where they defecate. It is normal for the excrement from these tiny plankton to be compact, and it therefore forms sediment more easily. The final result is that the solution of compounds of the most limiting chemical elements (phosphorus and nitrogen) takes place at a depth that is well below the level where they were assimilated. Gradually, the recycling process slows, and the average level at which the limiting elements have been returned to the water becomes distributed deeper.

The return of these vital elements comes about through deep waters rising to the surface. This occurs in an irregular manner, either the waters being mixed by the action of the wind or, in the regions where upwelling occurs, as a local manifestation of wider circulatory movements arising from the interaction between the atmosphere (mainly winds) and water. Elements coming from land, principally through the transporting action of rivers, are of secondary importance, and are limited to the coastal areas. The largest marine movements respond with local and irregular mixing processes when they come into contact with islands or reefs. Upward movements are always disorderly and not very effective.

In the continental part of the biosphere, the situation is completely different. It is clear that plants use nutrients from the soil and that they have the same problems of scarce elements, which limit the whole process, running out: new nutrients have to come from the erosion of solid materials found at higher levels. Recycling always occurs through the action of water, in a similar way to what happens in aquatic ecosystems. But on land we are dealing with rain water, which, after collecting the necessary mineral elements in the soil, forms a very dilute solution and rises through the interior of the stems and trunks of plants (in macrophytes, there is an extensive translocation over an inch, a characteristic which differentiates them from plankton microphytes) through the transpiration action in the leaves. The water circulation mechanism does not depend directly on the photosynthetic system but on external energy from the atmosphere, that is, rain and evaporation. Sap circulates through vessels extending vertically. This form of organization controls the circulation of nutrients more efficiently and more predictably than the plankton, which has to depend on a turbulent and often unpredictable mechanism that is rarely optimal.

The vertical dimension of recycling in continents is limited to the first 4-12 in (10-30 cm) of the active layers of soil and to the height of the plants. On the other hand, in oceans it can take place at much greater depths, which makes it a less effective mechanism and introduces a long delay. In fact, in the deep waters of the great oceans, concentrations of phosphorus of up to 50-75 mg/m^3 can be found, but are never observed near the surface except in the contaminated waters of eutrophic rivers and lakes. Naturally, this means that it is much more difficult to maintain a high level of marine production, as this only happens in a small privileged area. All in all, the difficulties of the ascent of nutrients or the long path that these nutrients must follow can be the principal reason why, per surface area, the primary production of oceans is only a third of the average primary production of that formed on the surface of the continents.

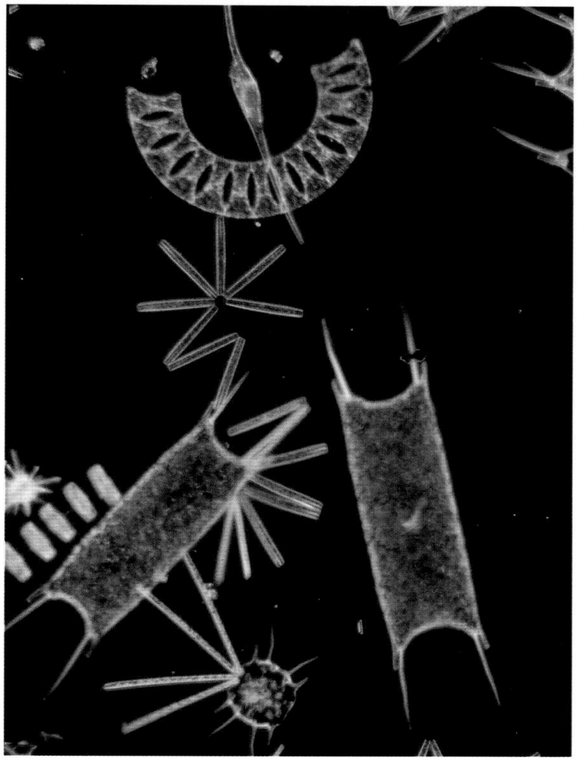

110 Plankton and woodland, aquatic media (below), and aerial media (above) require very different morphological adaptations from the organisms that live in them. In the case of plankton, the primary producers are basically unicellular organisms that live in suspension, and multiply very rapidly to compensate for the inevitable tendency to fall to the bottom, (sedimentation). Only some, such as the dinoflagellate in the lower part of the photograph, can swim on thier own. In terrestrial ecosystems, such as woodland, the primary producers are, above all, higher plants which invest a large part of production in creating and maintaining a support and transport structure which allow them to occupy a space, and stay there, so as to be able to take advantage of the suitable season for reproduction; also to occupy new habitats, such as these larches (*Larix decidua*) which colonize a scrubland in the high Engadine in the canton of Graubünden (Grisons), Switzerland.
[Photos: Hans Wolf / Image Bank and AGE Fotostock (x 200)]

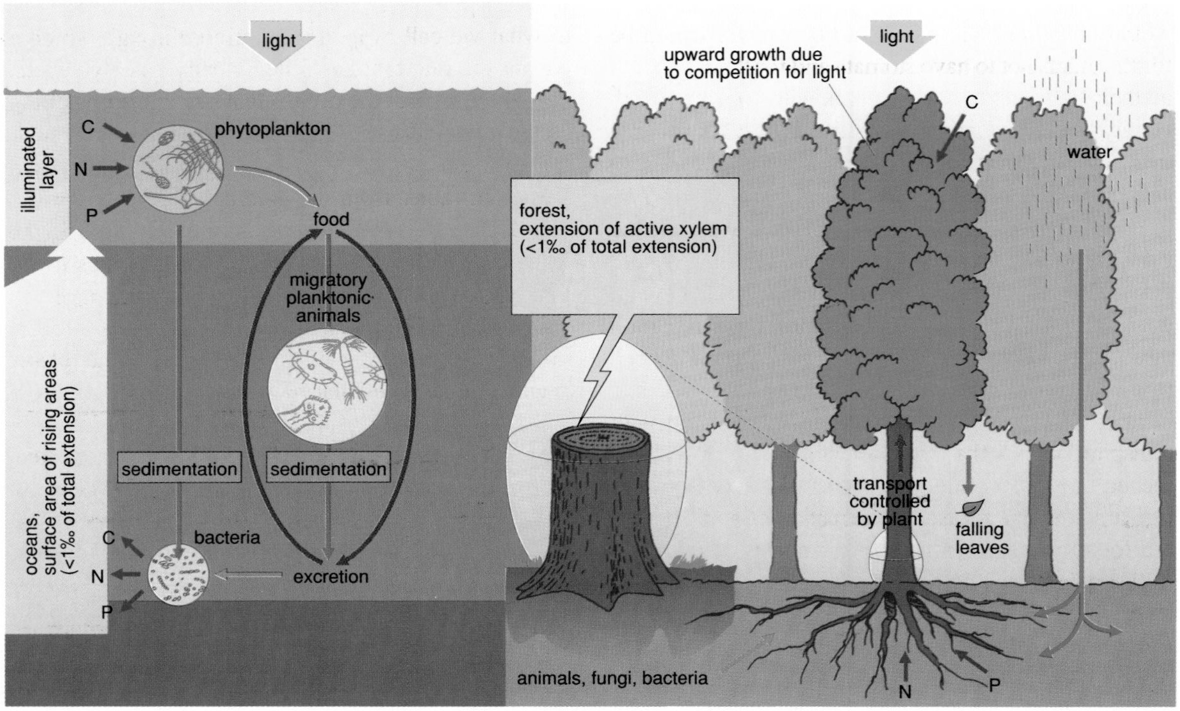

111 Despite the differences in size and structure between plankton and woodland, it is interesting to analyze the analogies they present, and their limits, which are nearly always related to the physical nature of the environment and the ways in which the cycling of materials is produced. The diagram shows some of these: the organization in horizontal blocks, already mentioned, which, in the case of oceans, can extend to columns of some hundreds of meters; the predominance of production at the upper levels, largely related to access to light, which is an essential source of energy for the producers. Also, the predomonance of breakdown in the lower levels, whether of sediments in the ocean deeps, or in the soil, also the slowness of recycling, more notable in the oceans than in terrestrial ecosystems. We can also draw attention to the similarity between the proportion of the surface of upwelling in relation to the total ocean surface; and that of sections of active xylem, by means of which raw materials that the plant extracts from the soil are transported to the leaves, relative to the sections of the trunk as a whole (less then 1‰ in both cases). And there are other similarities we could mention.
[Diagram: Biopunt, based on data supplied by the author]

The analogies and differences between terrestrial and aquatic plant life can be expressed in very different ways. If we look at a unicellular planktonic alga and compare it with a tree, which can be up to 10^7 times larger, this forces us to take into account other, important differences. Marine production is maintained at the present level because a fraction of the total area of the oceans, perhaps a little more than 1 part per thousand, contains water that moves upward at a speed of 3-33 ft (1-10 m) per day. If the concentration of phosphorus in this water was 25 mg/m^3, such an upward movement during one month a year represents a contribution of phosphorus that would permit a primary production of 100 to 500 g C/m^2/year, which can be compared with the average observed throughout the world (some 100 g C/m^2/year). Estimates of marine production are based on the results of incubating samples sealed in bottles, where the carbon fixation is measured through labelled atoms (the ^{14}C isotope is used) or through the exchange of oxygen. On the continents, as is natural, the periodical "harvest" of vegetation material gives a more direct assessment of organic production.

If we want to make similar calculations for trees, we would need to know the cross section of the stems of all the continental vegetation on a horizontal plane, and also the fraction of this vegetation taken up by wood vessels (xylem), which draw up water together with other materials in solution. Forestry technicians use a measure called a basal section, which is the cross section of all the trunks at an agreed height of 4.3 feet (1.3 m). This measure is expressed in square meters per hectare, which is equivalent to ten thousandths of the surface of the area, and normal values are between 20 and 50. The percentage of space that the phloem vessels occupy in a trunk is not an easy and constant function of the section, as it is related to height. In any case, for the trunks of European trees, of average diameter, it is between 1 and 10%. Multiplying the two previous figures we end up with a result between 0.05 and 0.2‰ of the soil surface, a value which we can compare with the 1‰ obtained for the oceans. It is difficult to understand the small amount of interest that has been shown in the search for useful or necessary information to calculate this approximation. As the surface of the leaves is at least four times the surface of the soil over which the foliage is projected, the most interesting index might be: surface of the leaves/section of the active xylem vessels.

But there has been little inclination to make these calculations from adequate data, and the few figures that we do have give values between 3,000 and 20,000 with respect to trees. Herbaceous plants have, unforgivably, been almost totally neglected.

Plants and water

Judging from the way the question of water is presented in many botanical works, it would seem that the life of plants depends entirely on how they can control and limit water loss. If this were the case, the remedy would be simple: all that would be needed would be for the plants not to have stomata and for them to cover all their leaves and even their bark with one of the high quality impermeable varnishes that nature knows how to make. But this is not the case: the water from the soil carrying vital mineral nourishment has to enter through the roots and leave through the leaves, and the flow has to be as active as possible. Evidently, a plant that habitually allows a lot of water to circulate, and grows rapidly, has to be able to control this circulation through the stomata, avoiding the risk of wilting. The stomata also facilitate the entrance of CO_2 gas and clearly, have to maintain a certain relationship with transpiration, so that the stomata and their control mechanism balance the two functions. The stomata, like little mouths measuring a fraction of a millimeter, are found in numbers of several hundred per square millimeter, especially on the underside of the leaves.

Everything works thanks to evaporation, which takes place in the tissues closest to the stomata, giving rise to what we call evapotranspiration, through which a part of the rain that has fallen locally usually passes. Like the waters of the oceans that rise in the upwelling areas, it should be mentioned again that this circulation of water is not paid for by energy from photosynthesis but rather from the external energy of the climate. The evaporation that takes place through the leaves takes up water from the soil and makes it rise through the plant. Conduction, that is, transport of soluble material through the plant, can be forced by other means: for example, in spring, when some plants "bleed" on surfaces that have been cut, it is because the sap rises before suction through evaporation, a process which also leads to the production of new leaves; it is not therefore a very diluted sap as there are reserve materials (sugars like those of the sugar maple [*Acer saccharum*]) which give it a high osmotic pressure capable of strongly drawing water from outside. We cannot trace exactly the evolutionary history of terrestrial vegetation. Probably, the first terrestrial plants derived from green *Coelochaete* type algae and

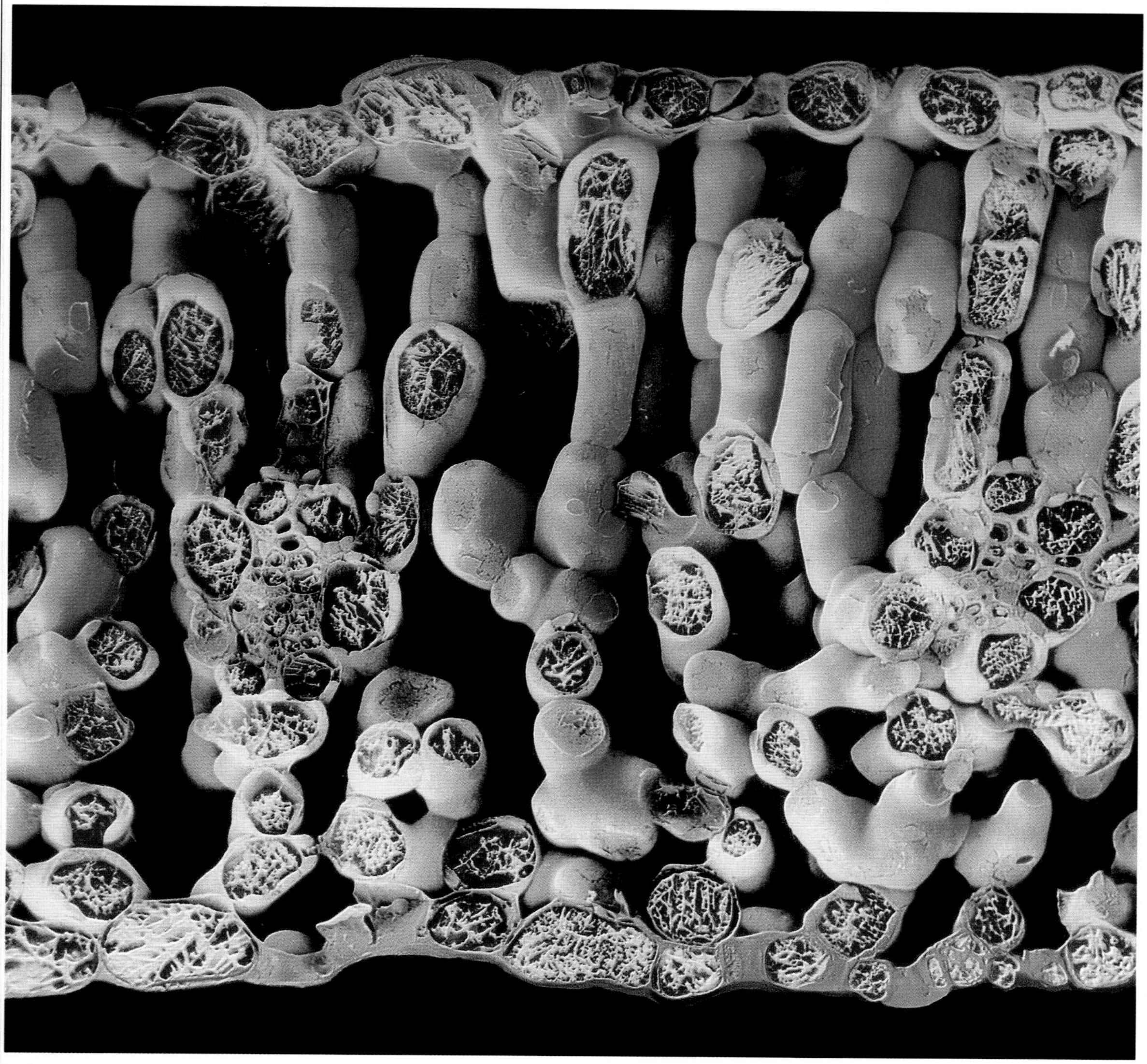

112 Image in false color of a leaf stalk of turnip (*Brassica rapa*). One can see, on both surfaces, the epidermal cells with their stomata, especially on the lower surface. Below the upper epidermis, we can see palisade parenchyma, which has most photosynthetic activity, and, below, near the lower epidermis, spongy parenchyma. *[Photo: Jeremy Burgess / Science Photo Library / AGE Fotostock (x 135)]*

113 Algae of the order Laminariales, such as *Macrocystis*, are by far those that have achieved the greatest dimensions, and a most complex degree of histological specialization, with differentiation into a cortical tissue with an assimilatory function and a colorless, internal medullar tissue. Because of these features and its at times gigantic dimensions, as in the photograph, the term macrophyte is well deserved.
[Photo: René Burri-Magnum / Zardoya]

other similar species, which we can easily observe with a magnifying glass and which are seen as tiny green disks on the walls of aquariums. On a larger scale we have mosses and a great number of cryptogams. Evolution has led to an increase in the size and the duration of transport systems. In this way, the plant, with its corresponding gene bank, survives unfavorable seasons, losing a part of its vegetational apparatus or of its leaves. When favorable conditions return, it can immediately make the most of them. This seems to guarantee for the larger higher plants, the phanerophytes, a long and relatively uneventful life. Botanists have always recognized the advantages conferred on plants having a persistent and well-developed structure above ground.

This belief is reflected in the Danish botanist Christen Raunkjaer's ecological classification, and in similar classifications proposed by other authors who proposing a system of Greek terminology (although broader or more complete) for the common concepts of grasses, shrubs, and trees. In plants, there are two very important ways of beating the competition: one is to trap light before it reaches other plants by growing taller, and the other is to capture water before others can use it by constructing a sufficiently deep and extensive root system, according to how the water is distributed in the soil. Trees can easily dominate the grass: they intercept the light above and extend their roots below. There are often other forms of competition, either from specific substances or from the accumulation of dead leaves. This means that throughout the process of ecological succession, we can not only predict the eventual dominance by trees, when the availability of water allows it, but also that the expression of the process, as far as the reduction of the production/biomass ratio is essentially tied to the accumulation of wood, that is, a largely inactive material but with an immense capacity to organize space and ensure dominance.

The tendency of trees to lengthen their life span implies a very slow turnover of generations and, therefore, condemns the higher plants to a relatively slow evolution. There are woods of diverse quality: one type is the white, light wood of poplars and eucalyptuses, and another the very dense prized woods of a fine quality and particularly resistance (mahogany, ebony), which have evolved under conditions of constant humidity in tropical environments where fungi are in abundance. It is clear that these woods could hardly be considered a renewable resource. They are not as far as the timescale of our civilization is concerned.

There is a whole series of marine algae (*Macrocystis* and others) that perhaps also deserve to be qualified as macrophytes, as they show transport of several substances, at least over distances of some feet. This is a parallel evolution to that of terrestrial woody plants, but one that never attains the same levels of persistence. The macrophytes that originated on the Earth have invaded the sea; this is the case of the posidonias (*Posidonia*), wrongly called algae, or turtle grass (*Thalassia*). There are few marine animals that can digest them, so they are mostly consumed by secondary invaders of the sea, such as some marine turtles and sirenians (manatees and dugongs), which are the descendants of terrestrial ancestors.

3. Energy to create and destroy

3.1 The driving light from the Sun

There is a mechanical equivalent of heat and electromagnetic radiation. Any mechanical labor implies a certain production of heat that spreads in many different ways, and part of which is never totally recoverable. This lost fraction gave rise to the concept of *entropy*, which represents a means of keeping an account of that sort of tax paid in all energy exchanges and which depends on the temperature at which the exchange takes place.

Life involves continuous changes in matter, which requires energy. The biosphere is organized so that energy may be transported wherever it is necessary, for example, circulation in plants, and animal movements. The Gulf War in 1990-1991 pro-

114 The Sun is the basic source of energy of the biosphere, the driving force, through which the photochemical systems of plants and of the photosynthetic bacteria feeds the majority of vital processes. Heterotrophic organisms, such as animals, have recourse to this same energy through eating the photosynthesizers, but at the same time they take advantage of it directly for thermal regulation: they warm themselves through the Sun's rays. Humans have found much more ingenious ways of exploiting this path, such as this solar oven—rudimentary but effective—with which a Tibetan family heats water in its courtyard in Lhasa. Heat is increased by concentrating the Sun's rays on a receptacle through a primitive parabolic mirror. Photosynthetic organisms, through a photochemical pathway, do something similar in many ways.
[Photo: Ramon Folch]

115 Some basic units and their respective dimensions. (*M*, mass; *L*, length; *T*, time). One of the most intuitive units is the calorie.
[Source: data prepared by the author]

DIMENSIONS		UNITS AND EQUIVALENCIES
Force	MLT^{-2}	dyne ; newton; 1 newton = 105 dynes
Energy	ML^2T^{-2}	erg
		joule; 1 joule = 107 ergs
		1 gram-calorie (cal) = 4.1855 joules
		1 Btu (British thermal unit) = 1055.055 joules
		1 equivalent of one gram of petroleum = 41.870 joules = 10 kcal
		1 electron volt (eV) = 1.6021773 x 10-19 joules = 1.6021773 x 10-12 ergs
		1 kilowatt hour (kWh) = 3.6 x 106 joules = 3412.14 Btu
Work per unit of time = energy flow	ML^2T^{-3}	1 Watt (W) = 1 joule per second

vided an extraordinary example of the importance of having the capacity to concentrate materials and resources in a particular place. This can be considered an example of fast top-down control by carnivores or organizers in ecosystems, which contrasts with bottom-up control by energy-assimilating primary producers. It is as if both trees and parasite hosts were so generous as to yield nourishment to other beings. Another example of bottom-up control is the lack of basic resources from the beginning, as in a desert.

Several speculations on the origin of life accept the initial and local availability of organic molecules, rich in energy, like those of petroleum, which had been synthesized abiotically or prebiotically. Now however, and quite probably from the very beginning, life depends on the use of radiant electromagnetic energy from the Sun. It is a rather concentrated energy that, given the nature of photons, travels through space without loss.

There exists a relation between energy quality and the size of a machine that may convert it into work. Thus, low-quality energy like hydraulic energy requires large plants. Organisms, on the other hand, are miniaturized and organized on a finely-tuned scale, and for their functioning they need high-quality energy, like electromagnetic energy and energy from chemical bonds. Chemical energy has its limitations: it needs a material base on which to circulate. This explains the primary adoption of electromagnetic radiation, which ties the biosphere to the Earth's surface,

116 Radiation from the Sun compared with radiation given off by the Earth.
[Diagram: Biopunt, based on Raschke, 1989]

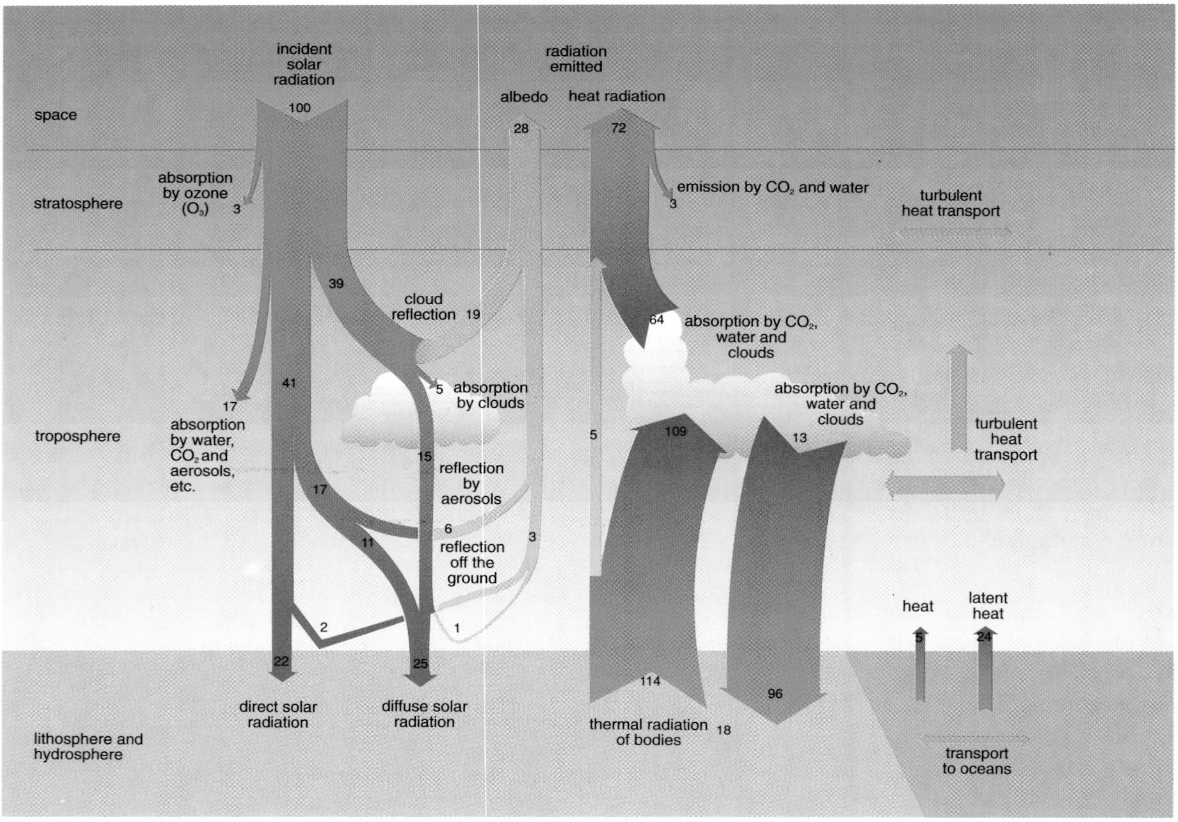

which is naturally exposed to this radiation. The fact that the availability of radiation is intermittent as a consequence of the rotation of the Earth is important although secondary. Other organisms depend on typical primary producers and may live in places without direct solar radiation, where it is brought indirectly through living or dead matter.

Radiant energy turns into other energy forms, which we can identify in the workings of the biosphere. Photons translate into probabilities of electron shifts, which in turn make it more or less probable that certain molecules intervene in some chemical reactions. The chemical energy of the components of the ecosystems is usually measured by combusting the materials in the presence of oxygen in a calorimeter. This records the resulting heat in calories, detected by the increase in temperature of the water surrounding the combustion chamber. Some of the numbers that will be used later are calculated this way. The evaluation of transfers or results of processes is referred to in terms of efficiency. Measured as the ratio between the actual result and the expected result, *efficiency* can be calculated as an energy quotient, and is therefore expressed as a simple relationship without dimensions.

3.2 The natural greens of autonomous life

Energy capture

The living receptor-detector of solar energy consists of a kind of antennae, whose essential elements are molecules that absorb radiation of defined wavelengths; they have color, they are pigments. The absorbed photons determine changes that affect the electrons in the receptor, so that the energy associated with certain bonds varies. Then electrons migrate to other molecules, where chemical changes may take place. Finally, the pigments are ready again to receive new photons. When organisms are seeking orientation to obtain light, and not energy, the detectors are made to operate with maximum refinement (visual organs), not with great intensity.

In the capture of solar energy by plants, a form of laminar construction is repeated at different scales. At the largest scale, the vegetation cover extends as a relatively thin stratum (maximal thickness of approx. 300 ft, or 100 m), which, compared to the Earth's radius, represents an extremely fine film (100 m:6,380,000 m = 1/63,800), where the basic activity that makes the biosphere work takes place. At the next scale, that of leaves (0.4-4 in, or 1-10 cm), the structures are also obviously laminar. In specialized leaf cells there are *chloroplasts*, which are disk-shaped structures of a few µm in diameter. In the chloroplasts there are smaller units or *grana*, 0.3-0.5 µm in diameter. Finally, at the level between molecules and chloroplasts are found laminar organelles, the *thylakoids*, flattened disk-like sacs whose continuous membrane is less than 6 nm thick (0.006 µm), supporting very complex and thickened molecular complexes. These molecular complexes are not uniform; there are at least two kinds, including those that correspond to the two different photosynthetic systems, *photosystems I* and *II*. Each unit contains numerous proteins and the pigments responsible for the assimilation of solar radiation.

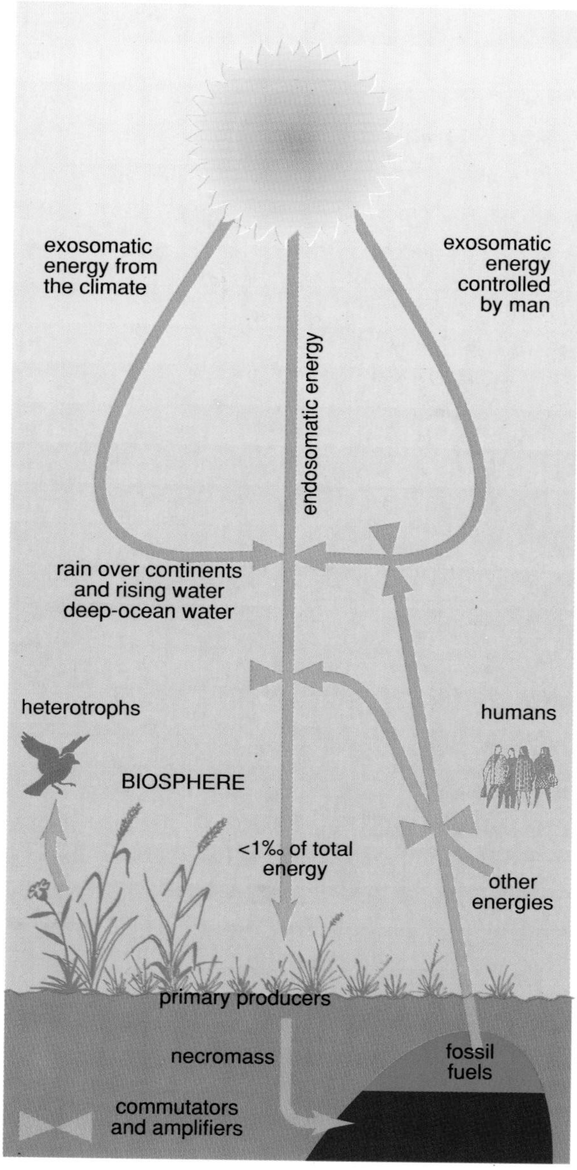

117 In the functioning of the biosphere there is not just light energy used initially by the primary producers and later, with food, by the consumer. Energy that circulates through the ecosystems in the form of light, and by chemical pathways from one organism to another and is known as *endosomatic* or internal energy. There is also a considerable part of solar energy that operates through pathways outside the organisms known as *exosomatic* energy, which plays an important role in ecological function. The circulation of marine currents and of atmospheric disturbances, rainfall, or upwellings are some of the phenomena which make this kind of energy possible. A part of this exosomatic energy channelled by humans, plays quite an important role today. *[Diagram: Biopunt, based on an original by Margalef]*

118 The systems of solar energy captured by the primary producers are repeated at different scales in a laminar structure. At a macroscopic scale, the leaf has the shape of a blade (lamina). Below the epidermis of the upper surface one finds a layer of parenchyma in the form of a palisade which contains the cells that are most active in photosynthesis. At cellular level, the chloroplasts tend to be in the form of small discs, a few millimeters in diameter. At ultrastructural level, the thylakoids form flat vesicles that bear the molecular structures that are active in photosynthesis.
[Diagram: Biopunt, from various sources]

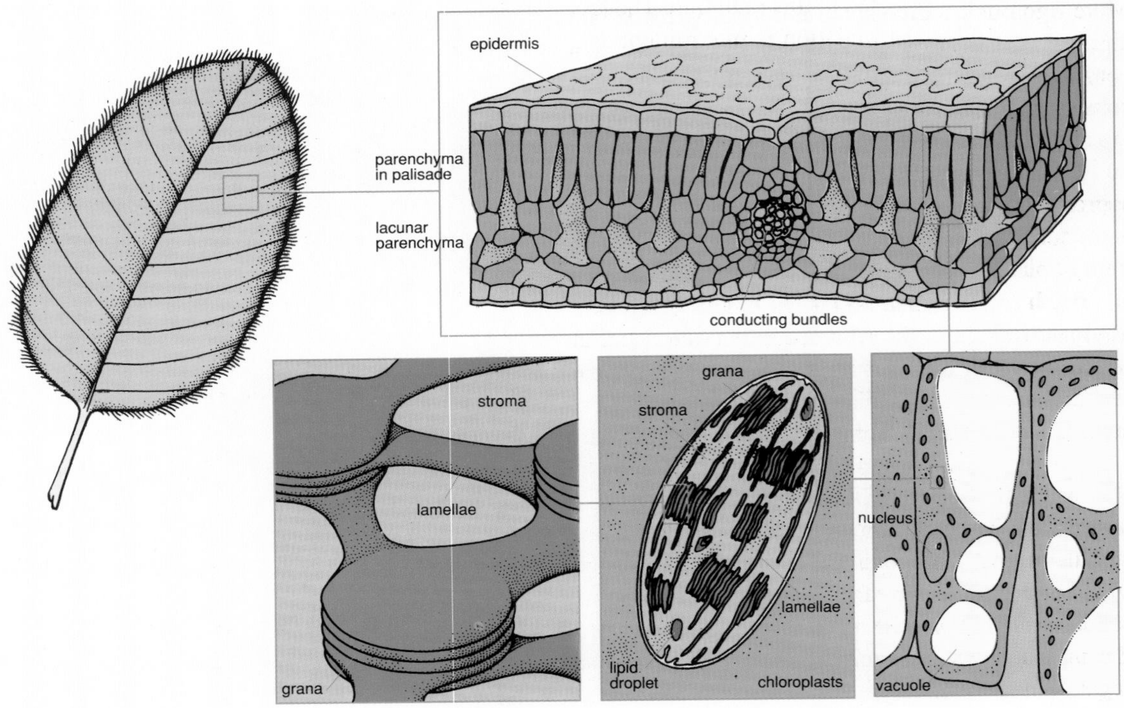

Pigments

The study of the photosynthetic apparatus is progressing rapidly. Here, we will only consider in a very simplified manner some features of special functional and evolutionary interest. Pigments, the molecules that absorb light, may belong to three different groups.

The first group includes the *chlorophylls*, whose molecule consists of a porphyrin ring with a magnesium atom at the center and a long tail of chain aliphatic alcohol (phytol). They have two absorption maxima: one around 430 nm and the other around 665 nm. For this reason they are perceived as green (the color corresponds to the unabsorbed light, of intermediate wavelengths). There are several types of chlorophylls: *a*, *b*, *c*, and some others.

The second group is that of *phycobilins*, comparable to open chlorophyll molecules, which are more linear than circular, and are associated with proteins. They absorb radiation whose wavelengths lie between the absorption maxima of chlorophylls, i.e. around 470-520 nm. For this reason their apparent color is bluish or purple.

The third group is that of *carotenoids*, derived from long-chain hydrocarbons, which absorb radiation of relatively short wavelength (blue), i.e. around 400-480 nm. For this reason their apparent color ranges from yellow to orange, the complement of blue.

Light absorption

Light passes through the atmosphere with relatively small loss. The most important absorptions are in the ultraviolet segment (UV) of the spectrum, strongly absorbed by oxygen and atmospheric ozone, and in the infrared segment (IR), which is absorbed by the *greenhouse gases*, among them CO_2 and water vapor. Other phenomena contribute to the modification of the quality of light: an increasing fraction of light becomes diffuse (ceases to follow approximately parallel paths) and an important part is polarized, which means that the planes of vibration of the various rays take on a different orientation. Some of these changes are not unimportant, however. For instance, chloroplasts are adapted to use diffuse light, and were they to have evolved to use light of parallel paths, their efficiency would possibly have been much higher. Many animals can perceive the polarization of the light plane, and they use this ability to orient themselves with respect to the light of the sky, even if they do not directly see the Sun.

Electromagnetic radiation is strongly absorbed by water, which has its maximal transparency around the band corresponding to greenish-bluish light (around 510 nm). On the other hand, the position of a leaf in the air makes little difference, but some leaves shade others. Plants tend to grow upward, and the resulting selection determines the progressive evolution in height of trees.

More rigorous conditions are imposed by the strong absorption of light by water. In order to measure it, a very simple method is that of Secchi's disc, which consists of measuring the maximum depth at which the disc, tied to the end of a line cast in the water, can be seen. This distance, multiplied by 2.2, is the approximate level at which light represents 1% of that at the surface and which, in practice, defines the lower limit of plant life, though some algae manage to grow at a depth of more than 660 ft (200 m), in especially transparent waters. The recorded maximum depth at which Secchi's disc has been seen in the eastern Mediterranean is 175 ft (53 m); in more fertile seas the depth of vision ranges from 15-65 ft (5 to 20 m).

The optimal use of light in the aquatic medium would require the concentration of chlorophyll (about 450 mg/m^2) right at the water surface. This is what happens in the green films sometimes seen on ponds, and also in the populations of duckweed (*Lemna*) and water hyacinths (*Eichhornia*). These vegetation mats rapidly exhaust local nutrients and can only survive in still waters fertilized right at the surface, conditions which are met in pools associated with rivers. Typical of these situations are the impressive plants with floating leaves (the genus *Victoria* in South America).

The mechanisms of photosynthesis

The battery of chlorophyll molecules is called a photocenter. This acts as a light antenna that is capable of capturing and focusing photons very effectively. The assembly could be compared to a funnel with a limited opening represented by the center, where the assimilated energy manifests itself. In simplified terms, this manifestation consists of giving reducing power to the cell, that is, the capacity to move electrons, and precisely, to add them to various chemical elements. This is a complicated mechanism based on the dinucleotide phosphates (nicotinamide + adenine) of pyridine (NADP + $NADPH_2$). The final result is the reduction of chemical elements that are usually found in the environment in oxidated form, for example, carbon, nitrogen, and sulfur. These reduced chemical elements become integrated in the substratum of life, and later they will eventually oxidize, thus returning to the environment. Nowadays this is a cause for deep concern, because in addition to these natural processes, there are supplementary oxidations caused by our civilization (combustions), which release CO_2 (increasing the greenhouse effect), and sulfur and nitrogen compounds (acid rain) into the environment.

119 The fleshy leaves of some Aizoaceae, such as certain species of the genus *Fenestraria*, have a translucent apical layer, rich in calcium oxalate crystals, which filters the light before it reaches the thin photosynthetic layer situated beneath. This permits the maximum use of the sunlight received.
[Photo: Elisabet Carreras]

Energy and photons

Each antenna has between 200 and 900 chlorophyll molecules, and any incoming photon moves practically without any energy loss until it reaches the reaction center. Chlorophyll molecules are not equivalent, but the biased transport probability is due to the general tendency to change short-wave radiation (equivalent to "smaller" photons of higher energy) with other radiations with a longer wave (equivalent to "larger" photons of lower energy).

The energy E per radiation quantum equals *Planck's constant* ($h = 4.14 \times 10^{-15}$ eV.s) multiplied by the frequency (equal to the speed of light divided by the wavelength). Thus, in the case of red radiation of 668 nm, the energy of a radiation quantum, of a photon, given in electronvolts is $4.14 \times 10^{-15} \times 299{,}792{,}458\ m.s^{-1} / 668 \times 10^{-9} = 1.858$ eV ($= 2.97 \times 10^{-12}$ ergs). In a radiation of shorter wavelength, around the blue-violet, for instance, 445 nm, the energy per photon would be 2.787 eV.

We now have instruments for measuring radiation quanta, and radiation is usually expressed in einsteins (E). An einstein of photons is a photon mol, that is, the *Avogadro number of photons*, equal to 6.0220943×10^{23} photons. The energy of an einstein of photons of lambda wavelength equals

120 A cyanobacterium that lives as an intracellular symbiont in the glands found at the base of the leaves of *Gunnera* undertakes, in them, the role of plastids in other assimilatory cell; and moreover, allows the plants of this genus, native to poor soils in the southern lands of New Zealand and Chile, and of the Andean mountain chain, to fix nitrogen. In the transmission electron micrograph, we can observe the thylakoids of one of the plastids of the cyanobacterium and, to the side (above, on the right) a fragment of its cell wall.
[Photo: Mercè Durfort]

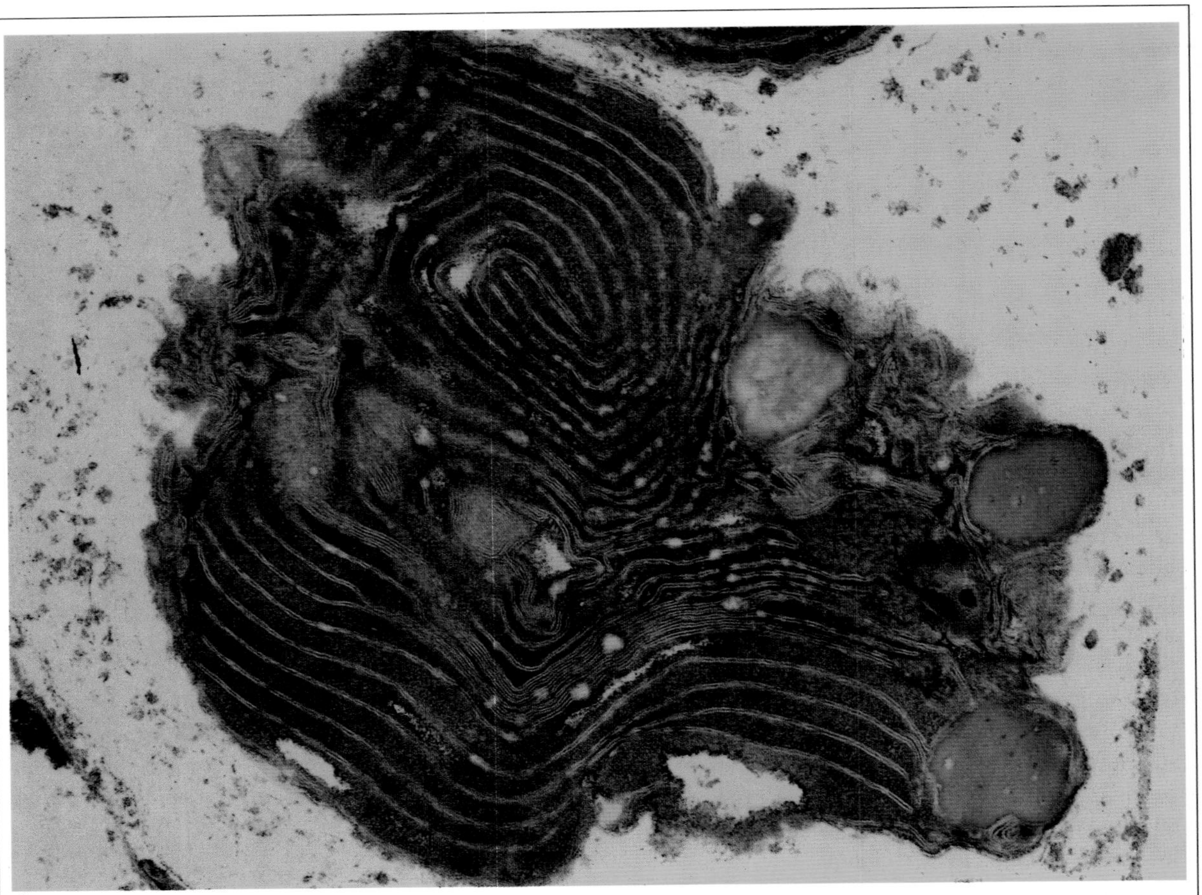

119,610,083 J divided by the wavelength expressed in nanometers (nm). If we multiply the number of einsteins per second by the energy that corresponds to them according to their wavelength, we obtain the energy expressed in watts (W). Thus, an E (einstein) per second of 500 nm radiation equals 239,220 W. It seems obvious that a more practical unit would be the microeinstein, μE. For 500 nm light, 1 W = 4.18 μE/s. This might have seemed a very dense presentation, but it was necessary to clarify, once and for all, the precise values of certain relations which are important in planetary ecology, and which will be repeatedly used.

Fluorescence

If the decrease in the energy associated with a photon corresponds to the growth of the wavelength, it is reasonable that as a natural entropic tendency, atoms and molecules return radiation of a wavelength generally longer than the one they received. This is called fluorescence. Photons "roll" toward the molecules that absorb a longer wavelength, and this happens in every receiving antenna. Thus, the reaction centers are functionally closer to chlorophyll molecules, which absorb photons associated with a longer wavelength. For this reason, when evaluating the energy in photosynthesis, it is acceptable to count the photons instead of measuring exactly the energy they carry. Currently, instruments for counting photons are widely used, and the result is given in einsteins, not in energy units. Their sensitivity window is limited by appropriate filters to the band of photosynthetically active radiation (PAR), approximately between 380 and 750 nm.

When there is excessive light, part of the electromagnetic radiation is not used because the processes taking place at the reaction center level limit the flow of light. Each unit behaves like a funnel that collects falling rain. If it rains excessively, water spills over the brim, and so not all the rain water flows away through the tube. Similarly, the excess of light warms up the tissues and may damage them. It may also increase respiration too much, or cause energy to be emitted as radiation of a longer wavelength, in which case a fluorescence effect is produced.

Manifestations of fluorescence are important in the biology of production: lichens contain highly fluorescent substances that absorb radiation of a very short wavelength and emit radiation of a longer wavelength, which is sometimes used for photosynthesis by symbiotic algae. Something similar happens in corals, in which the transmission of useful energy from the animal part to the symbiotic algae is really significant. Fluorescence is a means of energy transfer between the various photosynthetic systems within a plant, concretely from system I to system II.

Photosystems

A plant's different photosynthetic systems are called *photosystems*. *Photosystem II* has acquired a much more powerful function, and with a surplus of photons it feeds the more ancient photosystem I, which generally absorbs longer wavelength photons of lower energy. *Photosystem I* contains mainly chlorophyll a as its principal pigment, as does photosystem II, which also contains higher proportions of other chlorophylls and carotenoids. The effective absorption of radiation and its re-emission as fluorescence are naturally complementary. If photosynthesis is hindered at the biochemical level, using the appropriate means, e.g. DCMU, a substance which is also used as a herbicide, the fluorescent emission is intensified. There have been attempts to use this phenomenon for measuring the photosynthetic capacity.

Any photosynthetic system generates a difference in potential, which will move electrons between certain redox values when joining the biochemical machine. Photosystem I works between -0.6 and +0.4 volts. Quantitatively speaking, its main function in plant cells is the reduction of CO_2. Photosystem II works between -0.2 and +0.8 volts, and it uses the energy provided by photons to break up the water, whose hydrogen takes part in the reactions fed by system I. As a result, oxygen is liberated. If the environment is relatively reducing, the only necessary photosystem is photosystem I, the only one in organisms (photosynthesizing bacteria) that live in environments rich in hydrogen sulfide or with a lot of organic matter. It is reasonable to think that photosystem I was the only one in an era when most of the environment was reducing, before an oxidizing atmosphere was formed through the action of organisms. As evolution proceeded, photosystem II appeared. Both, functionally interwoven like athletes in a relay race, can move electrons over a wider band, practically 1.5 v. wide. The tension of domestic dry batteries coincides with the voltage at which life works.

The way in which the two photosystems are coupled presents still other interesting aspects. The antenna in photosystems of type II is between 2 and 4.5 times larger than in photosystems of type I: naturally, the former assimilate an excess of photons and may transfer energy within the cell through fluorescence to photosystems of type I. This is understandable and agrees with the different composition of pigments. Photosystem II contains a larger fraction of carotenoids and in general of pigments that absorb a shorter wavelength, i.e. of photons with more energy. Part of this energy is easily transferred through fluorescence to the other photosystem. As a result, it seems as if photosystem II were adapted to using lower light levels (more extended antennae). At the same time it acquires a privileged

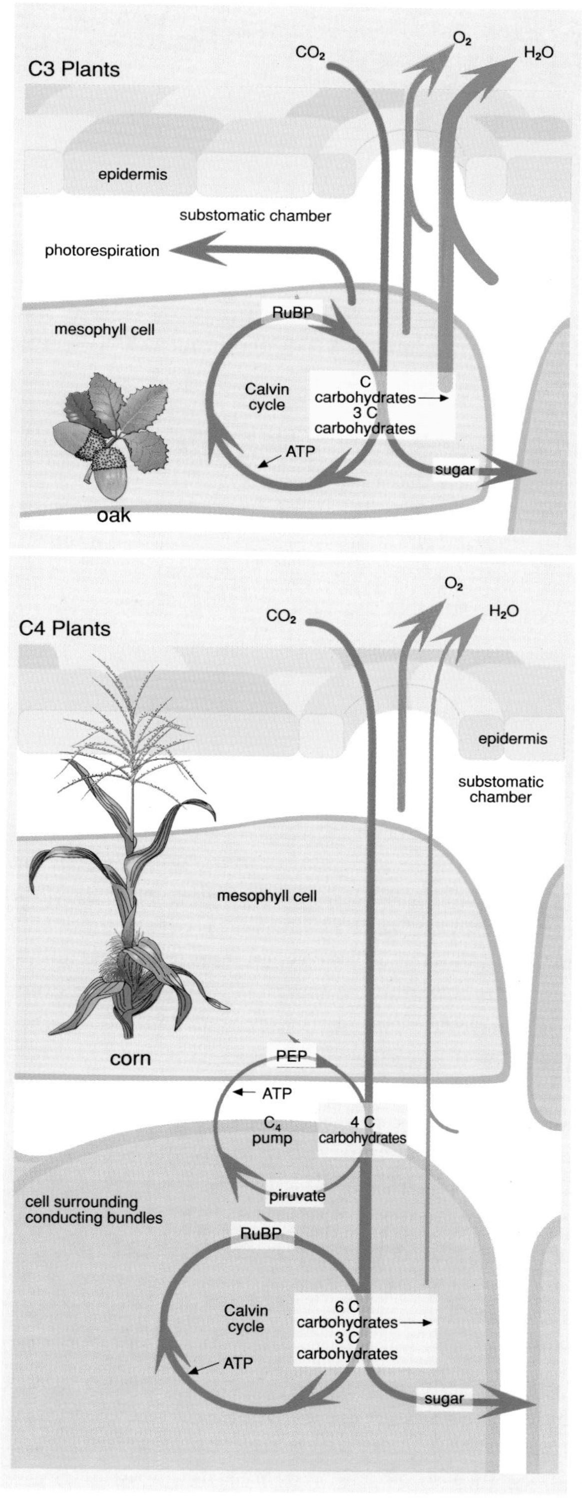

121 There are different ways of fixing atmospheric CO_2 by so-called C3 plants (most forest species in temperate zones) and C4 plants (many seed plant species of tropical origin). The photosynthesis of C3 plants leads to the initial formation of carbohydrate molecules with six carbon atoms, which split immediately into two molecules of 3-phosphoglycerate (phosphoglyceric acid), each 3-carbon. Because of this, this system of fixing CO_2 incorporated by ribulose 1.5-biphosphate (RuBP), is called C3. By contrast, C4 plants, which include maize and sugar cane, have a remarkable photosynthetic yield, even in situations of low CO_2. In these plants, the CO_2 receptor is phosphoenolpyruvate (PEP) and the carbohydrates formed have four carbon atoms, not three. First oxaloacetate (oxaloacetic acid) is formed and then malic acid; the pyruvate is regenerated and the CO_2 is again freed, which initiates a cycle similar to the Calvin cycle. These plants, called C4, tend to have anatomical differences, since the vascular bundles in the leaves are surrounded by a layer of cells rich in chloroplasts. The C4 pump makes for the concentration of CO_2 molecules near the active center of an enzyme, which is crucial for photosynthesis—ribulosebiphosphate carboxylase (Rubisco), by which oxygen fixation is prevented and thus the loss of energy through photorespiration.
[Diagram: Editrònica, based on Bazzaz and Fajer, 1992]

position, since it is able itself to provide energy to what remains from photosystem I.

Each photosystem moves electrons over a difference in potential of approximately 1 v, but the coverage of both photosystems combined is approximately 1.5 v. There is an overlap in this relay race. This could partly be seen as a safety mechanism, but there is another application for the excess of energy in the biochemical machine of the cell: it relates to energy storage and phosphorus assimilation (the step from ADP to ATP).

Photosynthesis in the biosphere

It is not the aim of this book to present the complex structure and function of the biochemical machinery of the cell and of organisms. Nevertheless, it is easy to understand that the input of energy that allows the biosphere machine to work is fundamental.

Photosynthesis is limited to the parts of the biosphere located at relatively greater heights, which contrasts with the less localized or more generalized distribution of respiration. This contrast results in the generation of a vertical gradient in the value of the redox potential. Light gives reducing capacity to the upper part of the biosphere. In lower parts, respiration generally predominates over photosynthesis, and respiration normally implies the use of oxygen. This represents a flow of electrons within the biosphere from top to bottom, like an electric current between an upper (negative) pole, and a lower (positive) pole. This current is balanced outside of the organisms, except when there is an accumulation of a large quantity of chemically reduced material in the soil or sediment. Another case of vertical electrical gradients, which are much more intense and erratic, occurs in clouds and between these and the Earth, most strikingly in storms and lightning.

Photosynthetic production

The solar constant at the atmosphere's limit is 139 mW/cm^2 (see section 2.1.3). Plants can use about half of this energy (photosynthetically active radiation or PAR), and since the Earth's total area is about four times the extent of its maximal circle, plant life may use on average about 172 W/m^2. This value should be locally adjusted for each case, as a function of latitude and season, not to mention other more unpredictable and inconstant factors, such as absorption and reflection by clouds.

When extracting leaf or plankton pigments with organic solvents (normally methanol or acetone), one can see that a solution containing 450 mg of chlorophyll uniformly spread over an area of 10.7 square feet (1 m^2) absorbs practically 99% of incident visible radiation. If chlorophyll, and other pigments, are not dissolved but compacted in small structures, as in leaves, there may be more pigment with same overall effect.

Phytoplankton almost never contains more than 0.5 g of chlorophyll per square meter of extension. This is also the concentration in the surface of leaves. Performance does not improve beyond this concentration. Trees whose leaves photosynthesize on both sides may be an exception, for example, very green trees in mediterranean climates, like the evergreen oak and accompanying trees, which have higher chlorophyll concentrations. Given that the total surface area of leaves in terrestrial vegetation is about four times higher than the area of the soil over which they grow, there is more chlorophyll than would seem strictly necessary.

Global primary production

The real primary production of vegetation may be estimated in very different ways. The most simple one is harvesting and weighing the result and evaluating its energetic content with a calorimeter. One can also do it by evaluating the oxygen produced by the process or recording the speed of carbon assimilation, using the radioactive isotope ^{14}C. Plant respiration and the increase in respiration as a result of photosynthesis are also measured.

Photosynthesis, because it is a photochemical reaction, is only slightly accelerated by a temperature increase. However, a higher temperature, which always intensifies respiration, often leads to the faster use of nutrients. An 18°F (10°C) increase approximately doubles the speed of a reaction or halves the time required to complete a process. A fluctuating temperature has a greater accelerating effect than one that corresponds to its arithmetic mean.

A fraction of the energy absorbed in photosynthesis is used in the reduction of nitrogen and sulfur compounds. Another fraction results in the energization of phosphorus compounds. However, the change due to carbon assimilation is the most important one, so that often, when speaking about production, one refers only or more explicitly to carbon. Therefore, the approximate mean primary production, integrated over an annual period, represents about 300 g of carbon per m^2 on the continents, and about 100 g per m^2 in the oceans. The global production of the biosphere would be around 78 x 10^9 tons of carbon per year, equivalent to 114 x 10^{12} W.

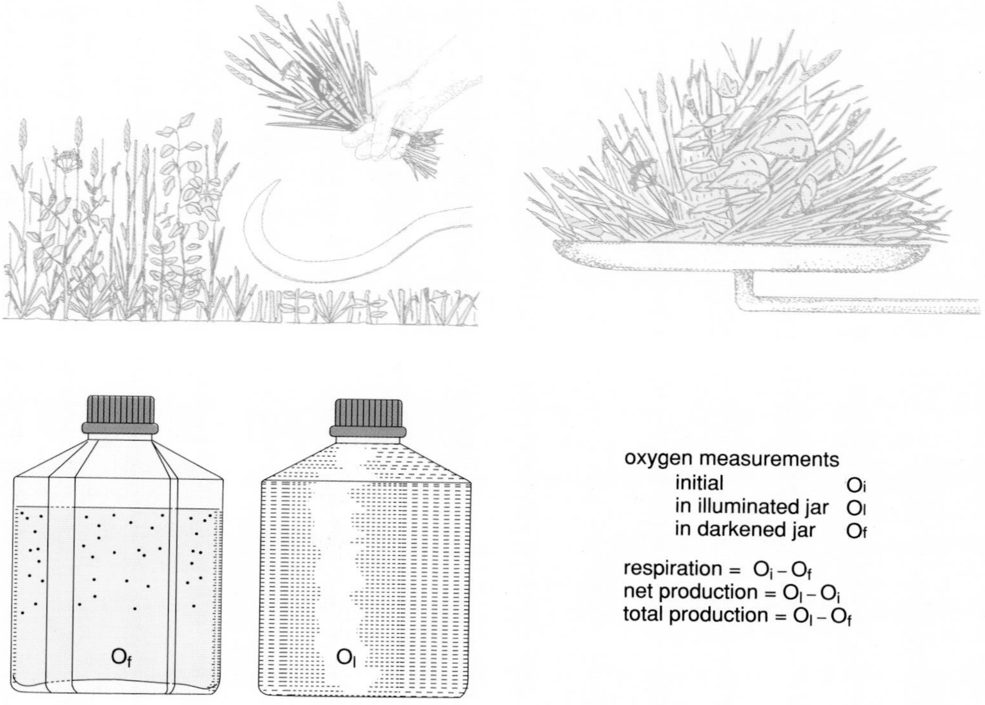

122 The simplest measure possible of primary production of terrestrial vegetation consists of harvesting a pasture or herbaceous crop and weighing the result. It has the disadvantage that one does not know the amount of production used in respiration. With plankton, by measuring the oxygen, it is possible to obtain more precise data. All one has to do is to fill two identical flasks, one transparent, one opaque, with the same suspension of plankton in water; measure the initial content of oxygen (O_i) and after a time the oxygen content of the transparent flask, which had received sunlight (O_l) and of the opaque flask, which had remained in the dark (O_f). By simple subtraction we can estimate the total production (O_l - O_f), respiration (O_i - O_f) and net production (O_l - O_i).
[Diagram: Biopunt, based on data prepared by the author]

The numbers given in books are based mainly on fairly old records, which are not all that common and often subject to different interpretations. Given the interest of these numbers for current research, it would be a good time to put some effort into obtaining new ones by using procedures in accord with the current state of knowledge and technical resources. Remote sensing from space may show the distribution of pigments, but it is less useful in showing their activity.

Considering that the total incoming energy from the Sun is 178 x 10^{15} W and bearing in mind the production numbers given above, it is obvious that only about 0.6 part per thousand of this energy reappears in primary production. Since this number is closer to net primary production, as evaluated at plant level, an estimation of plant respiration has to be added. One can easily conclude that about 1 part per thousand of the incoming solar energy is needed to make the biosphere work. This energy is called endosomatic because it circulates inside organisms.

All the remaining energy, both non-visible and that of appropriate wavelength but unused, is not lost from the biosphere's point of view because it shapes the climate, so making the Earth habitable.

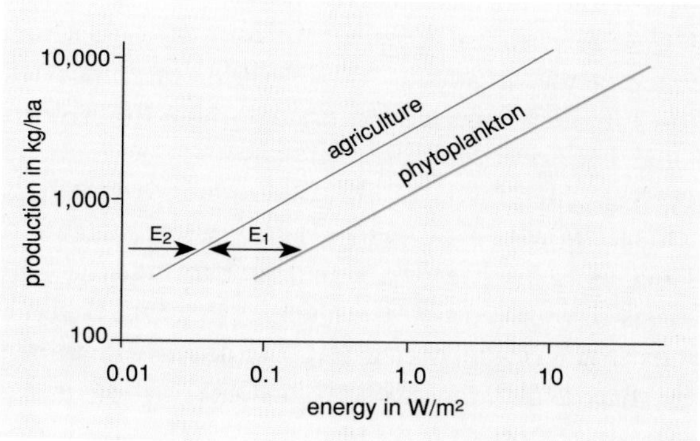

123 Exosomatic energy as well as endosomatic energy is involved in production. This is especially obvious in systems in whose exploitation humans are actively involved; an example is croplands, where energy is invested in tilling, fertilizing, irrigating, harvesting, and all the other activities that come under the umbrella of agriculture. But this also happens in the case of plankton, which receives exosomatic energy in the form of waves, currents, upwellings, etc., which help mix it up. In the case of agricultural production, we are not able to measure the evapotranspiration of the plants because of the lack of data. If such a calculation were made, it would result in a higher amount of total energy being consumed for a given amount of production, than in the case of plankton.
[Diagram: Editrònica, from various sources]

This is external or *exosomatic* energy, and is used by organisms.

The energy exchange that can be associated with the reduction of carbon (the energy released by the combustion of carbon or its compounds) is 116-144 kcal (between 485,668 and 602,900 J) per mol (12 g of C). Eight einsteins of photons with a wavelength of about the maximal absorption of chlorophyll (668 nm) represent an energy of 8 x 42.6 kcal (= 14,268,614 J). The conversion of light to chemical energy is achieved with an efficiency of less than 50%. Energetically speaking, three photons would suffice to reduce a carbon atom and to produce an oxygen molecule. In reality, eight photons are

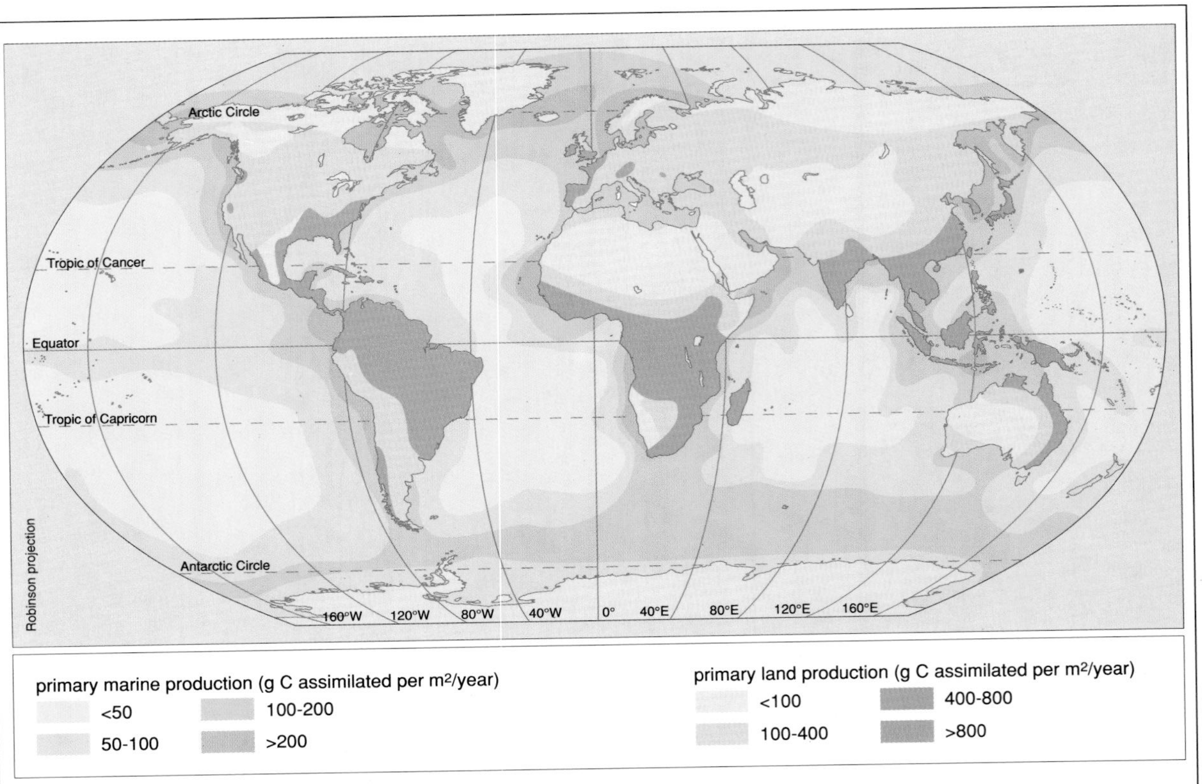

124 The distribution of primary production, expressed in grams of assimilated carbon per square meter/year, in the oceans and on the continents. *[Diagram: Editrònica, from various sources]*

required (there are experimental values between six and ten). This relative inefficiency cannot be considered important, given the way life works. Natural selection has favored the accumulation of structure over a more efficient use of energy.

Once inside organisms, the chemical machinery of life mobilizes and slowly breaks down the assimilated energy through more extensive biochemical cycles, which favor stability and organization over a fast mobilization of energy. Life uses the accumulated energy in chemical bonds prudently in the synthesis of more complex molecules that will become a part of living matter itself. The process is guided by the cellular mechanisms for information transmission (DNA→RNA→enzymes→substrates). Energy breakdown and transfer proceeds inversely. Characteristically, energy mobilization is achieved through the introduction of sugar molecules in a regular cycle of exchanges, involving phosphorated compounds (phosphate is always a good energy carrier), gradually and slowly converting the energy into usable form.

Production and productivity

The synthesis of new organic matter, and even living matter, may be seen as the interest on a capital. Capital could be compared to biomass and interest to *primary production*. There is a difference between *gross primary production* and *net primary production*. These concepts can be clarified by conducting experiments that measure production through oxygen exchange.

The simplest one consists in a suspension of unicellular algae, be it natural plankton or laboratory culture. The experiment is more favorable if an axenic or pure culture of an algal species is used. There is a simple reason for this. Natural plankton contains many bacteria which respire and therefore use part of the organic matter produced, thereby changing the result of the experiment. If there are heterotrophs in the bottle, that is, bacteria or animals, the results will be equivocal, since they will represent the exchange of a broader segment of the ecosystem, and not only the primary producers.

If, in other experiments, we follow the assimilation using radioactive carbon (^{14}C) it will be even harder to solve the problem, because a fraction of ^{14}C (for example, from the respirate) ends up in the water, and is partially recycled. The other more obvious method, which we should have followed, is to estimate the primary production from net increase in mass, or harvest, as it is done with the production of crops. If we followed the same method in the case of algae, we would probably neglect a small part of the matter produced, which algae release into the environment as soluble organic matter. But one can never take all the complexities of nature into account.

It has already been said that primary production (P) is like the yield given by the biomass (B) which is

125 The use of light is optimized inside a wooded area, since the part that is not absorbed by the upper leaves of the canopy is still used. Some light passes through, some is reflected. Thus, some rays of light can reach even the lowest levels through chinks in the foliage, at least in not very dense woods, where there are plants of nonarborescent habit. *[Photo: Zardoya]*

comparable to capital. It seems natural, then, that the ratio *P*/*B* should be widely used in ecology. If we use appropriate units (total weight, dry weight, carbon) or energy units like calories or joules, then productivity is given in watts divided by joules. The dimension of the ratio *P*/*B* is the inverse of time, that is, a velocity. Its inverse, *B*/*P*, is the average time of biomass turnover (turnover time). Obviously, the values derived from the total biomass, or estimated with reference to energy, do not need to coincide. Consider what happens if, in the development of the population, the energy value increases per unit of mass. The term *productivity* is applied to production as a function of some of its factors, the most important one being biomass. *P*/*B* is productivity.

Productivity can also be related to other factors of production, whether external like light intensity, temperature, etc., or internal like chlorophyll concentration. Due to the fact that chlorophyll (and in general all photosynthetic pigments) is easy to evaluate, the ratio production to pigments is frequently used, generally as grams of carbon assimilated in one hour divided by grams of chlorophyll. The maximal theoretical value is 25, though in practice the maximum value is 11, and high values often observed range between 3 and 4. These values are found in favorable light conditions (more than 70 $\mu E/m^2/s$). In less intense light, chlorophyll concentration becomes approximately proportional to the logarithm of light intensity.

Subordination to light and nutrients

The availability and use of light has a great influence on the organization and leaf arrangement and terrestrial plants. It is significant that the concentration of chlorophyll in leaves coincides with the quantity needed for a complete use, and also that terrestrial vegetation tends to have a *leaf area ratio* (LAR) close to 4 (ratio between the horizontal leaf expansion [photosynthetic area] over a given area of ground). Frequently, however, values may be higher, mainly in bulky trees, in which there is obviously more pigment than necessary. This does not happen in short vegetation, e.g. lichens, algae, liverworts, and some mosses. This leads us to believe that the spongy structure of a forest allows the optimal use of light, because only a fraction of the incoming light (maybe 1/3) is absorbed by the leaf, and the rest is mainly reflected, except for a small portion which traverses the leaf. Much of this light is finally absorbed by other leaves.

In addition to this, there always remain gaps in the foliage, through which a circular image of the sun is projected, and the movement of branches and leaves in the wind not only accelerates the gas exchange but also has some influence on the use of light. A white poplar (*Populus alba*) may be a suggestive image, but up to now it has only given rise to some considerations on the mechanics of leaf movement. Since four is the surface of a

126 In terrestrial plants, the leaf area index, that is the ratio of the total leaf surface area to the area of ground surface over which it is projected, generally has a value of four. This would be equivalent to a spherical surface whose radius was equal to that of a circle that had the same extent as the projection of the canopies. In the diagram the situations corresponding to leaf area indices of one and four respectively, are schematized geometrically. With a leaf area index of one, which would be the situation of a canopy in which there was no overlapping or interlacing of the leaves, the area of the circles that represent the surface of the canopy and that of its projection on the ground will be the same. With an index of four, although the projection would be the same (that of the two largest circles, that have the same radius as the circles in the first case), the development of each spherical surface would have an area four times larger ($E=\pi r^2$). *[Diagram: Editrònica, based on the author's original]*

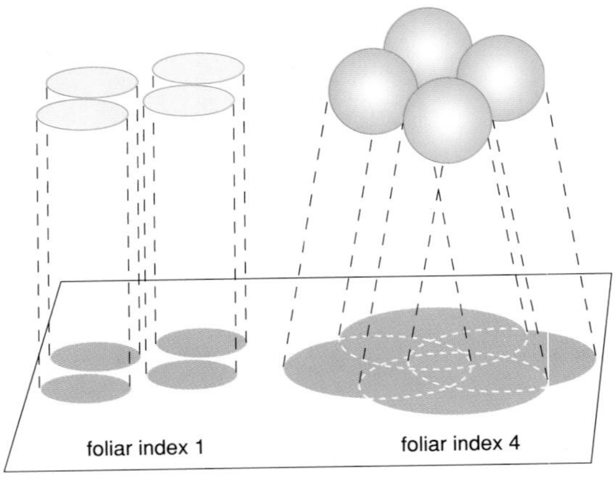

sphere with maximal circle equal to one, the leaf area ratio could be seen as a more general statistical expression of conditions of optimization in radiation interception, which could be an acceptable interpretation of the most common leaf area index, which is close to four.

The expanse and arrangement of leaves creates a particular climate of light in the forest, and some species adjust or become subordinate to others when sharing the available light. Competition is frequent and shown especially in the tendency for dominant plants to grow tall. All this combines with the conditioning of water availability and vertical transport from the soil through the roots. Botanists have interpreted the whole organization of higher plants, or macrophytes, as oriented mainly toward the transport and effective use of water, although this is correct only to a certain extent.

127 Estimates of primary production of different ecosystems in the world, expressed in grams of assimilated carbon per square meter/year. Since the International Biological Program, data has been gathered about the primary production of different biomes. It has to be pointed out that although some of these data, if not the majority, are debatable, some idea of the scales of values in the different areas of the world is available. In those cases where it is prudent to do so, the average biomass of the primary producers concerned is also given, in grams of carbon per square metre. *[Source: the author]*

	PRODUCTION ($g\,C\,m^2\,yr^{-1}$)	BIOMASS ($g\,C\,m^{-2}$)
Mediterranean Sea	60-100	1-2
Fertile coastal seas (North Sea, etc.)	100-500	1-8
Areas of upwelling (Peru, Sahara, etc.)	300-1,200	2-10
Benthonic vegetation of algae and phanerogams	300-3,000	50-1,800
Clean oligotrophic lakes	10-200	1-2
Eutrophic lakes	150-700	5-10
Tundra, subdeserts and steppes	25-300	50-700
Matorral	50-700	400-600
Savannahs	100-200	1,000-1,500
Deciduous forests	150-650	2,500-11,000
Coniferous forests	150-550	1,000-8,000
Moist tropical forests	300-2,000	3,000-40,000
Crops	550-1,825	

Productivity also depends, obviously, on the concentration of necessary available nutrients (carbon, nitrogen, phosphorus, sulfur, etc.). If one nutrient is not present or in very low concentration there often seems to be an excessive assimilation of carbon, which is recognized in vegetative structures and, in the case of algae, often in the excretion of mucilaginous substances. Usually the speed of assimilation is related to the concentration of a limiting nutrient (C_s).

Naturally, all the complexities of physiology must be taken into consideration in ecology, but they should not divert us too much from the more general goals, which often allow for rough approximations. However, we should bear in mind the necessity to improve them. Let us remember, for instance, that the alternation between light and dark periods subjects the physiology of plant assimilation to a very pronounced rhythm, whose study is of great interest.

Estimating production and productivity

Attempts are now being made to analyze productivity and to interpret the conditions of production through the use of images taken from space. The meaning of reflection at wavelengths attributable to chlorophyll and other pigments needs to be interpreted, too. However, in the sea, the maximal concentration of chlorophyll often lies 200-300 ft (60-100 m) deep, and it is not visible. In terrestrial ecology, the combination of color interpretation and texture details that may indicate, for instance, the height and "grain" of vegetation is often neglected. It is worth pointing out, though, that the information is ever more abundant and accurate, which leads us to believe that we are closer to a better knowledge of plant biomass distribution and its primary production.

It is fashionable to consider recent and possible changes in biomass and dead organic matter in relation to the increase or decrease in productivity and transfers of matter (mainly carbon) to other compartments of the Earth (e.g. CO_2 in the atmosphere) and in relation to possible modifications in the cycles of other elements like nitrogen. More attention is usually paid to nitrogen than phosphorus, although the latter is a better candidate for being the limiting nutrient of planetary production.

If we arrange the various production values on a map, both on land and the oceans, there are common features in their respective distributions: generally there are regions, usually not very large ones, with a high primary production, and increasingly large areas that correspond to ever lower production val-

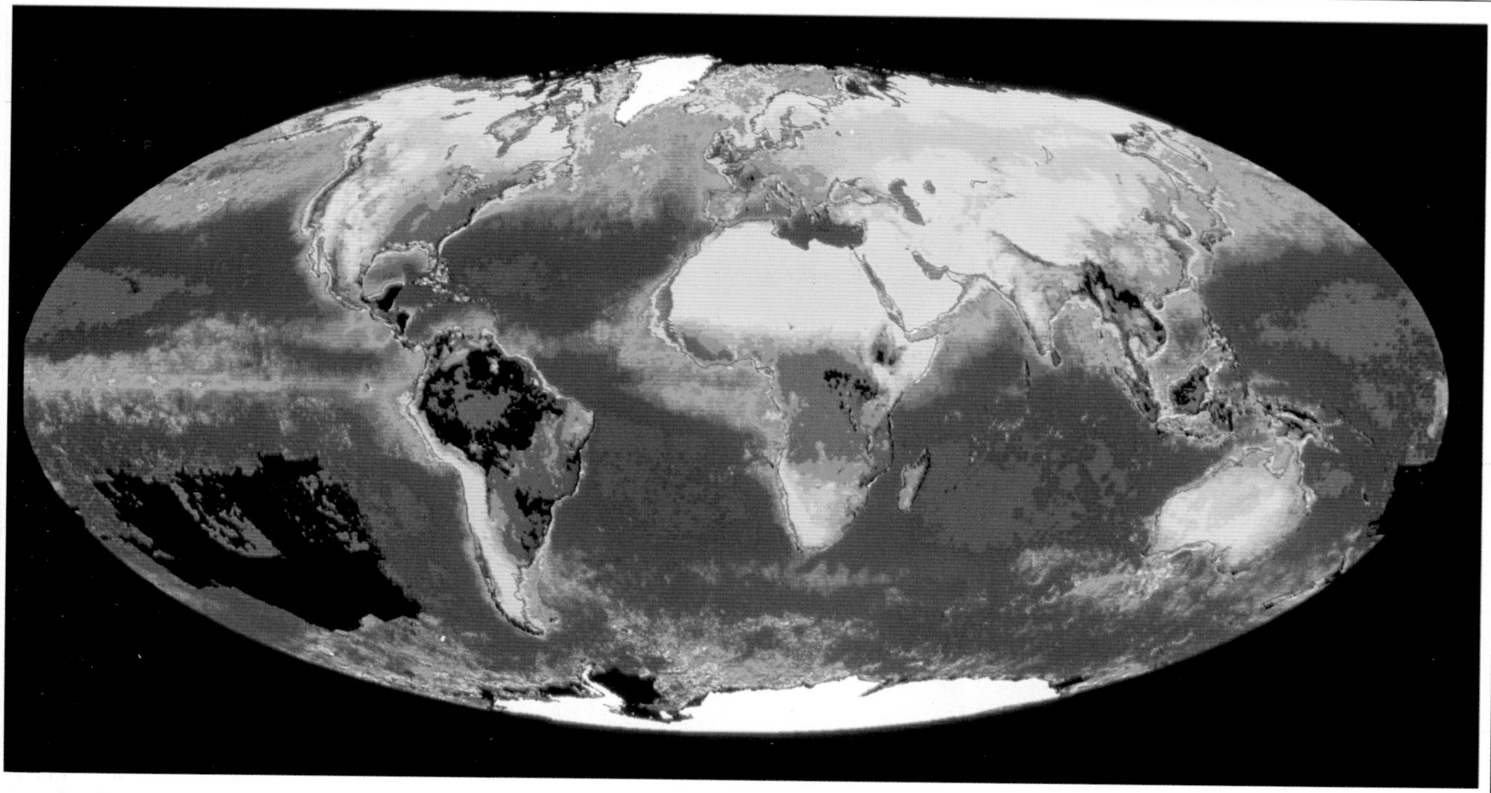

ues. Such an arrangement may be more regular in the oceans than on land. As far as oceans are concerned, we have already discussed the basic mechanism in relation to the availability of the limiting nutrients. If the way marine ecosystems work implies the accumulation of nourishment on the bottom, then what controls production is the movement of those deep water masses upwards, towards the surface and the light. Therefore primary production seems to be tightly correlated to the energy used locally in promoting the vertical movement of water. In terrestrial systems, the relationships are basically equivalent. We have always known that productivity on land was a function of the availability of liquid water and consequently also a function of temperature. The fraction of the year in which water is solid constitutes the most serious limitation, although not as serious as the scarcity or total lack of water. Empirically derived expressions which give primary production as a function of water availability and temperature have been proposed, for example, the one used in the maps elaborated by Lieth.

Farmers know that 200-500 quarts (200-500 l) of water are needed to produce 2 lbs (1 kg) of cereals. Obviously the cost of water may be expressed as the energy involved in evaporation, rain, and evapotranspiration. As in the case of the seas, we reach the conclusion that primary production is a function of some external or exosomatic energy that decays or is degraded in the peripheral space of our Earth.

In global terms, primary production is a function of a fractional power (about 0.6) of degraded exosomatic energy per area unit.

The average production of the oceans is calculated at about 100 g $C/m^2/yr$, a figure which corresponds to plankton. The coastal vegetation per area unit is more productive, but it occupies a much smaller area and its contribution to total marine production is probably lower than 2%. Coral reefs should be considered separately since their main primary producers are algae, which live symbiotically in the colonial animals and are in turn exploited by them. Therefore the eventual surplus of net production is extraordinarily small in relation to the net primary production of algae.

In terrestyrial systems, the average primary production is about three times higher than in the seas, around 300 g $C/m^2/yr$. If we take the relative extent of the continents and the oceans into account, we could correctly say, and it would be good and proper to bear this in mind, that the total production of the Earth is shared almost equally between them. The average distance traveled by the nutrients on their way back is much longer in the oceans, which are on average 13,000 ft (4 km) deep, than on land, where the soil is relatively thin and horizontal transport is not too excessive. In addition, terrestrial vegetation, and especially trees, control the upward flow of water very effectively through a well-organized system of channels. In the pelagic marine

128 Image in false color of the density of chlorophyll on the surface of the oceans and the continents, made up from images received by the sensors of two satellites: *Nimbus-7*, for the phytoplankton of the oceans, and *NOAA-7*, for the terrestrial vegetation. In the oceans, the density increases, following the colors of the rainbow, from dark violet in the center of the oceans to red in areas of upwelling. On the continents, it ranges from the pale yellow of the deserts to the dark green of some of the tropical forests. *[Photo: Gene Feldman, NASA GFSC / Science Photo Library / AGE Fotostock]*

129 In ecology, reference is frequently made when dealing with processes to the maximum values permitted (maximum velocity, maximum population, etc.). Logically, it is a doubtful practice but it continues to be used with some success. In the upper part of the diagram is shown an application of the Michaelis-Menten model that describes the speed of a process (*V*) and the concentration of the limiting factor, for example, the concentration of a nutrient (*C*). $K_{1/2}$ is the concentration at which the speed is half the maximum. Models can be constructed in which various limiting factors intervene, as shown in the lower part of the diagram.
[Drawing: Biopunt, from data supplied by the author]

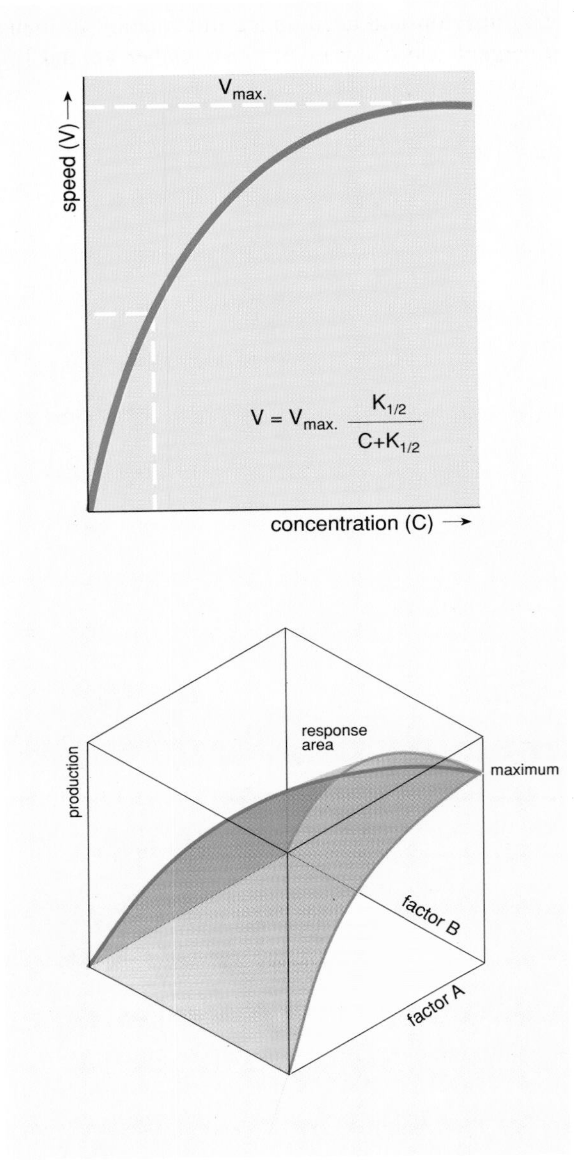

region, upward flows take place in a fluid, unorganized system. Therefore it is not surprising that these flows are much less effective when compared to the energy of the climate that takes part in them.

The biosphere must have worked in this way from the beginning, since its basic mechanisms do not seem to have varied much in the course of evolution. It seems as if Nature, if we may personify her, has intensified the richness of forms and diversity more than the mere quantity and capacity for physical work. Nevertheless, we cannot exclude some variations that may have been important. There are signs that in the glacial eras, the primary production of the whole biosphere was lower, maybe between 3/4 and 2/3 of what it is today, but it does not mean to say that any other changes in primary production have not been greater than this.

3.3 Food: the dependency of animals on subsidiary life

Heterotrophic life

We do not need complicated hypotheses to understand how dependent or heterotrophic life originated. In a regime of alternating day and night, the continuity of life during the night needed to be based on materials synthesized during the day. These materials allowed the continuation of life of the organisms which synthesized and then used them, and were also a constant temptation to start the evolution of a pure heterotrophic life regime in organisms that lost or gave up their capacity to assimilate, store, and use solar energy.

Osmotrophy and phagotrophy

There are two varieties of heterotrophic life. The first one, *osmotrophy*, consists in using molecules that are present in the environment, for instance, molecules dissolved in water that can pass through the surrounding membrane of the cell surfaces. This is done by osmotrophic heterotrophs, whose main representatives are bacteria and fungi. The other, *phagotrophy*, is related to the fact that the available concentration of organic matter remains high if the interior of other organisms is colonized (parasites), or when temporarily confining other organisms or parts of them to ones digestive system, so their decomposition results in a solution that is highly concentrated in all sorts of suitable molecules. This is the act of eating, as invented by the so-called phagotrophs, the animals proper.

The advantages of phagotrophy

The phagotrophic way of life permits different forms of specialization. The variety of functional forms that have developed manifests itself in the evolution of two systems that are associated, though less closely than one would suspect. One is the evolution of devices for detection, hunting, and capture. The other, parallel to the first though less spectacular or at least less visible and not so extreme, is the evolution of chemical mechanisms for attacking, decomposing, and using ingested materials. The development of very complete and balanced animal feeds, specially for chicken farming, allowed their use in zoos to keep alive such exotic animals as the hen (originally from southwest Asia), thus proving that often what lies at the base of the problem of introducing an animal species into its environment is how they obtain food and not how they digest it.

From an evolutionary point of view, it is obvious that the possibilities of phagotrophic nutrition allow

it to develop and accumulate information in many divergent ways: the enormously richer animal life with respect to plant life is a witness to it. So far the number of plants, animals, and microorganisms described may be higher than 1.4 million, and many more remain to be discovered. Flowering plants (250,000 species) together with other autotrophic plants (algae) represent less than 25% of the whole. Thus, the diversification of life has gone further in heterotrophs than in autotrophs, regardless of the fact that the latter are the first and autonomous form of life. There is also a vast number of fungi and lichen species. One might believe that there have been more stimuli among animals and that the multiple possible directions of evolution have been explored further than among plants. These sorts of statistics and considerations are widely used when discussing, with a certain sadness, the loss of biological diversity in the world today.

The nature of food

Food satisfies both plastic and energetic needs. It is both an input of energy and matter for an organism, and also an input of information: the role of vitamins

130 The best known osmotrophs are the fungi, such as these scarlet pezizas (*Sarcoscypha coccinea*). Their main source of food is cellulose from plant remains in the litter and humus, which they break down with enzymes to obtain glucose molecules that they absorb through the membranes of its hyphae. *[Photo: Joaquim Carbó / SCM]*

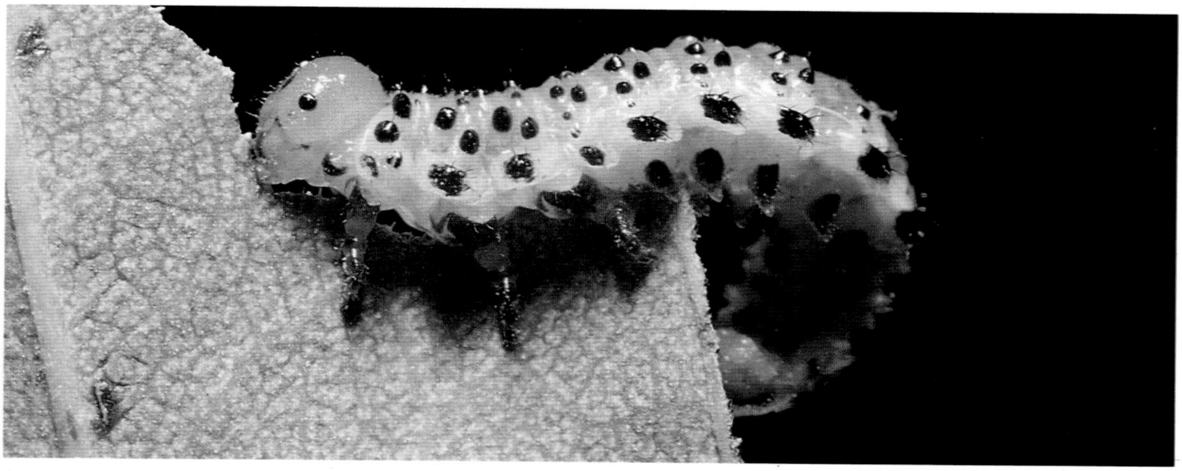

131 The diversity of the animal world is very great, especially as regards ways of obtaining food and the kinds of food used. Two very different examples are the false rose caterpillar (*Arge rosae*), a herbivore that feeds on rose leaves (above), and the red frog (*Rana temporaria*), a carnivore that we see trapping an insect. *[Photos: R.Campillo / Zardoya and Frank Greenaway / Bruce Coleman Limited]*

132 Tridachnid bivalves (giant clams) that live in the coral reefs of the Indo-Pacific region, expose the edge of their fleshy and brilliantly colored mantle to the sunlight so as to facilitate the growth of populations of intracellular symbiotic algae which supply them with food.
[Photo: AGE Fotostock]

and the cases of symbiosis would be examples of this added value of ingested food.

Energy from food

At levels of production beyond primary production, life uses energy stored in relatively unstable chemical linkages; the linkages between metals or those of crystalline material, for example, cannot be used. The energy that can be supplied by the total oxidation of one mole of normal organic material is around 2 to 8 x 10^5 J, which is 0.5 - 2 x 10^2 kcal. A gram of carbon represents around 10 kcal, an easy figure to remember when making rough estimates. Compounds that are rich in energy, such as ATP (adenosine triphosphate), and which are common currency in the metabolism of organisms, do not give more than 40 or 50 kcal/mole under normal physiological conditions.

Carbon accounts for roughly 10% of the weight of living matter, so that 3.5 oz (100 g) of total fresh weight contain between 40 and 160 usable kcal, as anyone will be able to remember from the tables which are often produced for diets. Materials with little water (wood, nectar, pollen, wax, resin, seeds, hair, and feathers) give values of up to 240-600 kcal per 3.5 oz (100 g) of fresh weight. They are not easily digestible, but organisms that manage to digest them have a monopoly over them.

Only in its reduced form can the carbon from organic molecules adopt the infinite number of variations of molecular structures. The substances in this reduced form can be oxidized when they come into contact with the oxygen in the air. Through respiration or combustion, we load the atmosphere with the most oxidized compound of carbon (CO_2). At the same time, oxidized compounds of nitrogen and sulfur are also formed.

The incorporation of living biological information: symbiosis

In very specific cases, living biological information, when it is different enough to be inoffensive, can be accepted. Sometimes, as with viruses, it only manages to copy itself. Or its continued functioning in a parallel fashion is tolerable, and this has been the origin of many symbioses, such as the algae or bacteria that live inside the cells of other organisms (corals and ciliates with endosymbiotic algae).

Since the beginning of the century, some researchers have thought that the adoption or assimilation of alien organisms or of some of their part was a process that has occurred repeatedly through the course of evolution. They think that this has enabled the formation of the eukaryotic cell and biological evolution to be speeded up. Most organisms could be considered monsters, along the same lines as Dr. Frankenstein's legendary monster—made of pieces created by life along independent lines and that the good fortune of archaeological finds and mutual interest have been able to combine. Complex organs practically devoid of biological information, and therefore that cannot be reproduced, can also be assimilated. An example of this are the stinging capsules of Coelenterata, which some species of marine molluscs seize with impunity without setting them off and then use them again in self-defense.

The case of vitamins

The question of the maximum level of complication and of molecular weight that assimilating molecules can reach is tied to the question of vitamins. The name vitamin is given to substances of an average molecular size, which are neither too simple nor too complex, which are produced by several organisms, and which other organisms continue to need, after losing the capacity to synthesize them themselves. The end result is that the second organisms are dependent on the first ones, which are capable of synthesizing them. The biological and ecological interpretation is simple. In bacteriology and experimental mycology, when the necessary molecules are added to cultures, it is easy to sustain defective genetic mutations unable to synthesize these molecules. Strains with this defect can continue to propagate themselves in media enriched with the substances they require.

There are very complex ecosystems that regularly have in their matrix or physical environment a whole host of relatively complex molecules. The presence of these allows for the survival of classes of other species, which need them, but which have lost their capacity to produce them. Clearly certain important changes, which lead to a faulty supply of vitamins, can mean that the species needing the vitamins are weakened and can even disappear. It is natural to find more species needing vitamins in those ecosystems that can offer them, in other words, those that are rich in species and have not experienced very frequent disturbances. It seems obvious that humans, Neolithic humanss, who are characterized by the adoption of a more sedentary life with a more routine diet based on a sharply limited range of cultivated produce, was accompanied by an epidemic of various vitamin deficiencies. Now, on the other hand, we use natural metabolic pathways for contaminants that are hardly necessary for the body to work, in fact quite the opposite; a clear example of this are the many products and by-products of industry, like metals which are dissolved and mobilized through the never-ending changes (acidification, for example) to which we subject our environment.

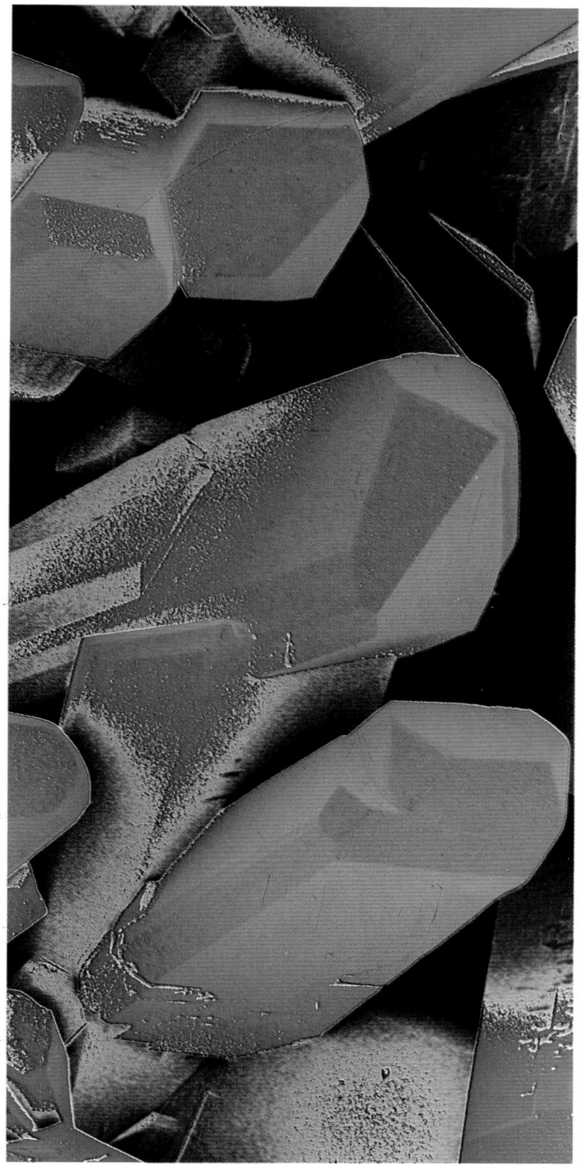

133 Vitamin C has the simplest molecular structure of any vitamin. It is the laboratory form of ascorbic acid, and at ordinary temperatures it occurs as a white powder which is easily soluble in water and composed of fine monoclinic crystals such as those seen in false color in the scanning electron micrograph. Vitamin C, which is abundant in most fruits and vegetables, acts as a regulator of cellular respiration. *[Photo: J. Burgess / Science / AGE Fotostock (x 113)]*

Food processing

In the evolution of life, the identity of a particular species is maintained. Organisms have a precise hierarchy of information carriers, which ultimately depends on nuclear DNA. Though this hierarchy does not admit important disturbances, it is flexible enough to handle recognition, acceptance and reaction, as happens all the time in the immune system. Food is broken down by the action of enzymes into sufficiently small fragments which may carry energy or serve as construction parts, but which do not present the risk of introducing alien information into the genetic systems.

The nutritional value of glycides and lipids

Glycides, carbohydrates and sugars are all typical foods. They consist of relatively unspecific molecules which contain carbon atoms often arranged in a ring, together with oxygen and hydrogen in the same proportions as in water. Basic molecules may combine forming other molecules of higher molecular weight. Lipids or fatty acids have the same chemical elements, though a smaller proportion of the water components. They form longer molecules. A gram of sugar releases 4,100 cal in a calorimeter. When used within an organism the release is a little smaller, 3,850 cal, because it is not completely oxidized in an oxygen atmosphere, as in a calorimeter. With respect to lipids and fatty acids, the release in a calorimeter is about 9,300 and 8,000 cal per gram, respectively.

The break down of these molecules is never a sudden one, as it would be if they were burned in a flame, but a progressive one, step by step without ever completely finishing. Life tends to reduce energy flow per unit of mass. The tendency is materialized in the metabolic cycles. An example is the Krebs' cycle, which separates energy from sugar following a succession of chemical steps involving phosphates. Thus ADP can be converted into ATP, one of the most commonly used energy accumulators of intermediary metabolism. The chains of fatty acids are consumed like a candle, starting from one end (or from both ends), and as slowly. Life will never burn itself out if it remains active, i.e. if the water concentration is sufficiently high. We should bear in mind that the quantity of calories required by the evaporation of water in "normal" temperatures is about 600 calories (or approximately 2,500 J) per gram of water, and that water represents between 70 and 80% of organisms' weight. Wood and dry plant tissues contain less water, though, which is why forests are susceptible to burning.

The nutritional value of proteins

Proteins also contain energy, but they are more important as sources of nitrogen compounds. Thus, amino acids are incorporated as such, and some are not synthesized by many organisms which, therefore, need to obtain them from food. Afterwards, amino acids are joined to form specific proteins. This is similar to the situation found in vitamins which have to be incorporated from food. It is easy to understand why life uses this strategy: it is wise to use as energy carriers bonds from ordinary molecules, avoiding for this purpose the use of bonds adjacent to atoms less common than carbon, oxygen and hydrogen.

Trophic webs

Alimentary relationships, like the one expressed in the popular saying "the big fish eats the tiddler," may be dignified with the scientific name trophic chain or web. The expression refers to the fact that some animals can eat others in a sequence that may include various stages, up to five or more. There may be more levels, especially when considering parasites and hyperparasites (parasites of parasites) which may add up to five steps. It is natural for the individuals of predatory species to be bigger (and to live longer, which is as important or even more so in biology) than the individuals of their prey.

There are no simple trophic chains. Lateral connections generally exist between them: two predatory species may go after the same prey species, or vice versa, different prey species are prey to one predator. For this reason, it is more appropriate to talk about trophic webs rather than trophic chains, while recognizing the limited number of levels. The trophic web could be seen as having a fibrous structure, since there is a certain tendency to eliminate, as a result of competition, an excessive number of horizontal connections at a given height of the web. Cannibalistic relations, or those in which predator and prey change roles, are rare or exceptional.

Trophic levels and parasitism

It has been customary, at least from the years of Charles Elton (1910-1993), between 1932 and 1938, to represent graphically some selected quantitative properties of the successive trophic levels in an ecosystem (vegetarians, first order carnivores, second order carnivores, etc.), in ways which remind us of the pyramids of the ancient Aztecs and Mayans. Vertically each floor depends on the one immediately below it, and regardless of the scale of magnitude used, its numerical expression generally decreases towards the top of the pyramid. The production or flow of energy decreases more rapidly than biomass, because the populations of higher-level carnivores renew themselves very slowly, i.e. the average life expectation of carnivores is usually longer than that of vegetarians. One reason for this, especially for the top predators, is that they are not prey to any other higher species. (A few vegetarian species have got rid of their enemies by increasing their size enormously, like elephants, rhinoceroses, hippopotamuses, and undoubtedly, several breeds of dinosaurs.) The relationship, according

134 The trophic relationships between organisms can seldom be expressed as simple food chains in which one organism eats another and in turn is eaten by a third. Different predator species can feed on a single species of prey, or different species of prey can serve as food for a particular predator. For this reason, even in simple representations such as this figure, which could represent a stream in middle Europe or in a Mediterranean mountain and its banks, it is preferable to treat trophic relationships as a web—the food web. *[Diagram: Biopunt]*

to which information-carrying subsystems are also the ones which renew themselves more slowly, is already found in the cell's internal systems (substrates—enzymes—RNA—DNA). Using a mechanical simile, each ecosystem could be compared to a gear, in which pinions spin faster than the respective cog-wheels of larger diameter with which they engage.

The segments of the trophic chains corresponding to parasites are very different, because the regularity described above is inverted, since parasites are smaller and have shorter life spans than their respective hosts. It is as if parasitic life abandoned actual control to the hosts. On the other hand, parasitism is very diverse. When a parasite metabolizes or cuts up long molecules from which it can extract sufficient energy, and the host further breaks down the remaining molecular segments, the parasite may become integrated into the host's metabolic machinery and may thus become necessary. We could then say that it behaves as a symbiont, but these descriptions (parasite, symbiont) are too loaded with anthropocentrism and ought to be discarded.

Energy flows

It is often accepted that the flow of energy from one trophic level to another through successive trophic levels is divided approximately by ten at every step, as figure comparable to the weight of pork obtained as a function of the weight of fodder fed to the pigs. This convergence around a common value is surprising considering the great variety of organisms involved in relations such as those existing between consumer and consumed.

In fact, the convergence may seem reasonable because of the fact that animals that automatically eat food of a low nutritional value (earth-eaters, mud-eaters, eaters or those that filter suspended materials, which could be qualified as "fork animals") usually work in a continuous way, often using material of low nutritional value. These animals have a low metabolic rate, are not very active, and a considerable fraction of what they have assimilated is used in reproduction.

On the other hand, carnivores, which may be very active, completely digest very nutritious pieces of meat. But carnivores have a high metabolic rate and move a lot, while a relatively smaller part of what they assimilate is destined to produce a new generation. In this case, naturally, a higher proportion of the diet may consist of sugars or fats which are simple suppliers of energy. Very active animals, like bumble bees or hummingbirds, have a diet rich in sugars.

135 The British ecologist Charles Elton devised a representation of the successive levels of the trophic chains using different descriptors (number, biomass, productivity), in the form of stepped pyramids, as in the upper diagram. These representations are often used in ecology, which are known as *Elton pyramids*. Other models that include energy flows, such as those proposed by Howard T. Odum—one of which is shown in the lower figure—can be both more subtle and more realistic. *[Diagram: Editrònica]*

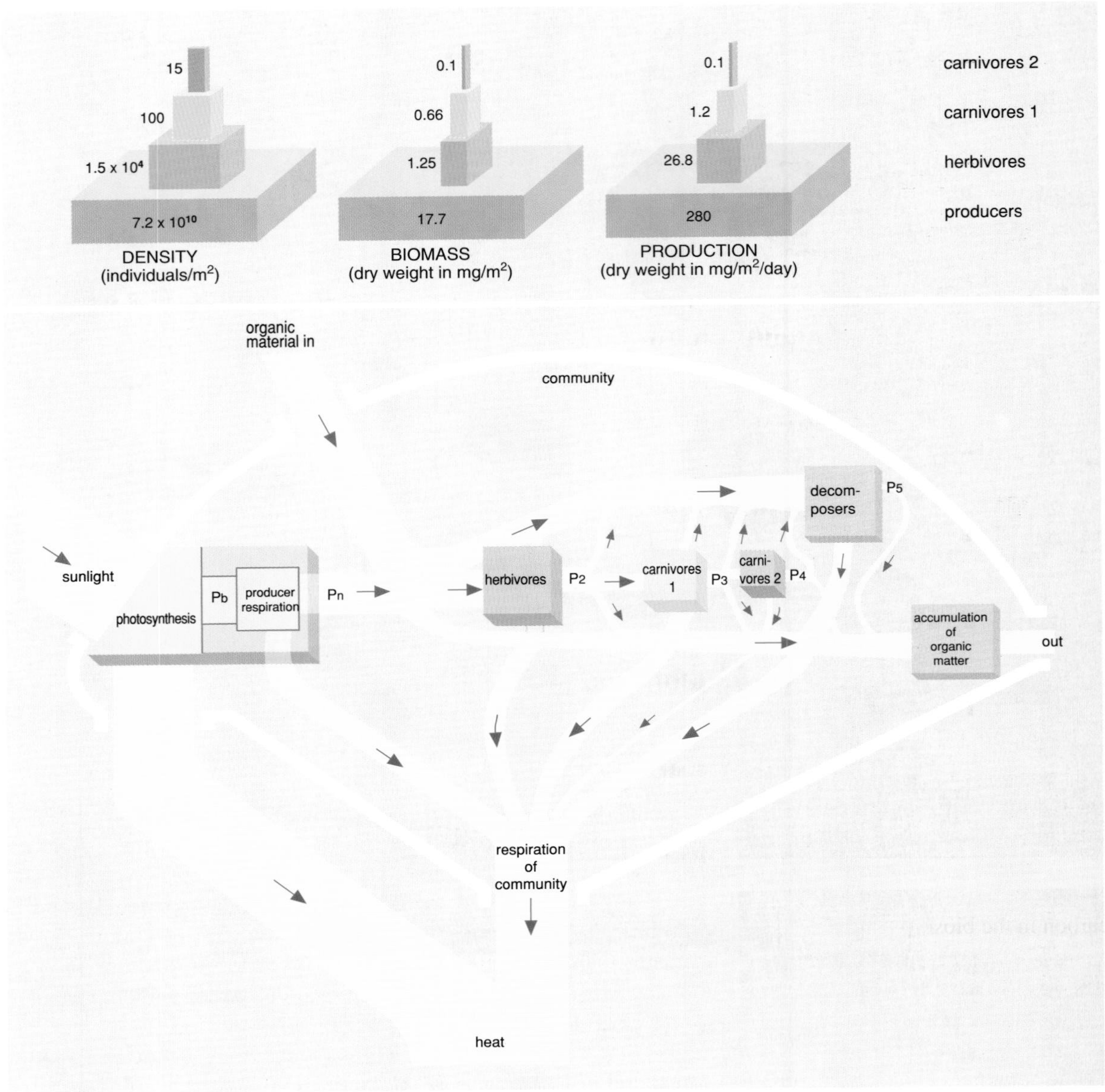

In the course of evolution, these are examples of animals which have regressed in terms of their trophic development. These animals, once "fork animals," are again "spoon animals." They have undergone profound organic reconstructions, like the ones observed in the beak and tongue of flamingoes when compared to other birds. The beak and the tongue are used by the flamingo, as tools which "sift" the mud very well while selecting small bulbs, seeds, and small crustaceans. A similar evolutive transformation can be observed in the mysticeti cetaceans (the true whales) which feed on relatively small crustaceans, molluscs and fish. These mammals have profoundly reorganized their mouths. They have developed palatal filters of corneous laminae, which constitute the so-called "beards." If the energy flow is roughly divided by ten at each level there would be no more than 10^{-5} of primary production left in the fifth level. This would be the most important reason, though not the only one, why trophic chains are relatively limited in length. The immediate conclusion drawn from this is the absence of big carnivores in areas of limited size: a tiger could not survive on a small island.

Plants offer a wide array of possibilities to phytophagous animals. The large number of insects adapted to live on any given species of plant is an example of this. The life of a tree, which can last for thousands of years with a high degree of genetic conservatism, contrasts with the thousands of generations of some insects that inhabit it, and which evolve at a much greater rate. This is a condition generally referred to when talking about the well justified "conservatism" of plants.

136 The differences in feeding strategy between filter feeders, which are generally stationary or with little mobility, and those that seek food actively are quite great. All are, however, consumers and cannot produce themselves what they need for their metabolism. Sponges, for example (below) are characteristic filter feeders. However, bats (above), both carnivorous and herbivorous, such as this American *Leptonycteris*, which feeds off the fruits of a cactus, are animals which have to expend a great deal of energy in the search for food.
[Photos: Merlin D. Tuttle / Bat Conservation International Inc. and Da Rocha Filho Rubens / Image Bank]

3.4 Dust from the dead

It has been said that many of the shortcomings in ecology nowadays are due to the fact that ecologists are not very fond of conducting observations at night, underground, or in excreta. Recycling involves a quantity of matter that lived once and is now dead: *Necromass*, i.e. dead organic matter, is greater in amount than the biomass itself. Meanwhile, the dead organic matter still carries an amount of energy, that is usable and used by many varied organisms, which are particularly abundant and diversified in soils and sediments. It has already been mentioned that there exist "twilight" situations in which death is not complete, e.g. that represented by wood.

The total recycling of dead material is not as fast as one might suppose because of the pressure that nature experiences in the form of selection that favored the appearance of molecules resistant to decomposition. This has been said before in relation to the support and transport system of higher plants. Reserve materials are also resistant to decomposition. They are locked up treasures and it is wise to keep the keys: the particular enzymes that alone can make them usable. Bacon and beans, and the way humans profit from them are also good examples. Chemical messengers and external hormones, or pheromones, are also very resistant molecules, which are difficult to break down.

It is marvellous at what distance insects of the same species and different sex can communicate chemically, although it is rarely mentioned that, in order to work, active molecules must have a long life. This is exactly what humans do with their antibiotics and biocides in general. DDT must have a long life, and a bottle made to hold liquid should not be biodegradable.

137 Leaf litter and humus are dead materials largely used by soil organisms. Soil organisms transform, recycle, and reincorporate leaf litter and humus' basic components into the ecosystem cycles, or they are transported—by water for example—and reincorporated into other connected ecosystems. The leaf litter still retains traces of the components from which it is derived, while humus is amorphous and integrated into the structure of the soil. *[Photo: Kim Taylor / Bruce Coleman Limited]*

Dead material

The presence and eventual accumulation of dead material, or chemically reduced carbon compounds that have been synthesized by life, has a mixed origin. On the one hand, it is due to the particular resistance that chemical bonds have, either in the original material or in molecules, that are smaller or that have been modified in some way and that remain after the most vulnerable bonds have been broken. On the other hand, molecules that could be oxidized are not, because they accumulate in oxygen-scarce places, e.g. in anoxic sediments on the sea floor, in lakes, or in peatbogs.

This dead organic matter is not only involved in the ecological cycles, with some positive or utilitarian significance in the case of wood, but also in other situations. It is often the basis of many reactions and decomposes slowly, like the humus in the soil and in natural waters. Humus is one of the most little-known compounds, as far as its precise chemical composition is concerned. Traditionally, *litter* and other names are used to refer to dead material which has a structure that allows us to recognise its origin. *Humus* is already one step further. It is amorphous and it hides, even under the microscope, its origin. Its molecular composition is still not sufficiently known.

Most of this material is used by soil heterotrophs and re-enters the ecosystem through recycling. The same is true for mineral compounds, like potassium and phosphorus, which are recycled in standing trees. Rain washes potassium off the leaf surfaces, but often it is assimilated by the roots not much later. A complete and local recycling of most required elements happens more frequently in humid tropical forests than in plant communities located on slopes or in seasonal plant communities, since these lose elements continually and gain others through erosion of nearby rocks or those at higher levels.

The interaction between biosphere and lithosphere

The continuous exchange between the biosphere and the lithosphere has determined much more important changes in the latter than the changes that would have occurred in it without the existence of life. The

138 The large accumulation of litter darkens the waters of rivers and streams, such as this stream in South-West National Park in Tasmania, which receives the debris from the luxuriant vegetation of laurisilva through which it flows. The final destination of the humus, which is dissolved in the water and dyes it these dark colors so common in many tropical rivers, is not known with certainty; such water dyeing also occurs, as in this case, in temperate latitudes.
[Photo: Kathie Atkins / Oxford Scientific Films / Firo Foto]

changes in carbonated rocks and the decomposition of silicates are both under the control of the biosphere. It is frequently pointed out that the alteration of the rocks of the periphery of the Earth has been twice as fast (it is difficult to make quantitative estimations) as it would have been without the existence of life. Overall, the accelerated selective transformation of the superficial solid materials of the lithosphere may be attributed to the maintenance, through the action of life, of the vertical redox gradient. Both the final phases of decomposition of humic materials and of alteration of clays are realized under conditions of low energy, which give a great variability of final products. Humus and clays are bound to adapt to each other as essential components of the soils, especially of the most mature ones, to which they give their most interesting properties.

There should be more research into the destination of the humus dissolved in water, e.g. the matter that gives the brown color to "black water" rivers which are frequent in the South American subcontinent, and in peaty waters around the world. It has long been known that there is a considerable amount of organic carbon in solution in the oceans, often around one or more milligrams of carbon per litre, which is intensely fluorescent and sometimes given the name "Gelbstoff" or yellow stuff. Its content of carbon 14 has certainly been studied, in an attempt to know the time that has elapsed since these materials were assimilated by organisms which were in equilibrium with the isotope composition of the atmosphere at that time. Surprising numbers of 6,000 years or more have been obtained for deep water levels of the Pacific and of half a millennium or more for superficial waters of the Atlantic, which appears to be younger or more active biologically.

In each ecosystem, most of these molecules are the ones which temporarily get out of control in ordinary and local cycles of organic materials. However, it is also suspected that in the oceans there is a relatively excessive fraction of materials, coming from these continents, whose synthesis depended highly on wood, fungi, and other materials which went through a humus phase. This is a little explored research topic, though it certainly has a great interest in relation to the global cycles of materials, especially that of carbon.

Soil destruction involves the oxidation of a fraction of the humic material that soils contain. Forest fires have the same effects. And it has been found that the destruction of humus by desertification, fires, and agriculture may represent an important contribution to the global greenhouse effect, i.e. the oxidation of all this material increases atmospheric CO_2 concentration. According to relatively recent estimates, this contribution ranges between 2 and 3 thousand million tons of carbon per year for the surface of the continents. This represents half the amount of fossil fuels burned by humankind.

Nuclear, solar, or fossil

The energy from chemical bonds, like that from the Sun, is of high quality. It seems natural that it should be exploited first and in the easiest form possible: gas and oil are easier to exploit than solid carbon (coal), but their exploitable reserves are limited. In 1988, 0.81 mi^3 (3.39 km^3) of oil and 461 mi^3 (1,922 km^3) of natural gas were extracted. Estimated maximum total reserves are equivalent to about 100 times this current annual use. Under optimal conditions we can predict that reserves will last for two generations, three at the most. Of course there is also a considerable quantity of coal that is hard to measure. Solar energy presents the difficulties that were so positive for the launching of organic evolution: its periodicity and the need to build reserves or storage devices.

Control centre in the nuclear power station of New Brunswick
[Alex Bartel - Science Photo Library / AGE Fotostock]

Most of the exosomatic energy directly controlled by humans originates in the combustion of matter that was reduced or assimilated by life in the Earth's past (fossil fuels) and present (wood, energy from the biomass). Most, but not all.

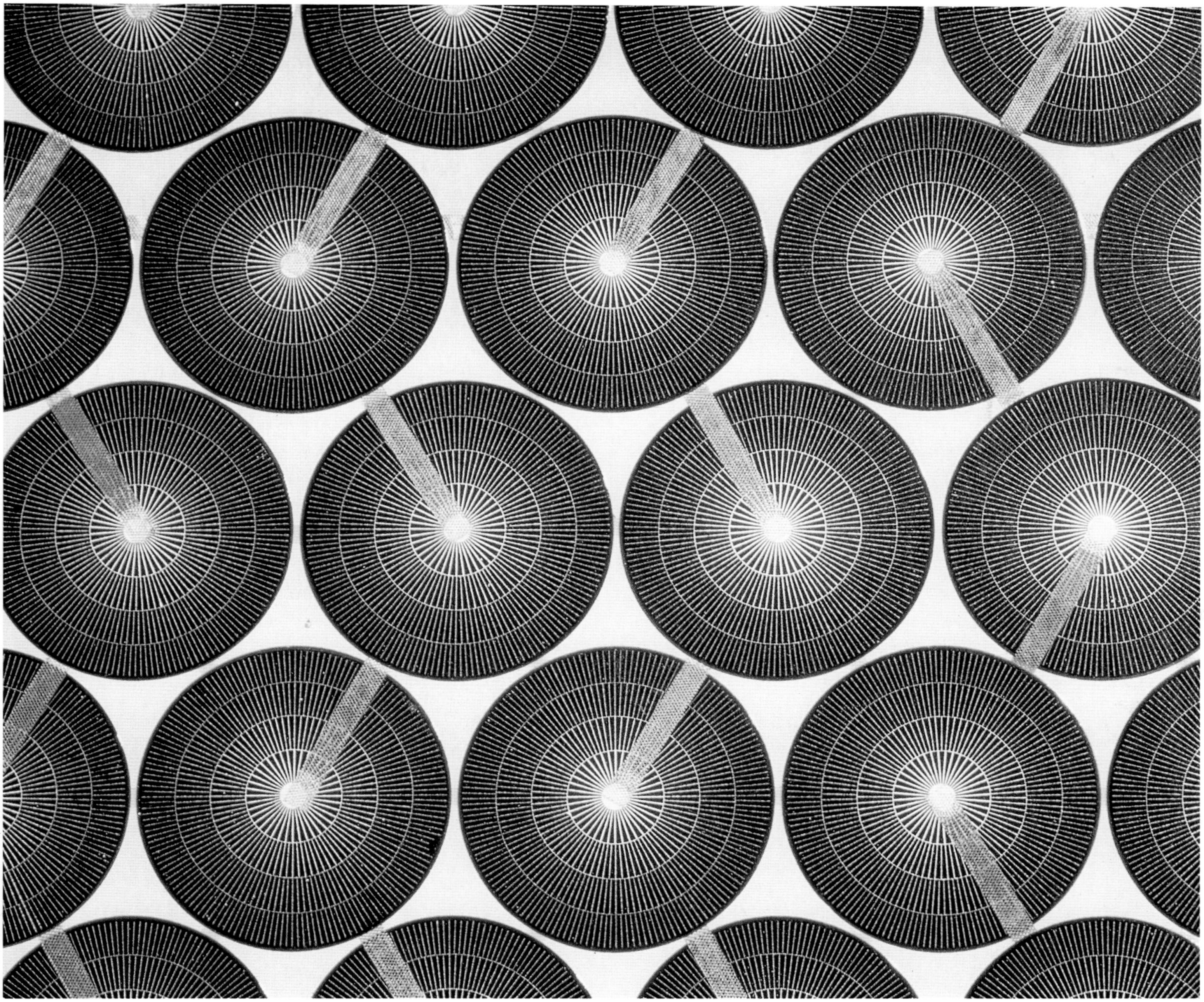

Solar energy is used in a very degraded form, as hydroelectric energy, and its poor quality is reflected in the size of the machines required to exploit it: dams, pipes, turbines, and alternators. The widespread use of electrical energy reduces transportation costs to a minimum, and will reduce them even further if in the future superconductivity is more widely used. Other energy sources look less promising. Maybe that is why they are called "alternative" energy sources. And the performance of biological conversion, as we know, does not allow us to expect much from exploiting the energy of the biomass, except in very modest terms and in exceptionally favorable local situations. It has been said, and it deserves repeating, that saving energy is a source of energy.

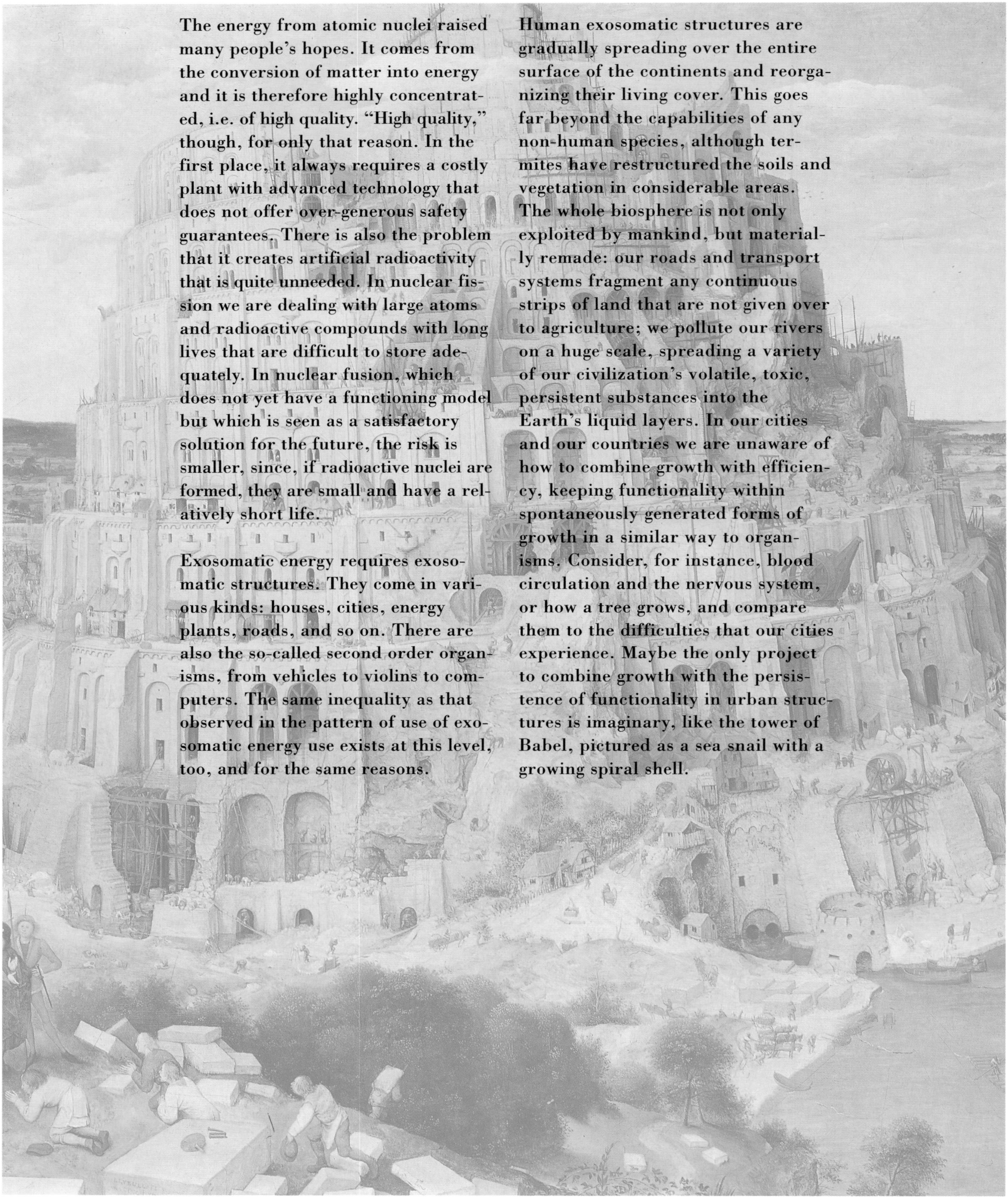

The energy from atomic nuclei raised many people's hopes. It comes from the conversion of matter into energy and it is therefore highly concentrated, i.e. of high quality. "High quality," though, for only that reason. In the first place, it always requires a costly plant with advanced technology that does not offer over-generous safety guarantees. There is also the problem that it creates artificial radioactivity that is quite unneeded. In nuclear fission we are dealing with large atoms and radioactive compounds with long lives that are difficult to store adequately. In nuclear fusion, which does not yet have a functioning model but which is seen as a satisfactory solution for the future, the risk is smaller, since, if radioactive nuclei are formed, they are small and have a relatively short life.

Exosomatic energy requires exosomatic structures. They come in various kinds: houses, cities, energy plants, roads, and so on. There are also the so-called second order organisms, from vehicles to violins to computers. The same inequality as that observed in the pattern of use of exosomatic energy use exists at this level, too, and for the same reasons.

Human exosomatic structures are gradually spreading over the entire surface of the continents and reorganizing their living cover. This goes far beyond the capabilities of any non-human species, although termites have restructured the soils and vegetation in considerable areas. The whole biosphere is not only exploited by mankind, but materially remade: our roads and transport systems fragment any continuous strips of land that are not given over to agriculture; we pollute our rivers on a huge scale, spreading a variety of our civilization's volatile, toxic, persistent substances into the Earth's liquid layers. In our cities and our countries we are unaware of how to combine growth with efficiency, keeping functionality within spontaneously generated forms of growth in a similar way to organisms. Consider, for instance, blood circulation and the nervous system, or how a tree grows, and compare them to the difficulties that our cities experience. Maybe the only project to combine growth with the persistence of functionality in urban structures is imaginary, like the tower of Babel, pictured as a sea snail with a growing spiral shell.

When we burn oil, carbon, or wood the reduced carbon, sulfur, and nitrogen are oxidized and so we return to something like a theoretical ancient atmosphere. This combustion has already reached 10% of the expected changes in the biosphere's normal cycle; in other words, the carbon of burned fossil fuel is nearly a tenth of the amount of carbon fixed every year by global photosynthesis. One percent or one part per thousand would seem acceptable figures, but if it goes above 10% there is cause for concern, even more so if the increase has come about quickly and continuously. However, some beneficial mechanisms like the absorption of CO_2 by the waters of the ocean, are in fact slower than we had hoped, as they are controlled (the end result is little known) by the ocean's "skin," to refer figuratively to the top layers of the ocean and the organisms that live there. The increase in oxidized compounds of carbon, nitrogen, and sulfur gives rise to the so-called greenhouse effect and acid rain. There is additional damage to the vegetation that has more complex causes, or that is due to particular chemical compounds that are also related to combustion or other industrial activities.

Today, with the domestication of the planet partly completed, our species' influence comes more from the manipulation of exosomatic energy than it does form the mere extraction of mineral resources. Leaving issues of justice to one side, it is obvious that we cannot continue with a philosophy of development based on the control of more energy. However, it has become very popular to talk about "continuous" or "sustained development." This may lie somewhere between political propaganda and paranoid delusion. In a more constructive manner, we could adapt the slogan to take into account the way nature works in the evolution of species and organization of ecosystems. The great initial energy flow would gradually be replaced by a more efficient use of the information obtained from that original, first expenditure of the principle. In other words, any sustained development should put more faith in a more cautious use of available information than in increasing the amount of energy used. Someone may say that this is equivalent to recommending someone to travel less and watch more television, something we would not find enjoyable if imposed on us.

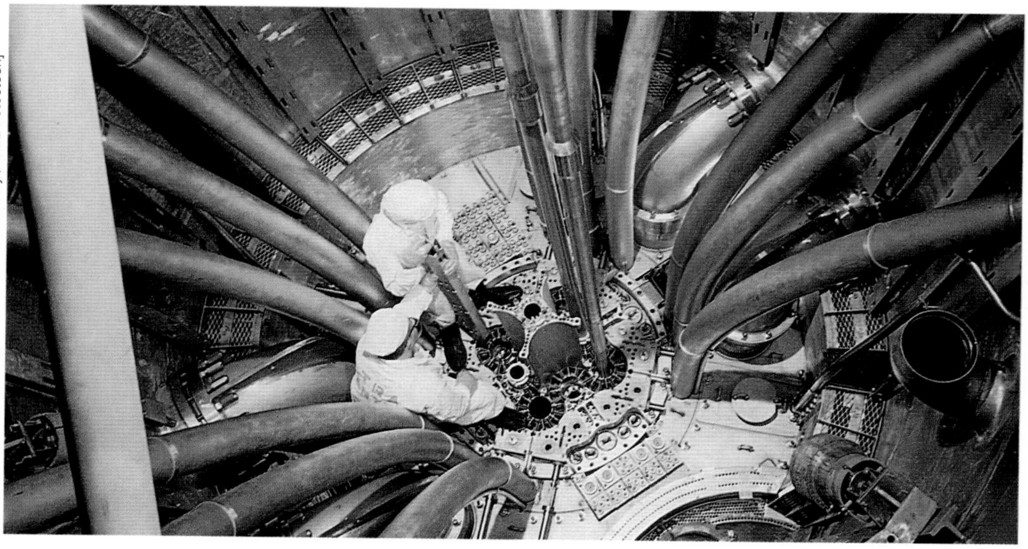

Reactor of the Idaho National Engineering Laboratory
[U.S. Department of Energy - Science Photo Library / AGE Fotostock]

3.5 Full sail or full steam ahead

Endosomatic and exosomatic energy

The maintenance of the biosphere depends on one thousandth of the solar radiation that reaches our planet and it is achieved with chlorophyll concentrations that are greater than one gram per square meter in terrestrial ecosystems and in fresh water ones, although this value is never reached by the oceans. But this is not all the energy that we end up using.

When quantifying the functioning of ecosystems, it is not enough to count only the energy that enters the ecosystem by means of the chlorophyll, i.e. following an internal metabolic path. This energy is qualified as *endosomatic*, since it circulates within organisms, first in plants and afterwards in a series of heterotrophs. The rest of the incoming energy from the Sun is also important. It is the climatic energy that makes the Earth inhabitable and determines the unequal conditions of different areas, which may be interpreted as more or less favorable to life in general, or favorable to some organisms and less favorable to others. Thus, this energy becomes an important factor for the definition of regional differences. This relevant fraction of energy is called *exosomatic* in relation to organisms, since it circulates or operates outside the body.

The energy of the tides is also exosomatic; it is not electromagnetic in origin, but gravitational. The energy that mixes seawater vertically is also exosomatic. It pushes elements towards the surface, like phosphorus, nitrogen, and silicon, which were more concentrated in deep waters, thereby assuring the continuity of production and of pelagic life. Also exosomatic is the energy associated with rain and evapotranspiration in leaves, which has an analogous function in the sense that it allows the necessary elements (phosphorus, nitrogen, potassium, etc.) to reach the level reached by light where photosynthesis occurs. In both examples, the exosomatic energy is quantifiable and lies between 20 and 50 times the associated endosomatic energy. As in any machine, the use of the external energy and the degree of irreversibility of the work accomplished is conditioned by the local temperature.

The relations between exosomatic and endosomatic energy often involve the organization of a physical environment or the construction of particular artifacts. Some species have attained energy control through material structures, resulting in an increase or regulation of biological production with the expected consequences for competition. It has already been mentioned that in life's history we can distinguish three evolutionary peaks, where there has been a considerable success in the production or regulation of biological production. The first one corresponds to higher plants, which possess stems, trunks, and roots. The second one corresponds to corals, which form coral reefs. And the third one corresponds to some kinds of higher animals: social insects to a relatively modest degree, and superlatively, our own species.

We have already compared the forest to plankton: the section of the xylem or ascending vessels of the xylem sap, multiplied by the speed of the flow, is comparable to the effect of ascent of nutrients obtained when oceanic waters mix. The rise of materials in plants is also limited by the quantity of available water.

The effects of exosomatic energy on life

The inequalities in the distribution, characteristics, and possibilities of use of exosomatic energy use explain the uneven distribution of species: the work needed to transport water transport may be more important than the supply of light in the determination of the geographic distribution of vegetation. The fluctuations in the amounts of exosomatic energy explain the changes that occur in the development of life and its activities. These are associated with day and night, the different seasons, and with other less regular and more mysterious fluctuations. An example of the latter is the existence of more humid years and drier years which may be irregularly or contagiously distributed, at least in pairs, which leads to speculations about the possible reality of cycles of long or indeterminate duration cycles of four, seven, or 11 years. On a longer timescale glaciations and other phenomena, and these are linked to changes related to the movements of continental plates, which depend on the Earth's internal energy, but energy which is external in relation to life and the evolution of organisms.

External energy is also important because it introduces an element of randomness. Fluctuations, intermittent periods and irregularities, contribute to the efficacy of ecological mechanisms. Consider, for instance, successions which are interrupted by disturbances. Irregular fluctuations favored the development of structures designed to persist during the period of least vegetative activity (trunks, roots). They also facilitated the evolution of exploitable plants and soils which are able to retain nutrients that make them suitable for agriculture. The tem-

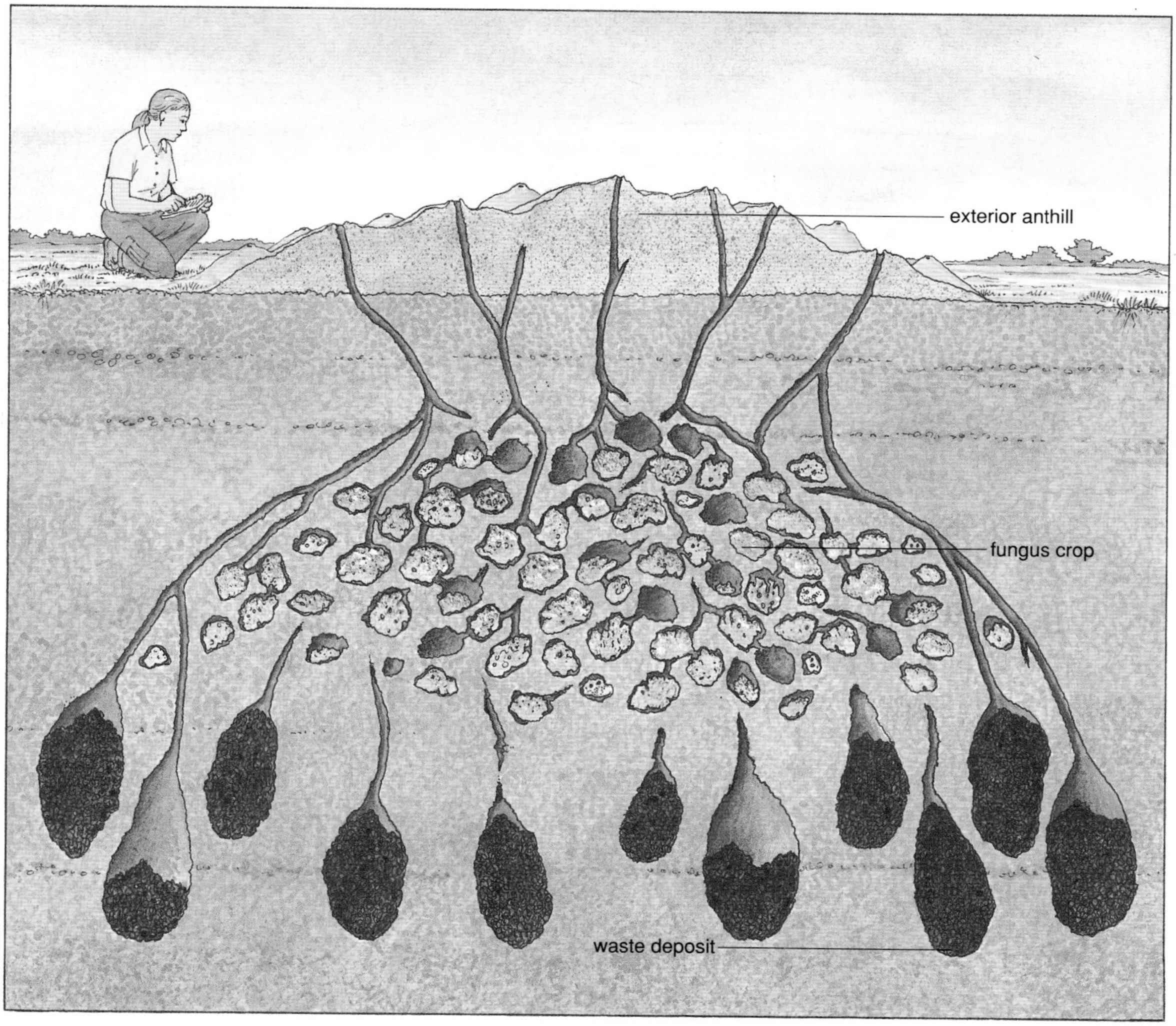

139 Ants of the genus *Atta* are social insects with relatively complex behavior, for example, their way of obtaining food is complex due to a kind of subterranean agriculture. The fragments of leaves that they cut off the trees only act as a substrate, once suitably ground by their jaws and irrigated with fecal liquid. What the *Atta* ants really eat are the mycelia of fungi that they themselves implant in the leaf pulp (obtained by chewing) kept in subterranean chambers of their nests, which function as true gardens. Some of these fungi have still not been identified and many are not found outside these "gardens." The drawing shows a vertical section of one of the ant nests, whose upper mound can be seen above, and which can occupy an area as big as 2,690 sq ft (250 m^2) and in whose galleries hundreds of thousands of ants can live. Further down, one can see the cavities, or gardens, in which the fungi are cultivated on the leaf pulp, and further down still, the large cavities that the ants use to store waste, where the leaf pulp not used by the fungi ends up.
[Drawing: Aina Bonner]

perate zones, particularly the northern ones, have benefited from these fluctuations since they are frequently affected by atmospheric fronts, which show more marked discontinuities.

Corals build enormous constructions of calcium carbonate, forming islands or reefs, which are able to transform the energy of marine currents into turbulent energy. This in part pushes deeper waters upwards and in general makes the surface waters more fertile, directly benefitting symbiont algae. Evidence has recently come to light which suggests that coral constructions can push nourishment from the sea floor up to the surface through the porous structure of their calcareous mass.

Social animals construct roads and nests which determine the environment in a variety of ways and at the same time help them obtain food. This is clear in the case of many insects, for which the harboring and storing resources means obtaining them in larger amounts and more regularly. The social life of ants and other animals involves constructing dwellings and roads, which are essential for termites and ants to establish intensive cultivations. The management and transformation of wood by termites is also associated with this.

The human species and energy consumption

Comparable functions and capacities are even more obvious in the case of the human species. Exosomatic energy may be measured by our use of wood, oil, electricity, etc. It ranges from values comparable to those of endosomatic energy (about 3,000 kcal per day, or somewhat less, or 120 watts, are accepted as normal values), corresponding to a simple life that involves the use of a little wood for cooking and heating, to a value with no upper limit. In an intermediate step we have to add the energy associated with food storage, packaging, etc., which avoids many losses (for our species, not for the ecosystem) such as those caused by bacteria, fungi and various pests, from weevils to mice. Lighting, transportation, air conditioning, and industry increase our use of energy enormously.

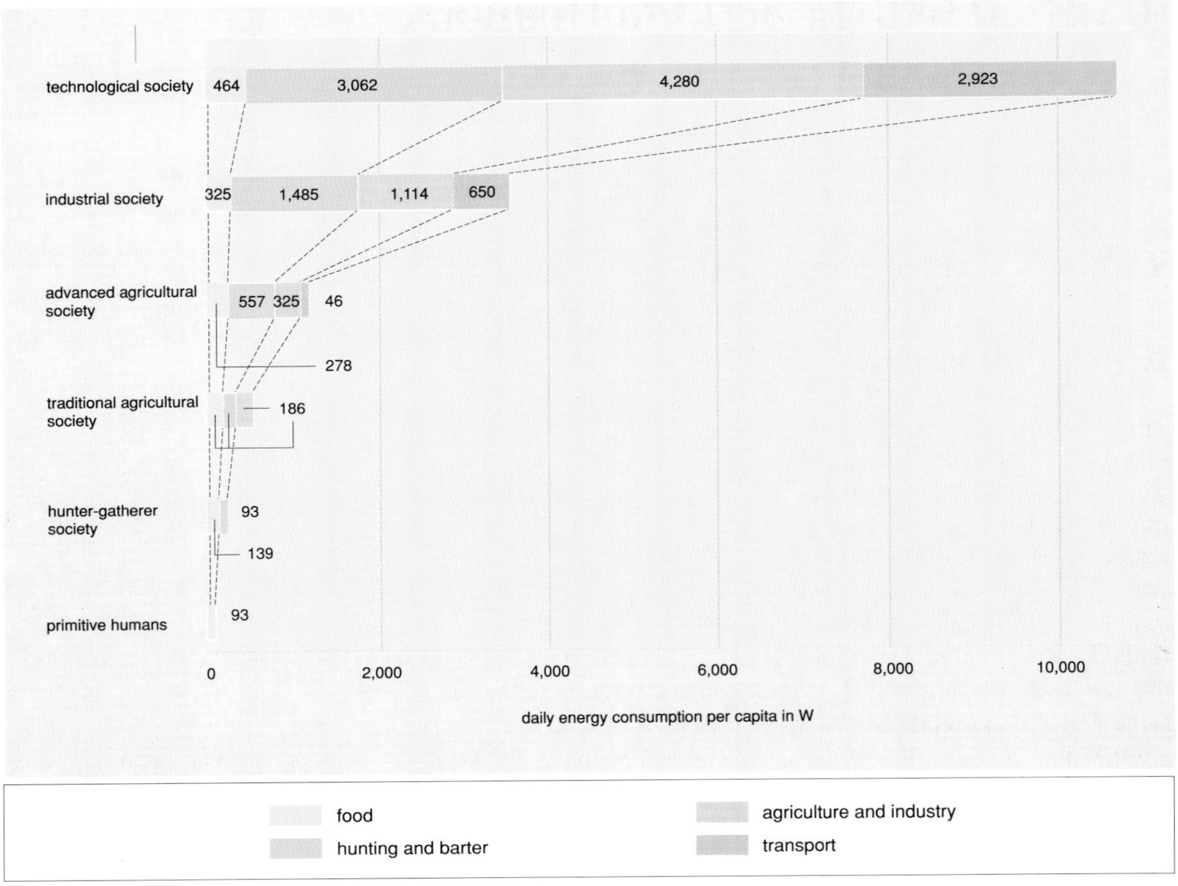

140 The consumption of energy by humans has varied from one group to another throughout history according to the state of technological development. Primitive human peoples confined themselves to consuming the energy necessary for survival, which they obtained from food. In hunter-gatherer societies, the consumption of exosomatic energy was nil or insignificant, but the use of fire to cook the food and to heat their dwellings, sometimes specially built, represents the first voluntary recourse to sources of exosomatic energy. The appearance of agriculture, followed by the adoption of a sedentary way of life, which implies the creation of surpluses of production and the accumulation of goods, signified the possibility of the appearance of consumption. In more advanced agricultural societies, the need for the transport of materials over ever increasing distances became evident. With the apperance of industrial society, and later, technological society, the consumption of exosomatic energy grew spectacularly. It has to be kept in mind that the growth of energy associated with the consumption of food does not represent a parallel growth in energy ingested through the food itself, but is the energy associated with the foodstuffs that are not used and that go to waste. The consumption of energy by a human being, both in early times and today, does not exceed 100 W per day. *[Diagram: Editrònica, from various sources]*

Nowadays the world's mean use of exosomatic energy lies between 15 and 20 times the endosomatic energy. There is no upper individual limit. A person may use as exosomatic energy 100, 1,000, or more times the basic reference of 120 watts. It is difficult to estimate it because the use of exosomatic energy is mostly collective. Exosomatic energy tends to multiply itself, therefore those who spend a lot of it are in a position to increase their consumption even more.

Endosomatic energy follows an almost normal distribution in human activities, since the extreme values, whether due to hunger or overeating, limit its distribution and keeps it contained. The distribution of exosomatic energy is very different and it is the logarithm frequencies of the use of energy which come close to a normal distribution. Thus, the distribution of exosomatic energy is close to a random distribution of brownian type movement, where each random path does not start from zero, but from the previously reached point where variance is proportional to the square of the mean. When increasing the mean use of exosomatic energy, its variance also increases. Such a feature may be seen as negative or unfair. The way our society works generates this statistical distribution and it seems there is not much hope to escape from it, no matter how undesirable we believe it to be.

141 In contemporary Western society, the consumption of exosomatic energy has reached spectacular levels, and is, moreover, one of the greatest expressions of the inequality between rich developed societies and poor underdeveloped societies. In the photograph, the city of Las Vegas, Nevada. *[Photo: G. Allison / Photothèque Stone International]*

4. Living beings and information

4.1 The rules of the game

Diversity, scale and time

There is a great variety of living beings. The organization of each individual is hierarchical. Each entity is composed of other smaller entities, and this organization is reflected in their functional relations. Hierarchical relations are also found within ecosystems, which are formed by many individual organisms generally belonging to different species. There are relationships of reproduction and descent within individuals of the same species, and relationships are of many kinds among individuals of different species. For instance, some species are food sources for others, or there are very diverse forms of interaction among them, direct or indirect: trees support creepers, many insects are pollinators, etc. Ecosystems contain groups of individuals of different species living together. The word ecosystem refers to or suggests the concept of system, something composed of elements related to one another by more or less flexible links. In this sense, atoms are also systems, and no system is absolutely rigid. We can say that the world is a great system formed by smaller systems of a diverse nature, on different scales. Within a system, what we call hierarchy is a consequence of the fact that not all possible connections are realized with the same intensity.

Living systems are much richer in structure if viewed at a small scale. Their homologous parts, at all scales, are seldom exact duplicates of each

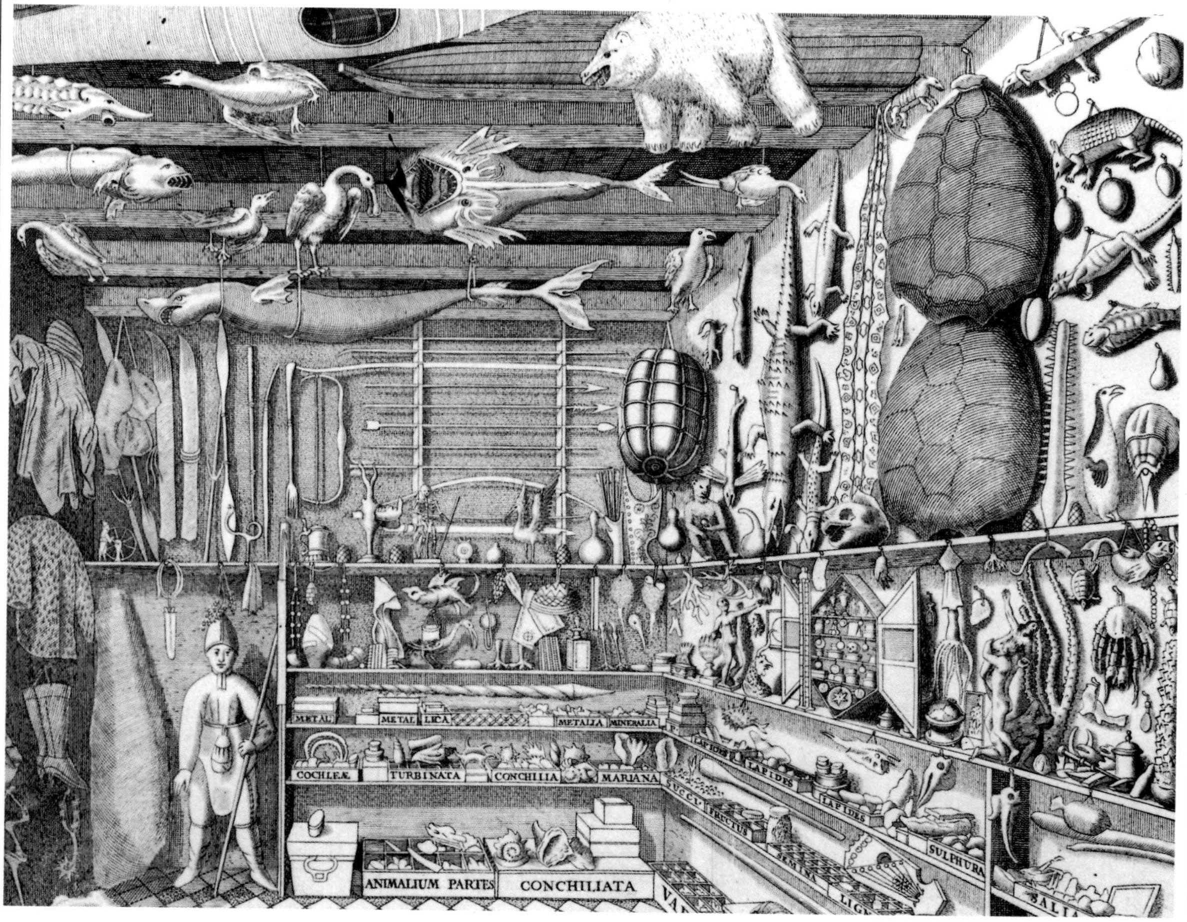

142 Nature is variety, but it is also organization. Collectors and hobbyists of the Renaissance and baroque periods understood it that way and attempted to make their cabinets of curiosities genuine microcosms that were at the same time summaries, compendia, and representations of the wonders of creation that followed an order that had been established once and for always by the act of creation. Their ignorance of functional relationships, and the inability even to conceive of the possibility that species had evolved in time, led them to establish classifications that we today find incomprehensible. The result was those storehouses where the most diverse objects were piled up in no particular order, such as this one of the Dane Ole Worm (1588-1654), published in Leiden in 1655. *[Photo: National Museum of Denmark]*

other. This makes it slightly inappropriate to use a type of statistical analysis designed to be applicable to comparable units, whose differences can be qualified as random. We will never find perfectly comparable sub-units, and the differences between them can never be considered random or haphazard.

These considerations are not sufficient when characterizing living systems, nor are similar ones also of a static nature. One has to introduce the concept of time. Time is inherent in life: we can feel it as a kind of internal conscience of the world, which serves as a clock. Certainly, living systems are physical systems: all living systems have the characteristics and limitations of physical systems in general. If there is any difference, it seems to consist mainly in the capacity of the former to recover effectively and efficiently, in the form of complexity or information, a considerable part of the entropy increase that has occurred in the organism and its close environment.

Entropy and the irreversibility of changes

The concept of entropy corresponds to a form of book-keeping for all physical and chemical changes that are taking place. We accept, in an oversimplified way, that entropy is the sum total of the values of an unrecoverable component of all changes, no matter in which direction they go. It makes sense because in all changes there are transformations between mechanical work and heat, and there is always a small part of heat that is diffused and irrevocably lost. There is no way of undoing what has already happened, nor to follow a trajectory which is the exact reversal of a previous material change. This irreversibility can be seen and interpreted in different ways.

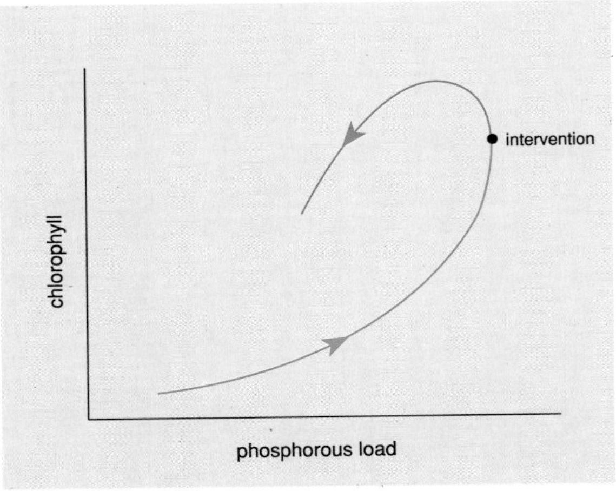

143 Processes of eutrophication and recuperation of a lake expressed through the relationship between the phosphorus load and the chlorophyll content. The outgoing and ingoing paths after an outside intervention are never the same.
[Diagram: Editrònica, from data supplied by the author]

In ecology the irreversibility of changes is a daily experience, and it is not only of scientific and conceptual interest, but also practical. In the process of the so-called eutrophication of a lake, for instance, the water is enriched with nutritient materials and becomes green. This is due to the fact that it contains a lot of microscopic algae in suspension (sometimes not so microscopic, but forming fine green threads). The change can be described by the variation in chlorophyll concentration which occurs in the zone of the lake that gets light, and which depends on the phosphorus load received by the lake, probably from sewage waters and irrigation runoff. If we try to remedy it and restore it to a state like the initial one, for instance, by building sewage treatment plants that work, the path described by the same function (phosphorus-dependent chlorophyll) during the recovery period is different from that of the eutrophication period. A graphic representation of the process in a system of coordinates (where *x* is the phosphorous load and *y* the chlorophyll) suggests that the part corresponding to the graph's area between the eutrophication path and that of acceptable recovery corresponds to the social cost of the operation. This might bring to mind the diagrams representing the functions associated with the properties of the gas mixture in an internal combustion engine, and even recognise the similarities with the lake example. In the case of a river, the recovery path can be closer to the one taken by the increasing pollution. The river becomes dirty fairly quickly but it is also easily cleaned. A lake, and even more so the sea, or an aquifer, become contaminated much more slowly, but afterwards they are much more difficult to clean up.

The reason for this is that the transport of materials and reactions between them that take place continually in living systems and their immediate surrounding and, to the extent that they correspond to irreversible changes, they can be attributed to entropy. The information or the complexity that the system itself acquires is a copy or reflection of this. Biological systems, at all levels, succeed in recovering an important fraction of that entropy in the form of what we call complexity or information. It is as if any given energy exchange leaves a trace or sign on matter. After this neither matter nor energy are exactly the same as before. A given energy cannot be used two consecutive times in the same way. Matter always stores some memory of the exchange. A record containing many signs of the matter and energy changes that took place in the past is also preserved by the earth's crust as information (folds, faults, and the enormous wealth of structures studied in geology). But in this respect organisms are particularly effective due, in the first place, to their inherent complexity and to their high aptitude to complicate different types of memory in different ways and to then relate them to each other.

It has been repeatedly written that systems are more than the sum of their parts. The opposite could also be said: systems are less than that, since, when each of the component elements enters the system, a good deal of its previous potential is lost. Its future development will be integrated in a system that limits and channels the possibilities of change and evolution that it had to begin with. We often complain that society limits our options. This is obvious in evolution: the fact that an organism has to adjust itself to the demands of its environment and to the conditions imposed by the individuals of its own and other species, determines that not all the possibilities of change that the genetic system could offer can be realized. For this reason the actual evolution of species never attains, or gets close to, the speed of evolution that the genetic system would allow if phenotypes were not subject to so many factors to pass the test of real life. In fact, in simplified situations, be they in the laboratory or in the biosphere, after destructive cataclysms, evolution has managed to recover a speed that is close to the attainable one. As has happened with the domestication of plants and animals by man, breaking species off from the ties that the usual relationships in ecosystems imply, has allowed them to accelerate their speed of evolution. Darwin was attracted to the study of the variability of domesticated plants and animals, which provided evidence of the variability of species. They have really proved capable of changing with exceptional speed after freeing themselves from the complex ties that existed in their respective original environments.

Complexity and information

Complexity and information have been used imprecisely and with a certain indifference. They could be considered synonymous, or at least, they present the same difficulties when it comes to quantifying them.

In ordinary language we notice complexity in a simultaneous or synchronous situation, while mentally information is more often associated with the message that carries with it a potential complexity from the past to the future. The problem

144 The evolution of domesticated plants and animals often shows a speeding up, which helps the selection of varieties that are of most interest to the humans who have domesticated, or who grow, the plant or animal. The bean (*Phaseolus vulgaris*), which originated in the eastern slopes of the Andes of Peru to northern Argentina, was domesticated not less than 10,000 years ago. Today, it is spread throughout most of the world, and it contains thousands of races and varieties with an enormous diversity of shapes, sizes, and colors, both in the pods and in the seeds, as can be seen in the market stalls of San Miguel in the Azores. *[Photo: Ramon Folch]*

Compiling information in chromosomes

Nucleic acids, composed of chains of nucleotides, are particularly noble materials. They are linear sequences, chains of molecules as in proteins, and potential message carriers. In terms of information they are comparable to conversation, music, and, in general, to our written or recorded messages.

Cell organization is three-dimensional, and we could even add a fourth dimension: time; but the manipulation of information in two or three dimensions is difficult. We have examples of it in games like crossword puzzles (two dimensions) and the Rubik's cube (three dimensions), which test our patience and ingenuity. The same difficulty is reflected in the management of information at the cellular level and the solution adopted has ended up by defining the genetic and evolutionary mechanism. Our brain provides representations of a great complexity, as well as generating "lines of thought."

Biological information is expressed in different "languages" and it can be translated from one into another. From the nucleic acids (deoxyribonucleic, DNA) of the nuclei and genes, it goes first to the ribonucleic acids (RNA), which act as intermediate carriers of information and are subject to a higher probability of spontaneous alteration; and then to enzymes that operate as catalysts on the substrates. Ribosomes are scattered in the cell and are essential intermediaries in the flow of information from RNA to peptide chains.

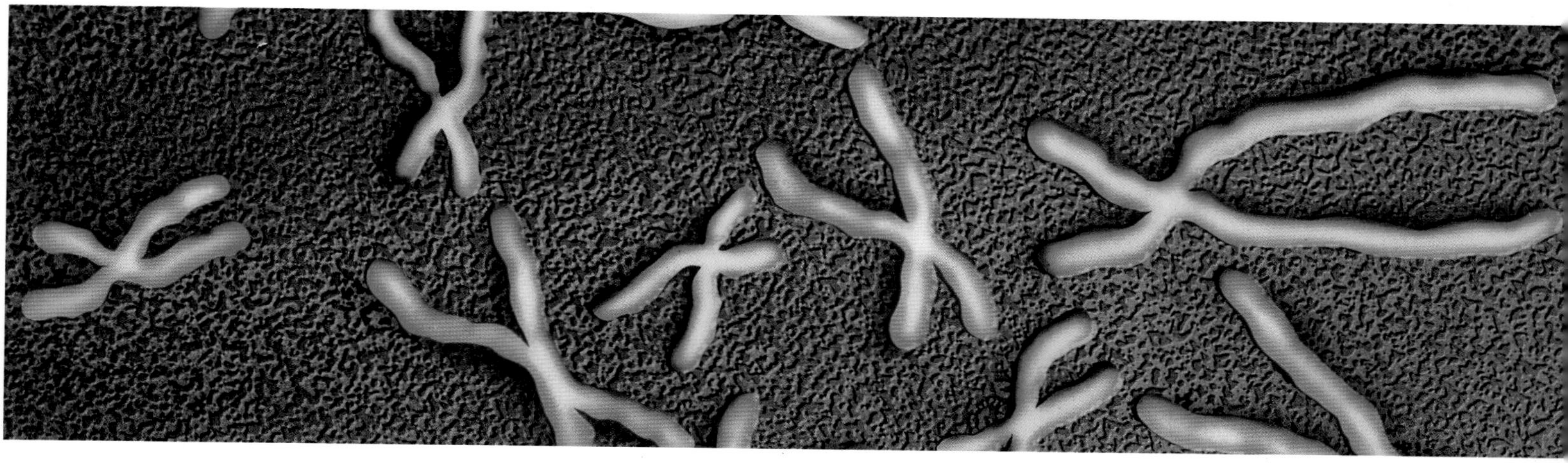

Human chromosomes [AGE Fotostock]

There exists a complete hierarchy in the organization of the cell and of life which we will not study here but which is important to keep in mind for the following reasons. Firstly, because it is the best-known structure which is close to the basis of life. Secondly, because it is the model or paradigm of a style of construction and functioning that is found time and again at other levels in the biosphere. Thirdly, because genetic manipulation adds new possibilities to the interaction between man and nature.

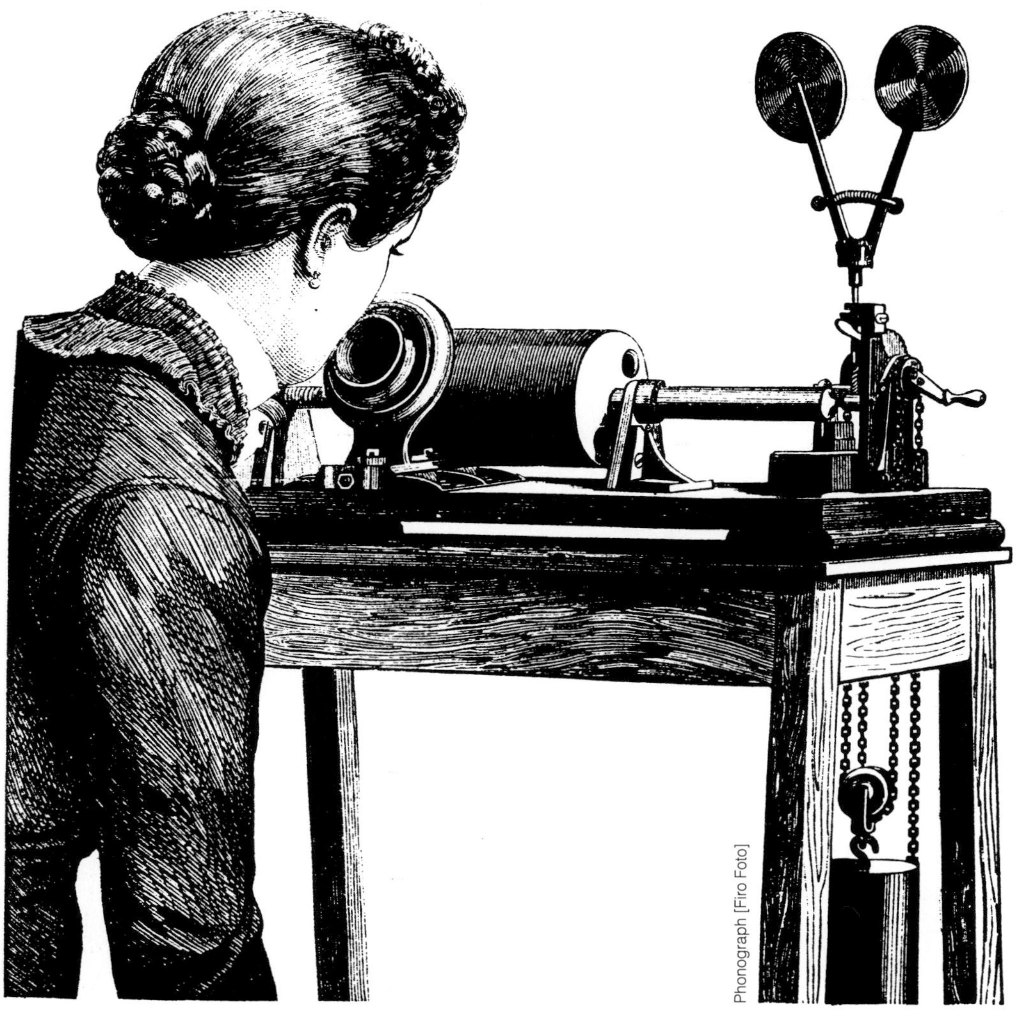

Phonograph [Firo Foto]

The most persistent information carriers are the nucleic acids, polynucleotides made of chains of modular units called *nucleotides*. Each nucleotide consists of a sugar: deoxyribose (in DNA) or ribose (in RNA), a phosphate and a base, generally adenine (A), guanine (G), cytosine (C) or thymine (T). Each molecule of DNA is made up of two parallel chains in the form of a helix; when they separate each of them may automatically induce the replication of another complementary chain. This requires a complex enzymatic system for the replication. Normally the guanine of a simple chain pairs with the cytosine of a complementary chain and the adenine with the thymine.

The chains of DNA that form the "hard" memory of organisms are very long and have a characteristic organization, which facilitates their operation. The RNA of a well-studied bacterium (*Escherichia*) is a filament consisting of three million pairs of nucleotides; human DNA is one thousand times longer. Along the axis of the double helix, the distance between two successive nucleotide is approximately one third of a nanometre (nm), so the total filament of human DNA is about 3 ft (1 m) long and divided among the 23

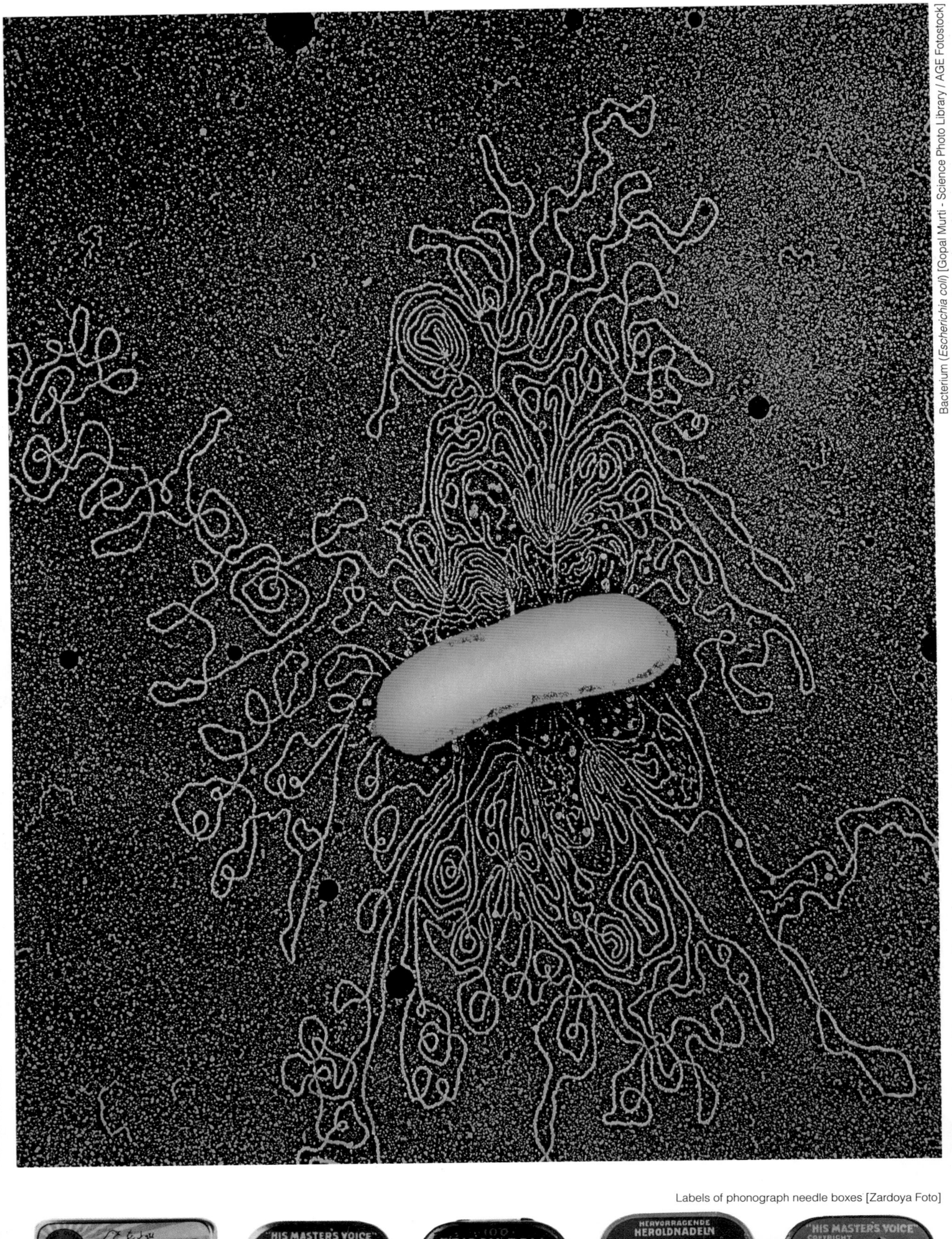

Bacterium (*Escherichia coli*) [Gopal Murti - Science Photo Library / AGE Fotostock]

Labels of phonograph needle boxes [Zardoya Foto]

chromosomes of each haploid set. In the chromosomes the DNA filaments are repeated, organized, and folded in various ways in order to fit into microscopic structures of a few micromillimeters long since the cell nuclei which house them are ordinarily no larger than 5 µm in diameter.

If we translate from a code with four symbols (nucleic acids) into a code with some 20 symbols (amino acids), it is necessary to use three of the former to specify each of the latter. Since the codification of one amino acid requires a group of three successive bases, the nucleotide "triplets" are called *codons*. Three thousand million nucleotide pairs, approximately the number found in mammals and in man suffice to specify at least 750 million amino acids and at least a million types of proteins, although it seems that the real number of proteins that are required and actually synthesised is less than one tenth of that. DNA also contains "punctuation marks," various instructions, many inactive sections and even viruses. It could be compared to a computer memory that has been used over a long period of time. Chromosomes are very complex structures, a good part of whose information is latent.

Nucleic acids are very resistant and have a limited turnover rate. DNA chains inform RNA chains, which are shorter, easier to renew, and more subject to accidental changes. RNA chains are models for the enzymes, and the enzymes manipulate the substrates, which are molecules with a high turnover rate that usually need relatively more energy. Such a situation offers the typical image of a kind of relationship found in different natural situations: the same opposed flows of energy and information may be recognized along the trophic chains of ecosystems, from the primary producers (plants) to carnivores, as well as in the technology of our civilization.

Genetic mechanisms and the expression of genetic information in development explain how the biosphere works and evolves.

Interest in the conservation of species and biotic diversity has to refer to their respective genotypes. It is also important to anticipate the results, which may be expected from what is now possible in the field of genetic engineering.

Humanity's most important role will not be one of producing more mutation-type changes, because nature has always had plenty of time to try them out and, in fact, evolution could have gone faster if selection conditions had not slowed it down. The importance of genetic engineering lies rather in being able to realize *in vitro* a sequence or combination of changes that would not have a chance in the wild, especially in the case of transitional forms of doubtful or low viability. Just as culture has been assimilated because it increases the possible speed of evolution, genetic engineering, in as far as it can accelerate the assimilation of complex (or otherwise impossible) changes, may eventually become an acceptable mechanism in the global evolution of the planet.

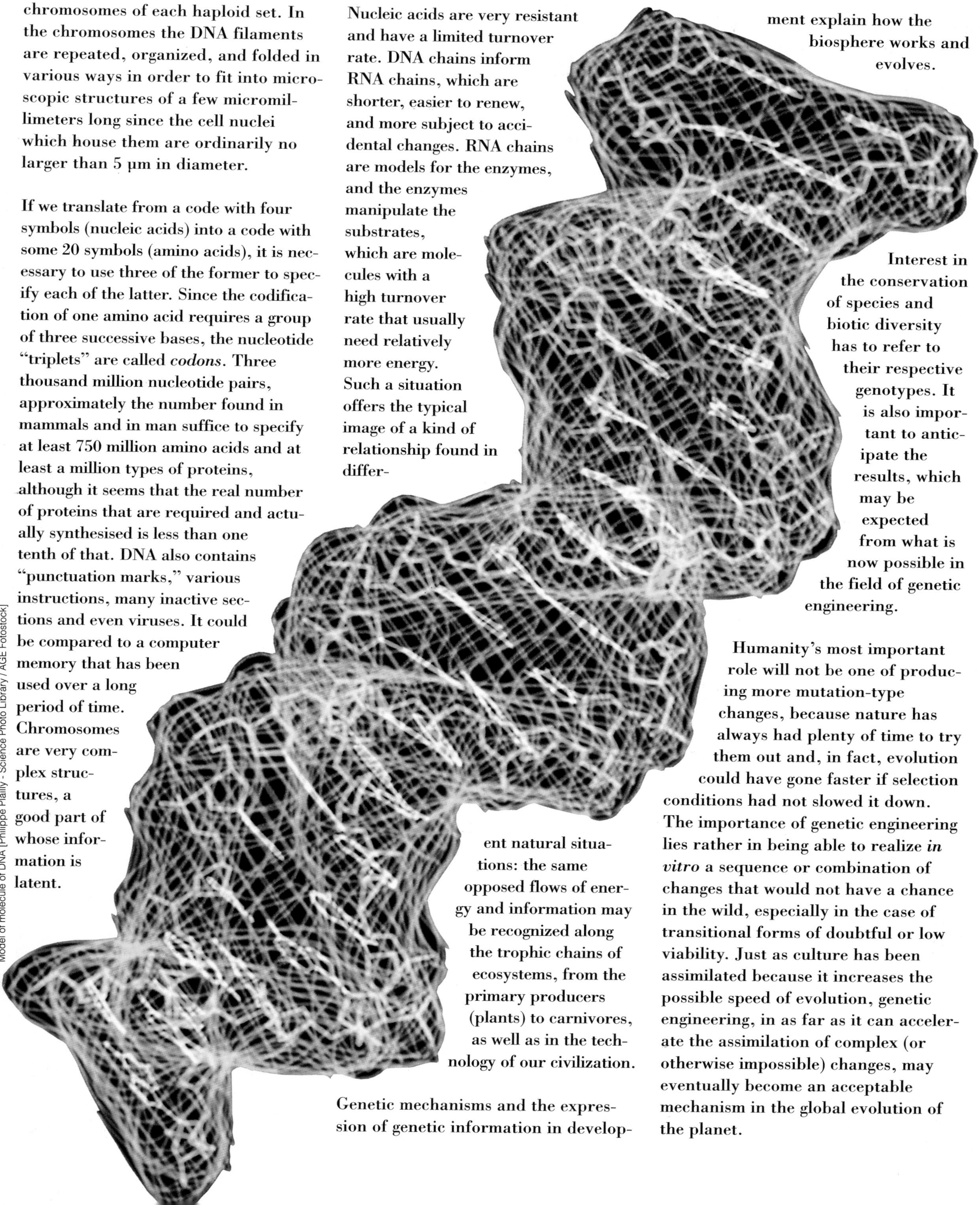

Model of molecule of DNA [Philippe Plailly - Science Photo Library / AGE Fotostock]

that makes these concepts scientifically intractable is quite simply how to measure them. Possibly the most reasonable proposal is to use as a measure an equivalent expression formulated in a normalized language, which describes the situation unambiguously. Currently, we are inclined to regard the description as a row of zeros and ones and to attempt to translate the primitive series into another series expressed in this same way. The difficulty, which is both suggestive and worrying, is that the "value" of an element of information, which is part of a message, is a function of the entire message. For this reason, two very long messages, like the genetic codes of human and chimpanzee, do not need to differ over a large part of their genome in order to be deeply divergent.

In terms of capacity to manipulate information, a double-sized computer is superior to two ordinary-sized computers, and a large brain is superior to an equivalent mass of small brains. This is one of the advantages of large organisms over small and short-lived ones, especially if, in addition, the former live longer. But, obviously, everything depends on the nature of the changes in the environment. Both the message and the capacity to manipulate the information it contains are information. We find, therefore, a parallel between the software and the hardware of our computers.

Information may be considered proportional to a power higher than 1 of the mass supporting it (or of some expression that combines this mass with its duration), in other words $I \rightarrow M^k$, $k > 1$. However, thinking of a quantity (or "unit") of information i, added to it, we can formulate the equation $I + i \rightarrow (M + i)^k$, $i \rightarrow (M + i)^k - M^k$.

Such considerations do not make it easier to talk about information, even more so if we take into account that many disciplines consider it immaterial, and would probably justify that attitude by saying that a similar length of a computer message may contain what some would interpret as something sublime and others as nonsense. The interpretation of the receiver of the message, the one who gives sense to it, is thus a relevant factor. Even if information may be regarded as "immaterial," energy is always necessary in order to process, transcribe, and reveal it. Furthermore, there is always an increase in entropy associated with material changes, at the basis of its generation and acquisition.

One way or another, life has managed to project into the future an endless repertoire of data: as in the "songs" of whales, the genetic record transmits a sort of epic poem, which each generation has had the possibility of correcting or adding to. It is an unstoppable flow of information, which is never totally annihilated by periodical disturbances. At most, these erase part of the basis and introduce partially new complications in the message of life, which is richer than an unending firework display. This is revealed at all levels, organic evolution being just one example. It is always present at biosphere and ecosystem level, and is one of the reasons why the study of the organization, evolution and complexification of living systems is so fascinating.

4.2 The rules of the game

Causal strategy versus inferential strategy

According to the naturalist tradition, there should be a reason for everything and any evidence of this is always welcome. It used to be considered a proof of the action of God's providence revealed in the care of His creatures; later, it became a proof of the effectiveness of natural selection, a process by which the best of all possibilities was chosen. All ways of contemplating and interpreting living nature incorporate what these two views have in common. It is significant that the observers of physical nature (e.g. the formation of planets and the Earth) did not need to extrapolate in this way and limited themselves to describing mechanisms and results. The fact that history is directly and obviously manifest in human beings, and the special role that time occupies in our lives, are factors that probably explain the basis of the interest shown in the historical development of humans.

The "different" ways of surviving are considered as the expression of nature's strategies, strategy being understood in a military sense: a plan followed with a definite purpose. But the persistence of an orientated trajectory, of something more than just living, rarely lasts very long in the presumed phyletic lines of evolution. We should also bear in mind that the various strategies explained by politicians and the military are made up ex post facto in order to justify or take credit for events that have already happened. It may not be worth insisting on adapting the concept of strategy, although it may still be said, figuratively speaking, that life plays a million chess games or fights a million battles every day, from which we can collect statistics of casualties, and even of the colors of the warriors' uniforms.

I	II
Species which leave many offspring that disperse easily and that have a life span that tends to be indefinite	Species that produce few offspring, which are well protected, sometimes less mobile, and generally have a limited life span
Species that are passive feeders, sometimes automatic, with a low metabolic rate, with less ability to learn	Mobile species that pursue their prey, have a longer life, and the ability to learn
Relationships with other individuals of the same genus tending to be violent, involving much energy and without much response expected	Relationships with other individuals of the same genus more conventional, diplomatic and respectful; sometimes with their own territory and respect those of others
More success in ecosystems that are at an initial colonization stage	More successful in well organized ecosystems

145 Parallels and contrasts in survival strategies. Although it is perhaps not wise to propose a scheme to formalize survival strategies, it is perhaps suggestive to believe that the ways of life, embodied in organisms, can be arranged along an axis according to certain tendencies, which can be homologized and recognized in many situations. The comparisons shown in the table can serve as an example. Although most are more applicable to animals than to plants, although their basic features can be found in some plant groups, they can serve as an example. In any ecosystem there is room for many organisms, but they nearly always show the relative contrast between those species that rapidly take advantage of the energy available and those that rely on the build up of material organization, and therefore seemingly use time in a more effective way. It should be noted that this classification is different from that which might be established based on distinctions between primary producers, osmotrophs, and phagotrophs in respect of the material cycle and energy flow; but even so it is quite clear that phagotrophs are more adapted to the evolutionary tendencies of the right hand column.
[Source: data supplied by the author]

The social compromise or ecosystem

We do not know whether at some point in the history of our planet there existed primitive ecosystem-organisms of particular organization, i.e. ones that were tailor-made for the environment where they originated, and fulfilling all functions, which are now diversified: from photosynthesis and the assimilation of necessary components, using it all in respiration. The subdivision of hypothetical ecosystem-organisms, if they existed, in complementary and separately reproducible fragments probably happened early (some would not speak of life until this moment) and gave rise to ecosystems like the present ones, made up of many species. Each of these species may evolve with a certain independence and relative speed, at the same time maintaining a succession of generations within the ecosystem.

An ecosystem may be difficult to define and limit: it is formed by a set of reproducible ready-made species or entities, which can be measured by their mass or number of individuals. Ecosystems have been compared with human society, where we can recognize diverse complementary skills or jobs, at least with respect to the function of occupying a place, and they persist at the crossing points between the respective biogeochemical cycles. An ecosystem has a real organization, made up of discrete elements, and is therefore never "in balance." Each of these elements lacks, or has an excess of, something, to stop it fitting in perfectly, and therefore tensions and fluxes are never cancelled out. Because they keep the system in tension, the quantification and discontinuity of the components of an ecosystem are considered factors of evolution.

Most of what is considered ecological theory centers around two questions: how individuals of different species fit together or organize themselves in order to form a functional set, the ecosystem, and how the population dynamics of each species, i.e. the series of births and deaths that constitute its history, are integrated into the ecosystem. Obviously, the deaths of individuals of species that are victims of other species, have to be related somehow not just to the births of new individuals of each prey species, but also to the births, availability and dangers of the predators, lying in wait. A stationary situation, in which everything worked with the exactness of a perfect watch, would be the mythical "ecological balance" that is never attained. This is due, apart from other less significant causes (like the fact that the world always works with sudden movements), to the very profound reason that the way the ecosystem itself works is reflected in the accumulation of new information and in the establishment of what could be qualified as new asymptotic conditions. There is never a lack of different kinds of disturbances: trying out a possible evolutionary adventure, the introduction of a foreign species, an unforeseeable catastrophe caused by factors external to the ecosystem (an avalanche or climatic change), or originating within the ecosystem (a species which changes its habits and becomes more aggressive, or whose power grows to a degree where it is dangerous, as is happening now on a worldwide scale with the human species).

Ecological guilds

Many ecologists have maintained a point of view which could be considered as "structuralist." They saw the ecosystem components distributed in ecological niches, or in guilds, which corresponded either to more or less similar or definable functions, or to certain signs, and which could be recognized in all or most ecosystems. Examples of these niches or guilds are the categories of primary producers, distributed according to their size and persistence in groups of annual herbaceous plants, trees, etc.; herbivores with different characteristics, like insects and large grazing species, small carnivores, large carnivores, parasites, etc. Each niche would have a particular way of carrying out the job, and evolution, responding to the pressure of natural selection, would try to optimize that ideal function. The division and subdivision of the niches could be pushed as far as convenient.

The concept of guild has been generally applied in a more restricted sense than that of niche. Dung beetles are a guild within the niche of arthropods which consume the excreta of large herbivores. Since each

146 The fitting of many species into the ecosystem sometimes is subject to an evolutionary selection, in terms of features or characteristics, which avoid or make difficult the attacks of predators. Aposematic or warning coloration is characteristic of well-defended animals who possess their own weapons—often they themselves are predators—or have a disagreeable flavor, which may indicate toxicity. Colors that have the maximum contrast (very often yellow and black) and that also contrast at the same time with those of the surrounding environment are combined. Some harmless animals adopt the strategy of imitating the coloration of others known to be dangerous whose distribution range and ecology they share; and this is usually effective against certain predators. Others adopt a coloration that passes unnoticed in its normal environment. Photograph *A* shows a coral snake (*Micrurus brownii*), a very poisonous species, which clearly shows aposematic coloration. In photograph *B*, a false coral snake, *Lampropeltis triangulum,* which mimics the dangerous coloration of the coral snake can be seen. In photograph *E* there is a view of the poisonous snake *Bothrops schlegelii*, which imitates cryptically the coloring of the fruits of the palm on which it lives. Photographs *C*, *D*, and *F* show human examples of aposematic, mimetic, and cryptic coloration. The red of the fire engines (*C*) clearly warns of danger, since it has to move rapidly through congested streets, and indicates the proximity of a fire or other incident when it is parked. The well know warning effect of the color red has been adopted by, imitation, for publicity purposes by well-known brands (*D*). Camouflage is widely used by military personnel to make soldiers less conspicuous to enemies (*F*). *[Photos: Xavier Ferrer / Adolf de Sostoa (A and B); AGE Fotostock (C and F); Antoni Comellas (D) and Michael and Patricia Fogden (E)]*

E

F

147 The migration of different species of shearwater (*Puffinus*) between distant points of the Atlantic depends, in part, on the relative abundance of the fish (green hatching: areas of upwelling) on which they feed, and partly atmospheric and marine currents. The quantity of information that has to be integrated so they might change their behavior to favorable combinations of circumstances, in an area as extensive as an ocean that extends through two hemispheres, seems enormous in relation to the size of the nervous system of these birds. [Blue arrows: ocean currents; red arrows: migration routes of *Puffinus*.] In Roman numerals the months of the year. *[Drawing and diagrams: Biopunt, from various sources]*

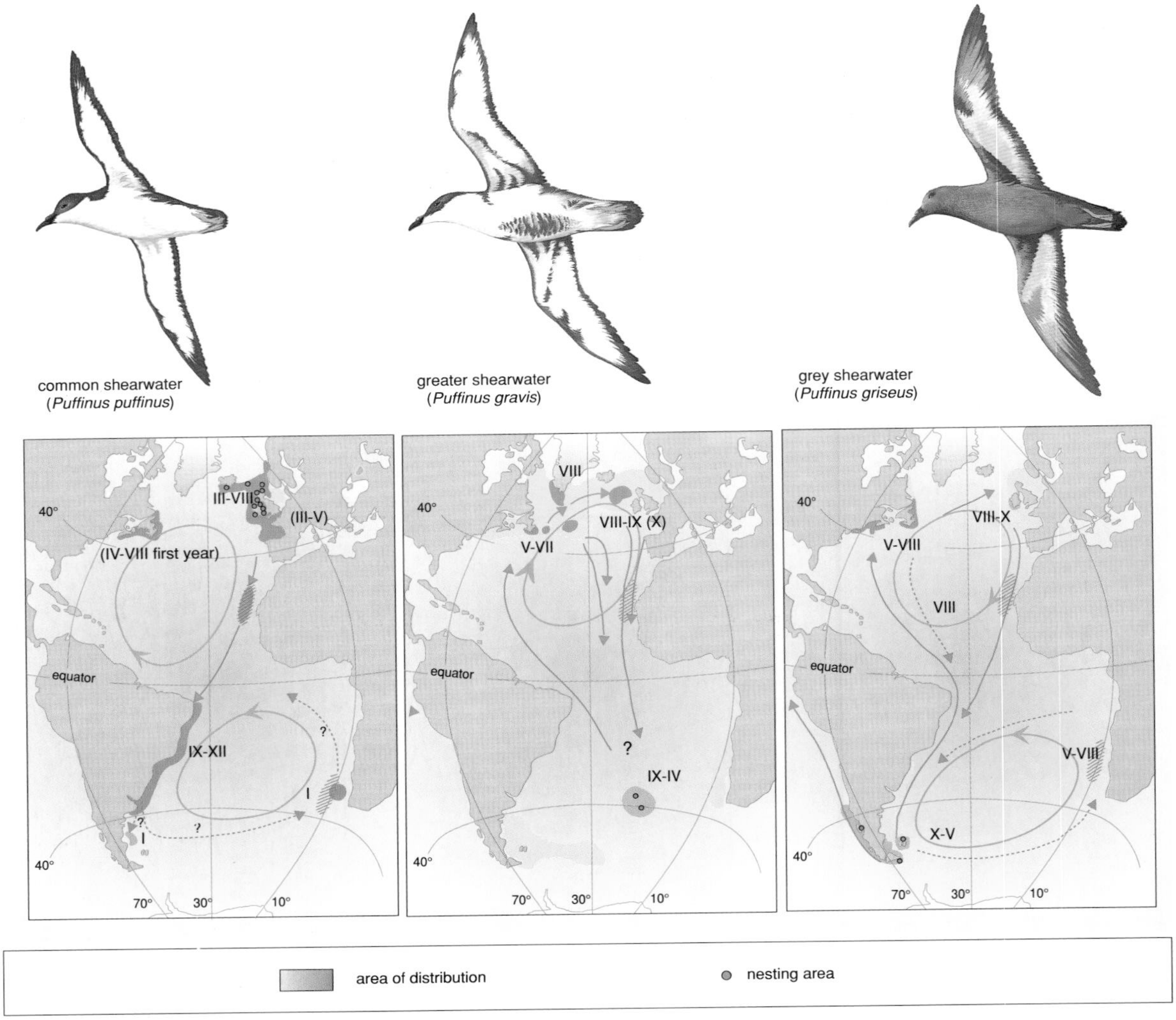

species has its own singularities, it is somewhat arbitrary to try to fit them into niches. It is probably an exaggeration to talk of unoccupied niches and whether they might make colonization more attractive, or stimulate evolution, thereby producing the appropriate inhabitant. For example, it was said that in Australia the niche for arthropods that consume the excreta of large herbivores was empty. The distinction and characterization of niches is so varied and indeterminate, and the descriptions used so diverse and arbitrary, that it becomes difficult and, perhaps, not worthwhile to develop the concept any further than an undefined and unambitious use.

The organization of relationships

Some intensive and quantifiable characteristics of ecosystems are biomass, the energy that circulates through it, and the time taken by biomass turnover. The turnover rate is not uniform and may be expressed in the form of a spectrum which is obtained by relating the series of decreasing values of turnover rates, which vary in a continuous way, with the respective amounts of biomass involved. Some parts of biomass have a faster turnover rate than others. Between ATP and wood, turnover rates vary as much as 10^8. Such differences do not exist only between species; on the contrary, within each individual some components change their matter faster than others. Whole ecosystems may be assigned global average values: the Amazon rainforest renews itself much more slowly than the communities that develop on river beds and in creeks that only occasionally carry water. The assemblage of species found in each situation reflects the general conditions of durability and the relative stability of their respective environments.

There is always a gradual, historical organization of ecosystems; through time some species die out, others enter the system or are chosen after a variable trial period. Pressure within the ecosystem stimulate the selection that will eventually lead to the formation of new races, or even of new species. Selection and evolution do not happen in the void, but within ecosystems themselves, which are evolutionary machines and at the same time the scenario of evolution.

Many species have different development stages in differently organized ecosystems. Consider the numerous insect species with aquatic larvae but aerial adult forms. The same transmutation, not just in their form but also in the way they integrate dynamically in the world, occurs in many other organisms, from batrachians to diverse parasites and sea-floor animals, whose larvae swim. Consider also migratory animals, the most spectacular and well-known of which are birds. Their populations extend over large areas: each species has its own peculiarities, but it generally adjusts to the normal differentiation of ecosystems, in the sense that they breed in environments with accelerated food production: Nordic countries in spring, or very productive coastal areas.

This model is generally valid: "young" ecosystems always offer more resources to those who search for them. Both in insects and birds, the necessity to shed feathers or tegument is organized and incorporated into their life history in a remarkable way. Many birds, especially marine birds, move over great distances and it is marvellous how a relatively small nervous system organizes and combines information from varied sensors into a sort of map of a very large environment. The brain not only remembers, relates and integrates, but it also makes decisions and forgets, functions in which artificial intelligence is much less successful.

Diversity and wealth

A considerable part of the world's beauty and of the difficulties in ecology originate in the complications in the way that ecosystems are organized and function. In the course of this work, we will no doubt have the opportunity of amusing ourselves with admirable details about complementation and evolution. Here we will only refer to two quantitative characteristics which are the external expression of what could be called the "social compromise" imposed by life in common. First, the richness and variety of forms that live together, i.e. diversity, and second, the kind and degree of completeness of the interactions between various species.

148 When one talks about systems of high diversity, one tends to think, first of all and rightly so, of the equatorial forests. There is a tendency to forget that apparently very poor systems, such as some deserts, can also have considerable diversity. In any case, diversity in deserts is much higher than that found in the immense wheat fields that have replaced large areas of what were until little more than century ago vast grasslands. In the photos, part of the Saguaro National Monument, north of the Sonora desert, in Arizona, and wheat fields in the United Kingdom (above).
[Photos: AGE Fotostock and John Shaw / Bruce Coleman Limited]

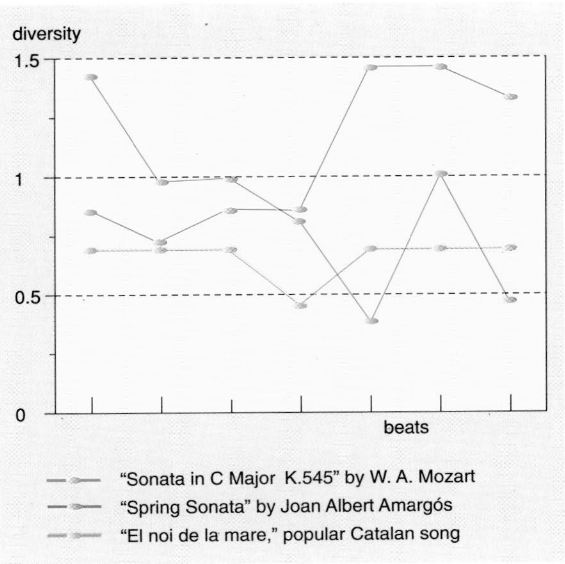

149 A piece of music, like any array of symbols, can be interpreted in terms of diversity. The diagram shows the spectra of diversity of the main melody of the first seven bars of three very different pieces of music: the "Sonata in C Major K.545" by Mozart (of which the right hand of the piano takes the main melody), the "Spring Sonata" by contemporary Catalan composer Joan Albert Amargós (the alto recorder that starts the piece), and the traditional Catalan cradle song "El noi de la mare" (the singing). The musical notes have been used as the symbol, and the number of "occurrences" has been measured in time—taking as the unit of occurrence the duration of the shortest note that occurs in the bar. Diversity has been calculated according to the formula of Brillouin. One can observe the low diversity and the almost flat spectrum of "El noi de la mare," an expression of the monotony required by a cradle song. The high diversity in the Mozart piece, from the fifth bar onwards, corresponds to the appearance of scales of semiquavers that ornament the melody of this piece. The spectrum of the piece by Amargós shows much more irregular variation.
[Diagram: Editrònica, from data supplied by Andreu Roca]

Some ecosystems are very rich in species, like the Amazon rain forest, or coral reefs; others are poorer, like the taiga or dune systems. Determining factors are the persistence and variability of the environment itself, and past evolutionary conditions, which could have provided a more or less rich reservoir of species. Diversity has to do with the total number of species, but not just with that: it is also related to the proportions between the number of individuals of the species present (or of their respective biomass, although according to this measure, the order of abundance may be different). In general, for N_i individuals of a species *x*, we may find one individual of species *y*, and for N_j individuals of species *y*, we may find one individual of species *z*. And in ecosystems which are rich in species, values for *N* tend to be, collectively and on average, lower than in ecosystems with low diversity, where the numbers of individuals in successive species, ordered according to their importance, fall rapidly when going from the most dominant one to the others.

Of course, nobody has ever been able to study an ecosystem up to the point of giving a quantified and relatively complete list of all its species. It is always to be expected that undescribed species may be found and now people often talk about the risk—and rather than risk, the certainty—that many ecosystems will disappear before we have a moderately acceptable knowledge of the species in them. Generally people talk about the diversity of particular taxonomic groups: diversity of tree species, diversity of species of butterflies, etc. Often the numerical values of those various samples of diversity are positively correlated, which is natural to a certain extent, since conditions of evolution (and structuring of ecosystems) operated simultaneously on the different groups, and lead to a similar degree of diversification or acceptance of immigrants.

Diversity may be expressed conveniently by the number of species present in a series of individuals of a particular group, taken at random. For instance, the number of species which may be counted in 1,000 specimens of nocturnal moths caught around a light bulb. Another widely used index is based on the distribution of p_i values of the probabilities (number of individuals of species *i*/total number of individuals), and it has the form $H = -\sum p_i \log_2 p_i$. This is the Shannon-Weaver expression, which gives the average information per symbol and is applicable to any set of symbols (messages, languages). Diversity may be interpreted as a message from nature.

A less descriptive and more dynamic approximation relates diversity with the processes that generate it: if it is a race to fill a space, or to take advantage of exceptional conditions, as in a continuous culture, diversity is reduced to a minimum; if it is a less dynamic system, it is probably easier to add species, and diversity grows. The maximum would occur in a display cabinet in a museum, where each species is represented by a single individual; it is, of course, a dead system. A similar example is the mythical Noah's Ark; many of the cartoonists who draw the animals getting on and off the boat are in fact making a comment on the small probability that numbers will remain low, if the system is dynamic. Their cartoons always show more rabbits and mice getting off than the mere pair who got on. Pairs are more likely to remain pairs in the case of larger animals with a longer life. To summarize, if it is easier to add an individual of a species that is already present than one of a new species, diversity decreases. If it is easier for genetic differentiation to proceed, i.e. if it is easier to add a new species than an individual, diversity increases. We humans are inevitably causing a decrease of diversity in all ecosystems, and it is unlikely that this tendency will be reversed, so long as humanity continues to press for the accelerated change of all the rest of the biosphere (and to slow down the renovation of its own biomass). Increased diversity is the result of periods of quiet and continuous evolution.

Interaction between species

If there are only a few species, it is natural that a forced interaction between them is established. An ecosystem formed by one plant species, one animal species, and one fungus or bacteria has, out of neces-

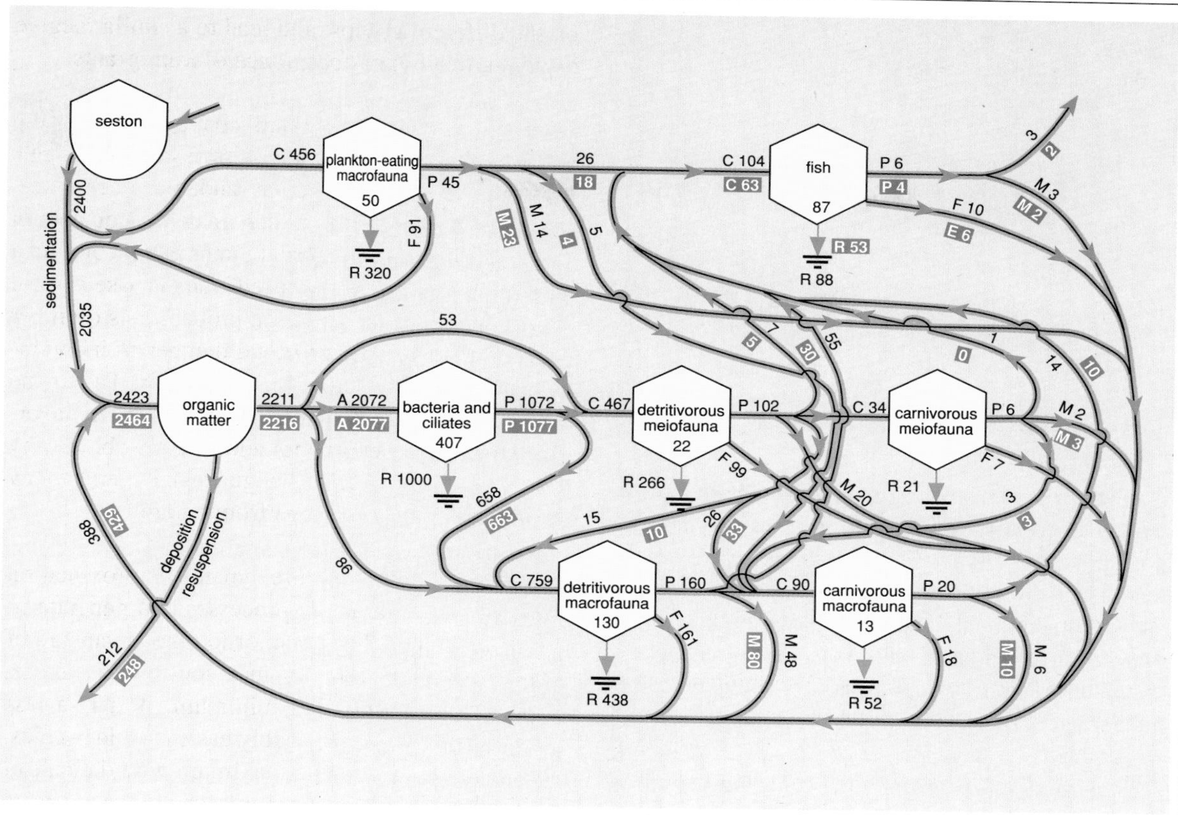

150 Idealized representations of ecosystems, imagined as a basis for constructing predictive models, are, as can be seen, very complex. Even so, they are but a partial reflection of the rich variety of facets that we find in the interactions between living organisms in real ecosystems. *[Diagram: Editrònica, from various sources]*

sity, to find its cohesion in a network of interactions. When diversity grows, with different species performing the same function (occupying the same niche, some would say), the saturation of possible connections is not that obvious. The notion of interaction needs to be made more precise, and we have to specify which interactions count: we could limit ourselves to observing only energy transfer, related to a circuit with feedback loops that leads to a certain regulation. The effect of competition (is it a relationship, anyway?) leads to cutting direct relationships between competitors. Therefore, if in every possible triangular relationship between species, one is interrupted, and this is indeed probable, the connectivity that remains is never complete or saturated, which is in agreement with the maintenance of a certain degree of inner flexibility in ecosystems and in systems in general. This applies most notably to nervous systems, where partial connectivity generates hierarchy and is the key to its functionality. All this runs counter to very common notions, e.g. that in an ecosystem everything is linked to everything else, and that, once we remove the most insignificant little flower, everything may break down, like a fragile castle of ecological niches.

The armchair ecologist, who attempts to construct quantitative models of ecosystems, is forced to define where links should or should not be accepted, and what kind of links they should be. The field naturalist realizes how difficult it is to synthesize in formal models the rich variety of details and nuances in the interactions between living beings. Confirming this fact does not undermine either view: we should eventually harmonize the perception of nature's richness and beauty with the acknowledgement that there should be ways for exploring it rationally.

Reference has repeatedly been made to relations between species linked by an energy transfer. Other secondary, though not less important ones, are the supply of vitamins, or mechanical support, like the one given by trees to creepers, or to epiphytes, like bromeliads and ferns, and other minor organisms that live off and depend on these subordinate plant species. Phagotrophs, which have to find their own food (especially "fork animals") are forced to lead a more active life which in turn has greatly stimulated their evolution. The improvement of sensory organs and nervous system came about as a consequence of evolution. The role of the nervous system is to get substantial information from the outside, to make decisions and act immediately. It manipulates information and has projected it outwards in all kinds of artifacts and organizations, like the ones developed by mankind. The nervous system is, like ecosystems themselves, a hierarchical system, in the sense that its inner connectivity is partial: each neuron is not connected to all others.

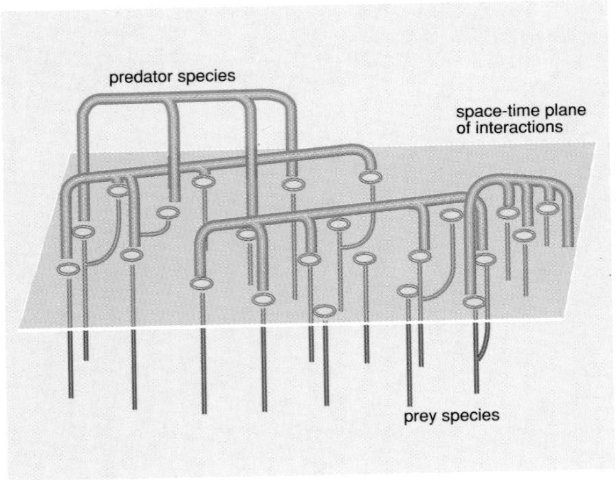

151 The interactions between individuals of two populations that share a space, one of a predator species (red) and the other of a prey species (purple), are always asymmetrical from a thermodynamic point of view. Due to the losses that are produced when moving from one trophic level to another, only part of the energy the prey obtains from its food passes to the predator. In terms of information, each predator interacts with more than one prey, while for the individuals of the species of prey, the first interaction is also often the last one. For this reason, in the predator natural selection favors its capacity to learn, while in the case of the prey, selection favors features of mimicry, camouflage, or good reflexes for escape. *[Diagram: Editrònica, from data supplied by the authors]*

Animals represent the unpredictable side of ecosystems. Clearly, for obvious reasons their biomass can not represent a very large fraction of the whole ecosystem. Their diversification, higher than that of plants, shows an additional dynamic, injected in their evolution. Most action takes place between animal species that interact intensively, such as very active predators, rather than between animals which feed passively.

As regards the interactions between individuals of two active species, we could imagine a common scenario, extending over space and time, in which the episodes are set, such as an individual of one species catching and devouring an individual of another species. The way that individuals that represent the respective species interpret the event is different. Suppose this time that the two species are an insect species and a bird species: each interaction will probably lead to the death of an insect, while for the bird it will just be one episode among many. As the saying goes, "the rabbit runs for its life, the fox only for its dinner." It is to be expected that natural selection will lead the insect to manifest physical characteristics that are immediately effective, like an unpleasant taste associated with a warning color, a hard and thorny shell, etc. or to disguise itself. On the other hand, for the bird the succession of hunting episodes has a special sense, because it can be fitted into a memory and experience frame. This requires a quite complex nervous system, capable of learning or of learning to learn.

This type of interaction should not be associated exclusively with being a hunter, not even with eating, and it was of great importance in our evolution. It expresses the positive value, in natural selection, of controlling a larger segment of time and space. Trying to extrapolate the general meaning of this dialectic of evolution, it is tempting to suppose that in any situation in which life had existed in discontinuous units and in conditions similar to the ones that currently exist on earth, the appearance of humanoids, capable of learning to learn how to learn, was unavoidable. On the other hand, one understands that there cannot exist in nature a large number of large and ferocious animals.

The social contract does not exclude great injustices, and the types of interconnections we discover in the functioning of our ecosystems may be qualified in many ways. Many of them do not have an easy analogy in human society.

Social organization

Bearing in mind these considerations, we can see that a comparable style of construction and organization of the surrounding area for self-benefit can also be found in what we could consider as certain other peaks of evolution. The forest tree is a good example of this. Another clear example is that of reef building corals. The plentiful deposits of calcareous material produce (they grow several millimeters a year) shape the environment and allow the animal tissues to lie in a suitable position according to the light and the marine currents. The corals live in symbiosis with groups of algae of considerable genetic simplicity (there is only one species of alga living in symbiosis with the most diverse inhabitants of the coral floor). The shape of the solid part does not only bring the algae closer to the surface of the sea, in other words to the light, but it also makes the water circulate vertically near the reefs which favors the arrival of nutritional material from the sea bottom.

The third peak where evolution shows considerable ingenuity in spatial organization is in the case of social insects and man. Anthills, termitaria, the nearby tracks, as well as cities and man's communication routes, are all exosomatic structures of great importance because they channel energy and facilitate the survival of the dominant species in very diverse ways. Social insects are very important in terms of quantity everywhere. According to recent data, each hectare of soil in the Amazon forest contains more than 8 million ants and a million termites. These two groups of insects, together with some hymenopterans such as bees and wasps, account for more than 75% of the total biomass of insects. Comparable figures have been quoted for other environments. It is not even necessary to mention man except to say that, as in the case of the corals, man has enormously simplified the genetic variety of the range of organisms which he uses for his own benefit, making them multiply under his "protection." We could compare crop

152 In abandoned fields, vegetation succession takes place, as in this abandoned vineyard on the slopes of Perafita (Alt Empordà, Catalonia). The stage of succession has led to the beginnings of a scrub of heath (*Erica scoparia*) with cistus, in which lavender (*Lavandula stoechas*) is still dominant, as is evident from its spectacular flowers. Less visible are the last remains of the vines (*Vitis vinifera*) that used to be cultivated on these terraces. *[Photo: Ernest Costa]*

plants, which numerically represent only a very small fraction of the total of known plant species, with the coral symbionts which are dinoflagellates. Also in the case of humans, what we indicated in trees and corals is clear: very extensive structures are not equal and, whatever the case, have an adaptive sense which allows us to use external or exosomatic energy in an efficient way. We could say that there is a material part, a structure which serves as both a support for organising energy flows and which, whether it is of direct or indirect (through some technology) biological origin, is of such a nature that it can always be evaluated in terms of information.

4.3 Memory and changes

History as we have so far related it, is continuous and predictable and would lead to a slow and unhindered development. However, it is well known that not even human history is like that. Rather it has always been a series of jolts and attempts to overcome misfortunes. It is true that many of them originated within human society itself, like wars. But not only wars: other mishaps of external origin without anyone being obviously, occur again and again. The most frequent ones, like daily and annual changes, have been assimilated by the organisms themselves as internal rhythms which anticipate these changes and predispose the organism to receive them positively and react accordingly, all in relation to the average life expectancy of the organism in question. Other changes exceed the memory possibilities of individuals and often have destructive effects which extend to greater or lesser parts of the ecosystem.

Changes that strike unexpectedly, not assimilated by life and therefore considered as catastrophes, have not prevented the projection towards the future of what could be called evolutionary memory. Evolution has probably overcome all great catastrophes, at the expense of numerous extinctions but rarely with the loss of an important acquisition of life, like complex nervous systems or thermoregulation.

And maybe, once all disturbances of relatively low intensity have been overcome, it has been easier to raise the level at which a catastrophe is considered as irrevocable. Currently the human species can subsist in considerable numbers in an acceptable civilization whose conditions would have been inhospitable for some of our ancestors. We think about the climate, but even the climate is not an obstacle any more in a world provided with strongly unifying transportation and communication systems. That this occurs just within a particular civilization, thereby accentuating the differences with other less technologically advanced human groups, is another issue.

Succession and disturbances

In the middle of the last century a fundamental idea in ecology was clearly expressed: that of *succession*. Living nature, as physical geographers perceived it, and as expressed by the vegetation cover and the soil characteristics associated with it, was subject to historical changes identifiable by aspects external to the vegetation or community itself. It is easy to trace the antecedents of this vision back to at least one century earlier.

The topic of ecological succession may be introduced very simply through a few examples. If farmlands cease to be continually cultivated, they return slowly and spontaneously to the previously existing vegetation, just the same as that which remains in other similar but uncultivated areas. The process takes a few years and even longer if the goal is reconstructing the type of forest which supposedly represents the final or "stable" vegetation of the land. This final type of vegetation was, and still is, called *climax* vegetation.

The word climax has generated considerable disagreement. On the one hand, it could suggest that there existed a previously defined path, as if ecological succession was comparable to the growth of an organism or at least to the development of an organization. Since obviously this was not true, climax vegetation was discarded as a simple utopia or fantasy of thev followers of a perhaps over enthusiastic school of ecologists. Often there have been attempts to extend this criticism to the concept of succession itself. It is understandable that it is often difficult to be able to show the differences between two successive stages of a process of change clearly. The usual statistical methods, and especially the way they are used, do not indicate the differences between neighboring stages clearly. However there is indeed a considerable difference between the beginning and the end of the process. The analysis of each single moment could make us doubt whether Achilles will ever catch up with the tortoise, but only a few doubt the final result of the race in Zeno's paradox, a paradigm of the use that is sometimes made of statistics in ecological topics.

We have to accept, then, the phenomenon of succession with some general rules. Firstly, that the quantity of chlorophyll or the capacity for organic synthesis grows very little during the succession, much less than the total quantity of matter, especially of wood. As a result, the quotient production/biomass (and even more the quotient production/[biomass + necromass]) decreases in the course of succession. The number of different species tends to grow, and so does, generally, the number of trophic levels in which they are arranged, that is to say, the food chains become longer. Unless seen through the eyes of the farmer who used to cultivate the field, the final organization is more beautiful or at least more complex.

If we continue with the example of the field, we should bear in mind that while it was cultivated, succession could not advance because the yield was harvested every year. If left on the field, nature would find a way to assimilate it and to organize herself and to complicate matters. It is easy to discover common adaptations in the plants that correspond to each of the phases or states of succession. For instance, the first invaders are often those that produce large quantities of seeds or little fruits that the wind carries away, while it is common for plants to be dispersed by fleshy fruits, attractive to birds, during later more advanced stages. At this relatively late stage, the entire biotic community has already organized jointly the expansion of its area.

Another example of succession is scree vegetation, where we can find some of the humblest components of flora: mosses and algae, and some small animals of the incipient soil. Succession is a complex phenomenon because it goes together with the differentiation and organization of the soil and the life it contains. Succession proceeds with difficulty in a scree. It is given just a short time to advance, because successive slippage of the rocks and pebbles forces it to start again. One realizes too the importance of the ability of plants and their diaspores to maintain their occupation of the space. The spontaneous capacity of nature to take away, with each avalanche, the biological material which had been produced, may resemble the effect of harvesting the crops in a field. Succession in screes does not advance much because they are environments subject to very intensive, but natural, exploitation.

Even longer (decades or centuries) is needed for a plant community, under relatively favorable conditions, to attain the form of a forest. Vegetation scientists have distinguished biological types of plants, which are really no more than the names grass, shrub and tree, dignified by the use of a terminology that sounds Greek (it could not be any other way): a megaphanerophyte is obviously a tree, and an hemicryptophyte, a grass (whose buds remain two or more years at ground level). Succession represents a constant reorganization with the introduction of taller plants and at the same time an increasing variety of all kinds of interdependent organisms, among them many animal species.

A forest may burn from time to time. This represents, after the combustion of a considerable mass of wood, the return to a phase equivalent to one which had already been surpassed. Succession has some features that remind us of a game of snakes and ladders. The players advance regularly until, with a stroke of bad luck, they are forced to return to a state that is equivalent to one they have already gone through. Notice the profound asymmetry between a forest fire and its regeneration. Regeneration is necessarily much slower than the action of fire.

There is an existential uncertainty in what we call disturbance. The only detectable regularity is that the most energetic disturbances, in other words the ones involving more exosomatic energy, are less frequent than the weaker ones. Our lives are also full of minor set-backs, and occasionally we suffer real blows of which the worst one is by definition unique. The biosphere works in a similar manner, kick after kick. Thus succession may be seen simply as a mechanism to restore and heal the wounds. We could even ask ourselves whether, for biological evolution to take place, a pruning is necessary from time to time.

In temperate zones, trees that lose their leaves suffer an annual interruption of vegetation, which could be considered equivalent to a minor fire or, at least, a minor disturbance. Vegetation undergoes a pause, but unlike what happens in herbaceous plants, trees have the advantage of being ready for the next spring with their buds. In this kind of forest, winter rest allows the soil to retain their nutrients. It is this quality that makes soils good for agriculture, which has flourished in fluctuating environments, both in the temperate and in the intertropical regions, on the mountains

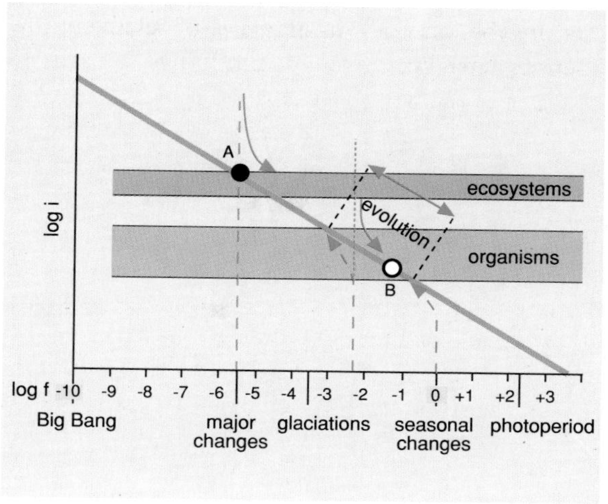

(cultivation of potatoes), or in marshes (cultivation of rice).

In tropical forests, or temperate forests with water availability all year round, without frosts, vegetation becomes taller and often very complex. For instance, it could be said that the climax vegetation types of the Amazon are "more climactic" than the climax vegetation of the temperate region. What that means is simply the replacement of that historical, impressionistic and aesthetic notion with a much more quantifiable concept, the quotient P/B (or $P/[B+N]$), as the expression of turnover rate (P= production, B= biomass, N= necromass). Succession is perceived as the result of a tendency to slow down. It may be helpful when trying to understand this to think that production depends on surface area, both for the availability of light energy and rain water, while the accumulation of biomass (and of necromass, which also helps to give it structure), however, is not limited in the same manner. A particularly illustrative example is that of tropical forests, since it shows directly the enrichment in species and life forms, with creepers, various types of epiphytes and diverse animals which depend on dead matter deposited on branches, which is equivalent to soils.

The notion of succession applies to all ecosystems. The development of plankton in fresh water and sea water shares the same characteristics, though the scales, especially the time scale, are different. Normally matter assimilated by phytoplankton moves downwards, due to direct sedimentation or to the contribution of animals which eat it and transport it through their own sedimentation or that of their excrements, or by active movement. The result is that the chemical elements most necessary for life are used up above.

153 One of the few generalizations that can be formulated with respect to disturbances is that stronger ones are less frequent than milder ones. This generalization can be expressed as the inverse relationship between the logarithms of their frequency and of their intensity (measured by the amount of energy involved). The maximum disturbance, the Big Bang, which initiated the universe, can be seen as a unique event on the scale of tens of thousands of millions of years. Other large disturbances such as the collision of the Earth with asteroids, occur much more frequently, on the scale of tens of millions of years. Glaciations are phenomena that occur at a frequency of tens of thousands of years. The seasons of the year are repeated on an annual cycle, and the succession of day and night follows a daily rhythm (except at polar latitudes). Life has inevitably assimilated or internalized the most frequent and apparently inevitable changes. Evolution leads to the overcoming of the constraints of the environment and its fluctuations, although it leaves open the possibility of unforeseen impacts that cannot be assimilated. On a broader scale, it is the ecosystems that internalize the less frequent disturbances, such as the glaciations or the movements of the lithospheric plates.

[Diagram: Editrònica, from data supplied by the author]

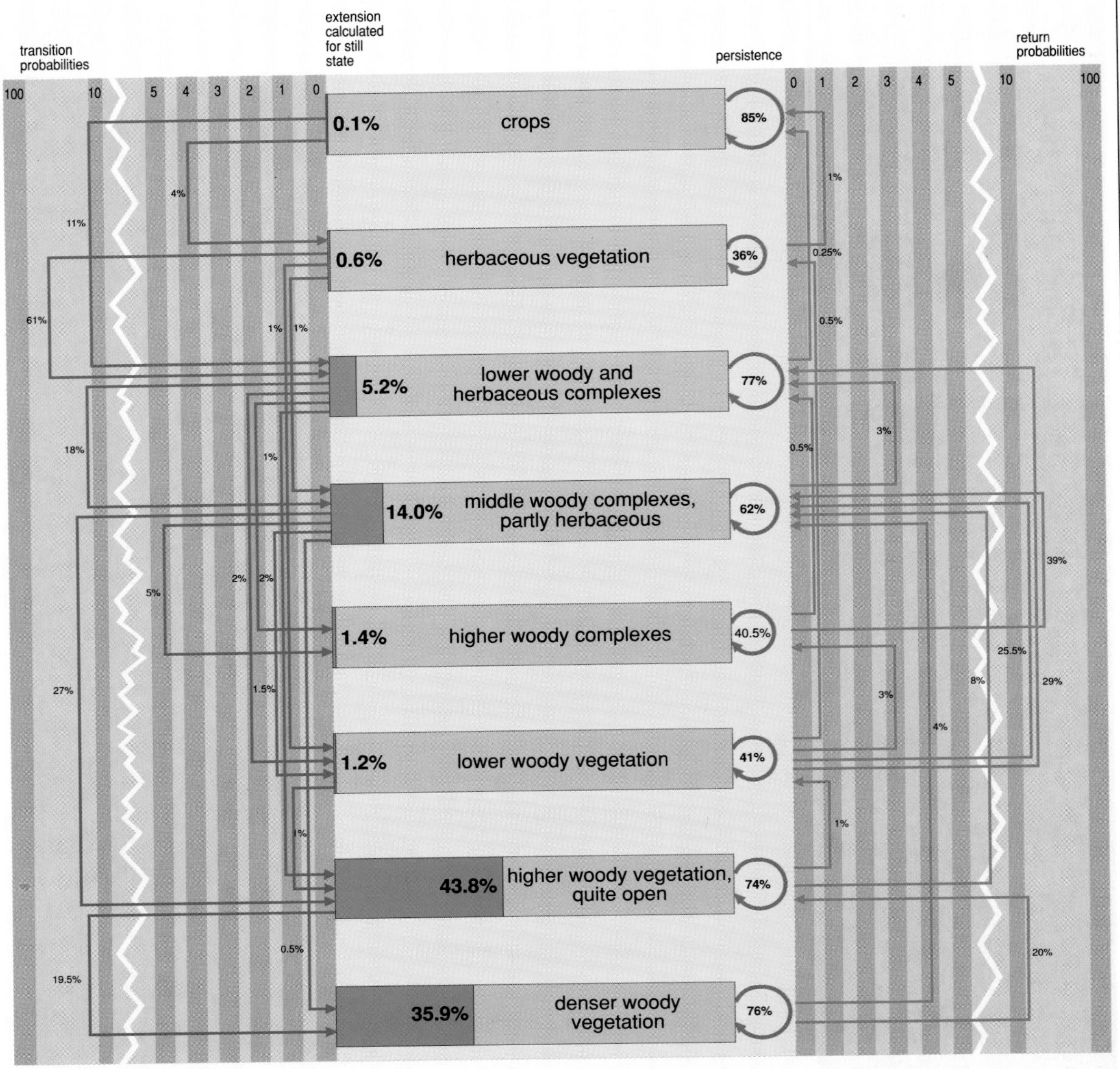

154 Succession is observable in a marginal habitat occupied mainly by Mediterranean woodland, matorral and garrigue near Saint Martin-de-Londres, N. of Montpellier, bas Languedoc. By means of an analysis of the changes recorded at a group of selected points on the map in a series of aerial photographs separated by a period of eight years, one can note the general tendency towards repopulation of abandoned cultivated fields and herbaceous vegetation, while the changes between more complex types of vegetation are much slower. One can also observe a change from advanced to less advanced stages of succession as a probable consequence of repeated fires, which are quite frequent in the Mediterranean basin. *[Drawing: Biopunt, from Rambal and Lepart, 1987]*

Nearly always the chain is broken at its weakest part, that is to say, by the most limiting elements or the first ones to disappear, i.e phosphorus and nitrogen, as happens on dry land. These chemical elements concentrate in deep water, where they accumulate because they are not assimilated due to the lack of light. When thermic stratification is destroyed, generally in cold and windy weather, the water is vertically mixed, fertililizing the surface and starting a new succession which naturally possesses a high *P*/*B* ratio. For this reason vertical mixing has been compared (though not quite correctly) to the ploughing of a field for cultivation.

In plankton the number of species multiplies progressively and succession develops faster than in terrestrial ecosystems. Its primary producers never accumulate wood, which does not imply that they do not "try to," in the sense that shells and all kinds of ornaments are more frequent in the species that develop later than in those which start the succession off. In water, the series of more or less truncated successions proceeds not only faster but also less regularly than on dry land. Nevertheless the result is similar: the increase in complexity of present life and slowing down the succession through the general principle of keeping separate the potential reacting agents, i.e. where there is light, no nutrients are left, and vice versa. Two popular sayings can be suitably applied to this mechanism of ecological succession: "when the going gets tough, the tough get going" describes the increasing complexity of nature on a local scale, so long as we leave it in peace, and "God gives beans to the one who has no teeth" expresses the need to have

155 The phenomenon of succession is evident on the banks of rivers, which meander, as can be seen in the tropical forests on the banks of the Amazon, in the photograph.
[Photo: Photothèque Stone International]

the reactants (the beans and the teeth) kept apart to create and maintain nature's complexity.

Another example of succession can be observed on a river bed which meanders with a dynamics proper to the river and its banks. At those places on the bank where the river recedes, terrestrial vegetation may advance or develop and does so in strips parallel to the sides of the river. In this way the more advanced stages are farther from the river. Given the nature of the geometry of meander formation, when the river advances it cuts almost at right angles the strips that represent successive stages of former successions. This is an interesting example for various reasons. The process we just described prevents great tropical forests from undergoing long periods without renewal. If forests interact with rivers of shifting beds there is obviously a continuous renewal of vegetation that favors the evolution of species in their own habitat. Through this example it becomes clear that what characterizes succession is neither a rigorously linear sequence nor the view of climax vegetation as the final culmination, but simply the lack of symmetry of any table or matrix that expresses the distribution of the probabilities of transition between the various stages or phases that we have recognized distinct in the whole sequence. We do not need to make reference to any problematic concept of climax. Rather, it is as simple as saying that in one year each one of us can either add one year to our life or die. What we cannot do is add two or more years. With this notion we hope to eliminate many false problems and quite a few discussions centerd around the concept of succession.

If we catalogued those disturbances known to affect certain natural systems, we would see that there is an inverse relation between the frequency of any type of disturbance and its violence. This intensity can be related to the (exosomatic) energy involved and the frequency ranges from the single event, e.g. the "Big Bang," the event that started the universe around 10^{10} years ago, to events which happen as regularly and often as the tick of a clock. The scale of frequencies may be expressed in decimal logarithms of the number of events per year, starting from -10. On this scale an annual disturbance (more or less intense depending on the latitude) would be represented by zero. Glaciations range between -4 and -6 and major wars between -2 and -1. Finally, changes associated to night and day range from between +2 and +3.

This distribution of disturbances is particularly important as background to all *succession* processes, in other words, the substitution of one system by others throughout time. Disturbance suggests unpredictability, regardless of the fact that we assign provisionally a frequency to each type of disturbance, although of little value. Its basic indeterminacy has always been the despair of ecologists. They have often pondered astronomic cycles, more or less well defined, which can account for days and for years, but which beyond these periods are of much more doubtful value. There have been attempts to describe numerous natural phenomena of fluctuating intensity through the addition of harmonic series of varying durations. However it is difficult to evaluate their possible interaction. In material systems oscillations are never symmetric, i.e. there are no phenomena (except for the oscillations used in the description of light) in which the "downslope" is symmetrical with the "upslope."

In relation to practical considerations and prediction, it should be borne in mind that a given global frequency may allow a very irregular distribution in time of the various episodes. To draw attention to the corresponding loss of predictability, two terms have been introduced among several others: the Noah effect and the Joseph effect. The Noah effect is a practically unique event, like the Flood, or maybe the collision of Earth with a planetoid. The Joseph effect refers to the tendency for some disturbances to occur together in time, while they are rare or absent in other periods, like rainy years or drought years. Hydraulic constructions are built to resist "the flood of the century," but cannot take into account a unique event like a deluge. This shows the hidden cards that an open world can play, as Popper would say, but any ecologist is put on the spot when asked to make predictions. Obviously, what he or she cannot say is that the crystal ball presents a spectrum of disturbances with such features that it would be unwise to take the risk of prophesying. It was easier for Joseph, the Egyptian.

Succession, a history matrix

Succession provides a useful historical vantage point from which to organize our own image or model of the world, in other words, history, or that of some of its components which may particularly interest us: life, organisms, and ecosystems. It is worthwhile examining the relationship between succession and evolution and even exploring the relationship between those interwoven historic threads and some aspects of our current views on the problems associated with the development of our civilization.

When trying to place evolution in a world subject to an uninterrupted process of succession, direct relationships between the two concepts are uncovered. The theory of natural selection states simply that in some cases the genotype of some of the descendants will gradually replace the one which was more widespread in its ancestors. If we try to relate this statement to a definition of fitness, we will encounter logical difficulties because fitness and survival cannot be characterized independently.

We need to find a criterion which is independent of the mechanisms of substitution over time and which allows us to distinguish the antecedent from the consequent systematically. This validation is independently and externally needed by the theory of evolution through natural selection, and it could perhaps be found in thermodynamics. One possibility is that a series of chemical reactions, comparable to an increase in entropy, which takes place in the individual members of a species and their immediate surroundings in a given time, could be recovered and recognized as an increase in information at some later time. This link with time is the essence of evolution.

A possible formulation inspired by the social and economic circumstances, whose study probably originated the idea of biological evolution, is the following: any increased body of augmented information is ready to assimilate a larger number of probable future states of the environment, and therefore, ready to allow a decrease in the production of new individuals in the unending attempts to occupy a larger fraction of the available space. The arrangement of a larger quantity of information involves, though not necessarily, a unidirectional and growing increase in the quantity of information that the descendants pass on from the past to the future and probably also an increase in the working time of each individual system. Some of these tendencies in change are also found in the study of succession. This proves the relationship between these two and very general thermodynamic or physical principles which may be specially valuable as prediction criteria, since they are practically the only ones that exist.

It may not seem very fruitful to attempt to establish all possible analogies between ecosystems and organisms, but they do share common properties because of their historical character: a change in the increase in entropy today to acquire information that may make persistence easier tomorrow. It is in this sense that succession may find an explanation or an unforced placement within a similar order of ideas.

There seems to exist another even closer operational connection between succession and evolution. It is possible to recognise certain common features between the different stages of succession, which manifest themselves in the species present at each respective stage, and even in the aspects or characteristics of individuals of the same species, when its life extends over various succession stages. Compared to the biological forms that preceded them, later species are generally better built, have longer lives, bear fewer offspring and protect them better, have a lower metabolism, etc. Nevertheless, the whole biosphere scenario slowly follows the general direction of succession, though from time to time there are sudden relapses to previous stages which had already been surpassed.

What this means is that the biosphere in evolution is subject, as if forced to walk on a moving escalator, to a *vis a tergo*, or smooth and continuous persuasion to adjust itself to the next stage in order to respond to a suggested evolutionary differential. The fact that the biosphere is continually upset and shaken, as if it were on a conveyor belt that will not give anyone too long a rest, must be a sufficient motive to induce a series of parallel and similar characteristics in many phyletic lines. Growth in size, complexity of many organic features, reduction in number of offspring and better protection of them are parallel characteristics of many breeds and had been considered a demonstration of a presumed *orthogenesis*, i.e. orientated or directed evolution. That many phyletic lines converge in many morphological and functional characters may be simply a consequence of the common denominator which allows the many successional processes which compose the scenario of evolution to occur.

Towards the final stages of succession there is little energy difference between neighboring situations. There may be many possible realizations of dynamically similar situations and it is not difficult for ecosystems to become locally differentiated from one another. In this domain there is hardly any difference in energy between situations that are practically equivalent and, moreover, the increase in the life-span of the individual is always favored.

This is a field prone to local differentiation, to the play of life in an indifferent domain, to experiment with life, to the apparent exaggeration in the design of all sorts of defense mechanisms, mimicries and imitations, to the establishment of very complex relationships between species or members of the same species. Now when speaking about the conservation of tropical rain forests, one has more or less consciously in mind the background of complexity that always keeps the mystery of the unexplainable. It is true that the concept of climax, though unreal, nevertheless has an aesthetic dimension: something complex though apparently not functional, with all the features of a work of art not imposed by everyday demands. And regardless of the artistic (and therefore gratuitous) interpretations they lend themselves to, these complex structures have a rather utilitarian *raison d'être* that becomes apparent when one tries to analyze each one separately.

Lazy nature

A system is a non-rigid organization composed of different and characterizable parts, often repeated or the product of production line, linked to each other through functional bonds of different kinds. With a relatively limited array of kinds of parts, and an also limited set of interactions, nature produces a great variety of systems. Examples of these are: atoms, the unified elementary living systems (i.e. organisms), ecological systems or ecosystems, insect societies and human societies in general, as well as particular examples of the latter, like industrial and political systems. The definition and explanation of such systems usually includes the formulation of a goal and tendency, often set by the observer, whose personal stand-point is ideally in the system itself in which he or she intends to recognize certain features. This happens probably because we are sys-

156 In the fundamental task of all living beings of passing their genes to the future generations, these whip scorpions (Amblypygi, above) and these sloths (*Bradypus variegatus*, below), represent two diametrically opposed strategies. The whip scorpions have numerous offspring, which are very liable to become the victims of predators, and against which maternal protection does not extend beyond the hatching of the eggs that have been carried about since fertilization. Yet, because of the large numbers of offspring it is likely that some will survive. The female of the sloth carries her single offspring around with her and protects it until it is able to fend for itself; this dedication to the survival of the offspring is fundamental for the continuity of the genetic inheritance of the parents. *[Photos: Michael and Patricia Fogden]*

tems too. Often the supposedly discovered tendency is given the form of a function to be maximized: maximum work production, maximum efficiency, maximum mass (biomass), projection towards the future, etc.

It could be said that the theory of natural selection contributed to the sanctioning of the Puritan work ethic. In many biology texts adequacy or fitness are identified with a capacity to produce more offspring. Success in natural selection terms does not mean leaving more descendants, but to passing more of your genes into the future, a goal which is sometimes better attained by reducing offspring mortality. It is better to have offspring that live longer and reproduce less than to leave excessive offspring that fail. Naturally it all depends on the world in which we live: if there are many unforeseeable dangers, the best thing to do is to leave many descendants: some of them will surely survive. If risks become more limited and foreseeable, it is better to reduce the production of descendants to the minimum. This is one aspect of nature's laziness.

The multiplication rate of species does not grow in successive generations, following the evolution of the breed, but rather it goes down and becomes adjusted to the permitted minimum. This may be seen everywhere, and one appropriate example is the course of evolution of life in rivers. There the product of the river's current by the probability (definable at a scale between 0 and 1) that the organisms that live in it will be carried away by water current itself defines the multiplication rate which is necessary to allow the populations to persist locally. The give and take of evolution is established between the probability of being carried away and the multiplication rate. Both values decrease simultaneously, in what could be called the syndrome of adaptation to fluvial life. Over long periods the difference is zero, but in a river it certainly fluctuates in response to floods or dry periods. Species need to have, if they are to persist in the long run, a slight excess of offspring which will allow them to survive extraordinary circumstances, whenever they arise. In our example, this means the capacity to colonise the river going upstream from the lower parts after a flood washed down the population that lived there.

The adaptations that allow the decrease of the probability or expectation of being washed away may consist in more efficient mechanisms for holding on to the river stones. In insect species that are aquatic only in their larval phases, aerial adult individuals usually fly in the opposite direction of the river current so as to compensate at a population level for the expected result of the river washing away some of the larvae.

Nature is lazy. If 10 copies suffice, she will not make 100. Even the copying strategy is an expression of the laziness of nature. Other diverse considerations confirm this tendency and clarify some of the possible ways and reasons why it happens. Even death comes lazily: the longer life is, the more possibilities there are for the individual's size to grow, for information to be accumulated and for life to be guaranteed in the future, if the environment is not a very changing one. The same tendency continues, culturally, in human nature. In order to lengthen life numerous resources, both sanitary and medical, are used. They are paid for with exosomatic energy and subject to the law of diminishing returns, since each year added to the statistical life expectation of people is more expensive in terms of exosomatic energy.

Nature, one could say, does not make the slightest move if she can avoid it. The prize, albeit a small one, is for the one who occupies space with the least possible effort, in the physical sense, i.e. expressed in joules, calories or kilowatts per hour. Obviously a system that is constantly tottering where survival is random, must rely on an extra number of trials, expressed in the form of leaving more descendants. But at the same time, a system with such characteristics is the only kind of system which continues exploring and thus the only one which may find novelties. It is not surprising that all phyletic lines, or new directions which evolution has taken have begun with a previous disturbance that launched life into making new experiences. This is valid both in relation to ecological succession and in evolution. We could think, and even believe, that this coincidence is the basis of an inevitable dependency of evolution on succession. The latter provides the cradle, the path, and the former follows it more or less grudgingly. The arguments we used to show the omnipresence of succession, at the mercy of changes in the environment, seem quite convincing.

The biosphere in the human age

"If his spirit is sensitive to works of art, if his cultivated spirit is broad enough to rise to the great conceptions of general physics, [Man], from the depths of his solitude and without having to leave his house, appropriates everything the intrepid naturalist has discovered by roaming the winds and the oceans, penetrating underground caverns and climbing the icy peaks. Doubtless, it is in this way that the lights of our civilization most influence our own individual happiness: they allow us to live the present and the past at the same time; they assemble around us everything nature has produced in all its various climes, and they place us in communication with all the peoples of the Earth."

Alexander von Humboldt
Essai sur la géographie des plantes (1807)

1
Humans in the biosphere

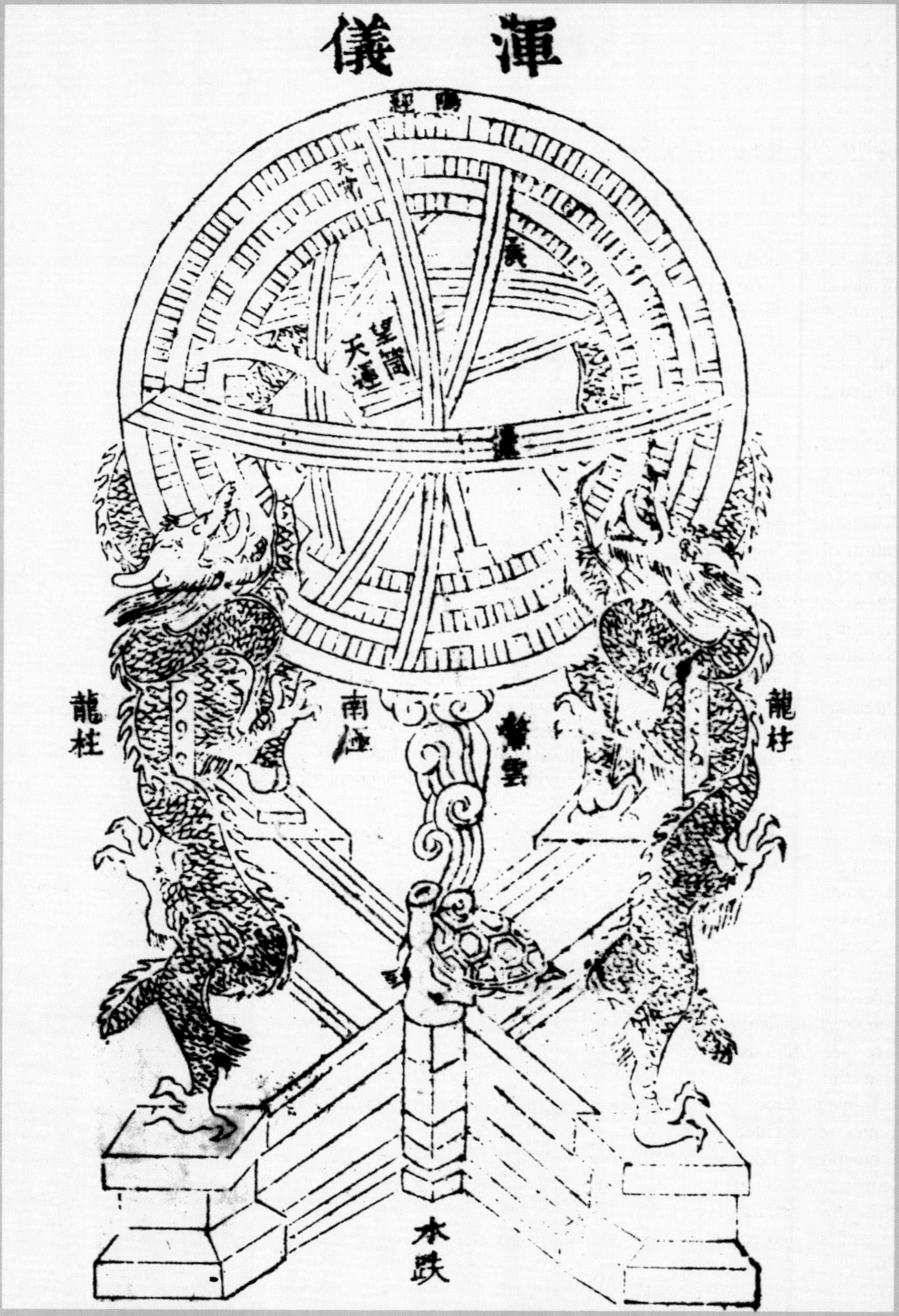
渾儀
望筒
天運
龍柱
南極
龍柱

1. The human race: the same, but different

1.1 Anthropocentrism, an untenable position

The human species has always had a very high opinion of itself. Anthropocentrism (regarding humans as the most significant entities on Earth) has been a constant in the majority of civilizations, many of which have seen the whole of creation as a convenient collection of elements entirely at man's disposal. The geocentric theory, widely accepted by western thinkers for centuries, is a logical consequence of this anthropocentrism: if humans are the inheritors of the universe, it is logical that the planet that they inhabit is at the center of the cosmos (a superficial observation of the apparent movements of the stars relative to Earth confirmed this). Naturalists themselves, when they put the taxonomic panoply of living things into some kind of scientific order, used the rather immodest epithet of sapiens to designate their own species, adding it to the neutral generic denomination of *Homo*. *Homo sapiens*, then, is the Linnaean binomial which enshrines the anthropocentric vision of 18th century scientists and their successors.

This rather unhappy perception is not, however, entirely unfounded. The zoological condition of the human species, which has been amply demonstrated by modern biology, does not necessarily mean that we have to deny its objective singularities, which are many. Thanks to the demythologization achieved by science, we now know that humans belong to just another zoological species, but we also know that we are obviously not just any species. In any case, the appearance of prehuman hominids followed by different human species, including modern man, represented a decisive turning point for the biosphere. For this reason, and putting anthropocentric self-satisfaction to one side, it is worth considering the appearance and development of humans, as well as their zoological and ecological characteristics.

Homo in Latin means "human" rather than a man, in the sense of an adult male human (*vir* in Latin). It is not derived from the Greek suffix "homo-", meaning "the same," as in "homozygous," "homosexual," etc.

1.2 The objective peculiarities of the human species

An intelligent, omnivorous, and accommodating species

The cybernetic control mechanisms developed by the nervous systems of many animals are particularly well developed in vertebrates, especially in mammals. Their brains and the structures associated with them are not limited to regulating movements and behavioral norms in accordance with a pre-ordained and immovable model. They also enjoy a substantial degree of freedom to respond unpredictably to stimuli: they perform voluntary actions that depend on decisions that are partially or totally unpredictable. On the other hand, they can recall previous decisions and experiences and infer from these new ways of responding to stimuli. They are, in other words, capable of learning. We could say, in fact, that they are more or less intelligent, but never more so than human beings.

This, together with the anthropocentric attitude we have already mentioned, has led to the assertion that only the human species is really intelligent. This position does not seem to be sustainable today, nor in any other epoch for that matter: leaving false cultural or religious prejudices to one side, it has always been known that dogs and horses, for example, understand messages and can perform tasks. Intelligence is not an exclusive property of the human species, but the degree to which it manifests itself is. For this reason the remarkable functional efficiency of the human brain is the main factor which sets human beings apart.

The extraordinary development of our intellectual capacity and our ability to memorize things is complemented by another skill: that of speaking. Sound modulation is common in many animals, especially birds, but once again it is the humans who are able to make the most of the anatomical possibilities of their larynx. When used in the service of a high intelligence, this skill opens the way for language, leading to better communication between individu-

157 Anthropocentrism, as a corollary of geocentrism, was a constant feature of human thought during thousands of years, as suggested by the classical armillary spheres. The various metal rings, which are concentric with respect to the Earth, represent the apparent trajectories of the celestial bodies, and also reflect the notion of the central position of humans at the heart of the universe. The engraving, which represents a Chinese armillary sphere from around 1090, described in the Xin Yi Xiang Fa Yao, shows that these attitudes do not occur only in western cultures. In fact, quite to the contrary, these geocentrically inspired structures were not known in Europe until they were "reinvented" by Tycho Brahe in the sixteenth century. *[Photo: The Needham Research Institute]*

158 The principal spoken languages in the world (five million or more speakers), arranged by the number of people who use them as their own language. (a) In millions. (b) Within Chinese are included different dialects that many linguists consider separate languages. Those having more than five million speakers are: Mandarin (761 million), Wu (89), Yue or Cantonese (76), Xiang (50), Keija or Hakka (41), S. Min (37), Gan (25), and N. Min (11). (c) Includes different dialects, some of which many linguists consider separate languages (Awadhi, Bihari, Marwari); those having more than five million speakers are: Khariboli (the basis of contemporary Hindi and Urdu, with 257 million speakers), Awadhi (with 55), Bihari (some 42) and Marwari (7). (d) Includes Brazilian and Galician. (e) Isolated language. (f) Includes Bahasa Indonesian; some estimates suggest 100 million speakers, but this is mainly due to its use as a "lingua franca." (g) Also known as Filipino when used as the official language of the Philippine Islands. (h) Includes Chichewa (the official language of Malawi), Malawi or Maravi and other dialects of Malawi, Mozambique, Zambia and Zimbabwe. (i) Includes Dzongkha, dialect spoken in Bhutan which is the official language of the country.
[Source: data prepared by the author after M. Ruhlen, 1987, and other sources]

LANGUAGE	FAMILY	GROUP	NUMBER OF SPEAKERS (a)
1. Chinese (b)	Sino-Tibetan	Chinese	1,066
2. Hindi-Urdu (c)	Indo-European	Indic	385
3. English	Indo-European	Germanic	331
4. Spanish (Castilian)	Indo-European	Romance	289
5. Arabic	Afro-Asiatic	Semitic	184
6. Bengali	Indo-European	Indic	175
7. Russian	Indo-European	Slavic	170
8. Portuguese (d)	Indo-European	Romance	166
9. Japanese	Altaic	(e)	123
10. German	Indo-European	Germanic	93
11. French	Indo-European	Romance	91
12. Punjabi	Indo-European	Indi	82
13. Javanese	Austronesian	Western or Indonesian	74
14. Korean	Altaic	(e)	69
15. Telugu	Dravidian	Telugu-kui	68
16. Marathi	Indo-European	Indic	63
17. Tamil	Dravidian	Tamil-kodagu	60.5
18. Italian	Indo-European	Romance	60
19. Annamese	Austro-Asiatic	Viet-Muong	58
20. Turkish	Altaic	South Turkic	52
21. Gujarati	Indo-European	Indic	41
22. Ukrainian	Indo-European	Slavic	40
23. Polish	Indo-European	Slavic	39
24. Malay(f)	Austronesian	Western or Indonesian	35
25. Kanarese	Dravidian	Kannada	34
26. Malayalam	Dravidian	Tamil-kodagu	33
27. Hausa	Afro-Asiatic	Chad	30
28. Thai	Thai (Tai)	Be-kam-tai	30
29. Criya	Indo-European	Indic	29
30. Burmese	Sino-Tibetan	Burmese	28
31. Farsi	Indo-European	Iranian	28
32. Sundanese	Austronesian	Western or Indonesian	28
33. Yoruba	Niger-Congo	Benue-Congolese	26
34. Paixto	Indo-European	Iranian	24
35. Romanian	Indo-European	Romance	24
36. Ibo	Niger-Congo	Benue-Congolese	22
37. Dutch	Indo-European	Germanic	21
38. Amharic	Afro-Asiatic	Semitic	19
39. Serbo-Croat	Indo-European	Slavic	18
40. Lao	Thai (Tai)	Be-kam-tai	18
41. Oromo	Afro-Asiatic	Cushitic	18
42. Sindhi	Indo-European	Indic	17
43. Azeri	Altaic	South Turkic	15.5
44. Kurdish	Indo-European	Iranian	15.5
45. Lahnda	Indo-European	Indic	15
46. Sebuan	Austronesian	Western or Indonesian	15
47. Tagalog (g)	Austronesian	Western or Indonesian	15
48. Uzbek	Altaic	Western Turkic	15
49. Shan (Zhuang)	Thai (Tai)	Be-kam-tai	15
50. Assamese	Indo-European	Indic	14
51. Hungarian	Uralo-Yukaghir	Finno-Ugric	13.5
52. Nepali	Indo-European	Indic	13
53. Malagasy	Austronesia	Western or Indonesian	12
54. Ruanda	Niger-Congo	Benue-Congolese	12
55. Greek	Indo-European	Greek	11.5
56. Singhalese	Indo-European	Indic	11
57. Czech	Indo-European	Slavic	10
58. Khmer	Austro-Asiatic	Khmer	9
59. Nyanja (h)	Niger-Congo	Benue-Congolese	8.7
60. Madurese	Austronesian	Western or Indonesia	8.6
61. Shona	Niger-Congo	Benue-Congolese	8.5
62. Kazakh	Altaic	Central Turkish	8.2
63. Swedish	Indo-European	Germanic	8.2
64. Pul (or Fulbe)	Niger-Congo	Senegalese	8.1
65. Somali	Afro-Asiatic	Cushitic	8
66. Kongo	Niger-Congo	Benue-Congolese	8
67. Belorussian	Indo-European	Slavic	8
68. Akan	Niger-Congo	Benue-Congolese	7.9

LANGUAGE	FAMILY	GROUP	NUMBER OF SPEAKERS (a)
69. Bulgarian	Indo-European	Slavic	7.9
70. Zulu	Niger-Congo	Kwa	7.9
71. Quechua	Amerindian	Andean	7.6
72. Makua	Niger-Congo	Benue-Congolese	7.4
73. Ruanda	Niger-Congo	Benue-Congolese	7.1
74. Iloca	Austronesian	Western or Indonesian	6.9
75. Catalan	Indo-European	Romance	6.7
76. Ibo)	Niger-Kordofanian	Kwa	6.7
77. Mossi	Niger-Congolese	Gur	6.7
78. Uigar	Altaic	Western Turkish	6.7
79. Tadjik	Indo-European	Iranian	6.3
80. Miao	Miao-Yao	Miao	6.2
81. Afrikaans	Indo-European	Germanic	6.1
82. Hiligaynon	Austronesian	Western or Indonesia	6.1
83. Luba	Niger-Congolese	Benue-Congolese	6.1
84. Tartar	Altaic	Western Turkish	6
85. Yi	Thai	Be-kam-tai	6
86. Bhili	Indo-European	Indic	5.6
87. Mongol	Altaic	Western Mongolic	5.4
88. Kinuri	Nilo-Saharian	Saharian	5.3
89. Albanian	Indo-European	Albanian	5.2
90. Slovak	Indo-european	Slavic	5.2
91. Kikuyu	Niger-Congolese	Benue-Congolese	5.2
92. Santali	Indo-European	Indic	5.2
93. Tibetan (i)	Sino-Tibetan	Tibetan	5.2
94. Danish	Indo-European	Germanic	5.1
95. Nyamwezi	Niger-Congo	Benue-Congolese	5.1
96. Finnish	Uralic-Yukaghir	Finno-Ugric	5

159 Racial diversity and the capacity to learn are the two outstanding characteristics of the human species, which is intelligent and accommodating like no other. In this class in a rural school in Queensland, aboriginal Australians and others of European descent show clearly the morphological diversification that our species has attained, and at the same time, its capacity, shared equally, to acquire new knowledge. *[Photo: Fritz Prenzell / Bruce Coleman Limited]*

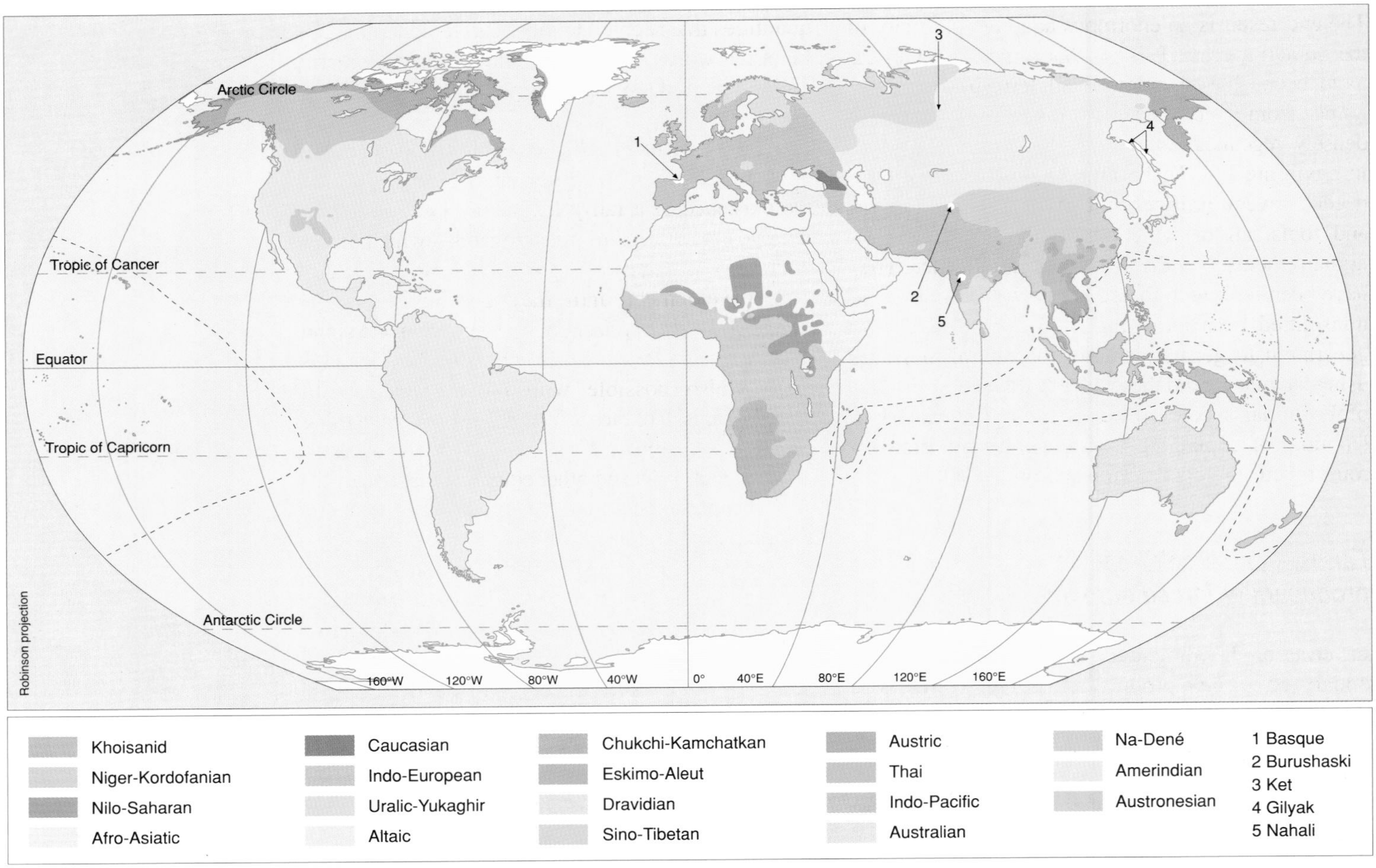

160 Areas of origin of the great families of languages in which the different languages spoken by humans are grouped. The areas correspond to the regions where the languages concerned are autochthonous (native), but do not reflect the linguistic reality of the modern world: the majority of the American people, for example, speak Romance or Germanic languages of Indo-European derivation, languages that have extended widely around the world. It is remarkable that besides the score of large areas occupied by the principal families of languages, there are a dozen tiny areas where minority languages of independent origin are still spoken.
[Cartography: Editrònica, after M. Ruhlen, 1987]

als of the species. Thus, what an individual learns can be passed on via language to other members of his/her group, which gives birth to the concept of culture: humans learn, exchange information and end up sharing certain standards of knowledge and culture, which bind the group together and differentiate it from other groups of humans. In this way, the idea of a social species is a complex one in the case of humans, because elements of one group are not all interchangeable with those of another. All this stimulates endogamous attitudes which, together with other factors, lead to the proliferation of (physically differentiated) races and (culturally differentiated) ethnic groups.

This social, intelligent and communicative species has yet another defining peculiarity: bipedalism. The adoption of the erect position effectively liberates the anterior extremities from their locomotive functions and means they can be put to different uses. Prehensile hands with an opposable thumb put the finishing touch to these locomotively idle arms. The anterior extremities are put to new use as the organ which executes the commands of the intellect. In fact, thought, language and the action of the hands give hominids in general and humans in particular a truly unique capacity to transform their surroundings. With these three resources, humans have established themselves as the most competitive species of all.

But there is still more. The human species is omnivorous, a compromise solution which enables it to exploit any alimentary resource. Its dental system is remarkably eclectic. All the characteristic elements of mammals are present, with no particular emphasis on one rather than the other. On the other hand, their offspring are born in a fairly advanced state of development, an apparent limitation which in the end is a great advantage: the exosomatic cultural inheritance that each individual receives from its parents finds a receptor in conformation phase, which does the job with singular efficiency. The touching vulnerability of human offspring, which is real and lasts for at least the first three or four years of life, is part of a rich phase of extragenetic information transfer, in other words, knowledge acquired through a cultural, non-instinctive way—and not accumulated in the chromosomes—but fundamental for life in society.

The end result is an enormous adaptive plasticity of the human species. It is for this reason that humans have been able to colonize all terrestrial environments, from the coldest to the hottest, from the most densely vegetated to the driest, and even some aquatic environments. To be able to do this, they have needed several artifices, notably clothing, dwellings and tools, all of which have been conceived by humans themselves thanks to their intelligence. They have been built with the dexterity of their hands and transmitted from individual to individual and from generation to generation through cultural messages using language. And these have been the trump cards of the human species, which is intelligent, capable of learning, of explaining and remembering, omnivorous, biped, equipped with hands and adaptable.

Farmers and stockbreeders: producers of forced surpluses

In terms of the alimentary chain, humans are secondary or tertiary producers, in other words, animals that eat plants and other animals (see chapter 2.3), a characteristic that they share with many other trophically comparable animal species. The novelty of the human species was the way they ensured the effectiveness of this alimentary chain: thanks to all their skills, humans managed to make use of other species for their own profit—not only by eating them, but also by making them live in places and quantities that seemed to them convenient. Humans, in other words, conceived and began to practice agriculture and stockbreeding.

Agriculture is the intelligent exploitation of a phenomenon that is a characteristic of flowering plants: the existence of a fairly long resting period in their embryos. The seeds of phanerogams—which are the embryos equipped with food reserves that guarantee their development until they become autotrophic organisms—allow transport, concentration and simultaneous germination of many individuals. This practice is also possible with other propagules of phanerogams, like tubers or bulbs, which make things even easier for humans. At first reduced to the chance collection of fruits and other edible elements, just like any other secondary producers (phytophagous or vegetarian animals), humans learned how to make use of the reproductive mechanisms of phanerogams. Having understood and controlled the germination mechanism—or the production of buds—agriculture was a fact, constantly improved by the acquisition of accumulated agronomic experiences.

A comparable thing happens with food of animal origin. In this case, the skill consisted of catching and domesticating certain species of wild animal. There is no doubt that the attempts were numerous and that only a small number of animal species were capable of tolerating the conditions of captivity or subordination to humans. But this was finally achieved and

161 Farmer and rancher, fisherman and navigator, constructor of cities and landscapes: all the capacity of the human species to transform its environment is brought together in this celebrated painting "The fall of Icarus" (1562, Musées Royaux des Beaux-Arts, Brussels) by the Flemish painter Pieter Bruegel the Elder, a graphic chronicler of the relationships between humans and nature at the turning point between the renaissance and baroque periods. The presence of nature transformed by every day life and the landscapes arranged by human hand, which was common in western painting after the Florentine quattrocento, would not have been alien to the consolidation of the anthropocentric vision of renaissance man.
[Photo: Bridgeman / Index]

162 Ideograms and abstract symbols of cuneiform type—symbols can be classed as true writing, not pictorial representation of reality—in a Mesopotamian terra cotta tablet (3.1 in x 3.1 in [7.8 cm x 7.8 cm]) of the Jamdat Nasr period (3000 B.C.). Starting with the transformation of drawings into ideograms and of these into abstract symbols, one managed to end up by representing words, syllables or letters. The so-called cuneiform script, referring to the wedge shape (*cuneus*, in Latin), of the symbols, was one of the first forms of writing notation with abstract characters (letters or syllables valid for any word) developed by humans, some 5,000 years ago. *[Photo: British Museum]*

stockbreeding and domesticated animals were a fact. Hunting, like gathering wild fruit, gradually became a thing of the past.

Both agriculture and stockbreeding, by themselves, are an exclusively human activity, a foreshadowing of their tendency to dominate everything that populates the planet. But their interest goes way beyond the confines of this question, and this is because, thanks to agriculture and stockbreeding, humans began to alter the trophic chains and biomass pyramids of each species and each place. With agriculture and stockbreeding, humans introduced the forced presence of surpluses into natural systems, something which was not forecast by ecological mechanisms. Because of these surpluses, humans were able to multiply beyond all expectations, at the same time as they altered the vegetational landscape and the circulation of mineral nutrients.

With agricultural and stockbreeding activities, which have taken up centuries of human presence on the Earth, the first big transformations of the ecosystems for nonautoecological reasons took place. For the first time in the planet's history, a species would interfere in a cultural way—extragenetic, in other words—in the systems of ecological homeostasis. Over time, this phenomenon has done nothing but grow.

Scientists and technicians: controllers of information and energy

It is customary to admit, in general terms, that the change from the nomadic, hunter-gatherer humans to sedentary, farming and stockbreeding humans coincides with the beginning of the Neolithic. In fact, forms of itinerant agriculture already existed then and they still do exist today but even in these cases mobility was, and is, much less than that of the long-range wandering of nomadic hunters and gatherers. There are also forms of stockbreeding which involve movements in search of pastures, of which transhumance is a good example, and still survives today in the Iberian peninsula, for example. However, in these cases too, there was usually a home which acted as a base and to which the shepherds regularly returned.

Exceptions apart, however, agricultural and fishing activities were linked with a sedentary way of life and the subsequent inclination to build progressively more comfortable and complex dwellings and the chance of making better and much needed tools and implements, first of polished stone, bone or wood, and later of ceramics and even metal. For this reason Neolithic humans represent a much more advanced civil state than Palaeolithic ones; and so, with a sedentary way of life, basic culture gradually developed into a more advanced forms of civilization. Sedentary human groups are the ones who spent time carving or painting rocks and, as a result, it was they who invented the first forms of writing: the extragenetic transformation of cultural information took a giant step forward because, compared to the ephemeral nature of spoken language, written language offers the gift of durability. Sedentary humans, as well as speaking, also write: civilization progresses.

At specific points in history this progress underwent notable quantitative leaps. Social structure optimised global profits—not always in a way that we would consider just today, but this concept belongs to another analytical perspective. Division of labor became the norm and the figure of the thinker appeared, or at least that of the enlightened person who mastered the art of writing. Knowledge became codified, and ideas became ordered. Knowledge and ideas brought with them spectacular changes in life styles and the artificial environment created by humans, giving birth to the great civilizations of antiquity, whether eastern or western, one of whose greatest intellectual splendours was atained, in relatively recent times by Classical Greece. Wisdom now becomes a subtle form of power, and the rudiments of science and of modern technology begin to take shape.

Between Neolithic humans and Renaissance Man there is, without doubt, an abyss. A cultural abyss, at least. An abyss that grows to dizzy dimensions with the development of science and technology, in other words especially from the 18th century onwards. It is the advent of the industrial society. The qualitative jump is expressed in terms of control of knowledge

and, an important novelty of energy. The fact is that the body of knowledge and the development of scientific method applied to the understanding of reality and to its transformation had, in the space of a few years, an effect comparable to that of the gradual Neolithic revolution in its time. Humans took a new giant step forward; they harnessed the power of the machine, of external energy which could be set to work under their control. Ecological Neolithic man, in fact, ended with the Industrial Revolution. The collapse of the western agrarian aristocracy was not a coincidence but rather the expression of the end of the pre-industrial agricultural economy. From the 19th century onwards science and technology rule, and the person who controls information and the recently domesticated energy resources is in charge. The human species, through its intellectual aptitudes, reinforces its domination over the others and over the planet as a whole. Anthropocentric philosophies continue to fall, while the central role of humans is imposed *de facto*.

Politicians and priests: masters of the visible and the invisible

The accumulation of knowledge leads humans to structure their thinking and so elaborate their ideological models. The establishment of scales of values and the ritualization of behavior which was intrinsically linked to these scales of values, are necessary consequences of the fact of reflective thought. For this reason, thinking humans must very soon have conjured up more or less mythical explanations of their origins and of everything that surrounded them. Explanations, naturally, about the uncertainty or transcendence of their very existence, in other words about life and death. Capable of thinking and of asking themselves questions, but lacking many of the essential elements to be able to answer these questions, they began to think up fables and myths in an attempt to translate to the realm of the inexplicable those things they could not in practise explain. Without commenting on the validity of what would later become religious options, it seems clear that, in historical terms, they must have been based on fantasy. Either one must accept this, or believe directly in an express revelation effected by a transcendent being, an explanation which is also somewhat based on fantasy, or is at least surprising for those who do not share the belief. In any case, ideologies and religious feeling must be as old as humanity itself.

This ideological component must have had, naturally, immediate repercussions in the sphere of human relationships, in other words, social consequences

163 The appearance of the industrial landscape, such as this iron bridge at Sunderland (England) and its surroundings, shown in this engraving published in London in 1829, represents the beginnings of the most recent territorial and cultural transformation experienced by humankind. In effect, the industrial culture has introduced countless artifacts into the landscape, has transformed the land in a way that no previous culture has done, and has modified the behavior of humans to the greatest degree.
[Photo: Ann Ronan at Image Select]

164 To admit the existence of a transcending divinity, fruit of the feeling of defenselessness of humans in the face of the forces of life and nature, is a constant feature of all cultures; it manifests itself in many different ways through various religious confessions. In the sanctuary of Dakshinkali, near Katmandu, for example, this Nepalese Hindu worships the the goddess Kali with propitiatory offerings and sacrifices—a manifestation of the severe, and even cruel, side of life. All these liturgical ceremonies tend to be linked with artistic expressions that symbolize respect to such an extent that art and religious feeling have always been associated in all cultures. The creativity and the mythical capacity of the human species excels when it is a matter of looking for a transcendent explanation of a daily event. *[Photo: Ramon Folch]*

165 Human beings raking through garbage: a sad truth, as seen in the picture of this man in a garbage dump in Karachi, is also a symbol of the grim side of the present day state of the human species. The pride with which engravings such as that in fig. 163 showed the initial thrust of industry some two centuries ago has been replaced by a growing concern at the environmentally negative and socially disastrous consequences of so much change in the land, of so much self-interested accumulation of wealth in the most favored sectors, and the concentration of so much poverty in the least favored. No other species and no other society before the industrial one had established, until now, such marked differences between individuals nor had compromised so seriously the future viability of its environment.
[Photo: Paolo Koch / Firo Foto]

based on the atavistic norms which the human species inherited, because of phyletic links, from its zoological ancestors. Thus the behavior of the group, for example the zoological hierarchical structure of roles, which one can observe in other primates, became modified—but never substituted or cancelled—by new cultural norms, the product of emerging ideologies. As in other orders of biological activity, extrasomatic inheritance, transmitted through cultural mechanisms linked to language, also upset instinctive social behavior through the introduction of new models to be followed. Social and political ideology, then, begins to govern the behavioral patterns of human groups.

Political and religious conventions had important ecological consequences. Human groups, with a rigid hierarchical structure, increasingly skilled and equipped with not strictly biological objectives, began to reorganize the biosphere and the space that surrounded them. The biblical injunction "go forth and subdue the Earth" came to be a legitimization of this typically human attitude of reconstructing the environment. Using religious and political principles—in other words, the explanation of transcendence, the organization of immanence—humans controlled themselves and governed the physical reality in which they lived.

Religion and politics, therefore, must be seen as a logical consequence of man's intellectual activity and have to be evaluated as the principal inducing agents of the ecological transformation effected by humans. Looking for a finalism in their acts and socially optimising the efficiency of their environment-transforming actions, the human species once again underlines its singular character and begins an unpredictable process of reshaping the planet's surface.

An ambitious and senseless species: plunderers and contaminators of the environment

The statistical unpredictability of intelligent acts is inevitably associated with their social and ecological dangers. Science fiction stories about robots which become independent and break away from the computer programs controlling them are a pale fantastical copy of the real history of humans. Curiously, all these imaginary androids share a common characteristic: they are all conspicuously perverse. The creators of futuristic fantasies, driven on by a shared instinct, take it for granted that release from computer tyranny triggers off the irate rebellion of those creatures which were suffering under it. There is probably a moralizing subconsciousness in this literary reaction, but in any case it reveals a real and inescapable fact: release implies apparent revulsion because it involves unpredictability, in other words, loss of control of the new phenomenon by the system that has generated it, something that is usually considered worrying because it is disturbing.

All this just goes to show that the unpredictable evolutionary emergence of the sophisticated human intellect led to a revolutionary change in the systems of ecological control of the biosphere, until then subject to a single and predictable norm. This is the reason for the lack of solidarity of humans with respect to the rest of the biosphere, a ecological lack of solidarity which would have no moral consequences—morality is a sociological not a biological concept—if it were not, paradoxically, for the fact that it can have adverse environmental consequences: the clever android destroys the surroundings which have generated it. Seen in this way, it is normal that humans should be ecologically ambitious and senseless. This is especially so if one takes into account the objective imbalance which has existed for millennia between programmed forms of nature and the astute, but initially somewhat powerless, capacity of humans for revulsion.

But the phenomenon has ceased to be a curiosity and become a problem from the moment in which the human species went beyond the point of inflection of its ecologically subversive path. Any other tertiary producer, any other carnivore or omnivore, consumes what it can manage and leaves what it cannot eat or does not want, and leaves useless waste in the form of digestive dung or metabolic urine. But humans can store great quantities and at the same time use small spaces—the outskirts of their great demographic concentrations or cities, for example—to deposit immense quantities of feces and garbage, some of which is not recyclable in the normal way (many substances are synthetic, for example).

For this reason their ambition and folly, although not unexpected given their history, end up taking on the character of a problem, an environmental problem for humans themselves. In their case, consumption and excretion become spoliation or pollution. The freed android devastates the nature from which it has come, without realizing that it is still dependent on it: it enjoys its information autonomy, but not energetic independence.

A civilized species, nonetheless: managers of natural resources

One of the highest achievements of the human intellect has been the subordination of behavior to agreed and explicitly codified norms, in other words the invention of law. Man has established the rules of the social game, which limit the unpredictability of human acts in such a way that it makes them less free as individuals but systematically more efficient, because it introduces factors of tranquillity and collective trust. Thanks to law, the social machine responds to a less entertaining, but much more functional metabolism. Humans have endowed their society with a legal order: they have become civilized.

Law, and the higher level of civilization with which it is associated, induces humans to a moderation or rationalization of their relationships with the environment. Law, as far as it represents an advanced product of the human intellectual process, is in fact driven to regulate ecological acts of humans, precisely because they threaten to become antihuman as much as they are humanising. Civilized humans thus rediscover environmentally regulated humans through law which is the human way of understanding ecological cybernetics, the poetic reconciliation with the android's environment in a storm of prose: civilized humans who, for the first time in their history as a species, are aware of their zoological origin, and for the first time can understand why they are the way they are and why they behave the way they behave.

They can understand it but they can also contradict it, through coherence and through loyalty to the profound reflexive nature of their very condition, in other words to be genuinely representative of the singular human species, the biosphere's exceptional exception. In fact, civilized humans are humans par excellance, et pour cause humans who substitute ambition for moderation, spoliation for management. The humans who extrasomatically regulate what they have extrasomatically learned to dominate.

1.3 The objective, zoological nature of humans

Humans: a group of primates

The simple description of human evolution is like a simple story with no surprises: a linear explanation starting with the dark past, which some present-day simians remind us of, to arrive, after some obstacles which can make us feel anxious, at the present happy ending, of the individual who explains it, listens to it or reads it, fully identifying with the obviously successful outcome of the story. And the fact that the product of the evolutionary process—ourselves—has been able to follow the thread, like an even more exceptional Sherlock Holmes, makes the end of the story even sweeter and at times helps us to forgive the uglier, dirtier and more difficult parts: the animal part of the origin of humans.

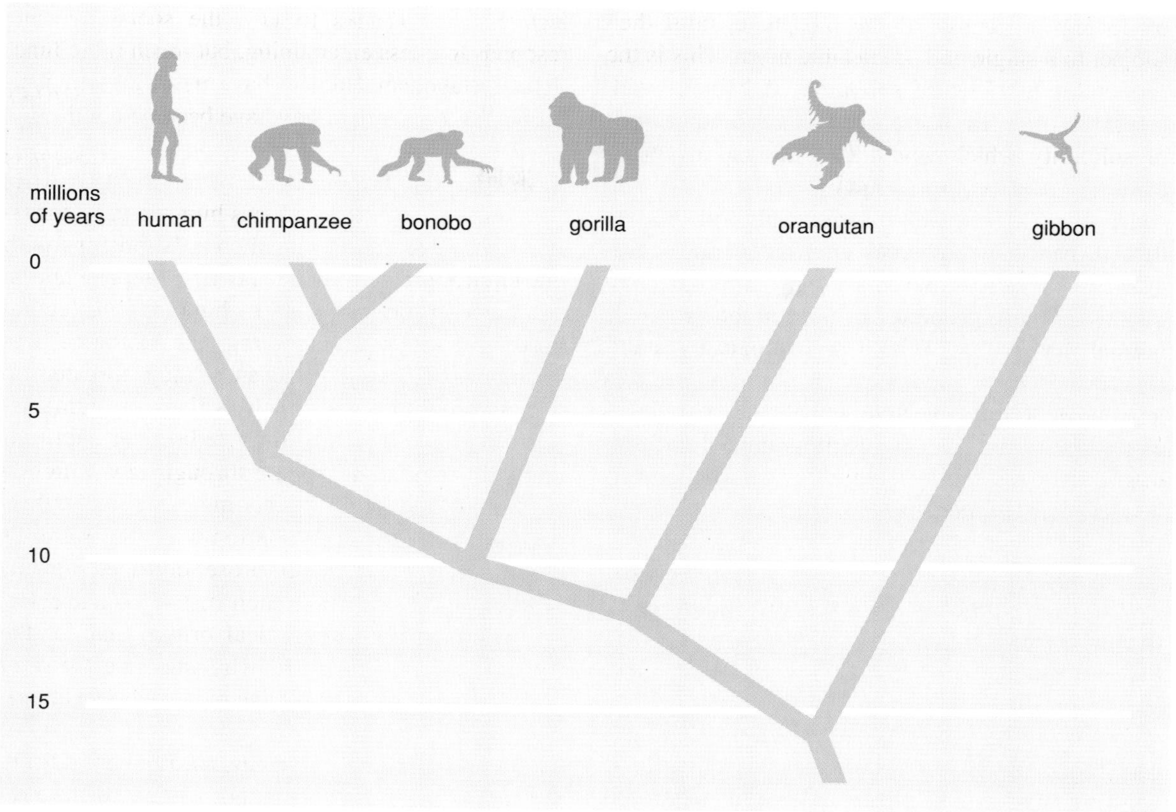

166 The ancestral relationship between humans and present day pongids is shown in this diagram based on traditional anatomical and paleontological data, and particularly on biochemical data such as DNA hybridization of the different species. The clear separation of the branches of the hominids and of the pongids stands out in particular; of the chimpanzees and pygmy chimpanzees (*Pan troglodytes* and *P. paniscus*), some seven to eight million years ago; that of the gorillas (*Gorilla gorilla*) and the orangutans (*Pongo pygmaeus*), which happened some 10 million years or more ago; and that of the gibbons (*Hylobates*), which happened some 15 million years ago.
[Drawing: Jordi Corbera, from various sources]

It is pleasant to observe how, historically, in the application of the evolutionary theory to the process followed by humans, we have continued to introduce tricks, small exceptions or supplementary explanations in order to understand what seemed an exceptional case of the general evolutionary process and which resisted classification within the simple framework of the theory. Even convinced evolutionists from the end of the 19th century and the beginnings of the 20th claimed an exclusive act of creation for our species, accepting that for others evolution alone was a sufficient explanation. And even today, with a general acceptance of the evolutionary process for our species also, there has often been a hint of linearity or of directionality in the evolutionary process in the sense of admitting, at times unconsciously, a progressive force in evolution, an increasing sense of improvement, which is not in any way implicit in the process of evolution itself. But it is more visible, perhaps, in our way of interpreting history or of explaining or understanding the story of the origin of man, for which all cultures have their own myths and contemporary society has formed its own.

We shall begin the story just at the point in which we can consider it our own and not shared with any other living species today: human and nothing else. We could start with the moment in which our ancestors had already become distinct from the ancestors of the animal species which are closest to them and which have been identified, for centuries, as those of present-day pongids or anthropoid apes, a branch of primates which encompasses the orang-utan, gorilla and chimpanzee. The way in which, in the course of evolution, the diversification between the different species of apes and hominids came about has been—and still is—controversial. Many researchers, starting either from the study of fossil remains or comparisons between present-day species, at a morphological or molecular level, have put forward hypotheses, at times with rather unconvincing or patchy arguments. At present there is a consensus—that means that it is the most probable option, although this may have to change in the future—that the separation took place between apes and hominids took place between five and 10 million years ago, probably around seven, and that the last separation between the ancestors of chimpanzees and humans, when the orangutans and gorillas had already diverged. We give the name *hominid* to the forms (we sometimes use this term to indicate a non-specific taxonomic group, whether peoples, races, species or genera) that we find among the descendants of this evolutionary branch which was separated from that of the chimpanzees around seven million years ago and of which we, contemporary humans, form a part. Our ability to recognize a specific fossil as that of a hominid, and not of an ape, makes it an important historical document, especially if, because of its age, it could correspond to one of the first hominids of which, as we shall see, very few remains have been found.

167 The morphology and skeletal structure of the gorilla (*Gorilla gorilla*), australopithecines, and modern humans. Although the structural plan is the same in all cases, in the three hominids, in addition to a general stylization associated with the erect posture, one can observe the lack of prehensile feet, the relatively modest mandibular system, and the notable cranial capacity. *[Diagram: Biopunt, based on Wood, 1976]*

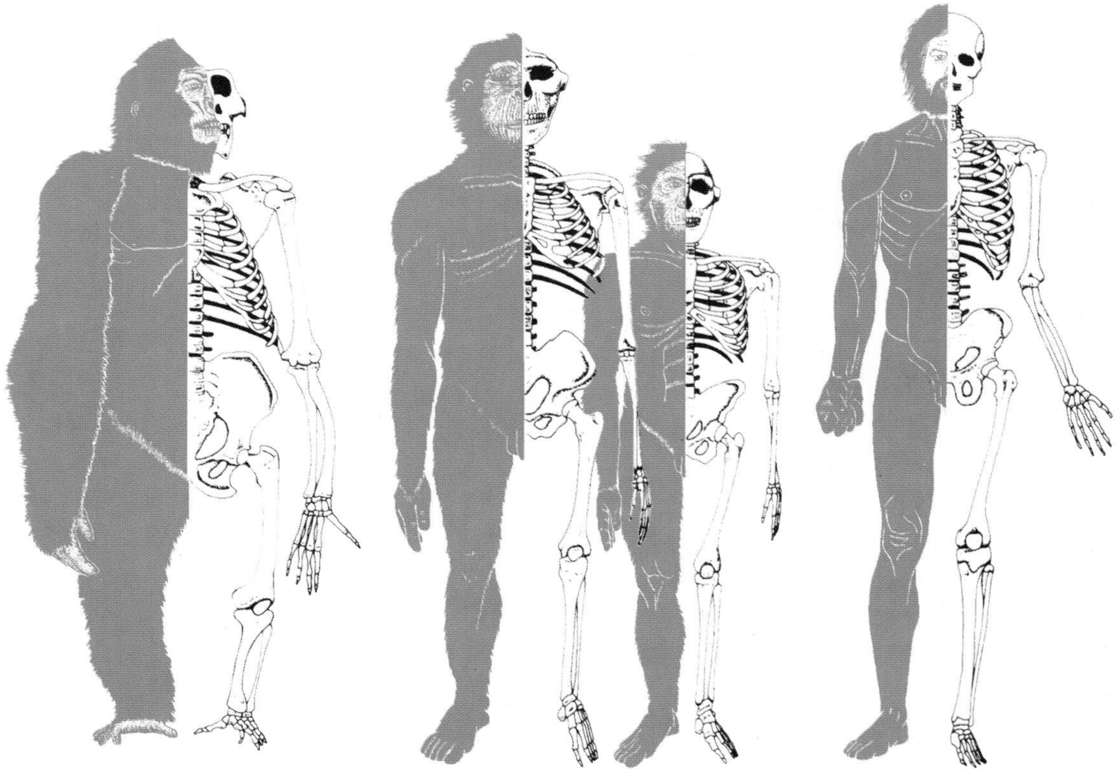

The characteristics of hominids

Hominids are characterized by a series of traits which differentiate them from apes and which we could consider as exclusive and typical adaptations. They can be found in the dental apparatus, in the postcranial skeleton and in the brain (including behavioural control mechanisms, mainly the making of instruments). In the first place the dental apparatus in hominids never has the large canines which are characteristic of the male apes; there is no separation between the different teeth and in general they are small in size. As for the post-cranial skeleton, it has a series of modifications related to erect posture and bipedal locomotion; the hands are freed from the task of propulsion and are capable of manipulating objects; the erect posture is reflected in a series of characteristics, from the position of the occipital cavity in the skull to the structure of the pelvis or the lower extremities. Finally the skull is rounded and globular in shape, with a high cranial capacity, around 91 in^3 (1,500 cm^3) in the modern races, and the brain is large; behaviour is complex, with the ability to make instruments and impose arbitrary forms on the environment; the culture that the hominids developed could be understood as an evolutionary strategy based on the modification of the environment to adapt it to their own needs. Within the group of hominids we will see that there are some forms which we can interpret as belonging to an evolutionary line which leads right up to present day, humans, and other forms which do not, but which have represented evolutionary experiments which are already complete. The groups or individuals which we can clearly distinguish as belonging to the human evolutionary line we assign to our own genus, *Homo* (even though within this line we consider them to be different species from our own), and we give them the name humans in the broadest sense of the word. In a strict sense, we will use the words humans or modern humans in this work to refer to contemporary human populations and their nearest direct ancestors.

The history which we will trace, then, will be that of e radiation of different species of *Australopithecus*; we will then look at the first humans (*Homo habilis*), with the first known material culture, that preceded a radiation of *Homo erectus* outside their African birthplace. It is only later that we can speak of *Homo sapiens*, our own species in its different forms or races, whether they be temporal or geographical, with the Neanderthal as the best known and which precedes the expansion of modern humans.

2. The process of hominization

2.1 The oldest fragmentary remains

In his classic book *The Descent of Man*, published in 1871, Charles Darwin wrote: "In all the great regions of the world, all the living great mammals are closely related to the extinct species of the same regions. It is thus probable the Africa has been inhabited by pongids closely related to the gorilla and the chimpanzee, and as these two species of primates are now the closest species to mankind, it is more than likely that our remote ancestors lived in the African continent than in any other place."

These precise and clear words are rather cautious but have turned out to be prophetic, considering that fossil evidence did not lead to acceptance of Africa as the site of origin of the hominids until long after Darwin's death. Africa was the only habitat for the hominids until the expansion of *Homo erectus* approximately a million and a half years ago.

The African cradle

The African sites where ancient remains of hominid or their activities have been found are basically restricted to eastern Africa, following the long Rift Valley, though to the south, in the South African republic, there is another group of very different sites, in caves.

The Rift Valley runs more than 1,243 mi (2,000 km) from the Red Sea, through Ethiopia, Kenya and Tanzania, and has been a region of great geological activity for the last million and a half years. In addi-

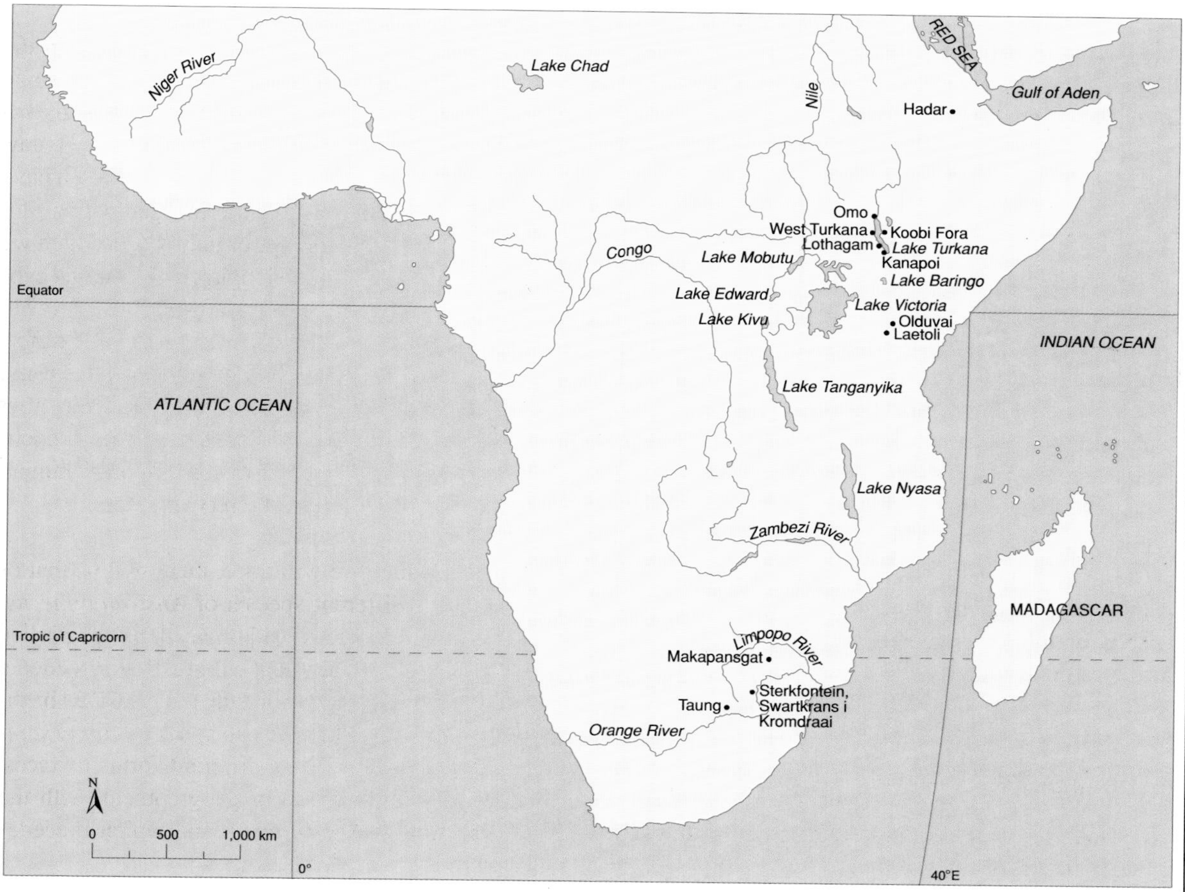

168 The australopithecines (Plio-Pleistocene hominids) are the oldest known hominids. Their remains have only been found in two areas in Africa. The first fossils were found in South Africa, and the others are from the east of the continent. The excavations in South Africa started in the 1920s, and all the australopithecine remains have been found in caves where the excavation methods have had to be much more aggressive than archeologically desirable. Fifty years later, in the 1960s, australopithecine sites were also found near what is now the Rift Valley, an enormous geological fault running down eastern Africa through Ethiopia, Kenya, and Tanzania. The sites in this region are not in caves, like those of southern Africa, but these prehuman bones are mostly found near former lakes or near the deltas of torrents and rivers.
[Map: Editronica, based on several sources]

169 The Olduvai Gorge in eastern Africa has become famous for the hominid remains that have been assigned to the genus *Australopithecus*. It is on the Serengeti Plains, near the Ngorongoro Volcano (northern Tanzania), now dry and dusty but formerly home to lush plant and animal life. The Olduvai Gorge dissects lower and mid Quaternary deposits consisting of a succession of river and lake sediments alternating with wind-deposited and volcanic sediments. Five main levels have been recognized, between 1.8 million and 50,000 years old, and so in some places it is possible to travel almost a million and a half years in a single day. The Masai called Olduvai Gorge "Ol duvai" ("the place of wild aloes"), because of the large number of spiny aloes growing there. The names of Louis Leakey and his wife Mary will always be connected with the Olduvai Gorge, where Louis Leakey excavated from 1931 till his death in 1972, and where his wife Mary continued working after his death. *[Photo: Science Photo Library / AGE Fotostock]*

tion to providing a habitat for the first hominids, with abundant lakes along its entire length, a series of earth movements have brought deposits to the surface that would otherwise be at a depth of several metres. Erosion also makes remains visible to fossil hunters, in good stratigraphic order, sometimes forming uninterrupted series lasting for millions of years. Volcanic activity has also played an important role in the Rift Valley, both because it has caused rapid burial of the remains (thus protecting them from scavengers and erosion) and because these materials can be accurately dated radiometrically. Many of the Rift Valley sites are now familiar names, such as Olduvai, Lake Turkana, Omo, Hadar, etc. Their strata still contain uncountable hidden remains that are landmarks in the reconstruction of our evolutionary history; some, however, have already been recovered and act as guideposts on our journey through human evolutionary history.

Very little is known of the first hominids. They appeared in the unknown past, probably about seven million years ago (a date of 10 to 15 million years ago is usually given, but these older dates are very improbable). Only highly fragmentary remains have been found of the period between their origin and the rich finds of *Australopithecus afarensis* in strata a little less than four million years old. All the remains of these first hominids come from the Rift Valley, especially the sites between Lake Turkana and Lake Victoria in Kenya. Despite all the scientific articles and discussions, all that can said with certainty is that they are hominid remains, but they cannot give us much idea of what the individuals of that species might have been like. Thus, for example, in the strata that are between 10 and four million years old, around Lake Baringo, in the Baringo District of Kenya, in the north of Nakuru, despite the hopes raised by the site, all that has been recovered so far only is few isolated teeth a jaw fragment with two teeth and a piece of the parietal bone, totally insufficient to give us an idea of the individual the bones belonged to. Further north, near Lake Turkana, also in Kenya, other sites have yielded remains from the same period, such as the fragment of jaw with a tooth in place, found in Lothagam in 1967, which has a clearly hominid morphology and is about five and a half million years old, as deduced from the fauna associated with this find.

All in all, as we saw, this is very fragmentary and not very informative. The entire early evolution of the hominids remains unknown. Though evidence from molecular biology is helpful, as we shall see later, to locate the possible starting point, fossil remains do not yet confirm it. Pliocene remains (between 5 and 1.8 millions old) have not yet been found from the initial strata, but are more abundant and informative in more recent strata.

The Rift Valley finds

Only the dentition of the remains mentioned above reveals that they were hominids. Nothing is yet known about the post-cranial modifications related to an upright posture or the cranial modifications related to the brain. For many years, there has been intense debate as whether these changes happened at the same time, and if not, the order in which they occurred. The resulting discussions were often biased, because adaptive explanations were given without knowing their morphological conformation, what they were really like. For example the "hunter hypothesis" considered the upright posture and cephalization as integral parts of the evolutionary process linked to making tools—manipulation required hands that are freed from locomotion and a developed brain to direct the process, in addition to the tools used in hunting big game. Thus social complexity and a basically carnivorous diet were assigned to this model, and in some cases, suppositions were made about possible rites or communication potential that were totally hypothetical. This might have fitted together in a single comprehensible strategy if there had not been an underlying mistake. The upright position was in fact acquired long before cephalization occurred. This is shown by the remains classified as *Australopithecus afarensis*, which lived in eastern Africa between three and four million years ago.

The total number of remains discovered corresponds to almost a hundred individuals, and this makes it possible to reconstruct a relatively clear image of the taxon *Australopithecus afarensis*, though there are still many points to debate. It is considered the most primitive of the hominid groups that are known, which means that it shows some non-hominid characteristics (shared with fossil and current pongids) and few of the specializations (derived characters) typical of the hominids. Thus both the dentition and the form of the skull, though accepted as hominid, show primitive characteristics. The brain capacity is small, with some specimens fitting within the range of variation of later forms of australopithecines, about 30 in^3 (500 cm^3) and others with lower values, lower than 24 in^3 (400 cm^3). The difference between the specimens can be attributed to the sexual dimorphism that appears to be characteristic of the group. They are shown to be genuine hominids by their bipedal locomotion, which is clearly demonstrated by the fossils. There is still debate as to whether this was a bipedal lifestyle or whether it was an inefficient form of locomotion that was only used for occasional movements on the ground by an animal that was essentially tree-living. However, the post-cranial morphology and the tracks found at the Laetoli site are clear enough to consider that by then the hominids were totally bipedal.

The Hadar site

The Hadar site is in the Afar region of Ethiopia, about 186 mi (300 km) northeast of Addis Ababa. It has already produced abundant material and more are expected in the future. Many hominid remains have been found, all of them belonging to the taxon *Australopithecus afarensis*. Dating, as always, is controversial, but they are between 2.6 and 3.6 million years old. In fact, the first discoveries at this site were revolutionary, as they made it possible to define a new species, the oldest of the currently accepted hominids, and they were reported widely all over the world. The remains of more than 36 individuals have been found, but the site is most famous for two extraordinary discoveries by Don Johanson and his collaborators in 1974 and 1975, "Lucy" and the "family." The name "Lucy" was given to the partial remains of a hominid skeleton discovered in Afar in 1974, and which has almost totally replaced its official name "AL-288-1" (from "Afar Locality"); the name is taken from a song the team listened to while digging, "Lucy in the Sky with Diamonds" released not long before by the Beatles. The most interesting detail is that the 40% of the skeleton that has been found means that it has for a long time been the most complete skeleton of a hominid more than 100,000 years old. And Lucy is three million years old! Some of the preserved pieces have provided information on two key aspects: the jaw, which shows typical hominid

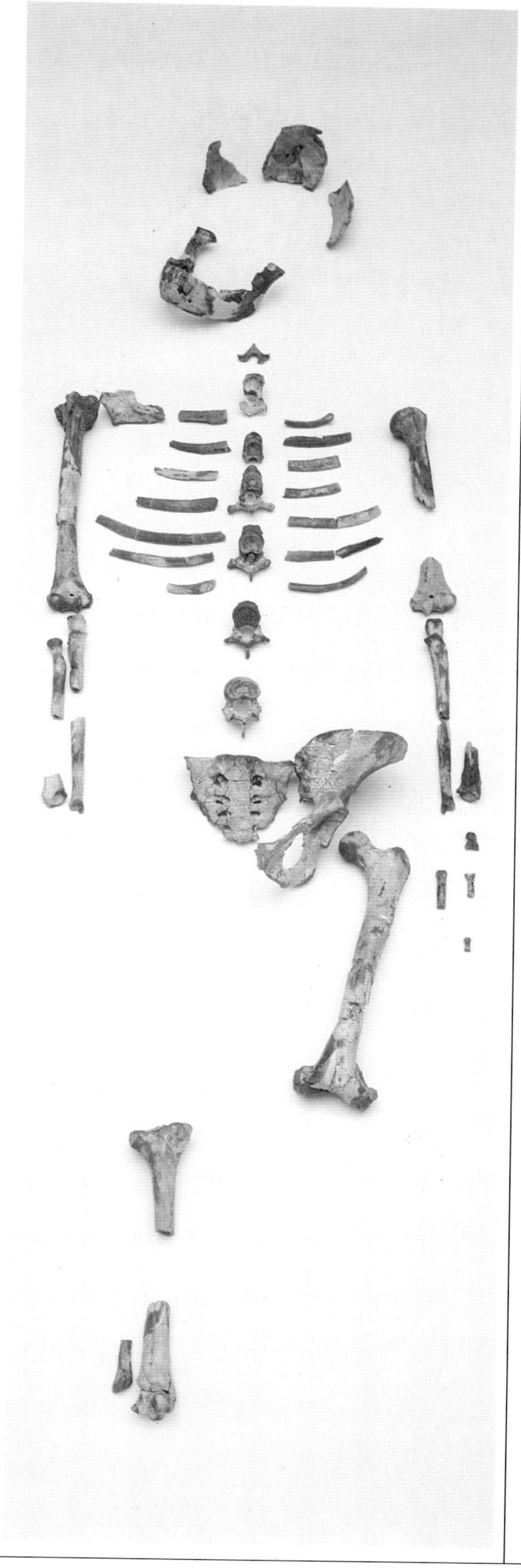

170 Lucy was a female *Australopithecus afarensis* who lived about three million years ago in what is now the Afar region of Ethiopia. Discovery of her remains was of great importance because almost 40% of the skeleton was present. Lucy's remains are a mixture of ancient and modern features; the skull bones retain ancient characteristics, while those of the post-cranial skeleton are modern. The curvature of the feet, inherited from tree-living ancestors, was adapted to walking in soft and sandy areas; the bones of the legs show that her posture was upright; the pelvis shows that she was female; and study of the dentition allows us to suppose she died at an age of about 20 years. The importance of Lucy's remains is that this group was ancestral to all the later hominids, both the australopithecines and the different genera of *Homo*. Unfortunately, the Afar excavations were interrupted several years ago when war broke out in Eritrea.
[Photo: John Reader / Science Photo Library / AGE Fotostock]

171 The hominid footprints found in Laetoli (Tanzania) by Mary Leakey in 1976 prove that upright posture preceded the increase in brain size. The Laetoli footsteps were left by two *Australopithecus* adults and a child. They walked over volcanic ash that consolidated shortly afterwards by crystallization, due to the combined action of rain and sunshine, and the footprints were fossilized in just a few hours. In addition to the hominid footsteps, there are tracks of other animals, such as giraffes, elephants, antelopes, hyenas, *Hipparion* (an ancestor of the horse), apes, birds and saber-toothed tigers. The Laetoli australopithecine footprints are the earliest proof of bipedal locomotion and suggest they walked with a slight limp—dragging the feet—and also show that the big toe of the foot was already parallel to the other toes, as in modern humans. *[Photo: John Reader / Science Photo Library / AGE Fotostock]*

dentition, and the pelvis and remains of the rear limbs, which show clear adaptation to an upright posture. The pelvis also appears to have belonged to a woman.

The following year, at the base of a hill, the expedition found dozens of fragments of a total of 13 different individuals, including children, youths and adults. The discovery is sensational for what it may mean, not only as the prototype morphology of the group, but also because, despite some difficulties, it is possible to study the growth patterns of the individuals (bear in mind that the difficulty of conservation means that infant remains are very rare) and the differences between them. It has been speculated that the different individuals belonged to a single group and all died at the same time in an accident or catastrophe, such as a flood. However, as in most African sites, these remains were found because erosion had brought them to the surface, and it is very difficult to know exactly where they were deposited. Thus, the fact of having been found together or at the same level of the site does not mean they were contemporaneous, something that is normally taken for granted. The Hadar site thus provides a wealth of finds, surprises and the first trace of the australopithecines.

The Laetoli site

Laetoli, the second major site, is in northern Tanzania, near Olduvai Gorge (discussed below), and has several different volcanic layers that can be used to date the sediments. The hominid remains recovered, mainly jaws and dental parts, are between 3.77 and 3.59 million years old. Because these remains are much thicker and tougher than the Hadar specimens, this raises the very controversial question of whether they belonged to a different taxon. The currently accepted response is that *Australopithecus afarensis* showed marked sexual dimorphism, and the thicker remains (related to the dentition, especially jaws and dental parts) were from males, and the more slender ones from females.

The feature that has made Laetoli most famous and has led to its picture appearing on the front of many books on human evolution is a quite remarkable discovery, the footprints of different individuals walking in different directions in an undeniably upright posture, on their rear limbs. About 3.5 million years ago, some hominids and other species walked over soft volcanic ash wetted by rain, leaving very clear footprints that were then covered by another volcanic eruption. This has provided the first and only evidence of the locomotion of the first hominids, which was undeniably bipedal and whose locomotion was similar to our own. It has also been possible to accurately estimate their stature, from 4-5 ft (125-145 cm) depending on the individual. Other footprints seem to show an adult walking with a child. To sum up, this gives us one of the clearest images of what the ancestors of modern hominids were like.

2.2 The typical australopithecines: Australopithecus boisei, A. robustus and A. africanus

The genus *Australopithecus* includes a group of very different forms, that now stretch from the earliest, *A. afarensis*, to remains about a million years old. About two million years ago there appears to have been a diversification of forms among the slender australopithecines, which are probably related to the first forms of the genus *Homo*, on the one hand, and the robust australopithecines, on the other. Many sites have provided fossils of both these groups and of later groups, either *Homo habilis* or *H. erectus*.

In eastern Africa there are many hominid sites in the sediments crossed by the Rift Valley, especially Olduvai Gorge, the valley of the River Omo and the edges of Lake Turkana (formerly known as Lake Rudolph), especially the eastern part (sites that have also yielded remains of hominids that are closer to modern human beings than the australopithecines, as shown later). However, the African finds of hominids are not restricted to eastern Africa, but also occur in southern Africa, where the sites are very different in nature. These are remains that have been discovered by quarrying, and it is almost never possible to assign them to a definite geological level. In general they are caves, clefts or cavities that have formed within limestone rocks, and which have over time filled up with animal remains transported by currents, dragged by carnivorous animals, or which sometimes simply fell in. They were thus not the site of settlements. Furthermore, due to the lack of stratigraphy and of volcanic layers suitable for radiometric dating, they are almost impossible to date, in absolute or in relative terms. All that can be done is relative dating based on identifying the fauna associated with the remains.

The eastern African sites: Olduvai, Turkana and others

With respect to the robust forms of australopithecines, these remains are extraordinarily robust, as is very clearly shown by the features of the skull and dentition. On July 17, 1959, Mary Leakey found one of the most important fossils in the history of anthropology, which was classified by her husband Louis as a new genus and species, *Zinjanthropus boisei*, known colloquially as “Zinj.” This is now considered to be a species of australopithecine, *Australopithecus boisei*.

It is extraordinarily robust in appearance, with large molar teeth, a very wide face, highly protruding zygomatic arches and a sagittal crest on the top of the skull. The cranial capacity is relatively large, 530^3. The remains have been reliably dated at 1.79 millions old by potassium-argon dating of a volcanic layer joined to the fossil (this method is based on the radioactive decay of potassium-40 to argon-40). Other remains have since been found and assigned to *A. boisei*, both in Olduvai Gorge and in other sites in eastern Africa, such as Lake Turkana or the valley of the River Omo. Not all these remains show the same robustness, despite having been included in the same species; there was clearly marked sexual dimorphism.

The South African sites: Kromdraai, Makapansgat and others

There are five South African sites where remains have been found. The first site is Makapansgat (in the northern Transvaal, South Africa), which is the oldest in southern Africa and dated at two and a half million years old, though doubts about dating mean it might be about three million years old. The second group is three sites near each other in the central Transvaal, halfway between Johannesburg and Pretoria; Sterkfontein (with remains more than two million—or more than three—years old) and Swartkrans and Kromdraai (with remains between one and two million years old). The last site is Taung on Cape Province’s eastern border with Transvaal, north of Kimberley, also in the Republic of South Africa.

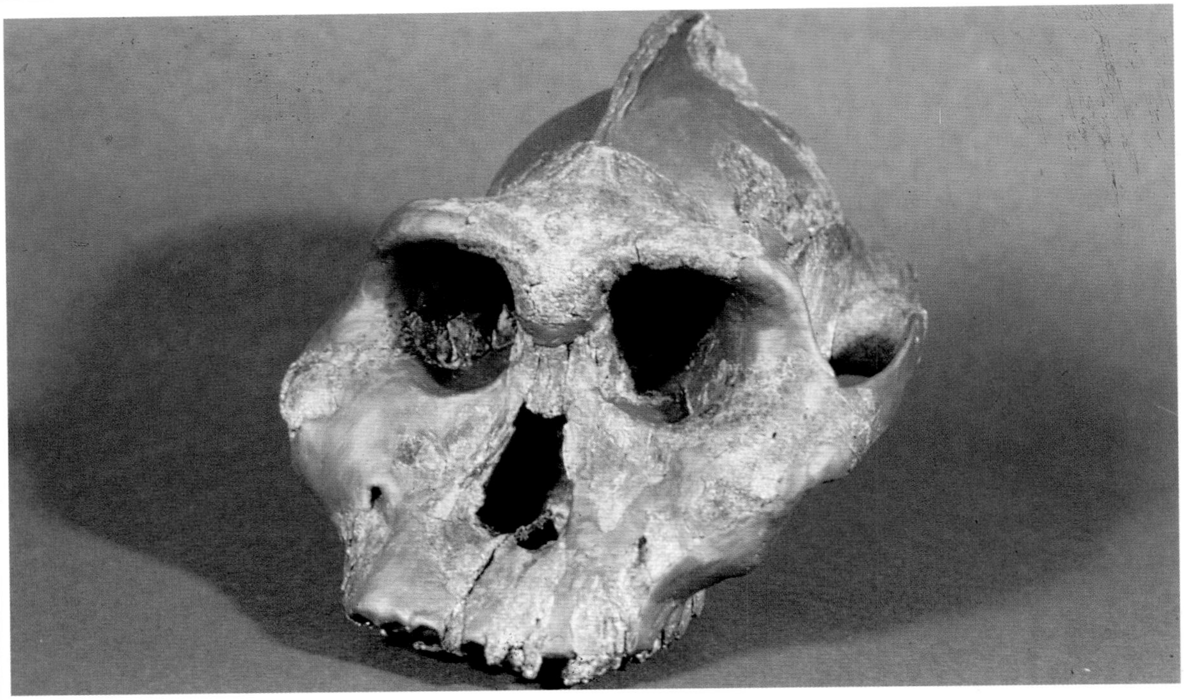

172 An animal's diet is reflected in its dentition. Both the skull of *Australopithecus boisei* (shown in the photograph) and of *A. robustus* show the same feeding specialization. The two species left fossils with a coarse morphology, and that were taller and had a longer life expectancy than previous forms. The robust forms of the australopithecines clearly show that they followed a vegetarian diet, while the other forms of hominid were omnivorous. Feeding specialization led to changes in the structure of the dentition and the chewing apparatus, with repercussions on the general structure of the skull. Their dentition consisted of small front teeth, with much larger rear teeth; the jaw, which had to support this dentition and make it work, was very well developed; and the skull supporting the musculature responsible for chewing the food showed a sagittal crest for the attachment of the masseter muscles, responsible for raising the mandible. *[Photo: National Museum of Kenya]*

Though it was the first site where hominid remains were found in South Africa (1924), their dating is very dubious, but they are perhaps more than two million years old. These South African finds tend to be hard to date, but to make up for it they are very complete. Skulls that are almost complete and pelvises in very good condition have been found.

Long before the east African remains, some of the fossils from these South African sites showed the same characteristics related to robustness, but attenuated. They were initially given many different names, the result of the belief that each new fossil found was the only representative of a new taxon, but they have now all been brought together in the taxon *Australopithecus robustus*, maintaining the species name given by Robert Broom (1866-1951) to the Kromdraai fossil, but within the genus that was already described from other sites, with which it shows clear affinities.

The robust australopithecines: feeding specialization

Australopithecus boisei and *A. robustus* are still considered to be different species, despite the inherent difficulty of classifying a species from its fossil remains. They are clearly closely related, and if they had been found in the same site, there would be no doubt about assigning them to the same taxon. The greater robustness of the remains from eastern Africa (*A. boisei*) and the great distance between the two groups mean that it is reasonable to use two different names for them. Anyway, they represent groups with clear dietary adaptations; their morphology indicates that they must have had a vegetarian diet specialized in small hard foods, especially seeds. The great strength and the hard surface needed to crush them would be related to the great development of the chewing apparatus, which has repercussions on the general structure of the skull.

The robust forms are dated at between roughly one and two millions years. A skull was found in 1985 that, while controversial, appears to establish a contact between the oldest remains of *A. afarensis* and the robust forms. This is the 2.5-million-year-old "black skull" found to the east of Lake Turkana, which some authors assign to a new species, *A. aethiopicus*. Its robustness might make it one of the first stages of the evolutionary changes towards the derived robust forms in both southern and eastern Africa. Sites less than a million years old do not contain remains of robust australopithecines or of any group that could be phylogenetically related to them. This suggests the robust forms became extinct, after lasting for about a million years with few morphological changes.

The slender australopithecines: the path towards the first humans

In 1924, when almost nobody considered that Africa was the place to look for fossils related to human evolution, in South Africa Raymond Dart

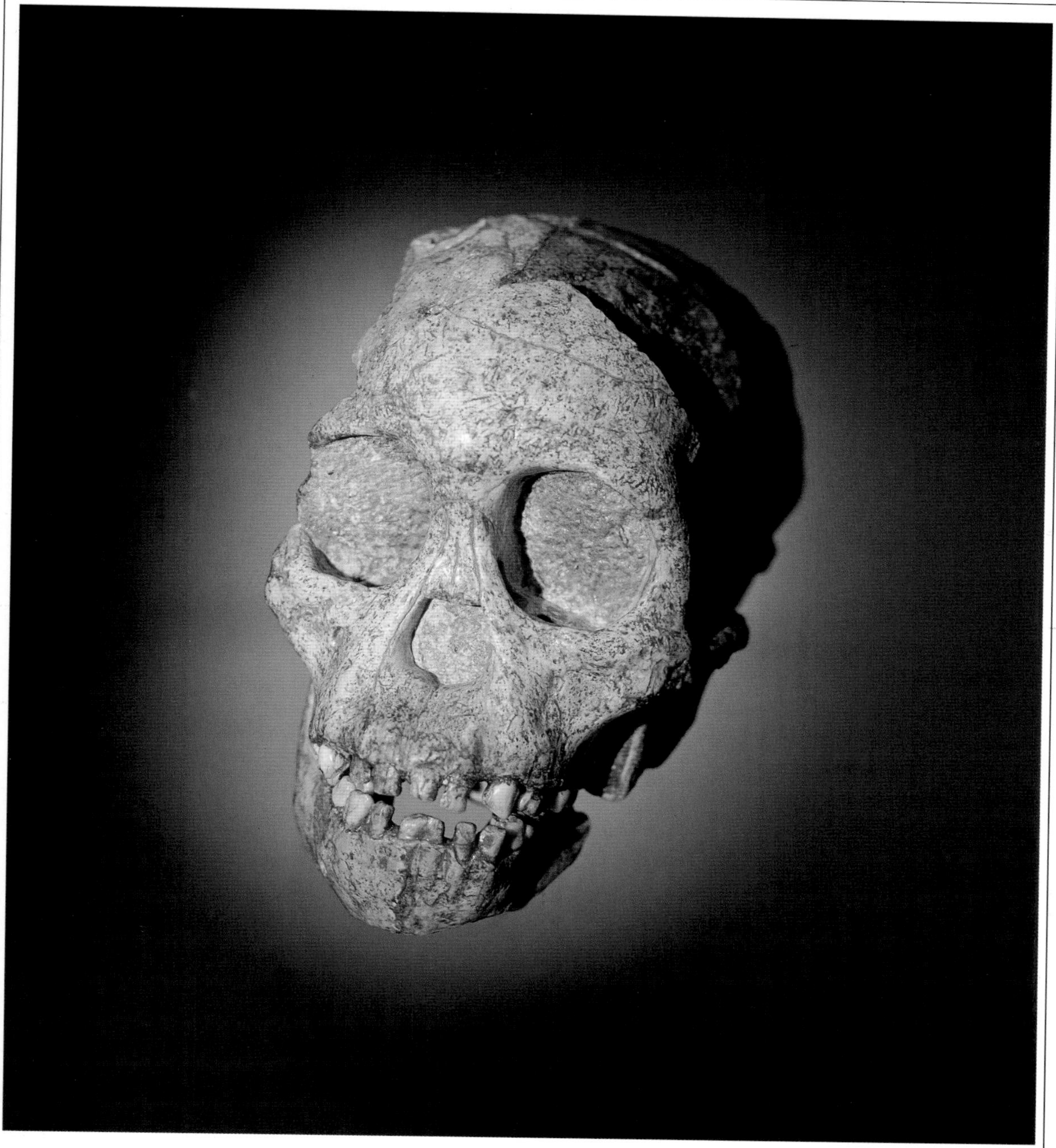

173 The Taung skull, discovered by Raymond Dart in South Africa, was considered by the international scientific community of the time to be an aberrant form of primate. Dart, Professor of Anatomy at Witwatersrand University (South Africa) first suggested in 1924, the existence of a form, *Australopithecus africanus* that he considered a link between the mankind and the higher primates. The name that he gave to the remains of an anthropoid that died at the age of six, was in keeping with his convictions: the term "australopithecus" means "southern ape," and might also have been influenced by the fact that he was born in Brisbane (Australia). The Taung skull consists of an endocranial mold, the forehead, the face and the jaw, still with the milk teeth. The capacity of the skull is about 25 in^3 (405 cm^3)—larger than that of a contemporary primate of the same size—and the insertion of the spinal column is in an advanced position with respect to primates. These features are not exclusively simian; they show the path towards hominization.
[Photo: John Reader / Science Photo Library / AGE Fotostock]

(1893-1988) started his study of the specimen that led him to coin the name *Australopithecus africanus*. This specimen later became well-known as the "Taung skull," and is the skull of a child aged three or four with its milk teeth, and which Dart, correctly but simplistically, described as the "missing link" in human evolution, that is to say, a fossil that showed both human and pongid features. After a great deal of initial controversy, it was accepted that the fossil was a hominid, and it is still one of the most complete and paradigmatic specimens of the group.

In addition to Taung, remains found in other sites in southern Africa have been assigned to *A. africanus*; there has been much debate as to whether it was present in eastern Africa, but there is more and more evidence that it was. To sum up, they were hominids with a clearly upright posture, though capable of climbing trees, without the primitive characters of *A. afarensis* and with related dental and cranial characters that separate them from the robust forms. As Dart pointed out, the basal location of the *foramen magnum* (the orifice where the nerve fibers of the spinal column enter the skull) shows an upright posture, confirmed by the post-cranial anatomy. The general slenderness of the skull means that some examples are difficult to distinguish from the forms assigned to *Homo habilis*, but the capacity of the skull is lower, as in the Taung skull it is 25 in^3 (405 cm^3), corresponding to about 27 in^3 (440 cm^3) in the adult.

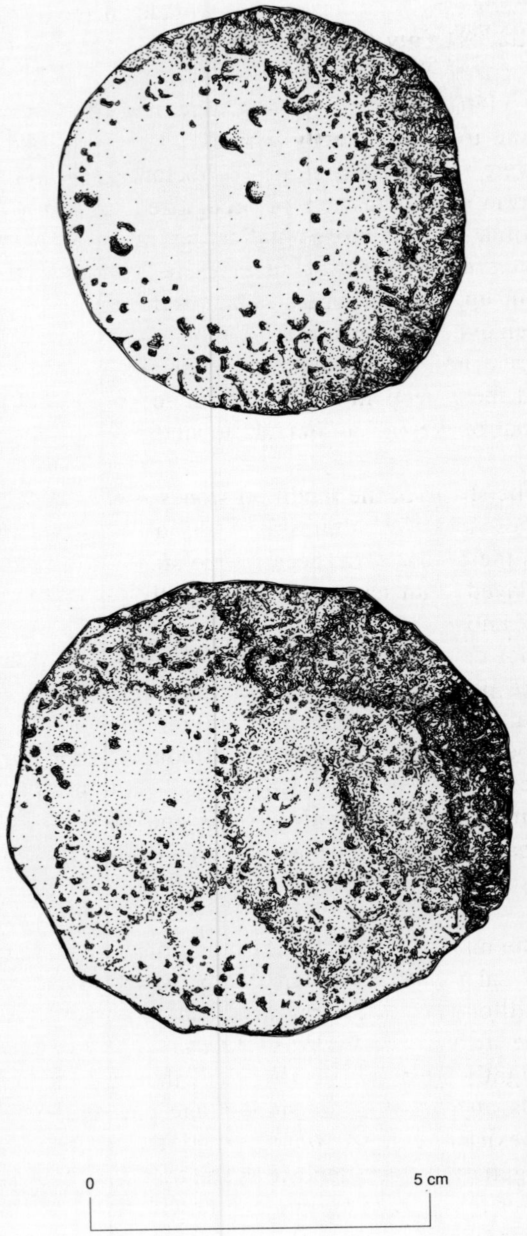

174 The oldest tools yet found are from the Olduvai Gorge site in eastern Africa. This primitive industry, known as the Oldowan industry, is attributed to *Homo habilis*, the first toolmaker, who lived by hunting other animals and collecting other foodstuffs. Using small stone tools they could cut the tough skin of the animals and cut them into pieces. This hunting behavior probably alternated with obtaining carrion from the kills of other predators. It is thought that competition for food and the presence of predatory carnivores conditioned the social behavior of the first individuals of the genus *Homo*. In Olduvai remains have also been found of a circular building (11.5-13.1 ft [3.5-4 m] in diameter) made of piled lava blocks.
[Drawing: Biopunt, from several sources]

It is difficult to date the remains of *A. africanus* because of the problems related to the nature of the South African sites. It is accepted that they are between three and two million years old, with some of the more modern examples perhaps one million years old, but it is impossible to be more precise. And the problem is made even worse by the difficulty of distinguishing the slender australopithecines from some of the forms already assigned to *Homo habilis*.

2.3 The dawn of the humans: Homo habilis

In 1964, when Louis Leakey proposed a new taxon, *Homo habilis*, on the basis of some fragmentary remains from Olduvai Gorge, many anthropologists were not convinced. It was hard to believe that the differences between these remains and the South African specimens of *A. africanus* were sufficient to justify establishing a new group. Later discoveries by the Leakeys' son Richard in the Lake Turkana deposits definitively confirmed the suggestion that they were the first humans (in the sense of belonging to the genus *Homo*) that showed morphological differences from the australopithecines, especially in terms of the capacity of the braincase, and who could, for the first time, be unequivocally associated with remains of cultural materials.

The makers of the first tools

Leakey's suggested *Homo habilis* grouping is now completely accepted, solving some old problems and raising new ones. Talking of a biologically distinct taxon at the moment when traces of the first culture appear (and it should be recognized that this is the oldest culture yet identified) and relating it to a larger braincase, and thus a larger brain, than in preceding forms, gives the term a satisfactorily global and humanist perspective. It does not however eliminate the difficulty of assigning specific remains to the taxon: the older remains are hard to assign because they are similar to the slender australopithecine forms, and the more recent ones are difficult to assign because they are similar to the group that followed them, *Homo erectus*.

In general, *Homo habilis* is characterized by its large braincase, an average of 39 in^3 (646 cm^3)—that of *A. africanus* is about 27 in^3 (450 cm^3)—a much more rounded skull perimeter, a small face in relation to the size of the skull, and much larger rear teeth than front ones. The post-cranial skeleton, and in general the stature and posture do not show differences from the slender australopithecines.

Although a cause-effect relationship cannot be established, this increase in brain size is implicitly related to the complexity of its use. On the other hand, there are abundant stone tools showing human action. Mary Leakey, the great archeologist of the Plio-Pleistocene in Africa, considers that the stones used by human beings can be classified by the context in which they are found, by their shape, by their marks, by the scrapings they may show or the use thought to have been made of them. Note that not only the stones that have been modified for use as tools show signs of activity or human "culture." In the Olduvai Gorge, it is often important to know exactly where and how the stones were found. Thus stones deliberately transported from other sites can be recognized, as can accumulations of stones indicating other activities; sites of settlements, sites where mammals were cut up, or sites where stones were extracted and removed for later use as tools. This shows the great importance of the context and associations of the objects in the reconstruction of the behaviour of the ancient human populations.

The shape of the modified stones is the aspect of these material cultures that is usually typified, and is the best known, because the stones can be displayed in museums. In this case, they are generally known as the Oldowan Culture (the Oldowan tool complex, to be precise). The typical stones are pebbles modified into spheres, polyhedra or cutting edges (and are often referred to as the "pebble culture"). There are tools referred to as "choppers" or "chopping tools," their presumed function. These modifications and processes are characteristic of behaviour that is typically and exclusively human.

The materials from Olduvai and the surroundings of Lake Turkana are dated at between 1.8 and two millions old. They are thus much more recent than the forms of *Australopithecus afarensis*, and slightly later than *A. africanus*, though some fossils appear to be of similar age and show they coexisted with *A. boisei*, (and are even found together in some deposits). The transition towards later forms, with specimens showing intermediate characteristics, took place in eastern Africa about 1.6 million years ago.

The jigsaw puzzle of the hominids

The jigsaw puzzle of the hominids is not easy to piece together, especially because there are few pieces and it is difficult to fit together their shape (morphology), their site of origin and their place in time. First, however, we have to ask if there are other pieces that may help in this reconstruction. Are there other remains contemporary to the forms described that should be taken into account? Are there hominids outside the African

GROUPS OF HOMINIDS	LIFE EXPECTANCY (years)
Australopithecines	15
Neanderthal humans	18
Paleolithic humans	19-25
Neolithic humans	20-27
Modern humans	
Classic and mediaeval societies	22-29
Present-day hunter-gatherer societies	22-29
Rural societies (Guatemala,1893)	24
Protoindustrial societies (Sweden, 1870)	38
Industrial societies (Sweden, 1903)	54
Advanced industrial societies (Sweden,1960)	73

continent that predate the later expansion of *Homo erectus*?

Though there have been several claims of great antiquity for sites and remains from outside Africa (around 1.5 million years), they have never been confirmed. It would not be surprising to find ones more than 1 million years old, but not much more. And the oldest datings, sometimes more than two million years old, are doubtful and impossible to confirm. This is the case of some remains in Java, or the Ubeidiya site in Israel. In Europe, for the moment, the oldest archeological remains are thought to be about 1 million years old, such as the Vallonet Cave, in the Mauras Massif (Provence, France). Other sites have been claimed to be older, but they have not yet been finally accepted.

Thus, human evolution, as far as the forms known as *Homo erectus* are concerned, is restricted to eastern and southern Africa. But how should these forms be placed in a phylogenetic tree? This a hotly debated question that remains wide open, but there is consensus on some points, explained below. It should be pointed out, however, that this is not a definitive perspective, and the discovery of a new fossil may mean it has to be totally revised.

It is generally accepted that *Australopithecus afarensis* is the ancestor of all the later hominids, that the robust forms are two side branches that became extinct, and that *Homo habilis* was derived from *A. africanus* and started the lineage that led through *H. erectus* to *H. sapiens*. The dubious points include the moment when the separation of the robust forms took place, and whether they are derived from *A. africanus* or if they had separated before this. The recent discovery assigned to *A. aethiopicus* would confirm the second hypothesis and would leave *A. africanus* totally within the human evolutionary lineage.

175 Life expectancy at birth has undergone a spectacular increase in the different social groups: the increase of these average values always suggests the introduction of sanitary improvements (both preventive and therapeutic), improvements in nutrition and improvements in certain social conditions that have repercussions on the population's quality of life.
[Source: data prepared by the author, from several sources]

Molecules and human evolution

Fossils have been the traditional tool for studying life in the past and a large part of the knowledge needed to date and reconstruct evolutionary processes has been based on them. Comparisons between the fossils themselves, as well as with present-day life forms, has allowed us, in effect, to build up an evolutionary tree in which fossils are the ancestors of current life-forms and links can be established between them. And, if the age of the fossil is known, this can be placed within a time scale.

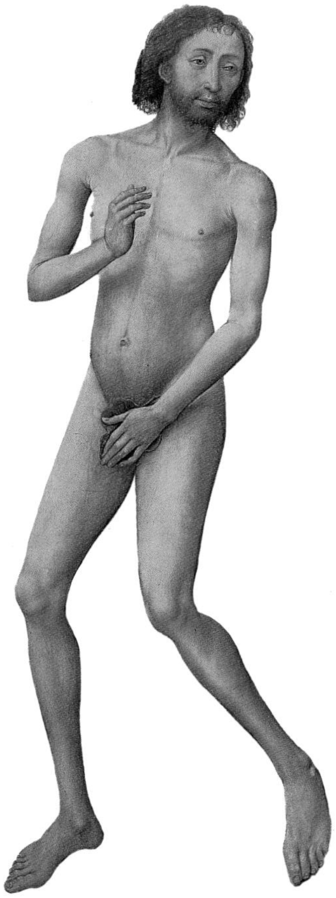
Fragment of *Adam and Eve* by Ignatius van der Stock [AISA]

The reconstruction of evolutionary progress mentioned above is, however often frequently inaccurate, both because of the scarcity of fossil remains and the state in which they are preserved, as well as the different ways they can be interpreted. Likewise, the dating is often less accurate than could be desired. As a consequence, in the last few years, there has been a great expansion in what is known as molecular systematics, which involves making comparisons between the biochemical composition of living species and then inferring their evolutionary history: the longer two species have been separated in evolutionary

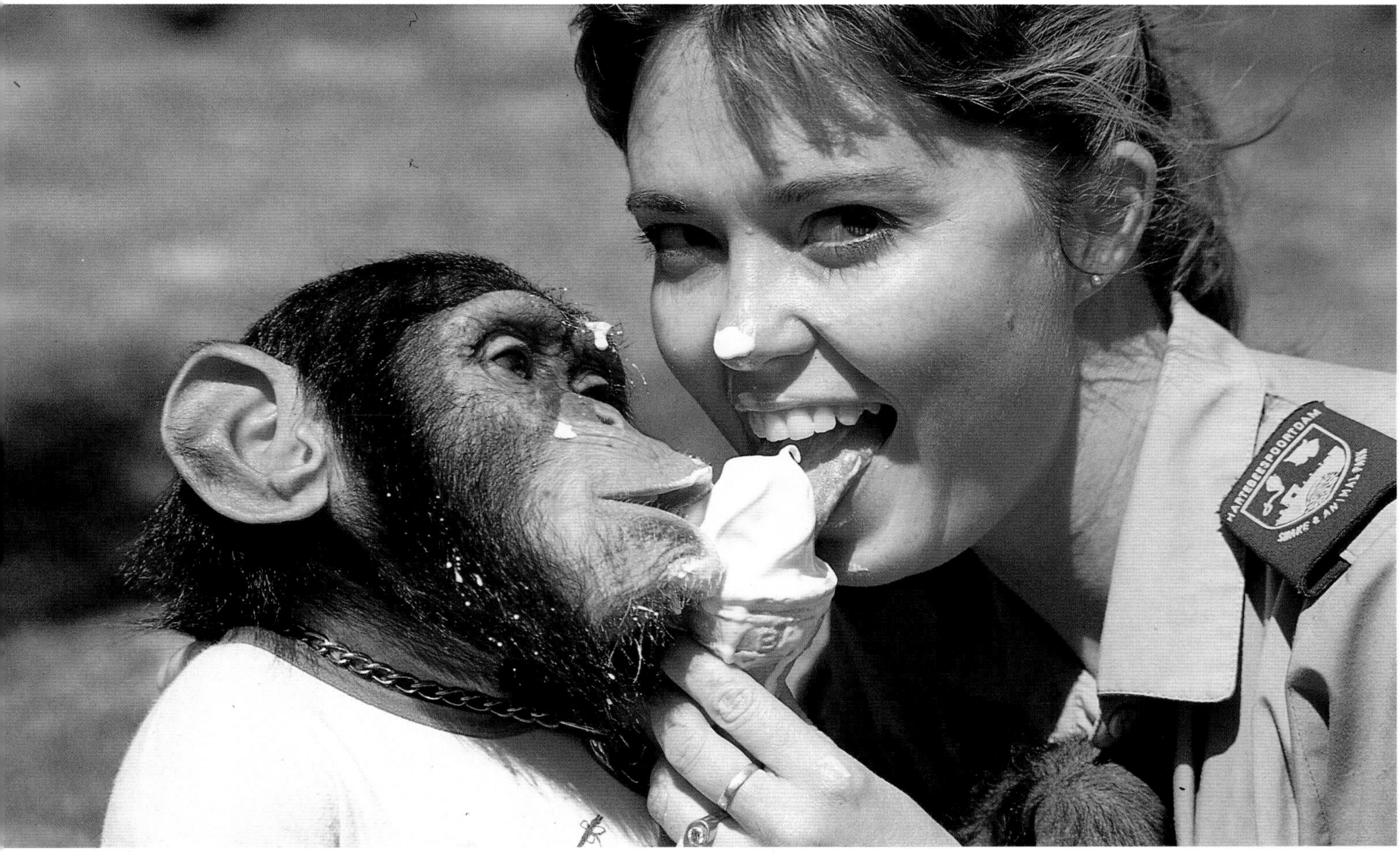

terms, the more different their biochemical make-up is.

The first important step in biochemical systematics was the measurement of the immunological reaction between apes and hominids. The method consists of taking a protein from one species, for example human albumin, and injecting it into another mammal, usually a rabbit, so that it produces antibodies that react, not only against the human albumin, but also against the albumin of other, related species, although to a lesser degree. The strength of the reaction is an indication of the relationship between the two species being tested. Using this system Vincent Sarich and Allan Wilson showed, in 1967, that the gorilla and the chimpanzee were closer to humans than to other simian species, such as the cercopithecoids. One of the problems of this system is that it does not directly measure the difference between two proteins (which are primary products of the genes). For that reason a method of directly analyzing the amino acid sequences of the proteins was developed and this has produced some very interesting results. For evolutionary purposes, however, this system has been partially superseded by direct comparison of the carriers of genetic information— nucleic acids. Using this latter technique more and more genes are sequenced and the amount of information available is constantly increasing.

Chimpanzee (*Pan troglodytes*) [Firo Foto]

In contrast with morphological evolution, which occurs at very different rates depending on selection pressure, molecular evolution, on certain occasions and under certain conditions, can act like an evolutionary clock. In other words the amount of change is proportional to the length of separation. For this to be true we must be sure that the changes being analyzed do not have an important affect on the living beings which are the carriers. In other words we must make sure that the process of natural selection is not operating. This is achieved either by choosing parts of the genome where we know this process is not active, or by making global comparisons that give statistically acceptable results. In these cases it has been possible to establish an evolutionary clock that has given some surprising results. In the first studies on immunological similarity carried out, Sarich and Wilson suggested that the separation between the line carrying the human gene and the one carrying the chimpanzee gene took place a little over five million years ago. Their theories were published at a time when it was generally accepted that hominids had been an independent branch for at least 15 million years, and that the first representative of that branch was *Ramapithecus*. These days the possibility that *Ramapithecus* was one of our ancestors has been completely discounted and it is generally accepted that genetic divergence was a much more recent event, even though the original proposal seems to be rather incomplete.

Orangutan (*Pongo pygmaeus*) [AGE Fotostock]

Other forms of molecular analysis, such as DNA hybridization, have also shown that the separation of the branch that originally contained both humans and chimpanzees happened later, between five and eight million years ago, which indicate where efforts to find fossils have to be directed. Overall, and using only molecular information, we can say that the human species evolved according to the sequence: humans, chimpanzee, gorilla, orangutan, gibbon, monkeys. Molecular analysis is, at the moment, a very useful method for clarifying and reconstructing evolution on many different levels, human evolution being a case in point. Nevertheless, we should remember that it is only one, additional tool, among many used to find out more about the evolution of living beings in general, and of humans in particular.

An analysis, in 1987, of DNA from mitochondria showed that all present-day human populations probably derived from one ancestor who lived in Africa 200,000 years ago. This evidence provides support for the theory that modern man originated in Africa and spread from there all over the world, replacing previous populations. This idea was later confirmed, in 1991, by a study based on the sequencing and comparison of a nucleotide sequences from a region of mitochondrial DNA which was called the "control region." These samples came from many different areas, including African populations and individuals from Asia and Europe. The control region is a fragment of 1,000 nucleotides, which are not codified and which show a high rate of mutation, a fact which means that there is a great variety of mutations within different individuals and populations. In the first place, great variability was observed between individuals: there are very few cases where the sequence is exactly the same, and whenever this does occur it is always in individuals from the same population. This implies a high level of geographical specificity and shows, furthermore, that geographical mobility over time has been greatly reduced, especially among hunter-gatherers. Using a computer program that is capable of reconstructing the genealogical tree from a set of sequences, and comparing it with the sequence of nucleotides from the same region of the mitochondrial DNA of a chimpanzee, a typology has been found which clearly suggests an African origin for all observed the variation: the first branches of the tree are occupied by sequences of individuals who all originated in Africa.

Further advances have been made by applying a molecular clock to the changes produced among present-day humans. Mitochondrial DNA mutates 10 times more often than nuclear DNA and therefore provides a very precise clock for use over short evolutionary periods, such as that proposed for the origin of modern man. The difference between humans and chimpanzees is 15.1% and by taking a particular period of time of separate evolution of the two species as a reference, it is possible to state how many mutations will be produced, on average, over a million years.

[Michael Freeman / Bruce Coleman Limited]

Considering that the separation between man and chimpanzee took place six million years ago, this would mean that our ancestors came into existence about 250,000 years ago. If other references are used the age varies: four million years gives an age of 165,000 years, whereas if we assume that the split happened nine million years ago that makes man 370,000 years old. Despite the inaccuracy of these figures, even the oldest case gives man a relatively recent origin. The fact that it was accepted that there was a single origin for the whole variety of human life led to talk of a "mitochondrial Eve," or an "African Eve," a symbolic term to represent humanity's female ancestor. The term, however, is incorrect, since the results do not imply that we are all descended from a single female ancestor (even though this is true of the fragment of the mitochondrial DNA studied), only that a specific mitochondrial DNA existed in a quite large population of African individuals and that it would have spread, by chance to the individuals who migrated from Africa. Other women could, therefore, have had the same sequence, as would their ancestors (men also could clearly have had the same sequence, but they cannot transmit the mitochondria).

The implications of these results are clear when we take into account the latest studies on human evolution. They rigorously support the idea that modern man originated in Africa and spread from there. They also emphasize the fact that no genetic contribution was made by earlier human species, which lived over large areas of Eurasia. Modern humans, during their expansion, would not have interbred with these earlier inhabitants, and that makes them our only ancestor. These results have been treated with scepticism by those who believe in the regional continuity of different populations, and so the debate remains open.

3. The expansion of humans

3.1 The first true humans: Homo erectus

The changes that took place in the course of time in *Homo habilis*, with a series of transitional forms in east Africa, gave rise to *Homo erectus*, a hominid with a larger body size, a more efficient bipedal locomotor system, a larger brain, a more complex culture, which can more easily be interpreted as an adaptation, with more or less permanent dwellings, and a greater alimentary dependence on meat, probably obtained from hunting.

The difficulty of delimitating the species

We must understand *Homo erectus* as a chronospecies, in other words, a series of more or less homogenous forms which lived in a certain period of time, without pretending to give a deeper biological meaning to the concept in terms of breeding relationships. In any case, the detailed image is not simple and some remains do not fit easily into the general scheme. We can probably find the most marked cultural changes in *Homo erectus*, changes that are linked to the conquest of new territories, with new evolutionary strategies which show the lead to growing cultural complexity which is strictly related to biological adaptation. There is a dependence on cultural adaptation in the evolutionary strategy. Complex activities can be recognized, such as the making of elaborate instruments, hunting, the use of fire or building huts.

In short, we begin to recognize the forms of *Homo erectus* more than a million years ago, at a date which is still under discussion, and, showing a remarkable continuity of both morphology and culture. We find them throughout Africa and Eurasia up until 300,000 years ago, by which time we can speak of archaic forms of *Homo sapiens*. The transition, however, is not always as clear in each place, nor is it possible to give them the same dates. *Homo erectus* must have occupied a good part of Africa, with

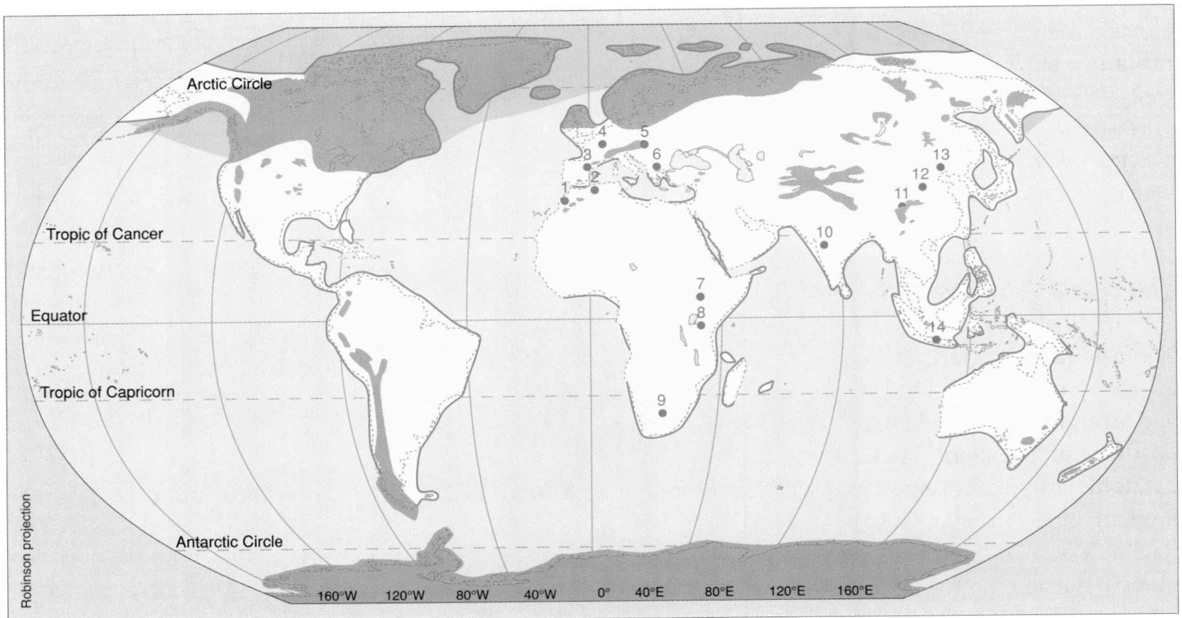

1 Salé, Morocco
2 Ternifine, Algeria
3 Talteüll, Catalonia
4 Heidelberg, Germany
5 Vérteszöllös, Hungary
6 Petralona, Greece
7 Koobi-Fora, Kenya
8 Olduvai, Tanzania
9 Swartkrans, Transvaal
10 Narmada, India
11 Lantian, China
12 Peking, China
13 Jinniushan, China
14 Trinil, Java

176 The discoveries referring to *Homo erectus* are found in very different geographical locations; the dispersion of this chronospecies led it to areas of south west Asia, east Asia, the Indian subcontinent, and, according to some authors, to Europe (the outlines of the coasts are those estimated for that time). It is to *Homo erectus* that we owe the conquest of the temperate zones of the planet, as well as other important discoveries in the history of humankind: such as the taming of fire, the discovery of symmetry (with the appearance of the first bifaces), the use of colorings, the technique of carving stone, and the first ritual activities (see also fig. 23)
[Cartography: Editrònica, from various sources]

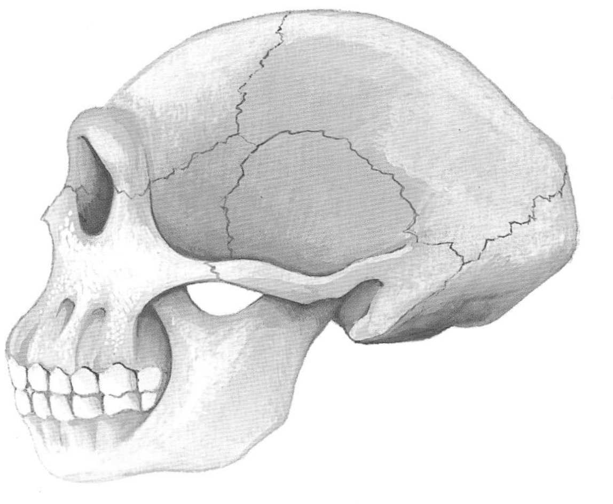

Homo erectus

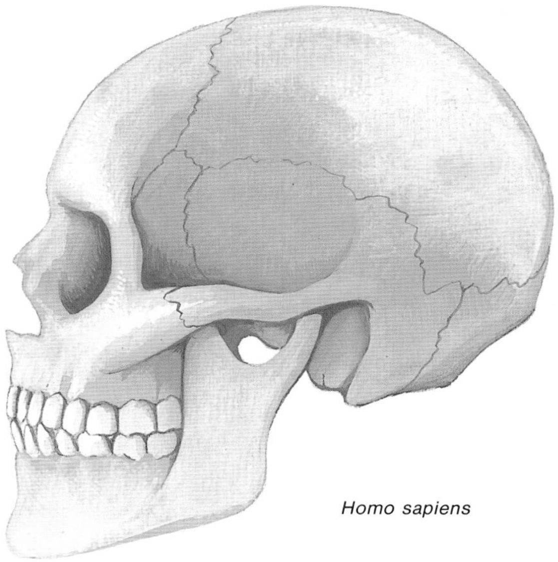

Homo sapiens

177 The somatic structure of *Homo erectus* was very similar to that of present day humans, except for the cranium, which was quite different. Its cranium had a pentagonal form—viewed from behind—and an important projection in the nape for the musculature of the neck. It also usually had a sagittal crest. The visage still presented some archaic traces, such as prognathism—the prominent or projecting jaw; very pronounced supraorbital arch, with bony thickening; small and backwardly depressed forehead; and a robust mandible without chin. The dentition of *Homo erectus* was in certain respects different from that of modern humans, and similar in others: the front teeth were large, the premolars, bicuspids, and the molars morphologically very similar to present day humans. The skeleton of its extremities was very similar to today's humans. *[Drawing: Biopunt, from various sources]*

remains in the east, and in the Maghreb and, as he spread out of Africa, we find him in the southeastern and eastern Asia, India and Europe. Here our knowledge is much broader because of the numerous fossil and archaeological remains which allow us to make an analysis, not only of the group as it is, but also of its variation in space and time.

Despite everything, it is often very difficult to define a species clearly, something which leads us to long and often useless discussions. For example, some authors, while still accepting *Homo erectus*, insist that the European forms be assigned exclusively to *Homo sapiens*. However, even though, as we will see shortly, there is some evidence to back this up, the overall panorama remains much more complex. It becomes especially complicated because of the need to distinguish between them when we speak about different species (*Homo habilis, H. erectus* and *H. sapiens*), which are distinct but not always definable entities.

The characteristics of the first humans

The general characteristics of *Homo erectus* do not appear to us to be much different from later forms and, even from the modern humans, as regards their post-cranial skeleton. They were tall in stature, extraordinarily so in some cases when compared to modern humans, and must have had a gait very similar to ours. The largest differences with respect to modern humans are found in the skull where there is often evidence of mosaic evolution, in other words, there are at the same time primitive characteristics, clearly typical of earlier forms, and other derived characteristics which are typical of later forms. All in all they present a characteristic morphology which we can find in fossil remains found in quite different geographical areas and which make it acceptable to place them all under a single denomination.

The skull of *Homo erectus* is large: the average cranial capacity is some 61 in^3 (1,000 cm^3)—oscillating between 49 and 73 in^3 (800 and 1,200 cm^3)—and this increases with time. This large volume is accompanied by a form which is characterised by a thickening of the bone above the orbits, forming a type of peak or occipital torus; the forehead is not vertical but slopes backwards and gives the cranial vault a flattened look. The rear part juts out and instead of being rounded as in modern humans is angular and forms a nuchal torus in the lower part of which the neck's musculature is inserted. Viewed in profile, the face projects forward, a trait known as prognathism; the mandible is chinless and has a greatly thickened bone, a trait which indicates a large insertion zone for a powerful mandibular musculature. The dentition is similar to that of modern man, but stouter and with typical characteristics. For example, the incisors are spade shaped, characterized by a thickening of the enamel on both sides of the rear of each tooth. It would seem that this characteristic is linked to a strong use of the front teeth, giving support and more resistance to wear and tear.

Known remains and the taxonomic confusion

The best picture of *Homo erectus* can probably be formed by reviewing the remains from the most important sites where they have been found. In many cases, and especially in the oldest ones, these fossil remains of *Homo erectus* were given their own scientific names which helped to create confusion, but since the unification of the group by Franz Weidenreich

(1873-1948) in 1940, these names have just become anecdotal although they are still used informally to refer to specific remains. For our purpose here the route will run from Asia (Java, China and India) to Africa (east and north) ending up in Europe. We will certainly not refer to all the remains or deposits: there are far too many of them to be mentioned one by one.

The Java man

In both a spectacular and accidental way, Java was one of the first places where remains of our ancestors were found. In 1887, a Dutch doctor by the name of Eugene Dubois (1858-1940) decided to leave his job as a professor of anatomy at the Universiteit Amsterdam to go to what were then the Dutch East Indies, in search of that hypothetical species which Ernst Haeckel (1834-1919) had christened *Pithecanthropus alalus*, the speechless human-ape which, according to Haeckel had to be *the* link between the other primates and humans. Because of his mistaken conceptions about the origin of the south east Asiatic primates, Dubois decided to go to Indonesia, first of all to Sumatra and then to Java. But it was not long before he made some great discoveries.

In 1891, near the town of Trinil, on the banks of the River Solo in eastern Java, he discovered the upper part of a skull with a previously unknown shape and which he originally thought was that of a chimpanzee (today we know that they never lived in that region). The following year, though, he discovered a femur at the same horizon, with a clear human appearance and, convinced that the remains really did correspond to the missing link that he was searching for, and observing that the erect posture was the most notable characteristic of this hominid, he announced them as a transitional form in the human line, giving it the name *Pithecanthropus erectus*: the human ape with an erect posture. As in other cases, the reaction did not take long to materialize both from anti-evolutionists and scientists who believed that the femur could be from a contemporary human and the skull from a giant gibbon. Dubois, offended and dismayed, hid the remains for many years until other finds opened up the way for the remains to be interpreted as the "Java man."

The overall panorama of the finds in Java is complicated by the extraordinarily complex stratigraphy, which in many cases has prevented accurate datings and in other cases has only produced very dubious ones. The datings have generally been estimated from fauna associated with the deposits. Very little is known of the type of life, as there are very few remains of cultural material and not a single dwelling site has been excavated. Some remains (like some of those from Sangiran) could be very old, more than a million years, but there is insufficient evidence to accept suggestions that they are older. With a continued increase in cranial capacity as time goes on, we come to much more recent forms which can still be attributed to *Homo erectus* lived there, but at that time formed part of the Sunda highlands, a peninsula which encompasses a large part of the present day islands of South East Asia.

Peking man

The history of the most important finds in Peking (Beijing), in China, was not as tumultuous as that of those from Java but the remains that were found did come to a much worse end: they disappeared for good during the Second World War. What happened exactly is still a mystery but, fortunately, Franz Weidenreich, before abandoning Beijing where he had directed the Tertiary research laboratory of the Chinese Geological Service from 1935 to 1941, managed to take a good collection of reproductions, photographs and drawings out of the country, despite the war. Today these still form the basis for the study of the remains.

The first remains were found in the upper cave of Zhoukoudian (Chou-kou-tien) and they were assigned to a new taxon, Sinanthropus pekinensis, but their similarities to the forms from Java led them to be included in the same group. The excavations were started again in 1949 and, luckily, a great deal more material was found, especially stone tools (over 100,000). Altogether there are six almost complete skulls and other remains belonging to some 40 individuals. Thanks to monographs written by Chinese authors, we have a good knowledge of the dating of the different levels in the cave, between 460,000 and 230,000 years, and we have been able to study the life style well. Thus, it has been said that Peking man was a cave man who used fire, hunted deer, collected seeds and made specialized tools. Compared to what we have so far seen, this description gives a completely new and much more complex and thorough perspective of its type of life.

Apart from the extraordinary remains from Beijing, other Chinese sites have produced important *Homo erectus* fossils. The oldest remains are from Lantian, near Xi'an, in Shaanxi, where a skull dating from 750,000 or 800,000 years was found with a cranial capacity of 48 in^3 (780 cm^3). The most recent remains, which some authors place within *Homo sapiens*, are those from Jinniushan in Hubei, with a dating of some 280,000 years.

The skull of Narmada

For many years, the remains from Java and China were the only ones known in Asia. But the discovery in 1982 of a skull in the terraces of the River Narmada, near the village of Hathnora in Madhya Pradesh State, in central India made the first link between the Asian and African populations. It was the *skull of Narmada*, of unknown age and a morphology which has been described as that of an evolved *Homo erectus*.

The African fossils

Much later than the Asiatic specimens, fossils of *Homo erectus* have been uncovered in the Olduvai Gorge and on the banks of Lake Turkana in east Africa. Louis Leakey described several remains from the Olduvai Gorge (known by their catalogue numbers OH9 and OH12) which are clearly from *Homo erectus* with a date of around a million years for the first and 700,000 for the second. The most interesting remains, however, come from the banks of Lake Turkana. The oldest remains, some one and a half million years old, were found on the east side of the lake in the Koobi Fora formation in 1975: two complete skulls (called KNM-ER 3733 and 3883, according to the catalogue of fossils of the Kenyan National Museum) which have a cranial capacity of 49 and 52 in^3 (800 and 850 cm^3) respectively and are morphologically related to *Homo habilis*. The most surprising remains were found on the western side of the lake later on in 1984: the almost complete skeleton of a 12 year old boy, of tall stature (5 ft [165 cm] which could have increased in adulthood) and a high cranial capacity (55 in^3 [900 cm^3]). The dating, which is also surprising, places it at 1.6 million years: the oldest we know of and with characteristics that are far removed from those of *Homo habilis*. These remains have led to the proposal of a later transition date and a higher rate of change. In the Swartkrans deposits in South Africa, a series of fossils was found that were also assigned to this taxon; their dating is rather imprecise, as might be expected. Finally, we must mention the finds of hominid remains, especially mandibles, in north Africa, with a dating between 700,000 years (those at Tighenif, the former Ternifine, south of Oran in Algeria) and 350,000 years (those at Salé, in Morocco).

The European fossils

The first settlements in Europe date from around one million years ago, even though some archaeologists suggest they were established earlier. The oldest known human remains are from Atapuerca, near Burgos (Spain), though there are older archeological sites that have not yielded human remains. This site is older than the Mauer site, near Heidelberg (Germany), considered until recently to be the oldest human

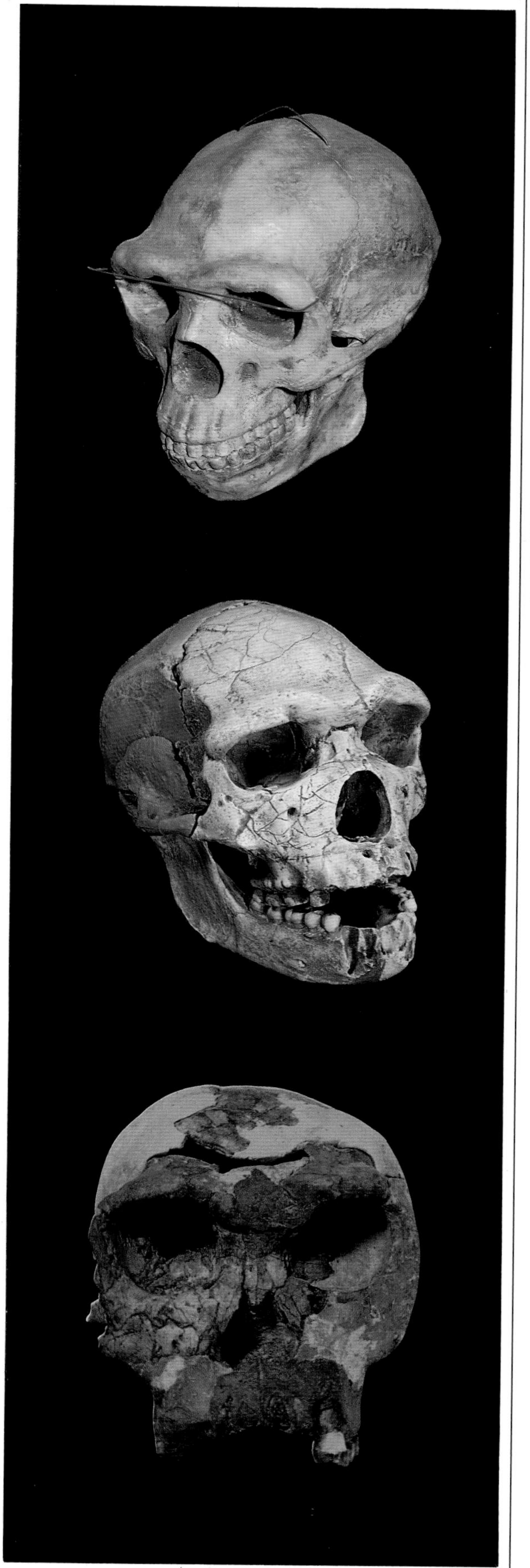

178 Various forms of hominids, corresponding to Peking Man (reconstructed from fragments found in Zhoukoudian, above), to the remains of the female cranium of *Homo habilis* OH24 from Olduvai (in the center), and to Talteüll Man (below). An age of 1,700,000 years is calculated for the oldest, Twiggy (OH24), discovered in 1968. The cranium of Peking Man, *Homo erectus* of China, was found in 1929 beside some stone tools and clear indications of the use of fire. Talteüll Man, found in a cave at Aragó, shows characteristics that are intermediate between the earlier *Homo erectus* and the later *H. sapiens sapiens.* Fossil pollen of wild vine have been found beside these latter fossils.
[Photo: AGE Fotostock / National Museum of Kenya and Jordi Vidal / ECSA]

remains in Europe. Other remains (Vértesszöllös in Hungary; Petralona in Greece; Bilzingsleben in Turingia, Germany; Aragó at Taltaüll near Perpignan, in France) are usually placed within the same taxon but not without controversy. In fact they are populations contemporary with those of *Homo erectus* in Asia and Africa. But the fact that they have certain characteristics which make us think of the oldest forms of *Homo sapiens*, and the lack of a discontinuity between them, make some authors prefer not to speak of *Homo erectus* in Europe and place all the fossils in a broad group of archaic *Homo sapiens*. Various pieces of evidence in many remains, and not only European ones, point to the fact that *Homo erectus* had the life style of a great hunter. The accumulation of bones from large animals would demonstrate this, some of which are marked in such a way as to indicate that they had been quartered by stone cutting tools. It has been deduced that some of the hunts were conducted in a group, an indication of social complexity. The tools themselves are much more complex, the bifacial tools being particularly worthy of note, which are characteristic of a culture or industry called Acheulean (a name derived from the French remains at Saint-Acheul in Picardie). In some cases, such as at Terra Amata in Nice, dwelling sites have been found were it seems there were temporary huts which served as dwellings and workshops for cutting stone.

The most probable route of expansion out of Africa is through the Arabian Peninsula, at that time still attached to Africa, and with routes that must have reached Asia on one side and Europe on the other. But we can not discount a path from the north of Africa to Italy and the possibility of another path across the Straits of Gibraltar is under discussion.

3.2 The emergence of our species: *primitive* Homo sapiens

The oldest fossils

According to some authors, the root of the problem of accepting that the first humans in Europe were *Homo erectus*, rather than including them in *Homo sapiens*, is the evidence of a gradual change towards this later species. Thus it is usually considered that forms dating from 400,000 years ago have cranial characteristics that are no longer typical of the *Homo erectus* we have seen and that lead us to speak of *Homo sapiens*.

The European fossils

It is in Europe where this transition can best be observed, perhaps because of the greater quantity of fossils. A discussion as to whether fossils like those from Aragó, Petralona, Bilzingsleben or others are cor-

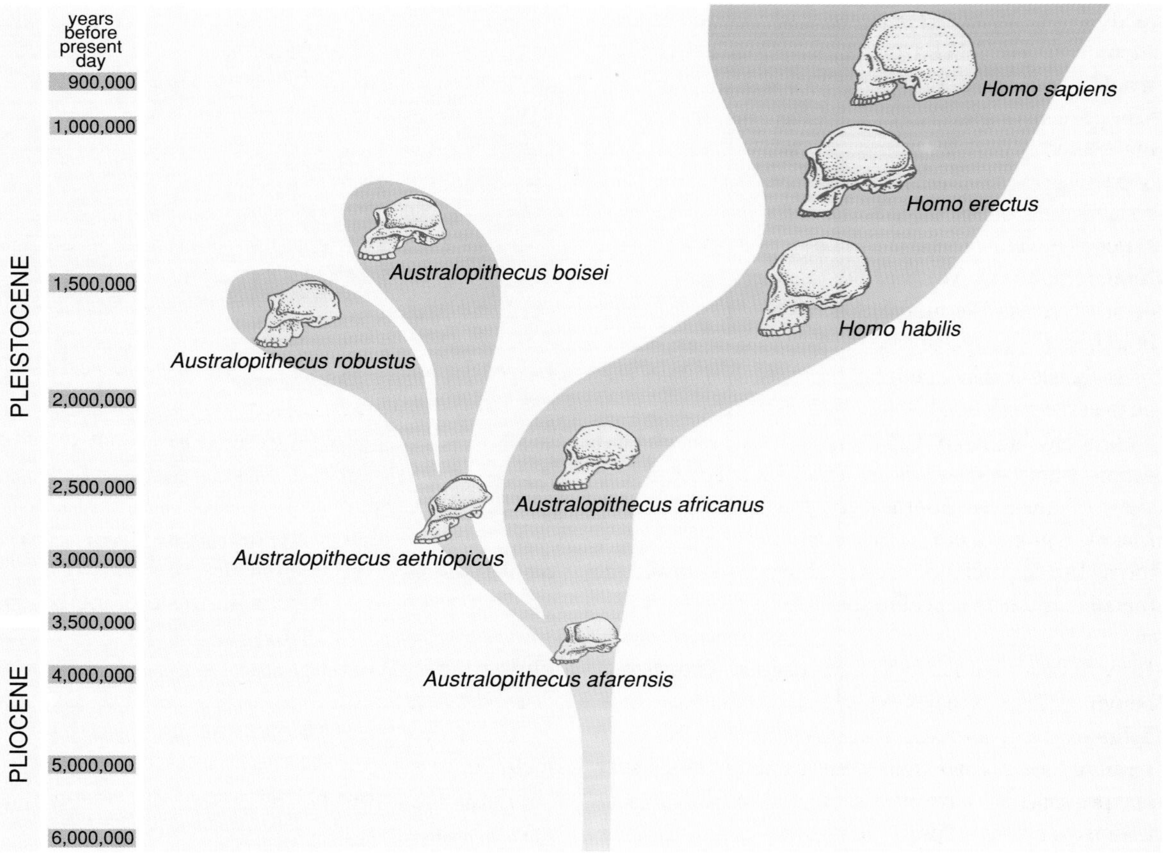

179 The evolutionary scheme of the hominids of the lower Quaternary, prepared from presently available data. The lineage of the hominids separates from that of the primates of tropical and subtropical Africa some five million years ago, when the first pre-hominids appeared (of which there are some four million year old fossils). One can say, therefore, that Africa has been the cradle of humankind and that humans have existed there for at least two and half million years earlier than on any other continent. It is presumed that there have been two migrations of humans through Eurasia, the second of which reached America crossing the Bering Strait. The first dispersal (*Homo erectus*) took place about a million years ago, and the second dispersal (*Homo sapiens*) probably took place between 60,000 and 40,000 years ago.
[Diagram: Biopunt, from various sources]

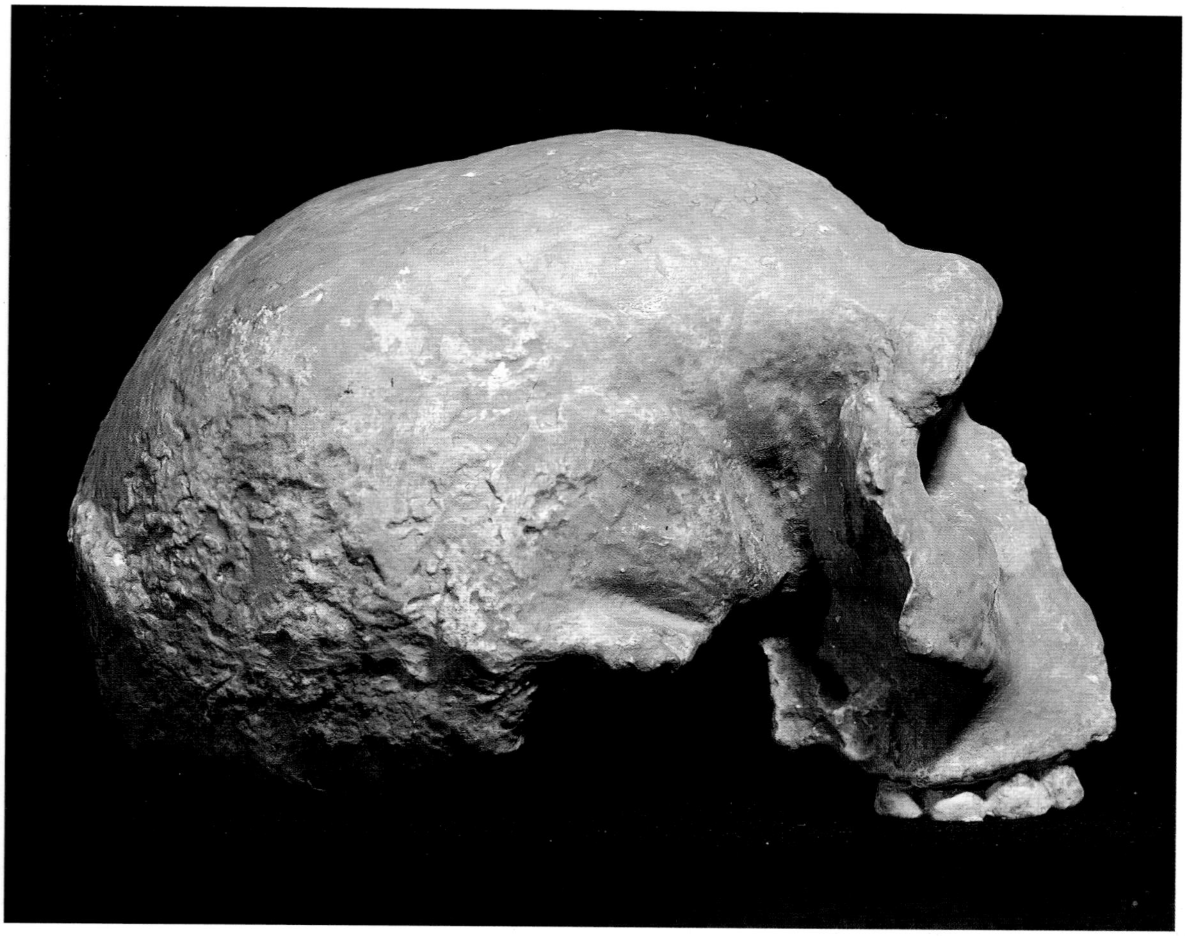

180 The Steinheim cranium (Germany), found in 1933 in fluvial deposits, corresponds to archaic *Homo sapiens*. The features that helped identify it are: the stout cranial bones, supraorbital arch and capacity of 70-71 in^3 (1,150-1,175 cm^3). Some of these characteristics are archaic, but they can be distinguished from *Homo erectus* by the expanded parietal bones and the more rounded occipital regions; because of its cranial capacity it is thought to be female. The skull is deformed in the facial region as a result of the sediments that covered it; no objects were found beside it, but the associated fauna suggests a date near that of the Swanscombe cranium (England).
[Photo: AISA]

rectly classified as *Homo erectus* or whether they should not have been classified as *Homo sapiens*, would be an endless one. Slightly more recent European remains, around 250,000 years, start showing characteristics that make us think of the human populations which, well-separated by their morphology and their distribution in space and time, lived in Europe between 30,000 and 70,000 years ago, those of Neanderthal man. We could refer to them as a "race" of our species. The morphological characteristics that link them to our species are those that refer, particularly, to the skull. The cranial capacity is very high, with an average of 82 in^3 (1,350 cm^3), very similar to that of present day human populations; the skull in general is rounded and slender; the vertical forehead with few signs of muscular insertion, especially in the nuchal (nape) region: there is no continuous superciliary torus, but superciliary arches above each orbit; the mandible is slender, with a small chin and dentition.

How shall we name the humans that we recognize as belonging to our species but are earlier than these well-delimited Neanderthals? There have been various suggestions, some good, some bad. Denominations such as "pre-sapiens" have not been accepted for obvious reasons, nor have "pre-" nor "ante-Neanderthal," as the reference to later forms gives them little identity and seems to indicate that they are the direct ancestors of the Neanderthals. Although this can be accepted, it does not necessarily need to be reflected in the name. Other denominations are more widely used, such as the first *Homo sapiens*, or the transitional forms, or archaic forms of *Homo sapiens*. Sometimes they are also called pre-Würmian forms, referring to the fact that they lived before the great Würm ice age, which the Neanderthals experienced first hand. Two sets of fossil remains are considered to be the prototypes of these first *Homo sapiens*, that of Swanscombe in the Thames Estuary, in Britain and that of Steinheim near Stuttgart in Germany. They tend to be put together because of their similar dating, between 200,000 and 250,000 years. But they are not by any means the only ones; other examples are the fossils from Biache-Saint-Baast in the French Flandes, several finds in the La Chaise series in Charente in western France, and the latest, now near the last glaciation, from Ehringsdorf in Thüringen, Germany, and those from Fontechevade in Charente, France. The Banyuls mandible in France, which for many years has been included in this group because of its morphological similarities, is now placed within the Neanderthal epoch thanks to recent dating.

181 In the Sierra de Atapuerca (in the north of the Iberian Peninsula) one of the most important sites of Europe was found, dating from the end of the Mindel glaciation (between 350,000 and 200,000 years ago). Excavation of the various parts that make it up began in the 1970s. The complex that has produced the most human remains is the Cueva Mayor. Linked with these fossils have been found large quantities of macrofauna and microfauna of the European middle Pleistocene and a considerable diversity of pollen. From these discoveries it can deduced that there have been a series of climatic changes during the period in which the materials were deposited, and even that—due to the richness and different biotopes found in the ecological system that has been reconstructed—it could be an ecotone. In 1994, the remains of at least six individuals dating from the lower Pleistocene were found in the Gran Dolina Cave. *[Photo: Eudald Carbonell]*

The Swanscombe remains consist of two parietal and the occipital bone of the cranial vault. This is a lucky find as the three fragments from the same individual were each found several years apart. The estimated cranial capacity is of 81 in^3 (1,325 cm^3), much higher than that of *Homo erectus* and it has a rounded occipital. The Steinheim skull is smaller (67-73 in^3 [1,100-1,200 cm^3]) and is partially deformed by fossilization. One characteristic, though, has provoked great discussion: the base of the skull is broken but in such a way that it indicates that it was cut to extract the brain. This has given weight to the hypothesis of cannibalism as it seems clear that the part was broken before fossilization began. In fact it cannot be proved that the mutilation was performed to eat the brain rather than as part of a magic or ritual activity, but the two facts could be closely linked. The possibility of cannibalism or at least of intentional fracturing of the lower part of the skull can also be seen in other remains.

The site that is producing the most material in Europe is the one at Atapuerca, near Burgos, in Spain. Every year new remains are unearthed, especially mandibles and tooth parts, some of an extraordinary quality. The most interesting have been found in the surveys of the Gran Dolina Cave, associated with fauna typical of the lower Pleistocene, more than 780,000 years old. The remains are very robust and recall the morphology of *Homo erectus*, but some characters suggest the later Neanderthals and even modern humans, and this is why those who discovered it wanted to call it a new species of hominid, *H. antecessor*, the common ancestor of Neanderthals and modern humans.

The African and Asiatic fossils

Outside Europe, several sets of fossils also show the transition to *Homo sapiens* even though they are very patchy. In no case, however, is there a link to the Neanderthal forms typical of Europe. On the other hand, some south African forms of more than 100,000 years ago are good candidates for the ancestors of the anatomically modern humans that we will see later on. In Africa there are also the remains at Broken Hill (now Kabwe) north of Lusaka, Zambia: a robust skull with a cranial capacity of 78 in^3 (1,280 cm^3); those from Bodo in the Awash Valley, east of Addis Ababa, Ethiopia, which have clear incision marks on the bone indicating that the individual was skinned with a stone cutting tool, and some others with a patchwork of characteristics of both *Homo erectus* and *Homo sapiens*.

In eastern Asia there is also a transition that has been interpreted by some authors as a sign of evolution, independent of the one from Europe and Africa, from *Homo erectus* to modern humans, in other words, to present day aboriginal peoples. This theory, which as we shall see is rejected by many other authors who defend the African origin of modern humans, implies a morphological continuity, and therefore one of origin and descent too, from the Zhoukoudian remains of *Homo erectus* up to the anatomically modern humans via the first *Homo sapiens* (the Chinese Dali fossils, found near the village of Jiefangcun, 74 mi (120 km) northeast of Xi'an, in Shaanxi province, and the Maba ones, found near Shaoguan, in the northern part of Guandong Province). What is accepted, though, is a much longer persistence of the *Homo erectus* characteristics in China and southeast Asia compared to other places where the transition to *Homo sapiens* had already taken place.

Tools and housing

From a strictly archaeological perspective, there are few differences between the instrumentation of *Homo erectus* and that of the first *Homo sapiens*. The Acheulean tradition continues, but deposits show few bifacial tools, especially in Europe, but a great number of chippings. These are pieces of stone, usually silex, which separate from a core on being hit; later they can be worked to achieve a more suitable shape. The basic difference is that in the bifacials the tool is made by whittling a larger piece down but the chippings, on the other hand, are pieces which fall off a block when it is hit.

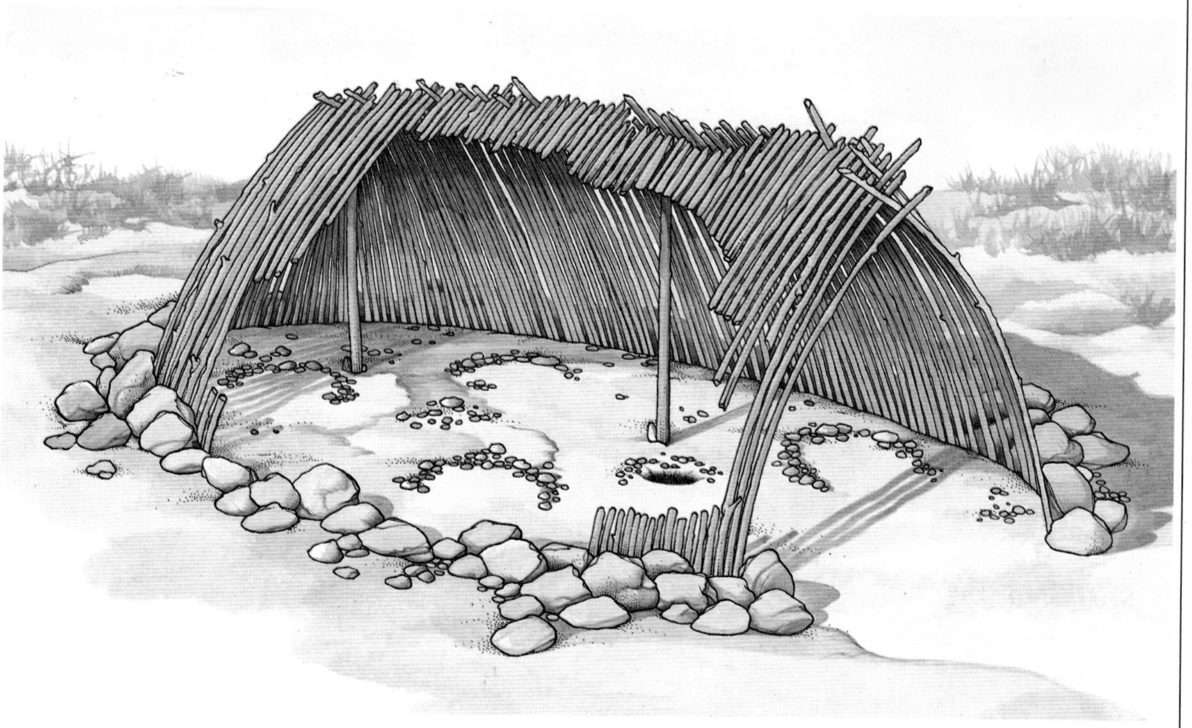

182 The Terra Amata site (Nice, Côte d'Azur) has allowed us to learn about certain aspects of the life of the inhabitants of Europe during the mid-Pleistocene. Traces of oval huts have been found, 23-49 ft long (7-15 m) and 13-20 ft (4-6 m) wide, sufficiently large enough to house up to ten people. The seasonal variation during the year had a major influence on the these human settlements; after spending some time in Terra Amata, the hunters dismantled their encampment and moved to other sites; on returning to the same site the following year they would have had to construct new huts on the previous settlement, since the old ones would have been covered by sand. Inside these huts, the humans who lived there made tools and excavated little hearths to light fires. There is sufficient proof available to allow us to think that the humans of this period were capable of exploiting the resources of the environment with considerable facility: they hunted elephants, rabbits, bears, and fished for aquatic mammals, fish and shellfish.
[Diagram: Biopunt, from various sources]

The first *Homo sapiens* lived both in caves and in the open air but with an ever more frequent use of caves. There is also evidence of the use of fire. The remains which best show us their life style are those of the cave of Lo Lazaret in Nice on the Côte d'Azur. There is evidence there of a hut that leaned against the wall of a cave, enclosing a space of 11 by 3.5 meters in which the remains of two fires and piles of small shells were found, perhaps brought in with the algae that were used to make their beds. There are no remains of stone chippings inside but there are outside, something that shows the delimitation of space. The presence of a wolf's skull at the entrance of the hut outside the cave is clearly significant. We can see that the resources varied according to habitat, with a great diversity of food. Marine resources were used and also, in some cases, fresh water fish. It has been suggested that among the first *Homo sapiens*, there could have been signs of interpersonal violence which could have provoked, for example, the breakage in the skull from Aragó; the evidence, though is not conclusive, even though it has to be accepted that there was ritual breaking of human remains.

The Neanderthal explosion

The Neanderthals represent a homogenous group which would perhaps correspond to the concept of a race as we know it today, with the complexity inherent that comes from dealing with past populations. Sometimes they are given the rank of subspecies and they are called *Homo sapiens neanderthalensis*. In short, they are human populations which lived in Europe and southeast Asia during the beginning of the Würm glaciation, between 75,000 and 35,000 years ago. They originated from populations which inhabited the same regions and which, suddenly, gave way at the end of this period to populations of what we call anatomically modern humans, associated with the Late Paleolithic cultures, and which are morphologically indistinguishable from present day populations.

The appearance of Neanderthal man

The skull of Neanderthal man is large, broad and long, with a rounded occipital part which protrudes but is not angular. The cranial capacity is large with an average of 94 in^3 (1,550 cm^3) , higher than that of present day populations and with some specimens with over 104 in^3 (1,700 cm^3). The forehead is not as vertical as in modern man and the supercilliary arches above the orbits are pronounced. The face is large and has a solid appearance, and protrudes forward. The nose must have been large, angular and prominent and has been interpreted as a device to warm up the air before it reached the lungs. The dentition is bulkier than in modern populations, especially the front elements; the rear ones, on the other hand, are already similar to those of modern populations. The mandible is usually chinless.

What makes the post-cranial skeleton different from that of modern humans is its extraordinary

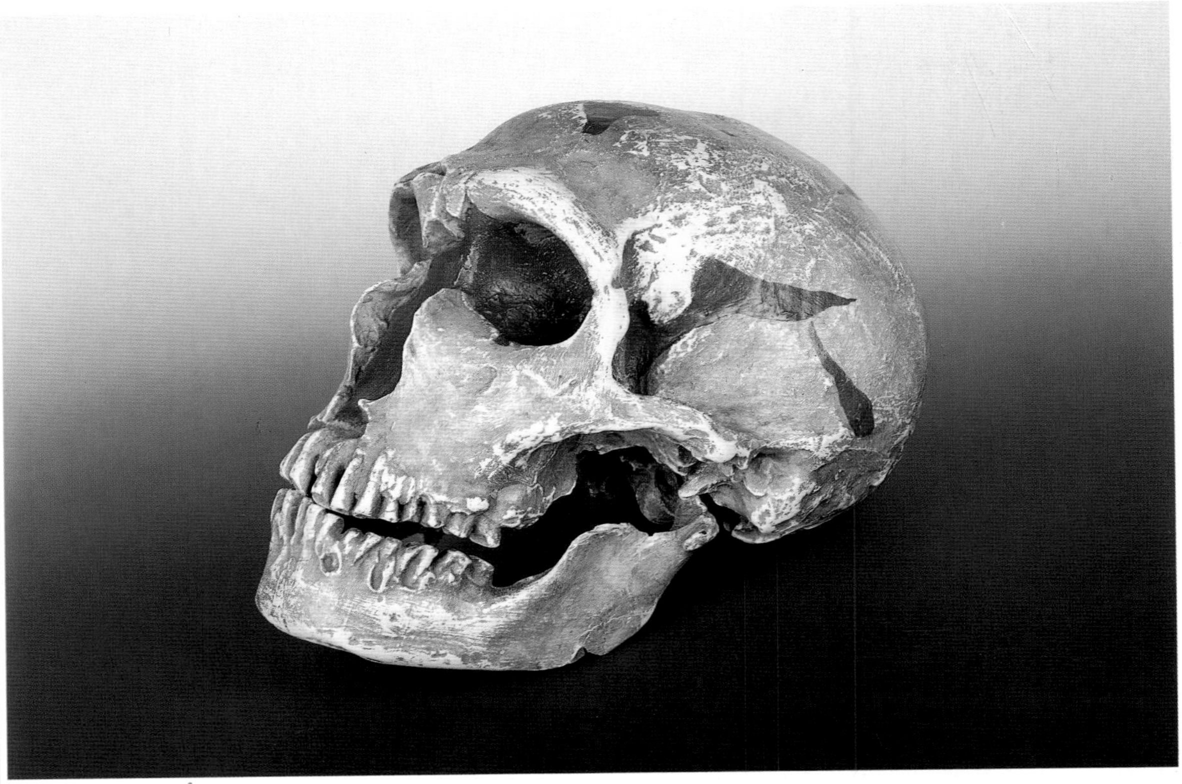

183 Cranium of a Neanderthal from La Ferrassie. The fossils called Neanderthal were found in the Feldhofer grotto in the valley of the river Neander near Düsseldorf in 1856, but were not described properly then: their finders thought they were the bones of a bear, but a schoolmaster realized that they belonged to a human, although somewhat abnormal. The schoolmaster sent the fossils to reputed anatomists of the country who diagnosed that the bones had belonged to a human who lived in the region before the Germans and the Celts. Later, the anatomist Rudolf Virchow (1871-1902) studied them and decided that the cranium was pathologically abnormal. The opinions of Virchow aroused interest in the country until the finding of other similar forms, which made clear the archaic nature of Neanderthal. *[Photo: Jordi Vidal]*

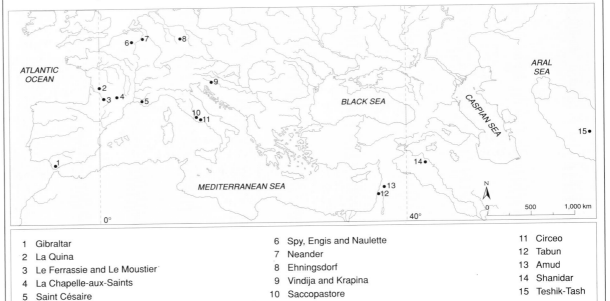

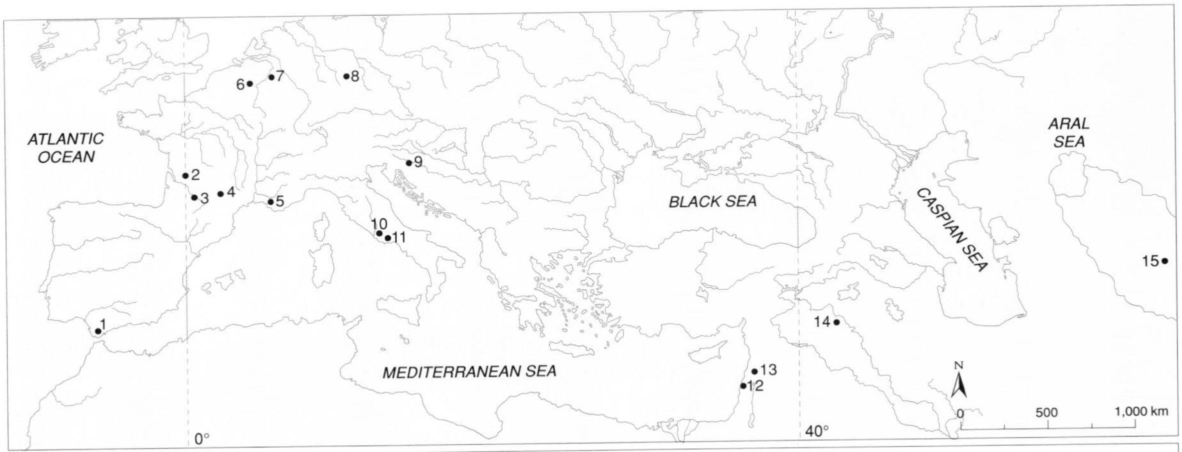

1	Gibraltar	6	Spy, Engis and Naulette	11	Circeo
2	La Quina	7	Neander	12	Tabun
3	Le Ferrassie and Le Moustier	8	Ehningsdorf	13	Amud
4	La Chapelle-aux-Saints	9	Vindija and Krapina	14	Shanidar
5	Saint Césaire	10	Saccopastore	15	Teshik-Tash

184 The distribution of Neanderthal fossils. Neanderthal remains are the most common and best known fossils of non-modern humans. They have been found from southern and western Asia to the extreme west of Europe, where they lived at the beginning of the Würm glaciation, between 75,000 and 35,000 years ago. It is not difficult to understand why they did not survive when humans with more modern characteristics appeared on Earth. Archaeological data indicate that in whichever aspect that is studied (implements, objects, construction of dwellings and others), the forms of behavior of the Neanderthals were very much inferior to their more modern successors. It is not known very well how the Neanderthals became extinct nor why. It is believed that in addition to their disappearance through competition, there occurred a phenomenon of displacement and/or genetic capture on the part of the more modern human populations. *[Cartography: Editrònica, from various sources]*

robustness. One characteristic in particular has attracted attention: the pubis, in the antero-inferior part of the pelvis, is long and slender, without the robustness which is found in other parts of the body and leaves a broad birth canal. This characteristic has been related to the extremely large head size, in such a way that is would have facilitated childbirth; but the larger opening could also be related to a longer gestation period. Even though this second hypothesis is speculative, if it were true, it would have interesting evolutionary implications. On the whole, this morphology becomes familiar after seeing just a few fossils and is a feature that is exclusive to this group.

The Neanderthal fossils

One of the most famous specimens is that from Chapelle-aux-Saints in Limousin, central France, which displays these characteristics in an exaggerated form and has often been considered the prototype for the group. In fact, when it was studied for the first time in the 1910s by Marcellin Boule (1861-1930), who gave a distorted and unreal description of it, as if

185 Pictorial representation of a a Neanderthal burial rite in the cave of Shanidar, Iraq. It is believed that the Neanderthals were the first humans to bury their dead with some form of ritual ceremony, at least occasionally, if not always. One of the many Neanderthal remains in the Shanidar cave was buried in early June, about 60,000 years ago. The traces of pollen include remains of the vegetation present at the time of year that the burial occurred. They also show human intervention, as there are far more pollen grains, and larger pollen grains, than could have been transported by the wind. Studying the pollen shows that when the body was buried it must have been covered with complete flowers. *[Diagram: Biopunt]*

it had been a ferocious and rather unintelligent ape. This error could be related to the clear signs of arthritis which he did not interpret correctly, or with the lack of conviction he apparently had about human evolution. The remains from central Europe (sites in Krapina and Vindija, both in Croatia) are of particular interest. On the one hand, they indicate the possibility of cannibalism or, at least, of the removal of flesh from corpses for a secondary burial, a practice which has lasted in many populations for millennia. On the other hand, the morphology does not follow the western European model so clearly and some characteristics have been interpreted as indicating a possible continuity with the Late Palaeolithic forms. This interpretation has a clear evolutionary repercussion on our understanding of the changes in the transition from Neanderthal to modern man, as we shall see.

In Asia, we find sites in Israel (Tabun, Amud), Iraq (Shanidar) and the previously mentioned one in Uzbekistan (Teshik-Tash). The morphology is similar to that of the European ones, with a lesser degree of robustness and some characteristics which remind us of more modern remains. Here the problem of the replacement of the Neanderthals is also evident because in other sites close by, very old remains have been found with a morphology which can be related to the modern forms of *Homo sapiens*. We will deal with this point later on.

The Shanidar site, where nine skeletons have been excavated, has become famous because of a series of indirect pieces of evidence that are of great importance to our understanding of the way of life and thought processes of these humans. The remains of one of the individuals clearly shows signs of survival after an accident that collapsed his left orbit. It also shows a deterioration of the upper right extremity and the right leg, probably the result of the cranial wound that could have affected the brain. It is doubtful whether he had his arm amputated; if this is confirmed it would be the oldest known surgical operation. Other individuals have also left us evidence of wounds; one of them, who suffered from advanced arthritis, probably died of a wound at lung height made by a penetrating instrument, which has left a clear mark on the rib. Another has a scar on the right-hand side of his forehead. These are some examples of wounds and illnesses that show that there was survival of some individuals who could not have looked after themselves on their own. Outside the area we have described, the fossils of the Neanderthals do not display the same morphological characteristics and so are not considered to belong to the same group or race. The humans who lived in Africa and eastern and southeastern Asia (the area of Siberia was not inhabited nor had the conquest of Oceania or America started) are not included in a single denomination because of the lack of sufficient remains to be able to construct an overall picture, and the old names of non-European Neanderthals or Neanderthaloids are not acceptable. They are referred to simply as contemporaries of the Neanderthals. In Africa there is considerable heterogeneity and, alongside fossils with primitive morphology, related to the first forms of *Homo sapiens*, we can find others which, surprisingly, show modern characteristics in the sense that they already remind us of modern humans, as we will see later.

Neanderthal culture

Neanderthal man's culture is largely associated with Mousterian industry, the name of which is derived from the name of the Le Moustier site at Perigord, France, which is characterized by the production of tools made from flakes carefully chipped off a stone core, which were then reworked to achieve the desired piece (a scraper, a scratcher, a spear point, a knife). The techniques used were much more refined and efficient than those of previous epochs. It is also possible that they used bone and horn, which do not become widespread, though, until the following cultural period. The typification of these tools is very complex and has helped archaeologists to define and delimit areas and periods with a common cultural denominator. The cave was the principal dwelling place, even though there are signs of life in hovels and huts. We must remember that they were living in the coldest times and places known in human history up till then. The sites indicate only a temporary occupation, which would imply a nomadic lifestyle. The diet was made up of vegetables that were picked, with evidence of different fruits, and meat from hunting which, judging from the abundance of remains, must have been very productive. The clearest signs of activity of the group can be seen in the large number of deliberate and ritual burials. Among the Neanderthals, then, we find the first signs of spirituality or religion: the body is deposited in a specially made hole in a specific position, normally the fetal position, and accompanied with offerings that could be carved utensils (for them to use in another life?), animal remains like the horns or antlers of deer and similar species. In several cases

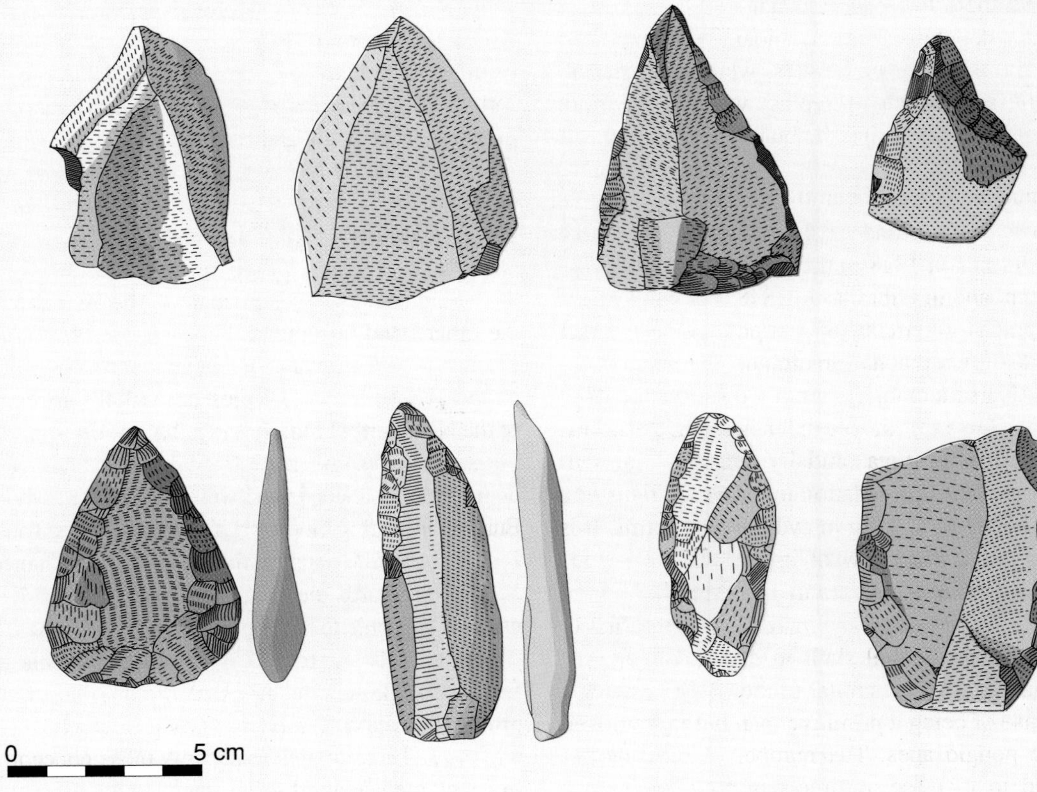

186 The tools made by the Neanderthals in Europe and west Asia are assigned to the Mousterian culture and correspond to the mid-Palaeolithic. The Mousterian industry fashioned tools mainly from stones of flint and, less frequently, limestone or quartz. The method used to make these tools is known as the "Levallois technique" and with it they managed to produce a series of tools. This Mousterian stone industry shows a notable unity in time and space, although a certain regional variety can be seen. In addition to their stone tools, it is thought that the Neanderthals also frequently worked with other materials because in some Mousterian sites the remains of wooden objects, such as staffs, have been found.
[Diagram: Biopunt, from various sources]

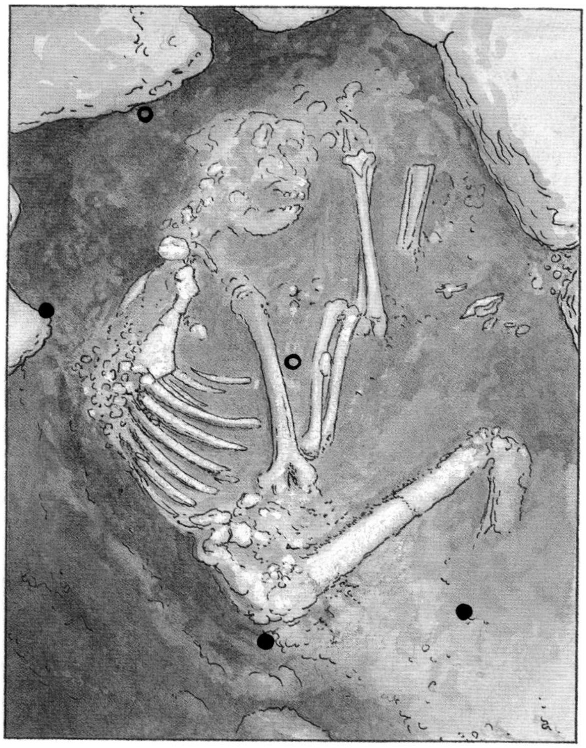

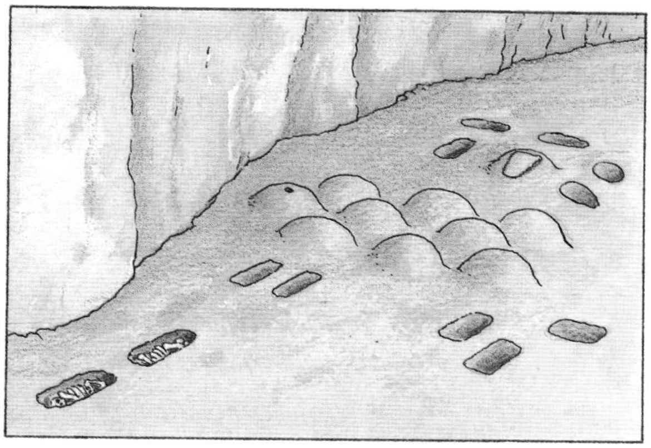

187 The discoveries of Neanderthal burials indicate that they were the oldest humans to bury their dead. The drawing on the right is a representation of how the Neanderthal skeleton of Shanidar IV (Iraq) was found. The archaeologists took samples of the soil that surrounded the corpse to analyze its composition [solid circles: samples with pollen; open circles samples without pollen] (see fig. 185). Thanks to these samples it was possible to identify the plants that had been used in the burial ceremony, some of which were medicinal. The drawings on the right are representations of the discovery of the burial site, also Neanderthal, from a rock shelter at La Ferrassie (Dordogne, France) where a family cemetery was found. Below the rock shelter a 45-year old man and a 35-year-old woman were buried side by side, separated by 20 in (50 cm); beside them were the remains of four children and two fetuses. It is believed that the Neanderthals knew the notion of burial since there are the remains of utensils and mounds of earth. *[Drawings: Aina Bonner]*

there is evidence of skinning and in some we can observe rupture at the base of the skull. The remains at Monte Circeo in Italy display this intentional breakage and the skull leads us to think that the individual died from a blow to the right hand side of the head and was buried in the middle of a circle of stones; some authors have interpreted this as an indication that there had been a ritual sacrifice. Around one of the skeletons from Shanidar, pollen analysis showed the presence of flowers, which flowered in the spring and which, it seems, would have been placed in the grave during the burial.

The distribution and dating of the deposits

The history of the Neanderthal discoveries began very early with finds in 1828 in the Engis cave near Liège in Belgium, and in Gibraltar in 1848, but which were not recognised as remains of past populations. In fact the first discovery that had any impact in scientific circles was that of a cranial arch in a quarry in a valley ("tal" in German) at Neander near Düsseldorf, Germany in 1856. It was initially seen as a representative of an ancient population in terms of prehistoric level but without thinking in evolutionary terms. It is known that Darwin knew of its existence when he wrote *The Origin of Species* in 1859, but he did not mention it. Thomas Huxley, in 1863, was the first to discuss the Neanderthal skull in evolutionary terms and he gave it a status similar to the one it has today, in the sense of being a primitive man but far removed from the pongid apes. The number of remains has continued to increase as time has progressed, to a point where we now have hundreds that allow us to make accurate studies of the populations.

Spatial and temporary delimitation is complex, as it depends on the way in which the group is defined. Thus we can arrive at the age of the oldest Neanderthals through remains that are beginning to display their characteristics or that already fully display them. Given that there is a large number of transitional forms, the delimitation remains flexible and some authors include in this taxon the previously mentioned Ehringsdorf remains and those from the Saccopastore quarry a few kilometers from Rome, which are usually considered to belong to archaic *Homo sapiens*. Delimitation from 75,000 years includes forms that are already morphologically typical and coincides with the beginning of the Würm glaciation. The later dates, on the other hand, are clearer. The remains from Saint-Césaire near Grasse in Provence, discovered in 1969 but not dated till 1991, at present mark the appearance of the Neanderthal morphology, that are dated as being more recent (some 36,300 years old). The spatial delimitation is clear in the western area: the whole of Europe, including Great Britain, or at least the south of England, with Germany and Poland as the northern extreme. Towards the east, though, the area of distribution is difficult to define because of the scarce and scattered finds, stretching as far as the Teschik Tach site in Uzbekistan. In terms of distribution, the rich group of western Europe, the group of central Europe and the Asiatic remains, especially those concentrated in Israel, are usually distinguished.

What was life like for the first humans?

Reconstructing human evolution is a complex task, involving numerous disciplines, where team-work is becoming more and more important. The times when fossils were collected at random or bought in Chinese pharmacies (as in the case of various dental fragments from around Peking) are long gone. Nowadays, this is one of the most interdisciplinary areas of modern science, an area where physics and chemistry, as well as various biological, geological and social sciences, all play a part.

Scenes reconstructed from the cave of Talteüll [Christian Vioujard - Gamma / Flash Pres]

Palaeoanthropology, or the study of early man, is no longer only concerned with our ancestors' physical appearance. These days, attempts are being made to reconstruct their lifestyle and behavior, eating habits, the natural environment in which they lived, the conditions of life, illnesses, etc. The aim, then, is to build up a palaeoecological picture.

The reconstruction of the physical environment in which certain groups of early humans lived, can be achieved through different areas of study. For example, by analyzing sediments, it is possible to find out how much erosion there was at the time, and which is related to temperature and climatic conditions. The analysis and identification of pollen grains found in sediments gives us a picture of the vegetation that existed at the time, and this is also related to climatic conditions. Animal remains can also be good indicators of climatic conditions, as in the case of the typical cold climate fauna that populated Europe during the last glaciation.

We can get an idea of early man's diet from different and interesting types of evidence, such as the remains of animal bones, especially when they show signs of having been stripped of their flesh or of having been cooked (with signs of fire). The results, however, are not always clear, since it is sometimes difficult to distinguish signs of human activity in hoarding and handling bones from that of certain carrion species. It is also difficult to say how important meat consumption was, since plant remains are rarely preserved, yet we know from anthropo-cultural studies that vegetables played an important part in the diet of groups of hunter-gatherers. It is therefore necessary to resort to other types of evidence, such as dental wear, and particularly the kinds of mark found in the interior parts of dental fragments.

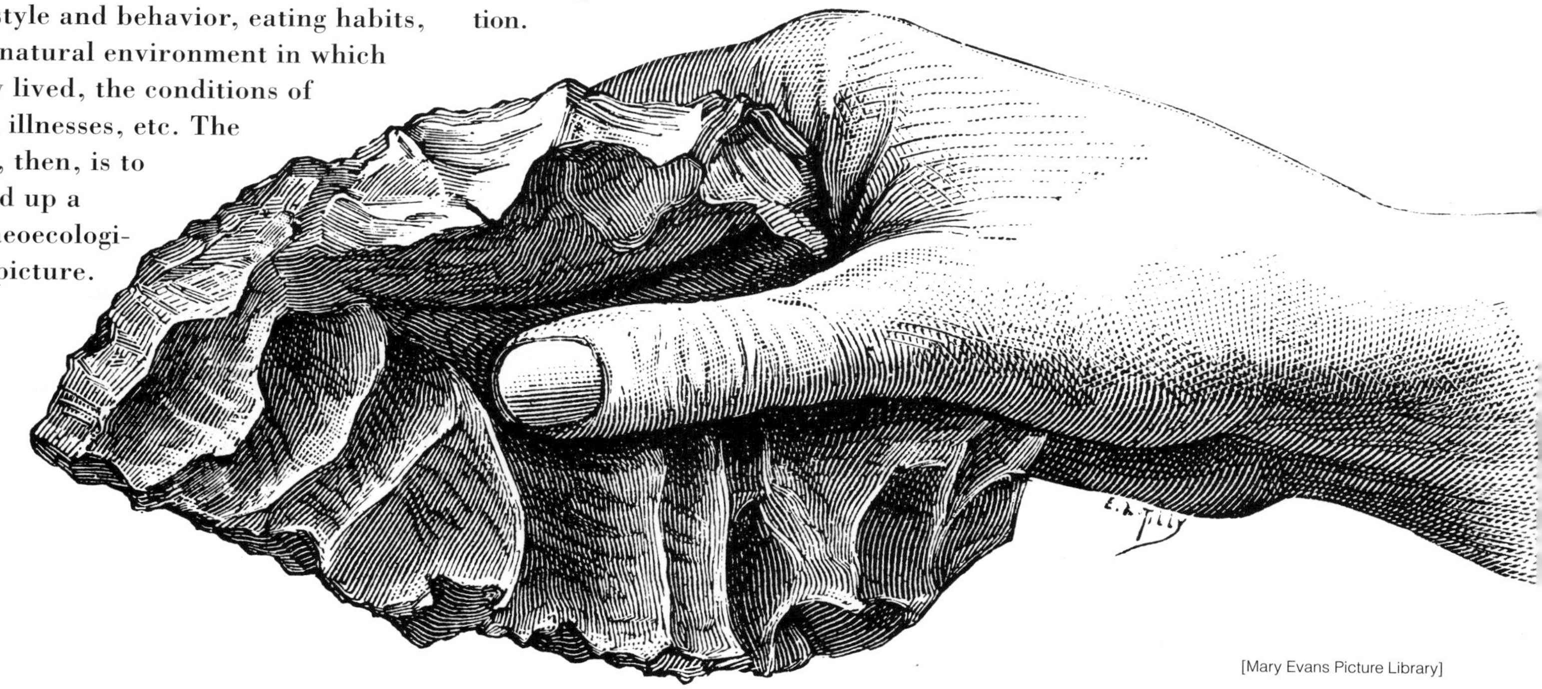

[Mary Evans Picture Library]

Scenes reconstructed from the cave of Talteüll [Christian Vioujard - Gamma / Flash Pres]

Different analyses of the quantities of very infrequent elements (called oligoelements: especially strontium, zinc or copper) contained in the bones have shown that the quantities varied considerably according to whether the diet of the individual was vegetable or animal, and even whether the meat was from land animals or sea animals. Taking known diets as a basis, attempts have been made to calculate the relative importance of meat in the diet as a whole. The results, however, are confused and have not really clarified the matter. Analysis of the amounts of the various isotopes of certain elements has more chance of success: by analyzing the amount of nitrogen-15 and carbon-13 it is not only possible to distinguish between carnivores and herbivores, it is also possible to say whether a particular carnivore ate fish or meat, and whether a particular herbivore ate grasses or woody plants. The nitrogen-15 content of carnivores is higher than that of herbivores, and, even more in carnivores that ate other carnivores, because the more common isotope is metabolized differently. The proportion of carbon isotopes is affected by the conditions in which a plant lived and by the type of photosynthesis.

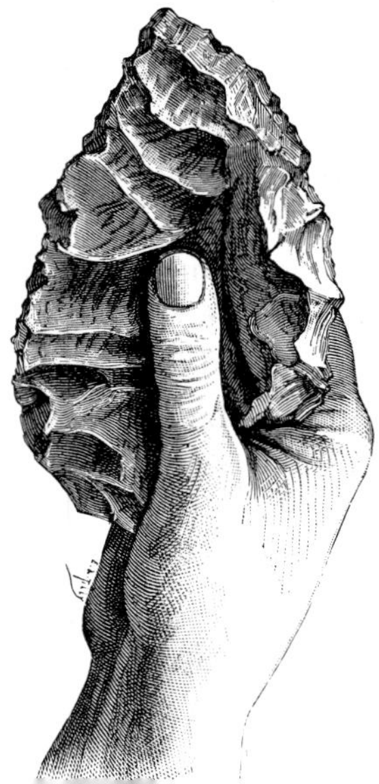

Scenes reconstructed from the cave of Talteüll [Christian Vioujard - Gamma / Flash Pres]

There are many demographic parameters involved in the structure and dynamics of a population. It is possible to estimate these parameters in early societies, from the number of individuals or population density, to details of birth-rate, migration and mortality. Any one of these parameters can give information about life style, social organization and sanitary conditions. Estimating the size of a population can be done in many different ways. For example, it is possible to get some idea of the size of a population by taking present-day societies with a similar economy as a point of reference (the usual comparison is with hunter-gatherer groups, as they were the only social model up until the beginning of the Neolithic Age). Approximate indications can be achieved using models based on the exploitation of resources and the carrying capacity of a particular ecosystem. Archaeological data also frequently allows more precise estimates to be made, on the basis of number and size of dwellings, food remains, number and kind of burials, etc.

Human life-span has changed throughout man's history. The point of departure for calculating life expectancy in the earliest societies is the estimation, based on bone remains, of the age of an individual at death. In the course of our lifetime various changes take place in our skeletons, especially successive welding of sutures between the bones, which allow us to estimate the age attained by an individual. By taking a representative sample of the population as a whole, it would be simple to calculate life expectancy, or other demographic parameters. In fact, however, estimations of an individual's age at death are imprecise, and the fossil remains in the majority of layers are on a slant, sometimes because adult skeletons are better preserved than those of children, and sometimes because burial rituals varied according to age. In fact, life expectancy did not increase noticeably throughout man's history until the coming of the industrial age. It should be noted that the great social changes which accompanied the beginning of food production in Neolithic times—greater food availability and greater population densities—were not accompanied by demographic changes at an individual level.

Magdalenian fauna and art

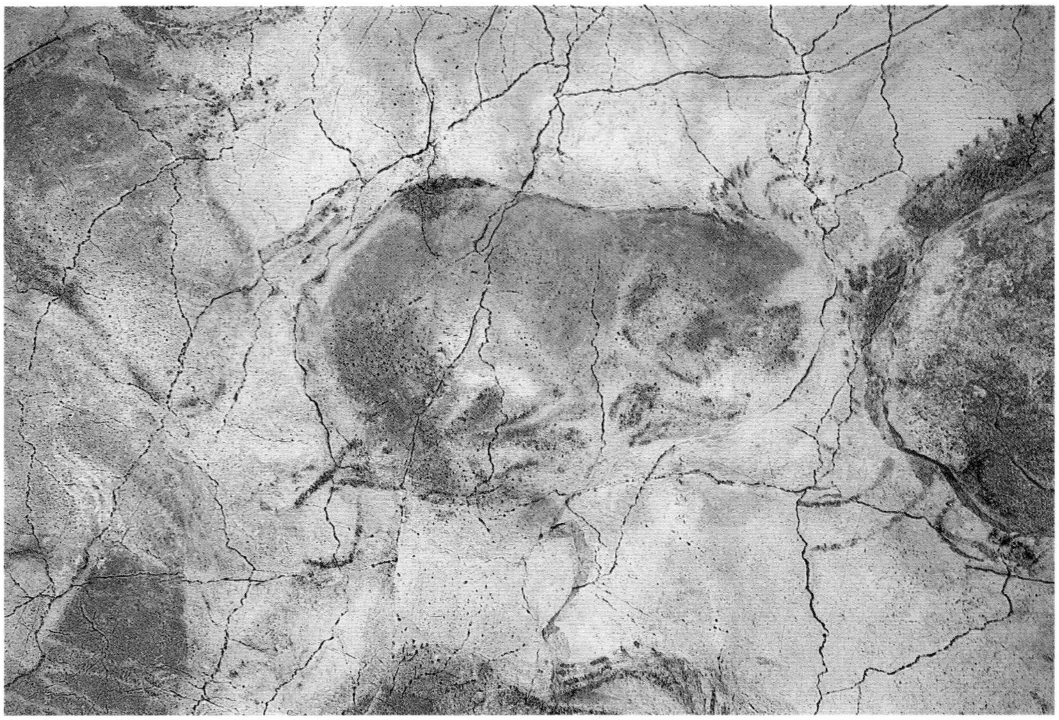

Bison, cave of Altamira [AISA]

When the ancestors of present-day man arrived in Europe, one of the innovations they brought with them was artistic expression. From the beginning of the upper Palaeolithic period, some 30,000 years ago, coinciding with the final millennia of the Würm Glacial Stage, man began to leave evidence of his ability to fashion symbols or images of the environment around him, although the Magdalenian period, which represents the culmination of Palaeolithic art, dates back to between 19,000 and 11,000 years ago, and, geographically, is almost exclusively confined to a relatively small area of southwest Europe.

The humans of the Upper Palaeolithic culture were hunting peoples, who produced characteristic artifacts (small-sized flint tools and all manner of implements, in particular harpoon tips and needles, making considerable use of reindeer bones and antlers), while at the same time regional and chronological variations can be noted. Shells and perforated stones—perhaps for personal adornment—marked with lines arranged in a sequence, or in a more or less regular order, represent the oldest expressions of plastic art. The earliest traces left by man, in several caves in Europe, can be dated back to as early as the beginnings of the Aurignacian culture, some 27,000 years ago: there were black and white outlines of human hands, drawings of geometric figures or outlines of animals drawn in the soft clay with a finger or stick, the edges of which were sometimes highlighted with a kind of pigment, and engravings in the rock of geometric or zoomorphic figures, which were also often highlighted by pigmentation. At the same time, a wide range of objects, from propellers to needles, including what appear to be buttons and maces, were decorated by their users with engravings, embossments and small sculptures, which were, increasingly, images of animals. Also belonging to this period of between 27,000 and 20,000 years ago are the small female figures known as "Venuses," often sculpted from reindeer antler or mammoth ivory, and whose sexual features are exaggeratedly enlarged, while the rest of the body is executed in a more schematic fashion (there are no facial characteristics, and the arms are mere outlines, often resting on enormous breasts, etc.). These have been discovered in many parts of Europe, from the Garonne (the Lespugue venus) to the Don (the Borodino and Kostenki-Borshevo venuses).

The paintings, engravings, reliefs, and sculptures left by Magdalenian man in dozens of caves in the Cantabrian Mountains, the Pyrenees, and in some of the neighboring areas, are truly astonishing. For the Magdalenian hunters did not confine themselves, as their forefathers had, to making utilitarian tools to enable them to fulfil their most basic needs, such as finding food, defending themselves from pillagers, and protecting themselves from the hostile cold in a Europe in the throes of the last great glacial period. They were also responsible for works of artistic expression, which strike us as impressive even today, despite the fact that their culture was so different, that many millennia separate us from them, and we find it difficult to grasp the full significance of the paintings, engravings and sculptures in the caves or of the small objects that they sculpted and decorated, so characteristic of their culture.

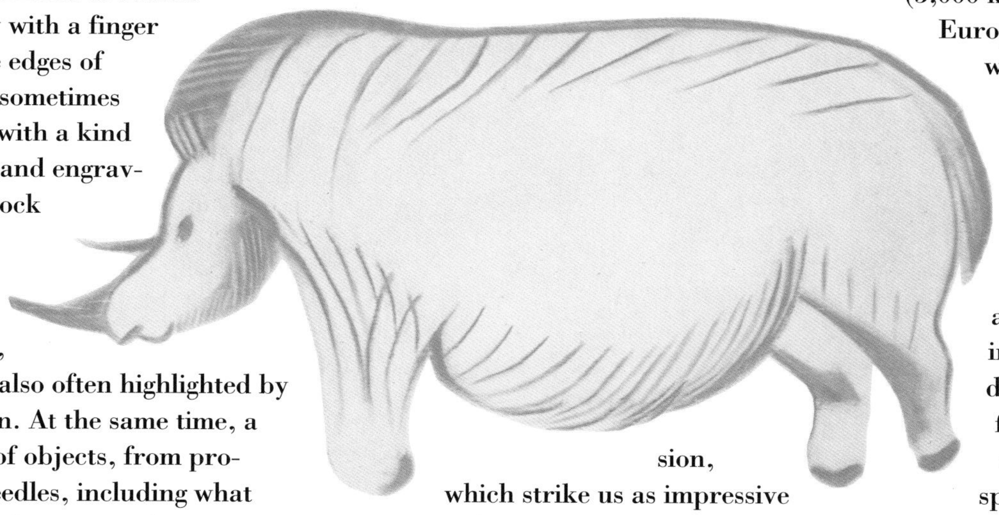

Rhinoceros, Dordogne [Coll. Musée de l'Homme]

It would appear that the Magdalenian hunters lived, during a period from 16,500 to 11,000 years ago, in a relatively limited area of western Europe, which included the length of the Atlantic seaboard free of ice at that time—the area from the Iberian Peninsula as far as Belgium and the south of Great Britain—, and in the hinterland extending from the Mediterranean coast of the Iberian Peninsula and of Occitania, to the Elbe basin. Caves with paintings are most densely concentrated in the area extending from Asturias, in the north of the Iberian Peninsula, to Périgord, in the west of Occitania, and from the old canton of Foix at the source of the Garonne in France. Further east, other hunting peoples of what was probably a Magdalenian-like culture hunted mainly mammoths, and built huts in the middle of the frozen steppes with the bones and skins of these animals. To the south of the Urals, in the Shulgan-Tash cave (better known by its Russian name, the Kapova cave), on the right bank of the river Belaya, at Bashkiriya, 3,107 mi (5,000 km) from the nearest western European cave, other humans, who were more or less contemporaries of the Magdalenians, also left evidence of artistic expression.

The fame of Magdalenian art is mainly due to the painted figures of animals, which are almost all extinct today. These images are often so realistic, drawn in such detail and so faithfully portrayed, that it is extremely easy to identify the species depicted: bison in Altamira, horses and bulls in Las Caux, deer, mammoths, woolly rhinoceroses, reindeer, goats and even birds in several caves. Magdalenian man has left us evidence of the fauna, which he himself helped to wipe out, completing the work of Neanderthal man before him, and adding to the effects of the climatic changes of the final glacial stage on animals that had adapted to habitats, only to see them progressively change until they were completely transformed. The mammoth, which for millennia had suffered the attacks of Neanderthal hunters, and had been driven north by the climatic changes, is only depicted in one Iberian cave (at Castillo, in Cantabria, where it has been possible to date positively two Magdalenian paintings to 13,060 ± 200 and 12,910 ± 180). Even so, objects of mammoth ivory and remains of this animal appear up until almost the beginning of the Neolithic period in more northerly locations, such as the open-air site at Gönnersdorf, near Koblenz, in the Rhineland. Here, mammoth remains have been found, dating 11,000-12,000 years ago as well as engravings in slate of the animal, which became extinct in Eurasia some 10,000 years ago (the most recent remains, found at Kunda, in Estonia, date back to 9,780 ± 260 years ago). At Shulgan-Tash there also appear various drawings of mammoths, together with horses and woolly rhinoceroses.

It is curious to observe that the reindeer is not among the animals most featured in Magdalenian wall paintings, since it was clearly an important natural resource for the Magdalenian culture; as well as its meat, use was made of its bones and antlers, and probably of its skin as well, and thus it appears to be the animal that was most hunted and sought after by Magdalenian man. For this reason, the initial interpretation of the

Horse, cave of Las Caus or Lascaux [Shelly Grossman /AGE Fotostock]

Bison, cave of Altamira [Ann Ronan at Image Select]

cave paintings by Henri Breuil (1887-1961), who suggested that they represented an invocation of a magic or religious nature, made in order to secure a successful hunt, is by and large rejected today, and even though this theory is not ruled out, it is more widely thought that it could be linked with a facet of the social structure of the peoples, among whom this form of artistic expression developed. Today, although it has not become totally extinct, the reindeer lives in regions that are markedly different from those it used to cohabit with Magdalenian hunters, since during the glacial periods the northern regions, where it now lives, were occupied by the Arctic polar cap.

More frequently drawings have been found of other large herbivores, which were abundant in Europe at that time, but which are now rare or already extinct, such as bison (only to be found today as a few populations in Poland and Byelorussia, and in zoos), horses (apart from domesticated horses, only a few groups of these survive in Mongolia), bulls (of which only domesticated breeds survive), and deer (it would appear that the giant deer *Megaloceros giganteus*, which is probably the animal depicted by the Magdalenian painters, became extinct during the Middle Ages in Ireland, where it had taken final refuge). Occasionally woolly rhinoceroses appear in the Magdalenian paintings (these probably became extinct between 14,000 and 12,000 years ago, although some sources believe that a few remaining groups survived in the Ukraine and in south Russia up until 3,000 years ago), and, more rarely, carnivores such as bears and felines are found. Very occasionally there are images of birds and fish.

In contrast with the faithful and detailed portrayal of the animal figures, human figures appear much less frequently, and are treated in a much more schematic fashion by Magdalenian painters: examples are the black and white outlines of hands, engravings of human heads, and the so-called "sorcerer" of the Lo Tuc d'Audobert cave, in the old canton of Foix. These drawings depicting human subjects never reach the degree of expressiveness achieved by the famous venuses that preceded them.

3.3 The expansion of humanity: present day Homo sapiens

The origin of modern humans

Mankind took a great leap forward in the Upper Paleolithic. At this time humans began to dominate the Earth.

Viewed as a whole, the men of the Upper Paleolithic were great hunters. Because of the partial thawing of the ice, game was abundant all over the tundra and the steppes of Eurasia. Hunting technology was well developed. Innovations appeared, especially in the last period of the Upper Paleolithic, the Magdalenian, including a device for throwing spears with great force, harpoons for fishing, and the bow and arrow, which had great power, precision, and range. Stone tools existed in great variety and were made with great precision and beauty.

The Upper Paleolithic was also a great period of art. Cave paintings, especially in the Cantabrian region and on the northern slopes of the Pyrenees, and human sculptures, called "Venuses," are the most outstanding examples. They are of great technical perfection, aesthetic sense, and a strong symbolic force which, when interpreted, speaks of beliefs, myths, and religion.

There is no doubt that these Paleolithic men were already full and proper *Homo sapiens sapiens*. Their exact origin and their relationship to Neanderthal man or other previous forms is not at all clear. Several hypotheses have been put forward to explain them.

The "out of Africa" hypothesis

The oldest remains which display modern characteristics are to be found in Africa. This fact has given rise to the hypothesis, within the substitution model, of the African origin of modern humans (called the "out of Africa hypothesis"). Anthropologists focus on two sites in South Africa: the Klasies River Mouth cave, on the southern coast of Cape Province and the Border Cave, in N. E. Natal, near the border with Ngwame (Swaziland). Both are dated as over 100,000 years old and show modern morphologies, especially to the absence of the supraorbital arch, the general shape of the skull, the presence of the chin, etc. Whatever the case, critics claim that the first site has produced few remains to confirm its assignation and as for the second, although indisputable at a morphological level, the dating is not definitive. They are, however, key pieces of a global explanation and their position as the first modern forms is accepted by most scholars.

Fossils from other parts of Africa have recently been reinterpreted as bearers of modern morphological characteristics. Thus the skull of Omo in Ethiopia and the remains at Jebel Irhoud in Morocco seem to belong

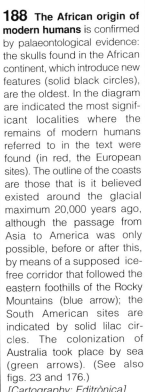

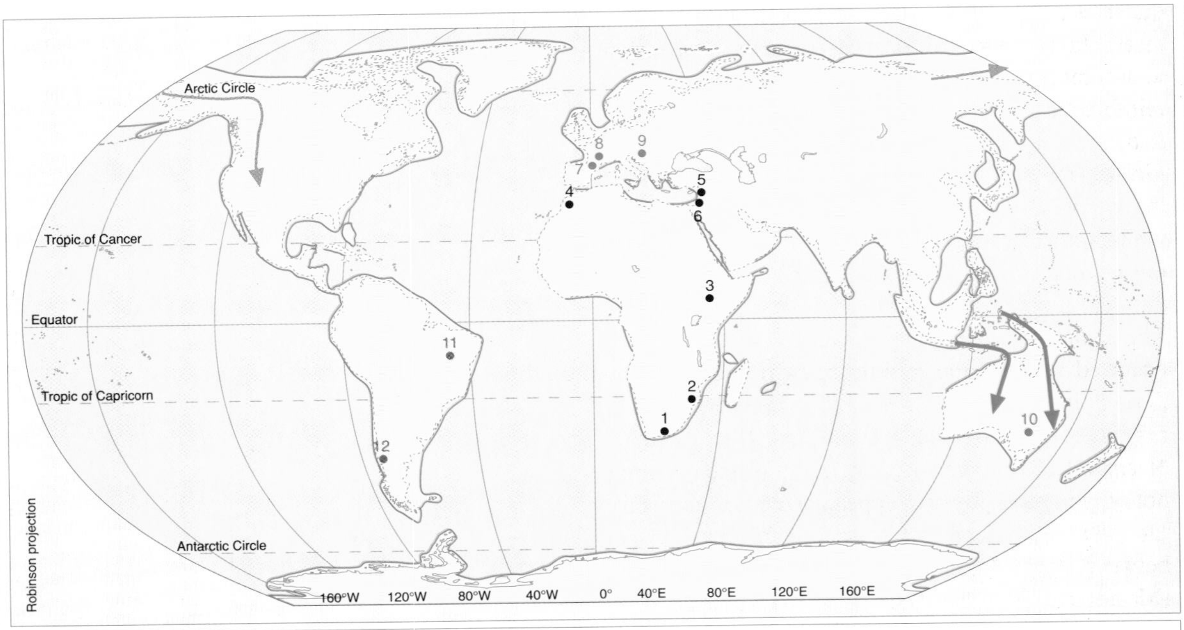

188 The African origin of modern humans is confirmed by palaeontological evidence: the skulls found in the African continent, which introduce new features (solid black circles), are the oldest. In the diagram are indicated the most significant localities where the remains of modern humans referred to in the text were found (in red, the European sites). The outline of the coasts are those that is it believed existed around the glacial maximum 20,000 years ago, although the passage from Asia to America was only possible, before or after this, by means of a supposed ice-free corridor that followed the eastern foothills of the Rocky Mountains (blue arrow); the South American sites are indicated by solid lilac circles. The colonization of Australia took place by sea (green arrows). (See also figs. 23 and 176.) *[Cartography: Editrònica]*

1 Klasies River Mouth, Cape Province
2 Border Cave, Natal
3 Omo, Ethiopia
4 Jebel Irhoud, Morocco
5 Skhul, Israel
6 Qafzeh, Israel
7 l'Arbreda, Catalonia
8 Cròs Manhon, Occitania
9 Vindija, Croatia
10 Lake Mungo, New South Wales
11 Pedra Furada, Piaui, Brazil
12 Monte Verde, Chile

to the same morphological line. If this interpretation is correct, the oldest remains of modern humans would be the African ones, possibly forming the basis and origin of all modern populations. From Africa there would have been an expansion to the Middle East, from where they would have spread towards Asia and Europe. In fact, the oldest non-European remains with modern characteristics are to be found in the Middle East and are more recent than the African ones.

Two sites, which have been known for some time now, have provided the most important remains: Jebel Qafzeh (normally referred to as Qafzeh) and Mugharet es-Skhul (referred to as Skhul—the best known skull is Skhul V), both in Israel. The morphology of the different individuals from these sites show, together with a considerable robustness, indisputably modern characteristics. In fact, for a time it was suggested that these forms could be the ancestors of modern European humans, and that they could have evolved from the Neanderthals from the same region. But later revisions of the datings have placed them earlier than the Neanderthals: between 90,000 and 100,000 years ago. There is, therefore, no evolution in the same place: on the other hand, there is the possibility that they could be modern forms which had emigrated from Africa before expanding into the world.

Lately a whole new kind of evidence has provided us with new data, the molecular anthropology. Several different types of molecular data (especially gene frequencies and sequences of mitochondrial DNA) have clearly favored the African origin model and the genetic differences between present day human populations reinforce the idea of a relatively short time of diversification, in accordance with the proposed African origin of modern populations and their expansion throughout the world, replacing previous populations. On the other hand, this does not support the idea that present populations have very ancient origins.

The apparent discontinuity, or sudden change, which occurred between the Middle and Upper Paleolithic Periods in Europe, and above all in western Europe, reinforces the theory that modern humans replaced the Neanderthals relatively rapidly. This change occurred not only in their physical appearance but in their culture too. It is clear that there is a sudden change between the technologies of the Middle Paleolithic (Mousterian, associated with the Neanderthals) and the first Upper Paleolithic technologies (Aurignacian, normally associated with modern humans). At l'Arbreda (Serinyà, near Girona, in northeastern Catalonia), for example, a detailed analysis of the site has enabled us to detect a rapid transition, dated some 40,000 years ago, a very old date and one which in other areas is still in the middle of the Middle Paleolithic, and with clearly Neanderthal remains.

The remains of modern humans from the Upper Paleolithic period in western Europe are numerous. Discovered a long time ago, they gave rise to the

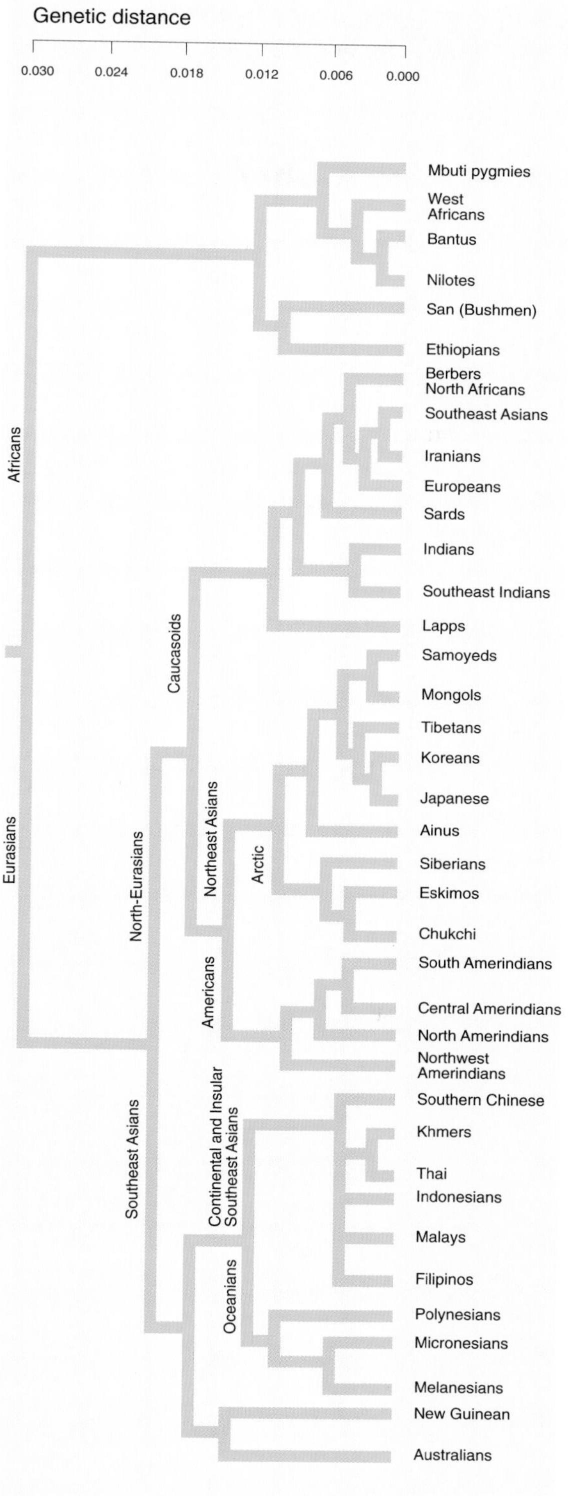

189 The genetic distances between different human populations are an accurate reflection of the past periods when they separated, and indicates their relationships. By studying their distribution one can prepare a genealogical tree that illustrates the distribution of humans on the planet. It is not surprising that many similarities are found between the distribution of the genes and the geographical distribution of languages.
[Diagram: Biopunt, from Cavalli-Sforza, 1992]

description of the so-called Cro-Magnon man, a nomenclature to be avoided as it only creates confusion. In fact the remains at the site of Cro-Magnon, in the Occitan village of Les-Eyzies-de Tayac, in the Dordogne, southwestern France, have been long considered as the prototype of the modern humans in Europe, but in fact there is a great diversity within their undoubtedly modern characteristics, and also the fossils are not very old, some 25,000 years, and are therefore much more recent than the transition. In central and eastern Europe the remains are much more hotly disputed: in some sites like Vindija and Velika Pecina in Croatia, there are individuals with modern characteristics but at the same time a robustness and other traits which remind one of Neanderthal man and which have led some authors to propose an evolution *in situ* rather than a substitution of Neanderthals by modern humans.

The multicentric or regional continuity hypothesis

The appearance of modern forms would have taken place independently in various different places according to the multicentric or regional continuity hypothesis which asserts that since the *Homo erectus* phase there has been a continual evolution at least in Africa, Europe and Asia. Promoters of this theory claim that, after the diversification of *Homo erectus* through natural selection and genetic drift due to reduced populations, migrations must have caused parallel evolution through selection and gene flow between populations. In fact it is in the Asiatic continent, especially the southeast, and Australia, where one can speak of a certain morphological continuity from old to modern forms, with examples of transition. There are, though, many opposing arguments, like for example the great morphological diversity of the first Australians which display characteristics absent in the ancient forms from Java but present in the modern African forms. On the other hand, there are no fossils anywhere which clearly indicate a transition, but we can speak about a substitution in some places. Finally, if the multicentric hypothesis were correct, there would have to have been a constant speed of evolution in several different places which does not, in fact, happen, on the other hand we can observe a step-like appearance of modern forms the further we get away from Africa.

Expansion and colonization of new lands

All these core populations of modern humans, whether they came out of or were implanted in Africa and Eurasia showed an enormous expansion in the last few millennia. The whole world has been occupied by humans, but we must not forget that they did not set foot in many areas until very recent times. This is the case with Australia, the islands in the ocean off the northern coast of Eurasia itself, and, extraordinarily, of the entire continent of America.

The complete occupation of Eurasia

The complete occupation of Eurasia came about with the settlement of the inhospitable lands of Siberia. It seems that this was not achieved until some 35,000 years ago. There are several fossil beds in the valley of the River Lena and an indirect proof of this is the population of Japan, which took place some 30,000 or more years ago, probably via the lands which joined the most important islands with southeastern Siberia during the last glaciation.

The colonization of Australia

The population of Australia dates back at least 33,000 years and probably some 40,000, which shows that technology was sufficiently advanced then to allow travel by sea. Even though the Indonesian islands were joined to Asia during the glaciations, Australia was separated by sea. Even making use of the intermediary islands, it must have been necessary to cover journeys of 19 mi (30 km) and at least one of 56 mi (90 km), distances which required a considerable technological level of development. The entrance was probably made via the northwest,nearest to New Guinea, and first of all they must have occupied the coasts. The whole of the territory, though, was apparently occupied about 20,000 or 25,000 years ago. The oldest human remains in Australia are those from Lake Mungo, in the southeast, dating from between 26,000 and 30,000 years ago. Their morphology is similar to earlier remains from southeast Asia but is different from that of Australian aborigines of recent times but which can be seen in more recent fossil remains. The colonization of Australia was probably a complex process of different arrivals and extinctions of groups. For example, the arrival of the dingo, a semi-domesticated dog closely linked with the aborigines, took place between 3,000 and 4,000 years ago. The numerous extinctions of marsupial mammals seems closely linked to the activities of man as predator.

The population process in America

The population of America is one of the great bones of contention. Although it is recognised that it took place via what is today the Bering Strait and, consequently from Asiatic populations, the dating of the first arrival is controversial. A generalized occupation 12,000 years ago is fully accepted, but the earlier datings, some of around 40,000 years, are doubtful. During the last glaciation a bridge of terra firma, more than 621 mi (1,000 km) wide, joined Alaska

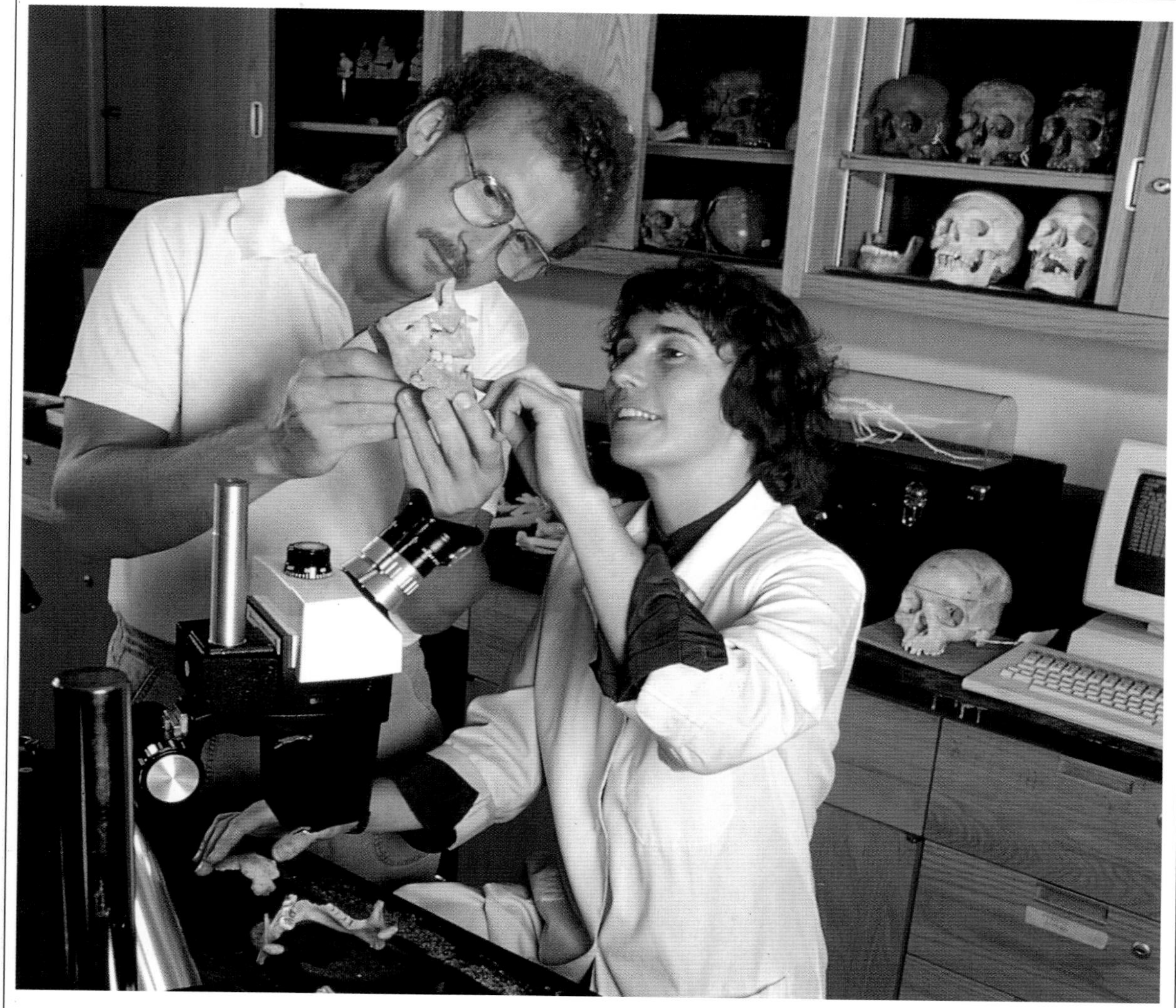

190 Current palaeontological and anthropological research studies, which can never be exact, of the characteristics of the various human groups. The correct classification of the variation within *Homo sapiens* only helps us understand the evolutionary history of these populations, but it in no way attempts to establish hierarchies. Existing hierarchies are already completely obsolete because of the knowledge we have, since the morphological differences observed within the human species are no more than adaptations that appeared as the different groups became established in different geographical regions. Thus scientists consider, for instance, that the discrimination of different human groups because of their pigmentation is a sign of ignorance, since this is no more than an adaptation to strong solar radiation—a characteristic color that is determined by only a few genes. Modern classifications of the various racial lines is based on more concrete points (such as protein polymorphism or DNA fragment's, etc.), which can give much more precise information about human migrations. *[Photo: AGE Fotostock]*

and Siberia and could have facilitated the passage. The problem is, however, the occupation of the more southern lands, as a large shell of ice covered what is today Canada. It has been suggested that if the penetration occurred 25,000 years ago or more, a narrow corridor could have been followed which was not iced over and separated the two great ice plates of eastern Canada. But the passage was quite impossible at the peak of the glaciation, between 25,000 and 14,000 years ago. Between the two proposals, there is a great time gap and at the moment there is a lack of consensus as to the acceptance or rejection of the supposedly oldest cases, like for example, some sites in Brazil (grotto of Pedra Furada, to the south of Piauí State) or Chile (Monte Verde, in the valley of the River Maullin, Los Lagos Province). If the later date is correct, the expansion must have taken place very quickly as the very southern sites have datings very similar to the ones in the north. Whatever the case, the speed of expansion seems compatible with the mobility associated with groups of great hunters and they could have traveled from one end of the continent to the other in a few thousand years.

The impact of man's arrival in America, or at least of the clear expansion which we can observe between 12,000 and 10,000 years ago, manifests itself in the massive extinction of large mammals. Even though this coincides with the climatic change at the end of the last glaciation, it all makes one think that direct human action in the form of hunting played an important part. In fact, the hunting capacity and in general the capacity of populations of the Upper Paleolithic to adapt made their action felt powerfully in terms of the extinction of species everywhere, but large areas of America seem to represent the clearest example known.

The diversification of the present human species

Just as the first step on the path of human evolution presents certain difficulties and needs justification, so the end is difficult to delimit or specify. After having seen the appearance of the modern forms, directly related to present day human populations, and their

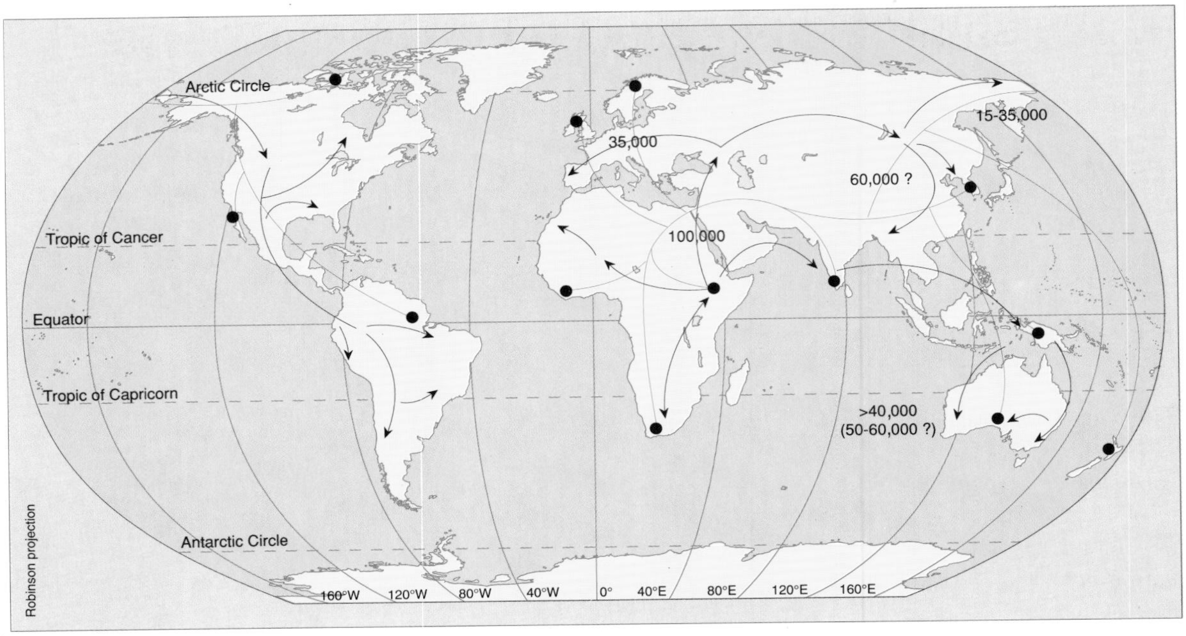

191 Genes, rocks, and languages all tell a similar story. The enormous diversity of human populations on the planet's surface is a reflection of events that took place in the past, when modern humans settled in various places, which they had to colonize, and began to differentiate themselves from each other. Humans, however, did not just carry with them their genetic features, but they also left major cultural impacts. This cultural factor, transmitted exosomatically, can provide a great deal of information about the origin of each person. One of the non-genetic features that is most characteristic of humans is language. Study shows that the distribution of language is totally comparable to that of the genes (except in a few cases in which there has been a language substitution without genetic penetration, or vice versa), since when *Homo sapiens* colonized the planet, they carried their language with them. This information allowed the elaboration of a first genealogical tree which, projected on the map of the world (red pathways), explains the routes followed by the first modern humans after their departure from Africa. The black dots correspond to present day populations. Recent studies appear to show that there were two migration routes from Africa to Asia (black pathways). The chronological estimates are based on archaeological evidence. *[Diagram: Editrònica, after Cavalli-Sforza, 1992]*

expansion over the Earth, we can now consider the description complete. But we cannot be truly satisfied until we have traced the evolution with more precision, and not just on the level of species but also of human groups, whether we call them *races* or simply peoples.

The problem is that in seeking to understand the history of a human group in detail we encounter an immense complexity as we examine its formation, its relationship to other groups, and its migrations, mixtures and adaptations. Furthermore, to these strictly anthropological considerations have to be added many cultural factors and the phenomenon (which is also cultural when all is said and done) of the continuous mixings of races or populations that have taken place over the last few centuries, or even the last few decades. Faced with all this, the physical anthropologist resorts to other tools, such as population genetics, in order to acquire a more precise frame of reference. But in order to acquire an overall view, still more tools must be employed, such as the study of history and prehistory, or historical linguistics, in order to acquire a coherent and precise picture.

In any case, modern physical anthropology bases itself on the study of genetic and biochemical phenomena and tends to ascribe much less importance to such anatomical or morphological features of populations as pigmentation or facial features. In other words, it reduces the importance of elements that were once taken to be decisive in determining the so-called races of mankind. The very concept of race has undergone a crisis among physical anthropologists and become obsolete due to the objective impossibility of applying it to the populations of a species such as our own, in which inbreeding populations are exceptional, while migrations and the intermingling of genes from one side of the globe to the other are frequent. As Johann Gottfried von Herder wrote in 1784: "The term race refers to a non-existent original difference [...]; in a word, there are not four, nor five, human races, and nor are there exclusive varieties [...]; physical types interpenetrate and hereditary traits continue and in the end they are no more than the shadows of a great mirage that extend over all the ages and all the continents; they belong less to a system of natural history than to a physical and geographical history of humankind." Today, only the proponents of narrow racist ideologies place any importance on skin color as a totally unjustified means of determining substantially different human groups. It is historically undeniable that, humans have established a long series of judgements and prejudices concerning their physical reality, from the belief that "negroes had no souls" (i.e., that they did not belong to the human species) in the epoch of slavery, or the racial hierarchies of the Nazis, to the way modern anthropologists have practically thrown out the concept of race, passing through the classification of mankind into black, white, and yellow races, or other more elaborate schemes (sometimes based on ethnological criteria). However, advances in scientific knowledge have established only one piece of incontestable evidence: that there were different species of men in the remote past, but at the moment (and this moment stretches back at least 40,000 years) there is only one, but with morphological features which are very similar although not identical, since the genetic characteristics of its populations varies geographically.

4. The anthropic modification of the biosphere

4.1 The gradual control of food production

The impact of primitive human species on their environment must have been scarcely noticeable. In any case, it would have been no greater than that of other primates. With the passage of time and the development of cultural activity, however, this situation began to change. The basic motive behind the attempt to master the physical environment was naturally the need to acquire sufficient food. In order to guarantee this, man first engaged in hunting and gathering, and then went on to agriculture and cattle-breeding.

Of course, they also improved their living quarters and clothing, especially as forced on by necessity, they colonized lands with hostile climates. All this was led to environmental changes with the passage of time and as his ability to transform it increased. In short, humans have shaped the landscape of the biosphere in accordance with their own needs.

The attitude of primitive humans

Apart from the extinctions of a few large mammals, to which his hunting contributed, ice-age humans exercised very little control over the natural systems in which they lived. Their role was scarcely different from that of other animals with similar eating habits or mobility. However, their ability to reason and transmit culture, or to make weapons and other simple or sophisticated tools, did indeed give them an advantage over the animals which might prey on him or compete with them for food, and made it easier to capture prey or to locate the plants they fed on.

The capacity of Paleolithic humans to shape the environment and control its energy sources and production were still very limited, but they grew over the course of time due to this capacity to conserve and transmit information which was for individual and collective survival, from one individual to another or one generation to another. At certain stages of human history, however, it seems that the

192 Until the domestication of plants and animals, the impact of humans on the environment did not begin to differ much from that of other powerful predators. The selective use of fire to promote the growth of herbaceous species attractive to the herbivores they hunted, or the bulbous plants they consumed directly, was probably the action of the populations of Palaeolithic hunter-gatherers who had the impact on the environment. But the domestication of plants and animals has been one of the principal cultural achievements of humans, and has significantly affected all subsequent history. The photograph shows some Egyptian agricultural workers as represented in the tomb of Nakht, 15 century B.C., in the necropolis of Sayh Abd-al-Qurna, near Luxor.
[Photo: E. Lessing / Zardoya]

193 In Jericho the oldest known traces of an urban civilization have been found. Around some modest adobe constructions, the oldest of which dates back more than 10,000 years, a society with a centralized political organization constructed stone walls, about 10,000 years ago. The excavations, of which the photograph shows the remains of a tower, have revealed a city of some four hectares in size, which could have sheltered a population of 2,000. At the time of its construction, the inhabitants of Jericho already knew about agriculture: at least they cultivated emmer wheat (*Triticum dicoccum*) and two-rowed barley (*Hordeum distichum*), but they did not have domesticated animals, apart from dogs, and they did not know about pottery. *[Photo: Zev Radovan, Jerusalem]*

stock of accumulated information became particularly fertile and introduced significant modifications into the human's way of life. These modifications went further than the simple maintenance or growth of the population, since they transformed the relationship of the human species with all other living creatures—with the entire biosphere—and humans acquired a growing control over the sources of nutrition, energy or information to their own benefit.

Most of the principal transformations brought about by this growing capacity of humans to control their environment can be summed up in three revolutions, two in the past and one that we are living through right now. These are the three "cultural revolutions" that have changed the face of the earth: the Neolithic revolution, the industrial revolution, and the information revolution.

The Neolithic revolution

The Australian archaeologist Vere Gordon Childe, in his book *The Dawn of European Civilization* published in 1925, coined the phrase "Neolithic revolution" to describe the whole series of changes (the making of pottery, and yarns and cloth from animal or vegetable fibres, weapons and vases out of polished stone, etc.) which came to light in the cultural material of human peoples in a period around some 10,000 years ago. This series of changes is associated with a no-less-important change in their relationship with their environment. Basically, the change was a move from gathering plant products to cultivating plants deliberately, and to rearing and feeding certain animals specifically for human consumption, or to use their strength to perform tasks which were too strenuous for man instead of just hunting them for their meat and skins.

The vision that we have today of the techno-ecological changes related to the domestication of plants and animals is much more detailed than when Gordon Childe first spoke of the "Neolithic revolution." However, this expression has survived in as far as it refers to a radical change in the ways of life even though, as we shall see, it did not happen either as rapidly as he thought, in the same way nor at the same time in all places where it did occur. Gordon Childe's teleological and self-satisfied vision of the dominant culture of the age (which is also that of today, if only in the developed world) and the direction it was leading in tended towards a facile acceptance of all the transformations that have gone to form the modern world (which was globally evaluated as positive) as a "natural" evolution, but in practice it is difficult to perceive the direct initial advantage of an economy based on the domestication of plants and animals over one based on hunting and gathering. Some anthropologists even consider that the mythical golden age that many cultures place in a remote past, in fact corresponds to

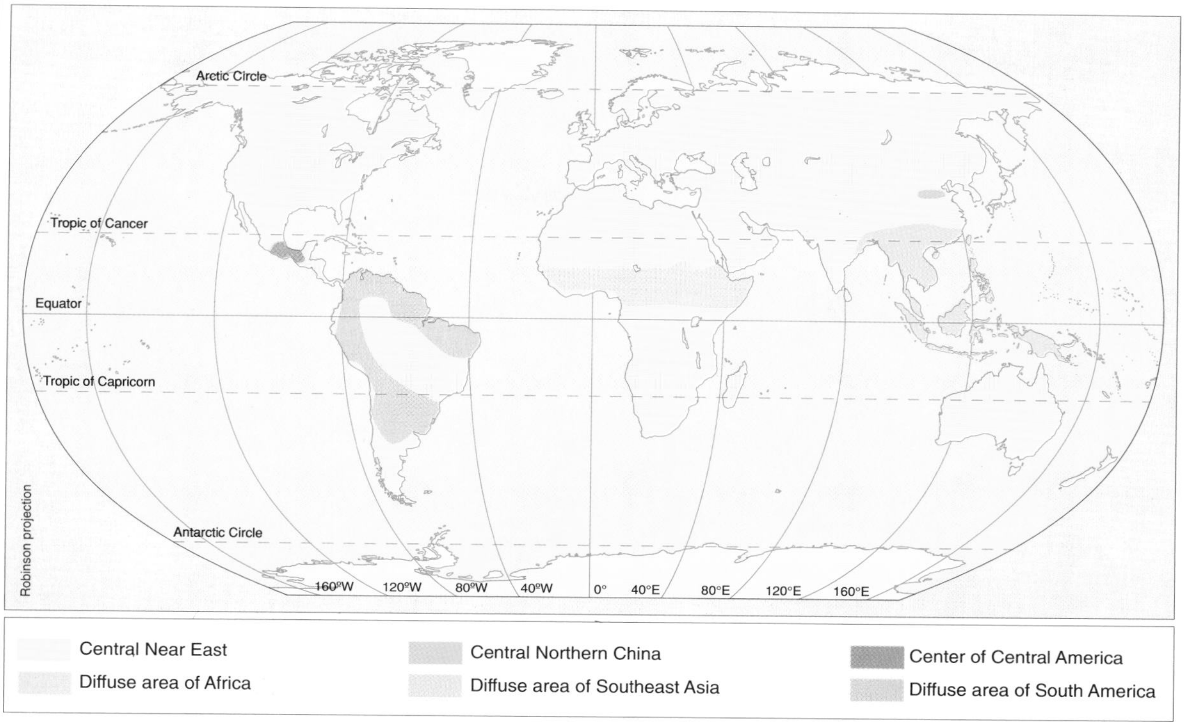

194 In 1926, the hypothesis was formulated that there existed a restricted number of centers of origin from which the majority of cultivated plants originated. Based on intraspecific diversity, the occurrence of wild forms of cultivated plants, and on known archaeological evidence, eight centers of origin of cultivated plants were proposed. Today, after further study of this topic, scientists tend to agree that some of these centers of origin are, not just of domesticated plants, but of agricultural complexes that were later very successful. On the other hand, many cultivated plants originated in areas that do not correspond to these centers. The hypothesis commonly accepted today is one proposed in 1971 of three double systems. Each with a center of origin and an area of spread of domestication (a non-center). Between the centers of origin and the associated areas of diffusion of domestication in each system, there must have been some stimulation and feedback until the later most widespread agricultural complexes crystallized in the recognized centers. *[Diagram: Editrònica, from Harlan 1987]*

the period before the introduction of agriculture when the acquisition of food by small groups of hunter-gatherers was far simpler and more agreeable, provided, of course, that they had access to an area particularly rich in resources or could migrate regularly in search of them. This is how pre-Neolithic society has come to be described as the first society of plenty.

Whether or not the domestication of plants and animals was "necessary" for the survival of some of the growing human populations 10,000 years ago, the birth of agriculture and the consequent adoption of a sedentary way of life of those populations is paralleled by demographic growth, which, although gradual and oscillating, is can clearly be seen in the archaeological record. Success in controlling the deliberate production of food (i.e., the modification of certain natural systems to favour the multiplication of certain species producing food suitable for man, and selection within these species of the varieties that would make production more secure and abundant) implied a growth in population.

The areas recognised as the centers of origin of the majority of cultivated plants are, to a certain extent, "preadapted" for exploitation. They are areas occupied by ecosystems exposed to a certain degree of destruction or exploitation by external agents in such a way that during long periods of time, before the intervention of the first farmers, there was no selection pressure which favored anything that which improved the capacity to replace damaged parts or to adjust to important fluctuations in environmental factors. This would be the case, for example, of the savannahs or prairies or, in the sea, areas where there is a rich eruption of life. The fluctuating climate, marked seasonality, the presence of large numbers of important herbivores, and more or less periodic fires would have been determining factors of the start of a more intensive and deliberate exploitation of the plant resources on the part of humans. In intertropical areas, with a more regular climate and more constant production, Neolithic agriculture was only able to develop in high altitude zones or in river bank ecosystems with naturally or artificial fluctuating water levels. Otherwise, as we shall see, the introduction of farming techniques in these areas has generally been much more recent than in those areas with a more variable climate.

The first domesticated animals and plants

Today it is generally admitted that the first attempts at plant and animal domestication preceded by many millennia the technical innovations normally associated with it and that in reality there have probably been many hunter-gatherer peoples which have in some way favored the reproduction and propagation of some of the plants which they used for food or which they valued for other reasons. This is how it was done by different groups of hunter-gatherers who have preserved their ways of life until today or at least until recent times, like, for example, many Australian tribes of aborigines.

195 These Indian women in the San Joaquin Valley of California, are probably from the Yurok tribe; they gathered the seeds of some species of wild grass even in the middle of the last century, using techniques that are probably no different from those used by the inhabitants of the Fertile Crescent in the centuries that preceded the domestication of wheat, barley, and other cereals. The engraving comes from the book by H.R. Schoolcraft *Indian tribes of the United States* published in 1865. *[Photo: The Library of Congress]*

In this way, when the Walmbaria women of the Flinders Islands off the northeast coast of Queensland, pull up yam roots, they always cut the top off, replant it and then urinate on it while uttering an invocation so that they may grow more and provide more food the next time. Similar procedures are known among the women in other Australian tribes (historically, harvesting has always been a woman's job in hunter-gatherer societies).

Some hunter-gatherer peoples like the Karuk from northern California grew and harvested different species of tobacco (*Nicotiana bigelovii, Nicotiana atenuata*) and had considerable knowledge of the morphology and physiology of the reproduction of these plants. In fact they invested a great deal of effort in the farming of these plants (and in no others) and employed very complex techniques including fertilizing the farming land with ashes, selecting seeds for sowing, then planting them, weeding the land and choosing varieties according to the quality of the final product, which clearly was not a food but a stimulant used in various leisure activities and ceremonies.

In the case of cereals, the basic crops of Neolithic farmers, it seems that before they became used deliberately as crops they had already been exploited in a selective way in different parts in the areas where they grew spontaneously. The Ojibwa Indians from north-west Wisconsin were still doing this in the 20th century with wild rice (*Zizania aquatica*) as were the Australian Iliaura tribe just over 50 years ago on the Macdonald Downs in central Australia, with a species of millet (*Panicum*), which they called *otteta*, and from which they obtained flour using rudimentary manual stone grinders.

As for the domestication of animals, the primacy of the dog (*Canis familiaris*) is indisputable. They had already been the companion and hunting aid for Palaeolithic humans and there is no present-day or recent hunter-gatherer people that has not kept domesticated dogs. It is more difficult to arrive at a date for its domestication but the oldest remains of domesticated dogs which have been found together with other traces of Palaeolithic humans could be dated around 14,000 years ago in the Old World (in Palegawra, Kurdistan) and around 12,000 in the New World (at Jaguar Cave, Idaho, in the northwest of the United States). But the real innovation associated with the Neolithic revolution is the domestication of livestock for human consumption and for work. Even then we cannot totally exclude the dog, which was an important source of food in some areas of America, and still is used as a draft animal in Arctic regions and in some Amerindian cultures.

Livestock and cereals in the Fertile Crescent

The oldest clear indications of the domestication of livestock that are known are no older than 9,500 years and correspond to fossil remains found at various sites in the Fertile Crescent (an arc of highlands, which stretches from the banks of the River Jordan to the Zagros chain, passing through the mountains of Kurdistan and surrounding the western, northern and northeastern sides of the basins of the Tigris and Euphrates—in other words, Mesopotamia). Some possibly older traces have been found at localities like Zawi Chemi Shanidar in Kurdistan, where the proportion of sheep and goat bones of different ages

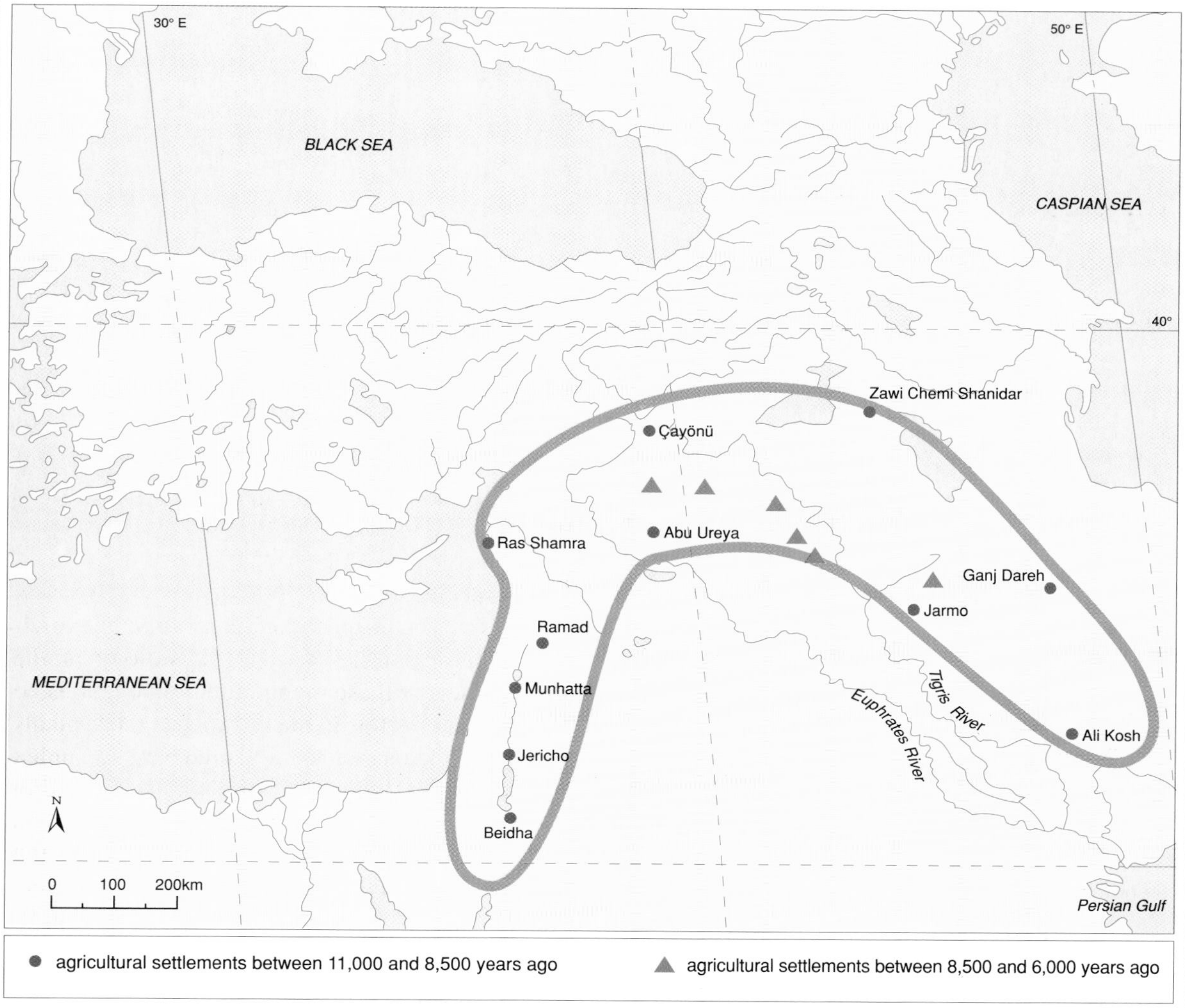

196 The arc of mountains and valleys that surrounds on the W, N, and NE the valleys of the Tigris and the Euphrates make up what has been called the Fertile Crescent, the oldest known center of domestication of plants and animals. In the whole of this area there appear traces, possibly dating back as far as the beginning of the ninth millennium B.C.—between 10,000 and 11,000 years ago—of human populations that were excercizing some control over animals or were harvesting some species of grasses from which the cultivated cereals were derived. From the middle of the eighth millennium B.C. (some 9,500 years ago), clear remains of domesticated plants and animals appear in many of the sites excavated.
[Diagram: Editrònica, from various sources]

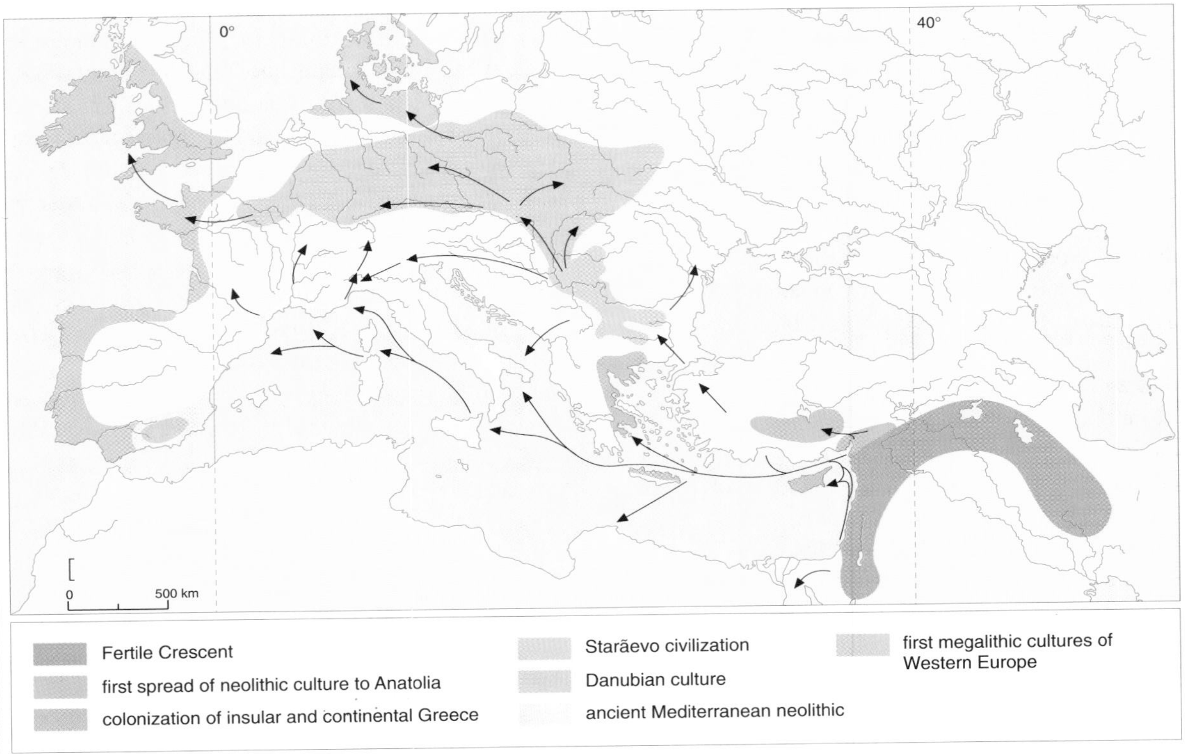

197 From the Fertile Crescent, the Neolithic cultural complex extended in all directions. The spread towards the west began in Anatolia, where there were already domestic livestock, agriculture, pottery, and urban settlements in the first half of the seventh millenium B.C. (more than 8,500 years ago); and towards the end of this age, the first Neolithic manifestations in the European continent were found in Thessaly (Greece). Fifteen hundred years later, around 5000 B.C. the Neolithic culture complex was already established in the whole of Greece and the Balkans, where there were cultures known as Starcevo (in Serbia and Montenegro), Körös (in Hungary), Cris (in Romania) or Karanovo (in Bulgaria). Navigators proceeding from the east Mediterranean or Greece, at about the same time, took the first elements of Neolithic culture to the south of the Italian peninsula, to Sicily, and the coastal regions of the west Mediterranean. From the NW of the Balkans, along the Danube, and extending across the lowlands of the north of Central Europe, the culture known as the Danubian was propagated, which around 4000 B.C. had reached the English channel coast. Around 3000 B.C. the whole of Atlantic Europe had already entered into the Neolithic world, and only residual pockets of hunter-gatherers remained in some marginal areas. *[Diagram: Editrònica, from various sources]*

in remains dating from around 11,000 years ago seems to point to a growing capacity to control the population of exploited sheep (but not of goats) which in turn suggests an incipient domestication of these animals. Information gathered from excavations of old farming settlements in Kenya in the area of Lukenya, near Nairobi would seem to suggest the dating of the domestication of bovine livestock to be not less than 13,000 years.

Whatever the age of the oldest forms of domestication, it is in the so-called Fertile Crescent that the new form of human life seems to have consolidated for the first time between 10,000 and 11,000 years ago. Indeed, in that area numerous human settlements have been identified with traces of farming and livestock activity which can be dated to the eighth millennium B.C. and even earlier. One of the oldest, the lower level of the Abu Ureya settlement in the Euphrates valley in northern Syria, with an age of between 11,500 and 10,500 years, already shows manual stone grinders and grains of einkorn wheat (*Triticum monococcum*), barley (*Hordeum vulgare*) and rye (*Secale cereale*), although in some cases they are apparently grains of wild varieties which have not been subjected to domestication. This would confirm that this was a settlement for sedentary hunter-gatherers who exploited the wide variety of resources that the area offered them at that time, like hares (*Lepus*), gazelles (*Gazella*), sheep (*Ovis orientalis*), goats (*Capra aegagrus*) and wild asses (*Equus hermionus hemippus*)—as well as fish and fresh water molluscs—among the animal resources, and lentils (*Lens culinaris*), fruits of terebinth (*Pistacia terebinthus*), hackberry fruit, capers, and esparto seeds (*Stipa*) among the plant resources.

The Abu Hureya finds bring together elements from different origins and, in the same geographical area in more recent settlements from some 9,000 years ago (Jericho, Ali Kosh, Çayönü, Jarmo), domesticated forms of the majority of cereals and legumes appear, as do domesticated animals like sheep, goats, pigs and, of course, dogs.

The first discoveries in these extremely old towns, some of which, like Jericho, were walled "cities," were the ones that led Childe to introduce the concept of a Neolithic revolution. But another factor also influenced him was the relative speed with which the new techniques of intensive use of plant production and livestock raising spread from the Fertile Crescent after the seventh millennium B.C. The complex farming system, mainly based on winter cereals, spread rapidly through Anatolia as far as Greece, where it was established more than 8,000 years ago and, across the Balkans, the Danube and Rhine valleys, it spread throughout the whole European continent until it reached the coasts of the North Sea and the Iberian Peninsula between 6,000 and 7,000 years ago. By some 7,000 years ago it had arrived in Egypt and from there it spread throughout northern Africa and what is today the Sahara. Before the civilizations of Mohenjo Daro and

Harappa developed in the valley of the Indus, the agricultural system that originated in the Fertile Crescent had already arrived there through a chain of old farming settlements which can be traced through Iran, Turkmenistan and Afghanistan. Wheat and barley were already being cultivated 5,000 years ago. In exactly the same way, at an unknown date, it would reach Ethiopia through Arabia and Yemen. It must even have arrived some 3,500 years ago during the Shang dynasty in China.

Rice and livestock in Chinese Neolithic cultures

More than 6,000 years ago, independently of that of the Fertile Crescent, a Neolithic revolution based on other cereals, like foxtail millet (*Setaria italica*) and common millet (*Panicum miliaceum*) had already taken place in China, specifically in the Wei He basin and the middle basin of the Huang He, north of the Qin Ling mountains and in the lower stretches of the Fen He, in the present day provinces of Henan, Shaanxi and Shanxi. This is the so-called Yangshao culture.

At the Bampo site near Xi'an in Shaanxi, with a date of some 6,000 years ago, remains of these two cereals have been found, as well as remains of hemp (*Cannabis sativa*), which was used for weaving, and of animals, both wild, (such as deer [*Cervus*], gazelle [*Gazella*], hares [*Lepus*]) and domesticated such as (dogs [*Canis familiaris*], pigs [*Sus scrofa*], bovids [*Bos*], sheep [*Ovis*] and poultry). As with the Fertile Crescent, the initial area of the Yangshao culture has a semi-arid climate with semi-desert vegetation rich in Artemisia but with large, mighty rivers and wooded areas on the mountains which surrounded the *loess* plains with tiers of terraces. As it extended towards the lower humid plains in the east, following the valley of the Huang He, two new plants of the utmost importance were added: soya (*Glycine max*) in the north, and rice (*Oryza sativa*) in the south. These eventually replaced the original cereals of the Yangshao assemblage and went on to become the staple food throughout the east and southern Asia.

Curiously the locality of Yangshao, which has given its name to the Chinese "Neolithic revolution" because it was the first to be discovered (1921) and described, is located near the southeastern limit of the area which makes up the main nucleus of this culture. One of the most important finds initially made in Yangshao was some traces of spikes, that could only be cultivated rice, in fragments of pottery. However it would seem that the oldest archaeological evidence of cultivated rice in China corresponds to a settlement of the so-called *Qingliengang culture*, later than that of Yangshao: that of Songzi at Qingpu near Shanghai in the delta of the Chang River (Iang Tse) with a date of 5,400 years ago. Similar dates have been estimated for other places of the lower Chang and further, on the basis of objects

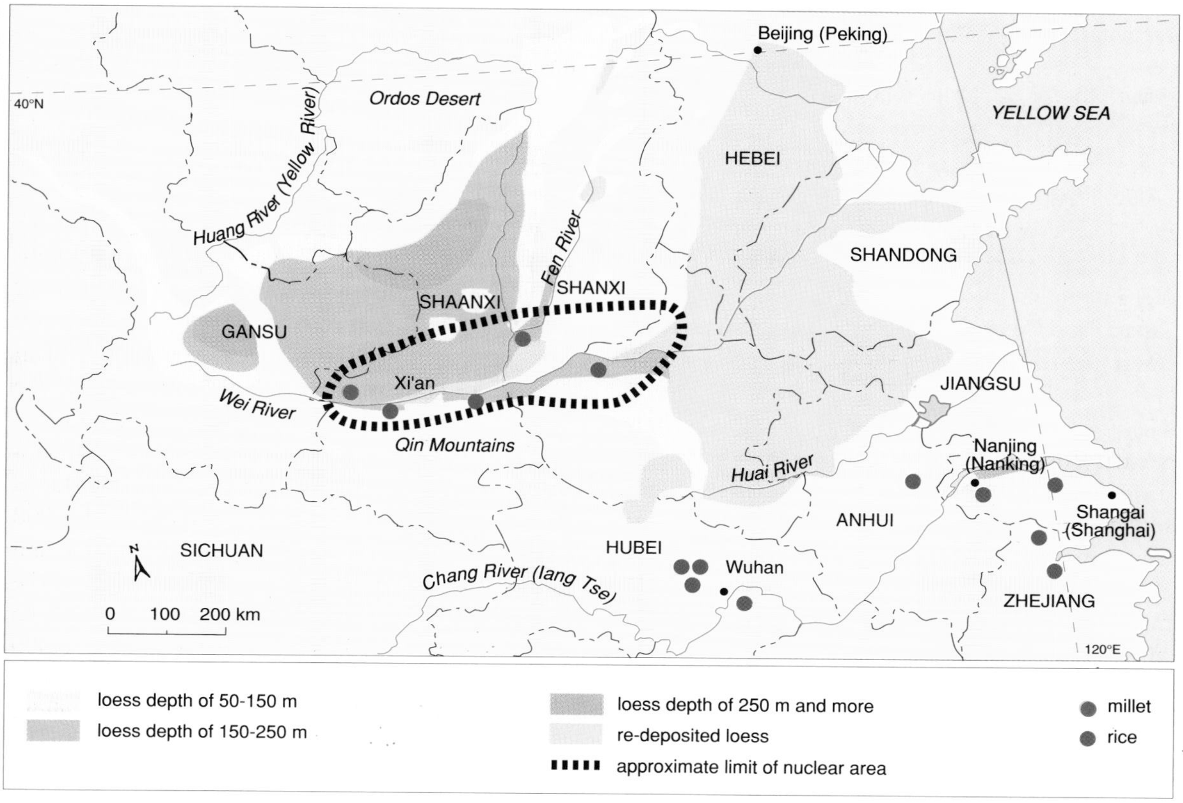

198 In the loess territories in the north of China, between about 8,000 and 7,000 years ago, a separate Neolithic revolution occurred that was comparable to that of the Fertile Crescent 2,000 years previously. A population that had arrived from the south of the Qin mountains established itself in the fertile lands of loess sediments in the mid-course of the Yellow River, and began to practice an itinerant agriculture which ended up as sedentary thanks to the extraordinary fertility of the soils. The basis of their agriculture was foxtail millet (*Setaria italica*) and proso millet (*Panicum miliaceum*). With its expansion towards the lowlands of the east of the initial core area, the agricultural complex incorporated soya (*Glycine max*) and rice (*Oryza sativa*) as basic crops and spread throughout the whole of east and southeast Asia. *[Diagram: Editrònica]*

199 The domestication of rice in SE Asia could have begun about 8,000 years ago in the valleys of the mountainous frontier zone between N. Thailand and Myanmar. At the upper levels of the so-called Spirit Cave, which can be dated from the first half of the sixth millennium B.C. (more than 7,500 years ago), remains of pottery were found, and in a nearby cave situated in the Banyan valley, at levels that can be dated from the second half of this millennium, there have been finds of not only pottery but some carbonized grains of rice. While the dating of these finds is not certain—nor is it certain if the rice grains belong to domesticated or wild varieties—what does appear to have been confirmed is that at the locality of Non Nok Tha in the eastern slopes of the central high plateau of Thailand, which descend towards the Mekong valley, there appear grains of rice, which are certainly of domesticated varieties, at levels which are more than 5,500 years old. The colonization of the central lowlands of Thailand and of the high plateaux of the region appears to have been later. *[Diagram: Editrònica, from various sources]*

found associated with one of the still undated finds, there are finds that we can presume are of cultivated rice from more than 5,500 years ago.

The oldest evidence of the domestication of rice on the edges of the plateaux of northeastern Thailand have also been placed near this date. Researchers have seen in these the origin of the agricultural complex of east and south east Asia and of the Pacific, based on rice and taro (*Colocasia antiquorum*) which could date back more than 9,000 years, the same as the Fertile Crescent.

Beans, maize and livestock in the Americas

The domestication of plants and animals was achieved much later in America, but it seems that it was totally independent of the first domestication centers of the Old World, and also developed independently in two centers (Mesoamerica and the Andes). The plant and animal species involved were completely different from those of the Old World, as were probably the ways in which selection took place.

The importance of domestication and its consequences in relation to its exploitation by humans in certain American ecosystems for the production of food surpluses are no less significant, at least as far as plants are concerned, than that found in the Fertile Crescent or in the Huang Valley. As for animals, it is not so important given that in Mesoamerica the only domestic animals before the arrival of the Europeans were the dog and the turkey (*Agriocharis* [=*Meleagris*] *ocellata*) and in the Andes region the dog, the guinea pig (*Cavia porcellus*), the llama (*Lama glama*) and the alpaca (*L. pacos*). There is a lack of consensus as to the domestication of different species of ducks and hens, evidence of which we can find in different points of America and which some authors attribute to ancient contacts across the Pacific or Atlantic.

In fact, some 7,000 years ago, maize was already being cultivated—or at least a precursor of this plant (maize only exists today as a cultivated crop and there is still debate as to its ancestry)—in the Valley of Tehuacan in the state of Puebla on the southern Mexican plain. Both in Tehuacan and in Tamaulipas in north eastern Mexico, beans (*Phaseolus vulgaris*) were being cultivated 6,000 years ago. Bottle gourds appear in Tamaulipas and Oaxaca in remains which can be dated as 9,000 years old or more, and in Tehuacan in remains dating back 7,500 years, but we do not know if they came from wild or cultivated plants. The first group of cultivated plants in Mexico, which later spread through Central America and a part of northern America, was made up of pumpkins (*Cucurbita pepo* and *C. moschata*), bottle gourds (*Lagenaria vulgaris*), maize (*Zea mays*), amaranths (*Amaranthus cruentus*), the common bean (*Phaseolus vulgaris*) and cotton (*Gossypium barbadense*). It would seem, however, that there had been no specifically agricultural practices in Mesoamerica earlier than the 7,000 years ago milestone.

In Peru the oldest known evidence occurs later, probably because most of the evidence is from the coastal area where complex techniques of irrigation were developed 5,000 years ago, but this very complexity, and the number and variety of the cultivated species, suggest that there must have been a previous development of agriculture on the higher lands, about which we still have very little information. In the Guitarrero cave in the Callejón de Huaylas, in the Ancash department of northern Peru, cultivated forms of the lima bean (*Phaseolus lunatus*) have been found with an age of some 7,500 years. Bottle gourds also appear in remains of a comparable age but, as in Mexico, we can not be sure in any of the cases, whether we are dealing with the fruits of cultivated plants or the fruits of wild plants. The domestication of the guanaco (*Lama guanicoe*), the ancestor of the present day varieties of lamas (*L. lama*) and alpacas (*L. pacos*), would have begun in the Puna de Junín between 7,500 and 6,200 years ago. Throughout this period the humans living in this area probably moved from an economy based on the specialised hunting of camelids to one based on breeding these animals in a state of semi-domestication. This was probably similar to the reindeer breeding

200 The first occurrences of cultivated plants in archaeological sites in America. *[Source: data prepared by the author, based on J.R. Harlan, 1987, and other sources]*

APPROXIMATE PERIOD	TAMAULIPAS (MEXICO)	TEHUACAN (MEXICO)	PERU
7000 B.C.	Gourd *(Lagenaria)* Scarlet runner bean *(Phaseolus coccineus)* spontaneous Marrow *(Curcubita pepo)* spontaneous?	Pepper *(Capsicum)* Avocado *(Persea)*	Common bean *(Phaseolus vulgaris)* and Lima bean *(Phaseolus lunatus)*[1] cultivated
6000 B.C.		Millet *(Setaria)*	
5000 B.C.		Maize *(Zea)* Pumpkin *(Curcubita mixta)* Marrow *(Curcubita pepo)* Gourd *(Lagenaria)*	
4000 B.C.	Millet *(Setaria)* Common bean *(Phaseolus vulgaris)*	Squash *(Curcubita moschata)* Jack bean *(Canavalia)*	
3000 B.C.		Common bean *(Phaseolus vulgaris)*	Gourd *(Lagenaria)*[2] Lima bean *(Phaseolus lunatus)*[2] Cotton *(Gossypium)*[2] Squash *(Curcubita moschata)*[2] Squash *(Curcubita ficifolia)*[2] Pepper *(Capsicum)*[2] Jack bean *(Canavalia)*[3] Arrowroot *(Canna)*[3] Guava *(Psidium)*[4]
2000 B.C.	Squash *(Curcubita moschata)*	Maize *(Zea)*[4] Peanut *(Arachis)*[4] Hot pepper *(Capsicum chinense)*[4] Manioc *(Manihot)*[4] *Amaranthus* Custard apple *(Annona)* Cotton *(Gossypium)*	Pacai *(Inga)* Lucuma *(Lucuma)* Jicama *(Pachyrhizuz)*
1000 B.C. Modern era	Pinto bean *(Phaseolus lunatus)*	Potato *(Solanum)*[5] Peanut *(Arachis)*[5]	Lima bean *(Phaseolus lunatus)*[5]

1: Andean valleys
2: First plants domesticated on the coast of Peru
3: Contact with southern Peru and Bolivia
4: Contact with North America, Mexico and Argentina
5: Contact with South America

(*Rangifer tarandus*) of many populations in northern Siberia, like the Chukchis, or to the vicuna breeding (*Vicugna vicugna*) still practiced in the Andes.

Cereals and livestock on the African continent

Finally, in Africa, it appears that the development of plant and animal domestication was diffuse out in space and time, with no area that could be considered a center of origin. However, it seems that most of cultivated plants can be placed in three groups, according to the ecological requirements of their wild relatives: those coming from the ecotones between the forests and the savannah, such as the oil palm (*Elaeis guineensis*) or the African yams (*Dioscorea* spp.): the savannah itself such as sorghum (*Sorghum bicolor*), pearl millet (*Citrullus lanatus*); and the high lands of eastern Africa such as tef (*Eragrostis tef*) or Niger seed (*Guizotia abyssinica*). Only a few plants domesticated in Africa, such as coffee (*Coffea*) and cola (*Cola* spp.) are of forest origin.

In the Sahara and the Nile Valley traces of hand grinders and polished stone sickles more than 12,000 years old have been found. However, as in many

201 Millet has been the staple food of the majority of the peoples of the savannah and of the African Sahel for thousands of years. The African millets belong to the genus *Pennisetum* and there are many species and varieties adapted to very different conditions of cultivation. Pearl millet, for example, is the variety that grows under driest conditions, and in the Sudan it is known as *aish*, which in Arabic means life. Further south, this name is applied to sorghum which is the principal crop. In the photograph women of the Malinki tribe (of the Bantu ethnic group) from Djenne, in the African republic of Mali, are milling millet to make flour. *[Photo: Antoni Agelet]*

202 The culture of Pharaonic Egypt, more than 5,000 years ago, was a fully developed agricultural society with differentiation of social classes. The fertility of the soil, irrigated and fertilized by occasional flooding by the Nile, allowed a large production of agricultural surplus and the growth of artesanal activities and services not directly related to food production. This painting of the tomb of Sennendjem, an official of the beginning of the 13th century B.C., comes from the necropolis of Dayr al-Madīna, near the Valley of the Kings, where social distinctions were made evident in their burials. Many of the workmen, artisans, and technicians who took part in the funerary constructions in the Valley of the Kings and the Valley of the Queens lived in the town that existed previously in this locality and were buried in its necropolis. The richness of the paintings in the tomb of Sennendjem, like these—which show the most typical agricultural tasks (ploughing, harvesting) as they were practiced at that time, and some of the scenes from the *Book of the Dead*—highlights their subjects social standing.
[Photo: William MacWuitty-Camera Press / Zardoya]

places in the Fertile Crescent of the same age or even older, these signs seem to correspond to a stage of exploitation of natural populations of grasses rather than real domestication and farming, and it is not until just over 6,000 years ago that the first evidence of the agricultural complex developed in the Fertile Crescent appear in Egypt. More or less contemporaneous, at different points of the Sahel, from the Atlantic to the Red Sea, the domestication of sorghum (*Sorghum bicolor*) would have begun at an uncertain date but probably later, both in the Sahel and in the transition between savannah and forests, than the domestication of other plants such as African rice (*Oryza barthii*), the African millets (*Pennisetum*), African yams (*Dioscorea cayenensis*, *D. rotundata*) the oil palm (*Elaeis guineensis*) and shia butter (*Butyrospernum parkii*).

On the other hand, from the beginnings of the fifth millennium B.C., in other words 7,000 years ago, the presence of pastoral peoples with flocks of goats and sheep is clear, and we have already pointed out the evidence that has been found in eastern Africa of even older hypothetical cattle herders.

The consolidation of agriculture and livestock breeding

Ten thousand years ago the vast majority of human beings were hunter-gatherers. Population density was insignificant and almost entirely in balance with the environment; and by not much more than 2,000 years ago, on the eve of our present era, most of mankind lived on agriculture and animal husbandry, involving a much more intensive exploitation of the environment and significant use of external (exosomatic) energy, provided mainly by domestic animals. In most parts of the world the last 2,000 years have seen agriculture becoming increasingly intensive, and new techniques requiring high energy input have increased the opportunities of peoples with cultures based on both agriculture and animal husbandry to take control of the natural resources of the planet and use them to their own benefit. Meanwhile, the hunter-gatherers have been reduced to peoples who are insignificant and totally marginalized in demographic terms.

The social repercussions of this change have also been considerable. Use of external energy by mankind, both individually and collectively, is not uniform, facilitated the differentiation of social roles within groups which were adopting agriculture and animal husbandry as ways of life. It also allowed the individuals, families or groups with the most ability to control energy flows, represented essentially by control of production and transport of foodstuffs. While one cannot regard the hunter-gatherer societies as being totally egalitarian, it is certainly true to

203 Chinese hydraulic wheel from 1637, as represented in the *Tian Gong Kai Wu* (*The Exploitation of the Works of Nature*). This is the oldest human invention for obtaining important quantities of energy without using human muscular force or that of animals. The first hydraulic wheels of which we have historic records appear some 2,000 years ago almost simultaneously in China and in Asia Minor. Initally, they were horizontal and used exclusively for the milling of wheat to make flour. Afterwards, they were made vertical and used in forges, and later in other industrial applications.
[Photo: The Needham Research Institute, Cambridge]

say that the appearance of complex social structures, with various differentiated and hierarchical castes or social classes, is one of the innovations associated with the Neolithic revolution.

Agriculture and animal husbandry allowed humans to begin to regulate food production, and were successful in ensuring the maintenance of gradually increasing populations within the limits imposed by weather and soil conditions, technological developments and social organization. Counterbalancing this is the simplification of the ecosystems mankind has exploited, which at times has exhausted the soil's productive capacity, or even eliminated the soil itself. Over-exploitation, or over-population brought about by the same demographic growth, has been the reason why some peoples, already possessing a Neolithic cultural baggage and some domesticated varieties of plants and animals, had to leave the lands they had originally been farming, abandoning the systems preadapted to exploitation where agriculture originated, to begin to open clearings in virgin forest, to burn steppes and savannahs, or to divert tributaries of rivers in order to be able to cultivate the land and establish new settlements.

But, with the exception of some particularly favoured areas where it was possible to set up artificial irrigation systems and build towns, Neolithic demographic growth, while being significantly greater than that of previous eras, was in global terms still relatively limited and locally subject to severe fluctuations (famines caused by poor harvests, natural catastrophes, epidemics, wars). This situation continued until, some 250 years ago, a new technological transformation enabled mankind (or at least, some groups) to take greater advantage of external energy sources: the Industrial Revolution.

4.2. Control of flows of energy and information

As with the Neolithic revolution, the Industrial revolution was not a sudden, isolated happening, but rather a long process of accumulation of knowledge and techniques which were crystalizing, in England and other European countries from the mid-eighteenth century onwards, bringing with it a profound transformation of the economic and social conditions of production and the impact of human societies on the biosphere. If with the Neolithic revolution mankind achieved highly effective control of the production and transport of foodstuffs by application of external energy, the factor that came into play with the Industrial Revolution was the control of the flow of this energy and the vast growth of its application in many fields, with social consequences that emphasized the differentiation of individual and class roles and the privileged position of particular individuals or populations.

The advent of the Industrial Revolution

It is worth remembering that, before the Industrial Revolution was termed as such, technological advances had taken place which allowed mankind to gain control of increasing quantities of external energy. This was the case with water wheels, which appeared in Asia Minor both under the Greeks and in China during the first century B.C., or with the improvements in navigation, using energy provided by the wind. However, the amount of external energy required was still relatively small, and in any case man's ability to control the winds or the rainfall which supplied the water courses where water wheels had been installed was non-existent. The true qualitative and quantitative change occurred between the mid-eighteenth and mid-nineteenth centuries, and the amount of external energy used and controlled by humans has been increasing steadily since then.

204 The horse-drawn seed-sowing machine of Jethro Tull symbolizes the agricultural revolution, which began in the 17th century in Britain preceding somewhat the industrial revolution. The prototype, constructed in 1701, was, in fact, the first piece of agricultural machinery provided with a moveable internal mechanism which, in this case, allowed seed to be distributed evenly in the furrows, while at the same time a rake attached to the back of the machine raked the ground and covered the seed that had been sown.
[Photo: Mary Evans Picture Library]

The very concept of the Industrial Revolution is a product of the social and economic situation of Europe in the mid-nineteenth century, the impact of the French Revolution and the successive civil wars which broke out in various European countries throughout the first half of the nineteenth century. This idea was first introduced (1845) by Friedrich Engels (1820-1895) in his book *Die Lage der arbeitenden Klassen in England* (*The situation of the working class in England*), in which he linked the situation to the invention of the steam engine and the machinery for textile production designed for the cotton industry in England, which was developing during the mid-eighteenth century. This idea was taken up almost immediately by John Stuart Mill (1806-1873) whose point of view was quite opposed to that of the German socialist philosopher, in his *Principles of Political Economy*.

More recent analyses of the phenomenon, which are more subtle than in the past, confirm that the Industrial Revolution was in part preceded by and in part accompanied by radical transformations in other areas. Thus, for example, before the revolution began to crystalize in the mid-eighteenth century, a whole series of events had occurred, above all in north-western Europe and specifically in England. This was the case with the changes in ways of thinking which identify the Renaissance, the Reformation and the Counter-Reformation in Europe, in the sense that they reaffirm a radical anthropocentrism (man as the measure of all things) which sets humankind apart from Nature and legitimises them to exploit it and bring it under their rule. There also took place the formidable expansion of territorial boundaries and of the peoples that fell within the reach of European powers and trade, thanks to advances in navigation and to the voyages of discovery and conquest first embarked upon five hundred years ago; these resulted in unprecedented growth in terms of trade and fortunes, particularly in the countries and cities which were engaged in some kind of production (agricultural or manufacturing) which could be commercialized. In addition to this, the development of a "new" agriculture, thanks to the work of agronomists such as Jethro Tull (1674-1741) or Duhamel du Monceau (1700-1782), led to the old routines being abandoned by the early eighteenth century, making way for the incorporation of the fruits of modern science.

One should also consider social phenomena, such as the spread of "enclosures" in England, which enclosed parts of common land; this caused collective land to be made over to the individual, and the appropriation of enclosed lands by rich landowners

205 The iron bridge at Coalbrookdale in a colored etching from 1836, published in a book entitled *Easy Lessons in Mechanics.*
[Photo: Ann Ronan at Image Select]

who exploited them for sheep pasture; in this way capital could be accumulated on top of the growing returns provided by this new way of exploiting the land (it also marginalized landless country people). Finally the population of most European countries, which had already begun to expand some time before, underwent a considerable acceleration of growth during the mid-eighteenth century, coinciding exactly with the dates which most authors attribute to the dawn of the Industrial Revolution.

The first industrial innovations

The first purely industrial innovations occurred in the textile industry. In 1733 John Kay (1704-1778) invented the flying shuttle, and between 1765 and 1779 spinning machines called spinning jennies were developed, which by the latter date were water (or steam) powered—Samuel Crompton's spinning mule (1753-1827)—and were capable of working 400 spindles at a time. During the 1730s there were advances in the iron and steel industry in England, many of them rediscoveries of metallurgical processes in use centuries earlier in China.

New processes: iron

In 1709 the Darby family, ironmasters from Coalbrookdale on the banks of the River Severn in the West of England, introduced the use of coke (free of the sulphur contained in coal) in the treatment of iron ore; in this way grey iron could be obtained, which partially prevented brittleness (caused by the impurities in fossil coal) and vastly increased production potential, which until then had been limited by the need to use charcoal (used in traditional metal working processes such as the Catalan forge) or the extreme brittleness of the product resulting from the use of coal, limiting its usefulness for certain purposes. Improvements in blast furnaces led, from 1760 onwards, to the widespread use of molten iron in steadily expanding industry. Industry also benefitted from the discovery made by Benjamin Huntsman (1704-1766) in 1750 of manufacturing molten steel in a furnace. Puddling, a procedure patented by Henry Cort (1740-1800) in 1784, enabled all impurities to be removed from the grey iron, obtaining optimum quality steel.

The last quarter of the eighteenth century brought the definitive consolidation of the Industrial Revolution in England and the beginnings of tentative industrialization, following the British model, in other European countries, and not long after in the United States, which had achieved independence in 1783. While in 1780 Great Britain exported 360,000 pounds of cotton textiles (a massive figure, considering that only fifty years previously England's cotton production was negligible), by 1792 export figures had reached two million tons. In 1779 Abraham Darby III

206 James Watt's steam engine, before the introduction of modifications, which allowed it to be applied to the production of rotatory movements, differed from that of Thomas Newcomen's in the introduction of a steam condenser (O), separate from the cylinder (Q), in which the pressure of the steam was applied to the piston. The transmission of the movement of the piston to the machine that it was to operate (in the engraving a water pump) was achieved, as in Newcomen's machine, by a pivoting arm. This modification doubled the thermal efficiency of the best of Newcomen's machines in use up till then, and, therefore, greatly reduced the cost of the energy used from burning fossil fuels. The engraving, from the *Cyclopedia of Abraham Rees*, published in London in 1820, represents a machine installed in Chelsea, near the Thames River, to pump up water from the subsoil. *[Photo: Ann Ronan at Image Select]*

built a bridge over the Severn River, in front of his factories in Coalbrookdale. Still used by pedestrians two centuries after its construction, it was the first iron bridge in the world, with a span of 100 ft (31 m) and a height of 35 ft (11 m); twenty years later iron bridges were common throughout England.

The steam engine

Of all the innovations, the most decisive one for the Industrial Revolution was the progressive replacement of traditional energy sources (human or animal traction, wind or water power, plant fuels) by energy derived from fossil fuels. Initially coal was used to drive the steam engine (and, in the last third of the nineteenth century, for the generation of electrical power) and subsequently oil, which was used not only in the steam engine but also from the late nineteenth century onwards, in the combustion engine. James Watt's steam engine (1736-1819), which was initially only capable of producing rectilinear motion, was perfected by Watt himself in 1784 with an arrangement of gears and connecting rods which allowed for rotational movement and enabled steam power to be applied to a wider range of industrial processes, particularly those pertaining to the textile industry. Virtually at the same time, in 1783, the Marquis de Jouffroy d'Abbans succeeded in navigating a section of the river Saône, near Lyon, in a vessel weighing 182 tons, the Pyroscaphe, which had been fitted with a steam engine driving a paddle wheel. In 1779 the first of Watt's steam engines to function outside England was installed in Chaillot, France, where it pumped Paris' water supply. 1785 saw the first installation in Germany. However, the introduction of the steam engine to other European countries and to the United States was still later (the first attempt in Catalonia was in 1805, to power a calico factory, but it did not come into general use until 1832). Even by 1830 the 15,000 active machines in Great Britain were matched by a mere 3,000 in France, 1,000 in Prussia (most of them in Silesia or in Rhineland Prussia, in other words the Ruhr basin) and even lower figures for Belgium (mostly in Liège), the Austrian empire (Bohemia) and other countries.

The consolidation of industrial society

Both cause and effect of the Industrial Revolution, a process of growth in population, of capital wealth, food production, markets, transport networks, and towns began in the last third of the eighteenth century, to gave rise to the capitalist society which, while being radically changed by the great upheavals of the twentieth century and having spread virtually worldwide by the end of this same century, has brought us to where we are today. This process has, however, been erratic, largely implemented by the exploitation of some social classes by others, of lesser developed countries by those which are more industrialized, and by humanity, in general, exploiting the rest of the biosphere and its

Poisoning the biosphere

***Silent Spring* is the evocative title of a book published in 1962, which alerted public opinion to the dangers of pollution, and in particular of pesticides. By her well-documented and also poetic attack, the author, Rachel Carson (1907-1964), sparked off a popular reaction, which led to a popular ecological awareness.**

Cover of the book *Silent Spring* by Rachel Carson [Jordi Vidal]

Until very recently, humans have tended to offload their domestic and industrial waste directly into the environment. It was thought that chimney smoke, agricultural pesticides, and radioactive isotopes from laboratories, would finally become lost in the vastness of the Earth. It was implicitly believed that nature would attend to finding a suitable place for these troublesome substances. Of course some of these pollutants disappear, or become inactive or harmless, but on the whole this is not the case, and indeed some are transformed into even more toxic by-products. Rachel Carson was not the first person to speak out against this, but no-one had done so with such vehemence before. Through her book, which is now a classic, she advised the federal government of the United States to introduce measures aimed at controlling air and water pollution. Carson's study of DDT, explaining how it enters the trophic networks and the hydrological cycle, and the overall impact it has upon the environment, was particularly striking (it is now known that even the penguins in the Antarctic have traces of DDT in their fatty tissues).

Effluent at Ebro, Catalonia [Jordi Vidal]

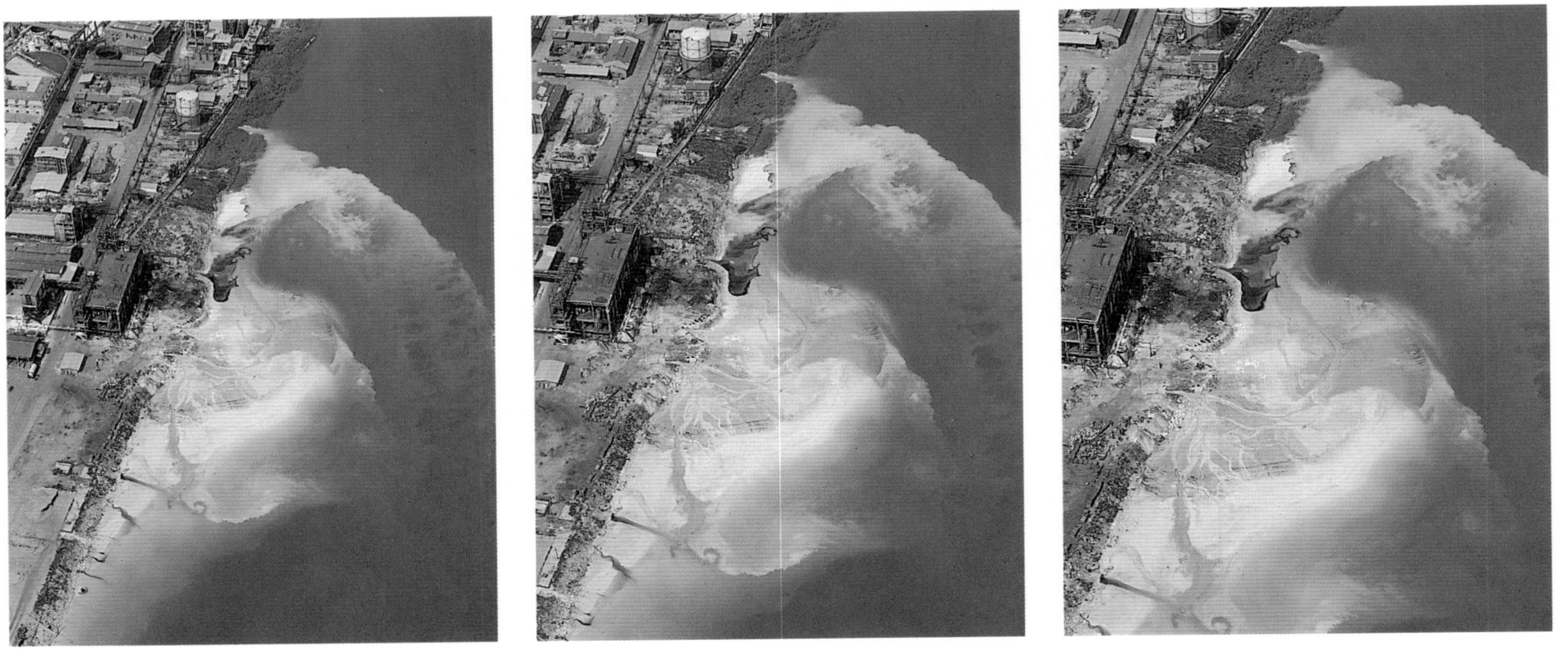

Effluent at Ebro, Catalonia [Jordi Vidal]

Bioaccumulation and "ecological deterioration" are two of the most worrying effects of the poisoning of trophic networks and of ecological cycles. Ecological deterioration means the progressive destruction of an ecosystem when it is constantly affected by pollutants. Acid rain is an example of this: forests are repeatedly exposed to pollutants, in this case acids, which arrive through the atmosphere and have a number of different effects upon the trees, from destroying the leaf cuticles to changing the balance and variety of microfauna in the soil, as well as causing stress in the trees whereby they become weaker and more prone to disease. The overall effect is a gradual wearing down of the resistance of the forest ecosystems, leading in some cases to the death of the whole forest. Bioaccumulation results from the concentration effects produced in the trophic networks when under attack from pollutants. This is particularly dangerous to human health, since foods obtained from organisms that are in the higher levels of the trophic network may have very high levels of contamination.

A typical example of bioaccumulation occurs in marine trophic networks. Some forms of waste that humans dump into the sea settle on the ocean bed where they evade ecological cycles, but others enter the trophic network.

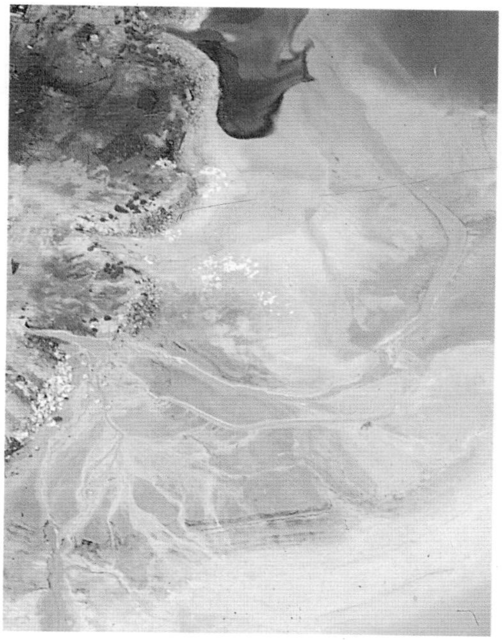

In the North Atlantic, for example, each kilo of a second-order fish caught by humans has needed 22 lb (10 kg) of primary carnivores to build it up, which in turn have consumed 110 lb (50 kg) of anchovies and planktophagous fish. These 110 lb (50 kg) of anchovies and oceanic fish need 220 lb (100 kg) of zooplankton, which in turn need 2,200 lb (1,000 kg) of phytoplankton.

So all the non-biodegradable waste that has been absorbed by this ton of phytoplankton ends up concentrated in this modest secondary carnivore (a hake weighing a kilo, for example), which is situated towards the top of the chain. When we eat this fish we expose ourselves to the biological concentration of waste products, which we thoughtlessly tipped into the sea in the first place, in diluted quantities. The concentration levels can reach proportions that are frankly alarming.

Pollution has developed as a result of the increasing number of activities undertaken by humans. In many cases, the natural processes of regeneration are incapable of keeping step with the rate of increase in pollution. Thus, as we have seen, serious problems arise not just locally, but on a world scale. Hardly any of the materials humans use for social, agricultural, or industrial ends are retained, but rather they are scattered across the surface of the globe. In the light of this, sweeping steps must be taken, which should not only be corrective, but above all, preventative.

Resources that are becoming scarce

Abundance by Maarten de Vos [Index]

Earth is not a cornucopia, although humans have tended to believe it is. Few of us consumed little for millennia, and we have helped ourselves to what was available without any problems. In the twenty-first century, however, we will be many; and the many will consume vast quantities. Natural resources, which are finite by definition, are already beginning to become scarce.

556
MARTÍN DE VOS
La Abundancia

Detail from *Abundance* by Maarten de Vos [Index]

Natural resources may be defined as the riches that nature has freely provided us with, from sunshine and water to forests, fish, oil, and minerals. We consume these riches directly (drinking water, for example), or use them to produce other commodities, (such as wood for paper production), or to produce energy (natural gas, for example).

Natural resources are considered renewable or non-renewable, according to whether or not they are able to replenish themselves within a human time-scale. Thus fish, wood, and solar energy are, generally speaking, renewable resources, while coal, soil, and oil are non-renewable. One may repeatedly fish from a shoal of sardines over a period of time, because the population will recover over and over again (as long as the fishing is carefully controlled, of course), but the same principle cannot be applied to an oil well. The quantity of oil in the well is finite and will last for a limited time. Perhaps, in many millions of years, it will have replenished itself, and so it might be considered to be renewable, but for practical purposes oil is not a renewable resource. On the other hand, certain renewable resources, such as fishing grounds for example, may eventually become non-renewable, if they are exploited in such a way that the fish populations are drastically reduced or completely exhausted.

The case of water, essential to life, and perhaps the most valuable element provided by our planet, may be taken as an example to illustrate the environmental problems involved in the management of natural resources. Although water is theoretically in abundant supply, if it is ill used, the future of the human race and of many other species may be placed in jeopardy.

Water is a renewable natural resource. In fact the water underground, and in lakes, rivers, and reservoirs, constantly replenishes itself—albeit slowly at times—according to the hydrological cycle. Every year this cycle makes around 9,000 km^3 of water available for human consumption, which would be enough to supply 20,000 million people! But it is unevenly distributed. Thus Iceland receives 89,598 yd^3 (68,500 m^3) of water per person per year, Bahrain, one of the Arab Emirates, hardly has any fresh water at all, and is totally dependent on the desalination of seawater. While some industrialized countries can even consume large quantities of drinking water for various uses, such as the maintenance of golf courses, in some developing countries people do not even have enough to satisfy their basic needs.

The growth in the world population, the ever-increasing use of water (agriculture is the greatest consumer with 73%), and pollution (salinization, acidification, lixiviation of nitrates, nitrites, organic waste, and heavy metals in aquifers, etc.) are all threatening to turn water, into a resource, which is, to all intents and purposes, non-renewable. This is becoming particularly clear in the case of underground water sources, where very often the rate at which water is extracted exceeds the rate at which it can replenish itself.

Detail from *Abundance* by Maarten de Vos [Index]

The problem of availability of drinking water is particularly severe in developing countries, where there is hardly any treatment of sewage. Every year millions of people, particularly children, contract illnesses that are often fatal, due to polluted water. The problem is so serious that the United Nations declared the decade of the 80s to be "The International Decade for the Provision of Drinking Water and Sanitation", with the aim, still unattained, of providing risk-free drinking water and adequate sanitary conditions for everyone by the year 1990. Indeed the natural processes of evaporation, sedimentation, and filtration of water through the soil no longer provide sufficient supplies of pure water. Humans have had to resort to sewage treatment plants to make up this deficiency, which has also meant considerable expenditure on infrastructure and energy.

When considering possible solutions to the far-reaching problem of the management of water resources and of natural resources in general, an integrated approach becomes essential. The areas of land to be administered should be delineated according to the natural processes taking place there, taking into account the presence of hydrographic catchment areas and aquifers, for example. Above all, the administrative bodies must have total control over these areas. International cooperation is also necessary, since the hydrological cycle transcends political boundaries. Preventative measures must be taken that will avoid the need to concentrate so much effort upon decontamination. More efficient use must be made of water resources and wastage of water avoided. The use of underground water sources should be restricted and these should be considered, to all intents and purpose, as non-renewable resources. Finally, there should be a greater focus on research into the hydrological cycle and into clean technologies. There are many steps that we, as individuals, can take; we can begin by only consuming the water that we really need; we can limit the use of substances that may cause pollution, and we can play an active part in applying pressure upon the authorities, encouraging them to adopt policies that will conserve our surroundings, while taking an integrated approach towards protecting the environment.

The increase in population, particularly in developing countries, and the growth in the rate at which natural resources are used per capita, especially in industrialized countries, mean that the biosphere's natural resources are diminishing at an ever-increasing pace. Developing countries are often criticized for their immoderate growth in population, and the repercussions this has upon the environment. That this is a problem cannot be denied, but industrialized countries are in fact applying an even greater pressure upon the environment when, in spite of their small, and in some cases even negative, population growth, they consume natural resources per capita at a far greater rate than developing countries. For example, although the population of India is more or less three times that of the United States, on average, the American citizen consumes far more natural resources than the Indian citizen. Certainly the United States, as a whole, is putting considerably greater pressure upon the planet than India is. The rich and the powerful, simply because they are so, have an obligation to act with the highest degree of responsibility.

207 Stephenson's steam engine opened the way for a real revolution in land transport, which helped to consolidate the economic and social changes that characterized the last two centuries and to extend the impact of the industrial revolution to the whole world.
[Photo: José Latova]

irreplaceable natural resource. This process has also been subjected, on a more or less regular basis, to crises and imbalances, from the food crises that occurred in many parts of Europe during the 1780s—and which, combined with other social factors, led to the revolution in France in 1789—to the oil crisis of the 1970s, which was perhaps the harbinger of the move to a new epoch during the last quarter of the twentieth century.

The increasingly widespread use of steam as a source of energy for industry and transport (and likewise coal as a fuel), although it initially delayed the rapid destruction of forests in European countries, later had negative repercussions on the environmental conditions in cities and industrial areas throughout the nineteenth century. Conditions improved at a local level when the use of electricity began to become widespread, but worsened again in our century with the extensive use of the motor car.

The development of new modes of transport and transport networks is another distinguishing feature of the Industrial Revolution, and one of the factors which has allowed socially and politically dominant groups to take control and exploit resources and work-forces from a distance. During the eighteenth century most European countries put great effort into building networks of navigable canals. By 1760 Great Britain had more than 990 mi (1,600 km) of navigable waterways, although the majority of them had been created by diverting rivers. By the end of the eighteenth century there were important networks in France, the Netherlands and Russia, while throughout the first half of the nineteenth century more canals were constructed not only in these countries but also in Germany, the Austro-Hungarian empire, Sweden, Denmark and, on the other side of the Atlantic, in the United States and Canada. The application of steam power to overland traction, that is to say the invention of the locomotive, opened up a new transport network which was even more efficient, albeit more expensive. The first railway line to carry passengers was built in 1829 between Stockton-on-Tees and Darlington, in the north of England, by George Stephenson (1781-1848). By 1900 more than 21,700 mi (35,000 km) of track had been laid in the United Kingdom (which at the time included the whole of Ireland), 146,900 mi (237,000 km) in the rest of Europe and 198,400 mi (320,000 km) in the United States, to which should be added many lines built by colonial powers in their territories and colonies. An example of this is the Trans-Siberian Railway (begun in 1872 and not completed until 1915), or the networks which the British constructed in Canada, India and Australia. These networks, along with the opportunities offered by steam navigation from the beginning of the nineteenth century, created a new economic system which expanded rapidly, in which a small number of power-wielding centers could exercise their influence over the exploitation of resources in increasingly large areas. In the long term this gave rise to the current situation in which, ecologically speaking, mankind as a whole tends to act as a single system which exploits the entire biosphere as a united body, and then spreads the waste generated by its activity throughout the world.

Although in a very unequal manner in relation to the use of external energy by individuals and groups, the whole of humanity has simplified and modified the ecosystems, created artificial ones, preparing forests and meadows for cultivation, introducing domestic animals to areas where there were none, moving cultivated plants and weeds from one continent to another, transporting all kinds of products from one country to another, discharging the waste from industrial processes into the atmosphere, into the water, and onto dumping grounds. The increased population growth rate, the ability to provide transport, and the accumulation and disposal of waste, giving rise to pollution, have become the most significant features of the dominant role of humans over the rest of the biosphere since the dawn of the Industrial Revolution. To this should be added the expansion and increased density of urban areas and the risk, which can be very significant on a local level, of exposure to ionizing radiation.

The biosphere was protected from this radiation, or at least that coming from outside the Earth's atmosphere, by the ozone layer, formed hundreds of millions of years ago. Among mankind's most recent contributions to life on earth is the introduction of radioactivity within the biosphere, arising from various applications of nuclear energy and leading to a noticeably decreasing density of the ozone-rich layers of the earth's atmosphere; this has happened in the areas around the Earth's poles, exposing them to dangerous levels of ultraviolet radiation.

4.3 Control of information flows

Humanity as a whole, then, tends to act as a single system. But, as has already been pointed out, it is by no means a homogenous system in space (on the other hand nor is the biosphere either) in terms of population density, the energy consumption of each individual or group, or their capacity to influence the exploitation of living systems or non-renewable resources. Today, the generation and cultural transmission of information is on the way to achieving the role which, during the years that have gone by since the beginning of the Industrial Revolution, was occupied by the increasing use of energy, the intensive exploitation of raw materials and the work force for the industrial production of consumer goods, and the transportation of these goods or of the raw materials necessary for their production.

The information revolution and informatics

In fact the transformations that we associate with what, in short, we term the computer revolution, are after all very recent (the first computers with integrated circuit date from 1964), and have their origin in advances made in the rapid transmission of information over long distances, already represented in the nineteenth century by the telegraph and the telephone. The North American essayist Neil Postman emphasized with considerable accuracy, and a touch of bitterness, the qualitative change which the telegraph brought to life in North America from the mid-nineteenth century onwards—the first permanent telegraph line, running from Washington to Baltimore, was installed by Samuel F. B. Morse (1791-1872) in 1844—turning the transmission of messages into something banal. His argument is that by moving on from a "typographical" culture, where communication was based on coherent discourse, supported by the printed word, to a telegraphic culture based on simplified discourse assisted by electronic impulses which were made to imitate letters, information became a consumer product (the first news agency, Associated Press, was established in 1848, just four years after Morse installed the first telegraph line), something that could be bought and sold according to market conditions, and not according to the use to which it could be put or the sense it might have.

Postman's characteristic rancor is understandable if viewed in terms of the progressive loss of the influence of written means of communication in the face of audiovisual media, the origins whose origins can be found in telegraphs and photography from the mid-nineteenth century onwards. But it is hard to deny that the immediacy in communications provided by the telegraph and subsequently the telephone and other means of transmitting information via electronic impulses or electromagnetic waves has been useful in transmitting a lot of very functional and relevant information, and has been the basis for much of today's capacity to control processes. It should be pointed out, however, that the first applications of these advances and facilities for the transmission and manipulation of information, and even more so of those in use today, have been directed at reinforcing the tendencies which were already apparent at the beginning of the Industrial Revolution in the sense of further hastening the increased exploitation of natural resources and reaffirming the power of the dominant classes in industrialized countries over their own societies and over their respective colonial or economic empires.

The substitution of energy by information

We know that man uses up a considerable amount of external (exosomatic) energy and that he obtains it mainly from the construction of external objects which act as vehicles for this energy. The history of mankind and its interactions with the rest of the biosphere is complex, and in some ways displays characteristics of developments based on exploitation of the rest of the biosphere. In other words, mankind has acted as a regressive factor on the rest

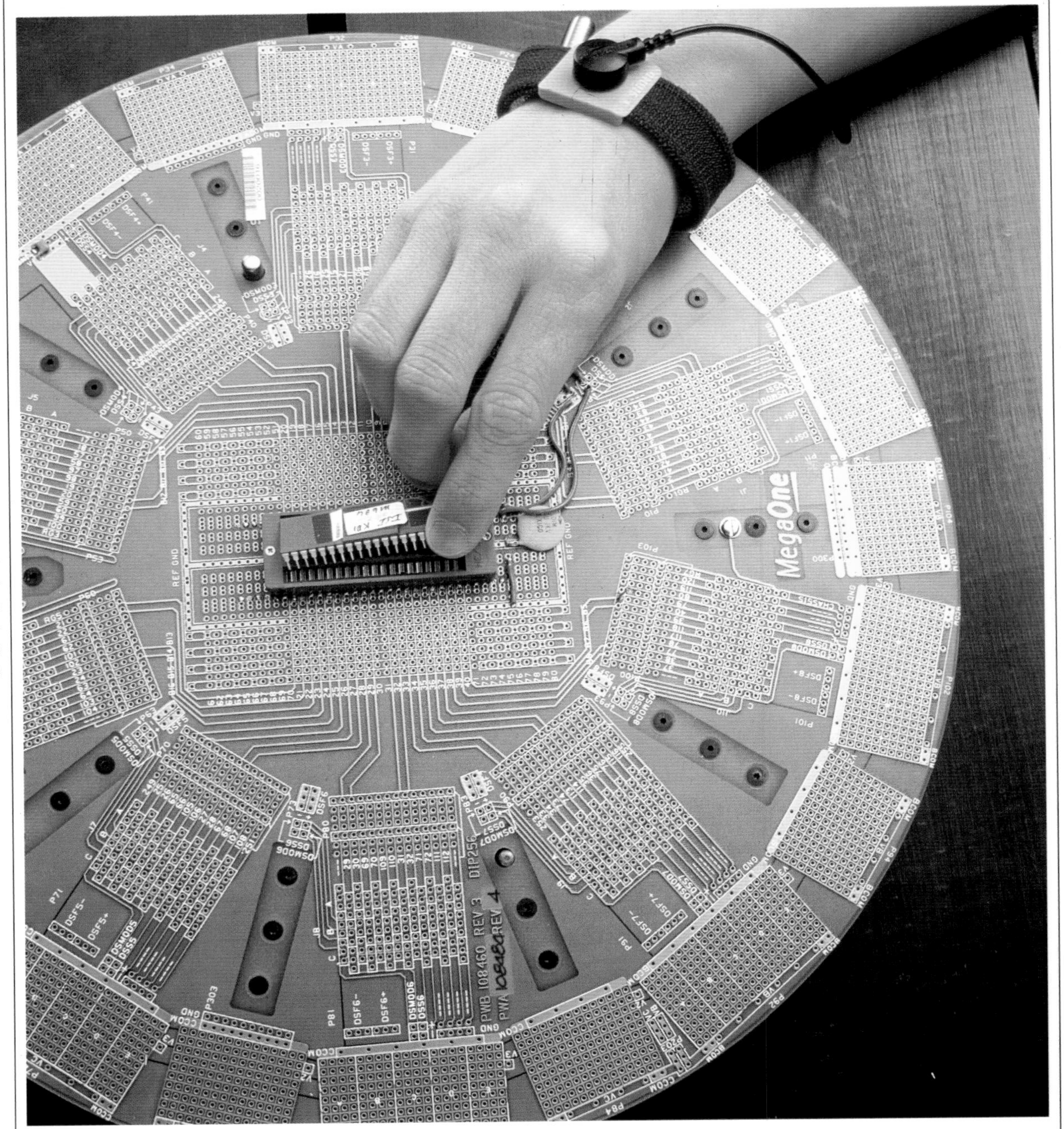

208 Integrated circuits or "chips" allow both the miniaturization and the increasing integration of electronic and logical circuits in computers, thus profoundly changing both the individual and social capacity of humans to handle large quantities of information. Unfortunately, a large part of this capacity is used in programs for complicated armaments that threaten the future of humanity; or in the transmission of publicity on consumer products, which we can do without, and by television, for trivial or violent programs that are even less necessary. However, it is true that the ability to handle large amounts of information places humanity in a radically new situation as regards its relationship to the rest of the biosphere and makes it particularly responsible for its future and that of future generations, so little valued by the industrial civilization that is coming to an end.
[Photo: AGE Fotostock]

of the biosphere and has set it back to a much earlier stage of development. In this way, humans have been able to extract from nature those resources they need to support their life thereby provoking a regression in the rest of the biosphere.

Within the concept of succession we can include the changes undergone by humanity, together with the array of domesticated animal and plant species and the artifacts mankind has surrounded itself with. Demographic change, brought about by a decrease in mortality and birth rates, is equivalent to the decrease in the production/biomass ratio in any natural population. An increase in average life expectancy is another characteristic, paid for by external energy invested in improving living conditions (improved water supplies and food distribution) and medical and health care. This is not reflected in the lifespan of each generation, since the child-bearing age in women is one of the least variable factors in human population.

Biological evolution having come to a halt, the increase in information occurs at a cultural level and, in a material form, in the construction of all sorts of objects. The slowing down of significant changes in civilizations makes way for the development of a vast range of codes of behavior, many of which would probably be dispensed with under a more demanding way of life under tougher conditions.

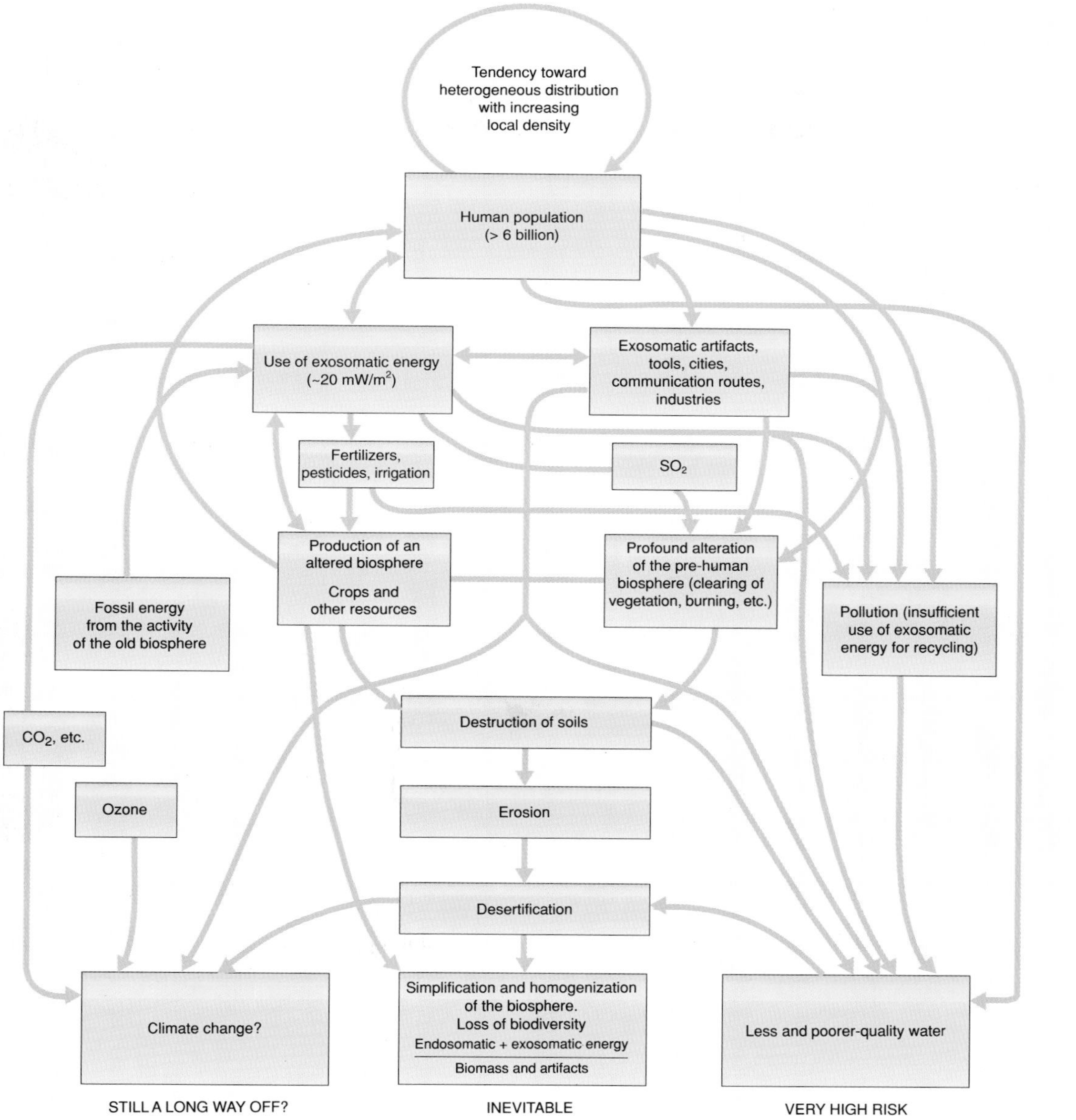

209 Humans have acted, and continue to do so, in a regressive manner on the rest of the biosphere, which is leading to a stage of succession that is nearest to its beginnings. It is all too often forgotten that in the initial stages of succession, species like the human one had little to do. With a population of 6,000 million (which could exceed 8,000 million by the year 2025), certain dangers related to human behavior are particularly threatening. Only the incorporation of guidelines that have been revised in light of our expanding knowledge about the organization and function of the biosphere; and in particular, the role of humans in it, could partly remedy this tendency. In a similar way to what happens in ecological succession, a way to maintain a hypothetical "sustainable development" has to take into account the need to reduce the consumption of energy, and the need for wise and careful use of available knowledge. *[Diagram: Biopunt, from an original by Margalef]*

In ecological development energy is substituted for by information. The work carried out to begin with persists as a structure and, so to speak, lightens the task later on in the development process. The accumulation of live and dead wood in a forest, and the enriching of persistent organic matter (humus) in the soil, is all part of the domination of living organisms over their environment, which is one of the characteristics of succession. Wind and water can disturb low-growing vegetation, but trees benefit from of these natural agents. It is clear that the initial price mankind must pay for the accumulation of information is relatively high in terms of energy, but that this is paid back later, as if the energy were invested in a savings account. This is adequately demonstrated by the history of technology. The initial efforts are not wasted because they give rise to equipment and procedures for subsequent use which are more economical in terms of energy. We can regard the history of technology as a magnificent process of exchanging information for energy with an increasing body of information supplied by the most recent stages of history.

Perhaps it would be advisable to go deeper into this perspective, since we now find ourselves facing the exhaustion of our energy sources. The excesses of the past cannot continue. But largely thanks to our past excesses we have a vast quantity of both scientific and technological information, which could

210 The large libraries, to which today we have to add the large bibliographic or documentation data bases, are enormous storehouses of information accumulated by humans in the course of centuries of intellectual work. Advances in informatics allows us ever more easy and convenient access to all this information, so that the need to record new information in published volumes is progressively reduced. In the reading rooms of many libraries, especially the larger ones, such as this one at the former British Library, it is increasingly more common to find—alongside traditional catalogues—computer terminals that allow consultation and also make standardized bibliographies readily available to the readers. *[Photo: AGE Fotostock]*

make the maintenance of our future civilization more economical in terms of energy. It may be that this possible exchange of energy for information is the only basis on which we can continue to speak of "ongoing" or "sustainable" development. It is only justifiable if there is a significant replacement of energy by information, and in a way similar to ecological succession. In other words, energy consumption must be reduced and made more effective by means of more sensible and economical use of the knowledge we have.

To go back to the meaning of the manipulations of the production/biomass ratio, starting with the ratio P/(B+N) we progress to; endosomatic energy = (biological production) + (external energy) / (B + external artifacts + accumulated information).

As long as that quotient diminishes, this is possible. This obviously implies the question of devaluation, be it gradual or sudden, of accumulated information. This is the inherent problem of all information: if it is useful or if not and can only be considered as noise, in the sense that it cannot be used for statistical or technical purposes. We believe that war, like a forest fire, represents a bad investment of energy; it cannot be regained as information, although it may clear the way for the use of other information that may have previously been suppressed.

Awareness of the exploitation of the biosphere

During the 1960s, when integrated circuitry or chips were incorporated into computer technology, allowing for speeds of some 100,000 operations per second, the way was paved for the world to begin to be conscious of the fact that the exploitation of the biosphere and of its irreplaceable natural resources by humankind was reaching its limits. This was also the time when the first images of Earth seen from space popularized the metaphor of the Earth as a spaceship, lost in the immensity of space, with mankind as its crew. It could be said that the history of mankind includes a past phase of local interaction with other natural ecosystems which regulated populations and stabilized the environment; a future phase of regulation which would be very similar but on a universal scale; and in between a transitional

211 The gradual shortage of many resources and the obsolescence of crude technology makes images such as this of an abandoned metallurgical workshop (Charter Towers, Queensland, Australia), ever more common in the industrialized world at the tail end of the 20th century. At the gates of the post-industrial society, this 1800s idea of industry seems destined to be forgotten along with the socio-ecological ideas linked with it: all-out expansion, ignoring aesthetic values, forgetting optimal criteria for the exploitation of resources, etc. Certain moral ideas are also likely to be forgotten, including the lack of solidarity in the distribution of economic benefits resulting from production. One could say that the collapse of the iron and steel industry, a remnant of the industrial society of the 19th century, precedes the dawn of the progressive post-industrialization of the 21st century. *[Photo: CLB-TPS / Index]*

phase of accelerated expansion and border strategies, the end of which we are rapidly and fatally approaching.

Accelerated expansion, which experienced a profound upheaval in 1973 with the oil crisis, and a subsequent series of minor disturbances, is still not over, but the growing capacity to manipulate information, both in cultural terms via new means of communication and in genetic terms through genetic engineering, are perhaps making way for the beginning of the third phase. If nothing else, it looks as if a change of attitude is beginning to occur which will bring humankind back to a consciousness of their integration with the rest of the biosphere and an awareness of the fact that, without renouncing the dominant role they have reached, humans should make an effort to maintain the viability of that role under conditions that are compatible with the survival of the species.

Given that the effect of mankind's increasing but unequal use of external energy, both in the past and the present, has been to increase the rate of renewal and slow down the rest of the biosphere, in addition to polluting the atmosphere (burning fossil fuels, for example), these efforts should be based on the ability to foresee, to control the present and mould the future,together with the accumulation of information and putting it to effective use. It appears that this has begun to happen over the last few decades of the twentieth century during which, for the first time, a growing number of people outside specialist circles, has become awareof the unity and limits of the biosphere and the fact that it is the only habitat where mankind can survive, as well as being the only conceivable supply of a series of resources necessary for survival and quality of life. A decisive contribution was made by media coverage of the pictures of Earth taken from space, particularly from 1973 onwards when images were provided by satellites, purportedly designed for observing the Earth, such as the LANDSAT, or meteorological satellites, which are now a feature of everyday life. Another contributing factor is the widespread knowledge of problems on a global level, such as possible climatic change or the disquieting thinning of the ozone layer over the Antarctic and the Arctic. The pursuit and solving of these problems has only been made by possible by technological advances linked to the rapid progress of computer technology during this period.

While there are many good reasons to distrust any hypothetical capacity of mankind to learn from his own mistakes or to work collectively on projects which do not bring tangible or immediate benefits, it would appear that a moderately optimistic view of the times we are living in is still possible. The twenty-year gap between the 1972 "Earth Summit" Stockholm conference and the one held in Rio de Janeiro in 1992, could constitute the dividing line between "before" and "after" for future historians as regards a widespread new awareness of the debt mankind owes to the biosphere which we originate from, on which our existence depends; and from which we cannot be separated, but which we are also capable of leaving in a state which will not permit our survival, even if we do not actually destroy it. We have moved on from the reports which apocalyptically warned us that we only have one Earth and that its resources are limited, and that these resources will not support indefinite demographic and economic growth, to reports which offer proposals for changes in collective attitudes, giving us the opportunity to make a conscious effort to redress the current state of our planet and to plan for the management of the future of the biosphere, as an inescapable condition for ensuring a future for generations as yet unborn.

2
The visible biosphere

1. Soil and bioclimate

1.1 The atmosphere on the Earth's surface today

The visible biosphere, as we see it today, is the result of a very long process, as we have seen in the previous chapters. But this result shows itself and is organized according to prevailing atmospheric conditions. In effect, history allows us to understand the past, but not to explain the present. The present results from combining the factors inherited from the past in accordance with the possibilities allowed by present-day conditions.

We cannot even begin to understand the present-day biosphere without considering the processes that have shaped the oxygenated layer (21% oxygen, 78% nitrogen, as basic components) suitable for the maintenance of life or, without taking account of the even more fascinating string of events, that have caused life to be organised in the form of the species existing today. These issues have been covered above.

However, our perception of the present, our only immediate and obvious reality, is not limited to the schematic and frequently inductive or deductive ideas to which we can reduce the past. The present-day biosphere is all around us, diverse, effervescent and alive. we ourselves form part of it and we intervene—in no small way—in the processes that take place in it. A summary description, for all that it leaves out details, still requires a lengthy consideration of factors and elements. This is in fact the object of this work.

The arrangement and functioning of the different elements of the biosphere are conditioned more than anything by the climate, and also by the soil. For some time the human species has also played an important organising role (or disorganising role, according to one's point of view) and has left its mark in all the biomes it has occupied. All these factors have combined to shape the biosphere we know.

1.2 Bioclimatic factors

The distribution of climates on the planet is related to the rotation and orbit of the Earth. Rotation determines the difference between day and night while the orbit gives rise to important differences in the amount of solar energy received per unit area, not because the distance between the Sun and the Earth changes significantly during the year but because of the inclination of the axis of the planet's rotation in relation to the plane which contains its orbit around the Sun. The main factors which determine the climate are very much influenced by latitude, even though other parameters such as the degree of continentality or altitude tend to vary them. Each zone, then, on the planet represents a combination of climatic variables which basically depend on its location.

Climatic variables

The climate is an essential conditioning factor of the biosphere's landscapes, especially in the case of terrestrial ecosystems. The climate acts as a whole, but it can be broken down into factors to allow us to studt the effect of each one on the others. The most important climatic factors are temperature, humidity and atmospheric pressure, even though the last of these only has an influence on landscapes as far as it affects the distribution of the first two.

Radiation and temperature

Solar radiation passes through the air without heating it up and falls on the Earth's surface. This heats up and as a result emits long-wave radiation at the same time as it gives off heat through conduction to the layers of air which come into contact with it. Nevertheless, this can produce a flow of important latent heat associated with the changes in the state of the water (melting, evaporation).

As a consequence of the inclination of the Earth's axis of rotation, solar radiation strikes each zone

212 The present appearance of the biosphere cannot be disassociated from human activity. Practically no landscape is free from changes directly caused or indirectly induced by human activities. Throughout the past few centuries, communication systems in particular have been weaving a dense network of roads and telegraph and telephone wires that connect, anatomically or physiologically, every corner with virtually every other. This view of a wood with a road running through it represents one of the most common landscapes: the humanized landscape, the biosphere we see. *[Photo: AGE Fotostock]*

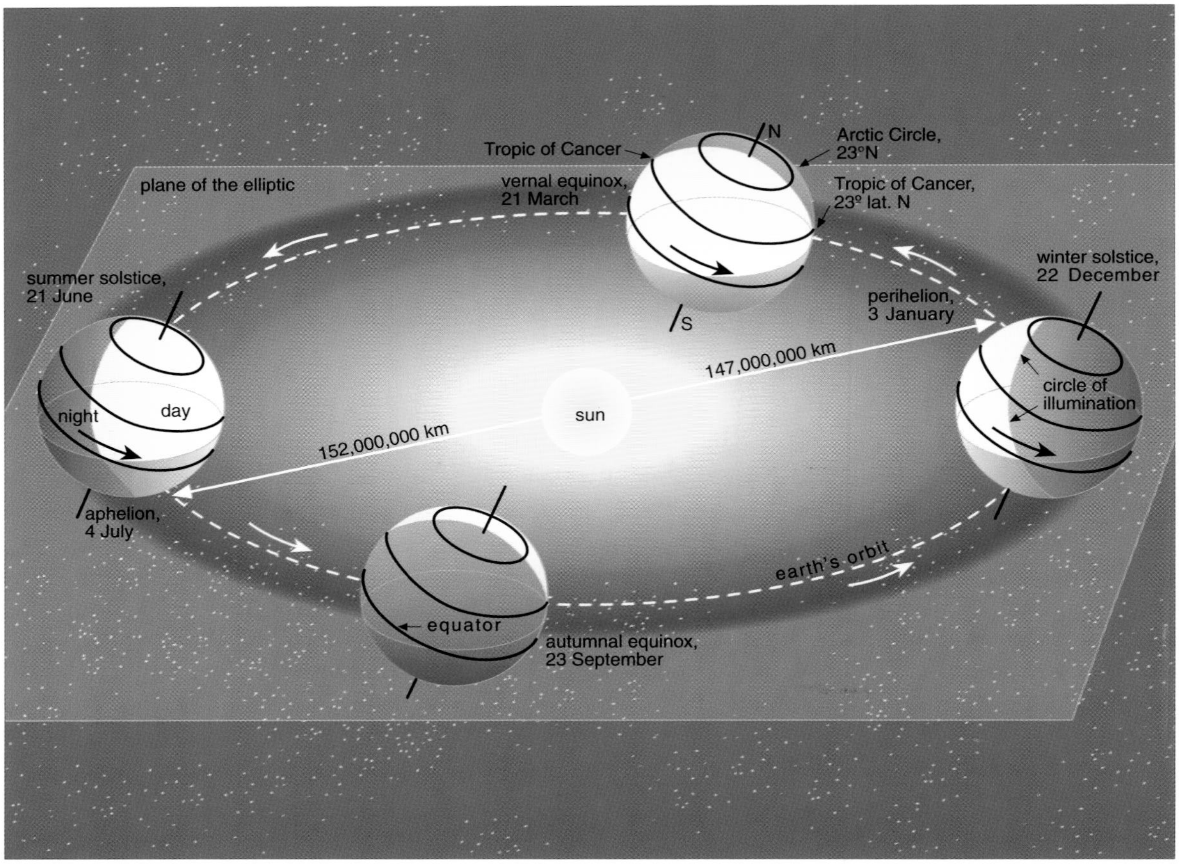

213 The Earth rotates during the year around the sun, describing an orbit whose intersection with the plane in which the sun occurs is called the ecliptic. During its rotation the Earth is at an angle and this inclination is what determines the seasons, since the sun's rays do not fall on the entire Earth's surface at the same angle. *[Diagram: Editrònica, from various sources]*

on the planet at a different angle, depending on the distance from the equator (latitude) and the time of year. This means that the lower latitudes receive the radiation almost perpendicularly while the higher ones receive solar radiation at an oblique angle and so they heat up much less than the former. What is more, the low latitudes receive the same radiation throughout the year, contrasting with the high latitudes where the angle of incidence of solar radiation changes in a very markedly, giving rise to much colder periods than in the other latitudes. This phenomenon is called *seasonality*.

Despite these difficulties, the extreme temperatures recorded at different points on the planet vary within relatively narrow bands because of the efficient mechanism for the transport of heat through masses of air and water. Thus, apart from phenomena related to geothermometry, temperatures go from extremes of 176ºF to -126ºF (80ºC to -88ºC). The temperature on most of the planet, though, varies little (104ºF and 14ºF [40ºC and -10ºC]), an ideal environment for living beings.

Humidity and precipitation

The availability of water, relayed to atmospheric humidity and precipitation, is another important climatic factor. Also important are, the changes in the state of the water, associated with it's circulation cycles which imply quantitatively important transfers of heat. We have to bear in mind that the calorific capacity of the air is around 0.20 cal/g while the heat involved in water melting and evaporating is 79.7 and 540 cal/g respectively. This means that the hydrological cycle leads to the transport of large quantities of heat without there necessarily being important changes in temperature.

Both atmospheric humidity and precipitation are easily measurable. The first is usually expressed as *relative humidity*, which is the actual vapour pressure expressed as a percentage of the saturation vapour pressure which would be possible at the same air temperature. Precipitation is measured in litres per square metre (l/m^2), equivalent to millimetres of rain. The average or total values have a limited value as climatic variables as their distribution in time is fundamental in defining the climate. Variation in humidity and precipitation over time is very irregular, contrasting with temperature which is closely linked to seasonal variations in the amount of sunshine associated with latitude. The spatial and temporal distribution of precipitation is closely related to atmospheric and oceanic circulation.

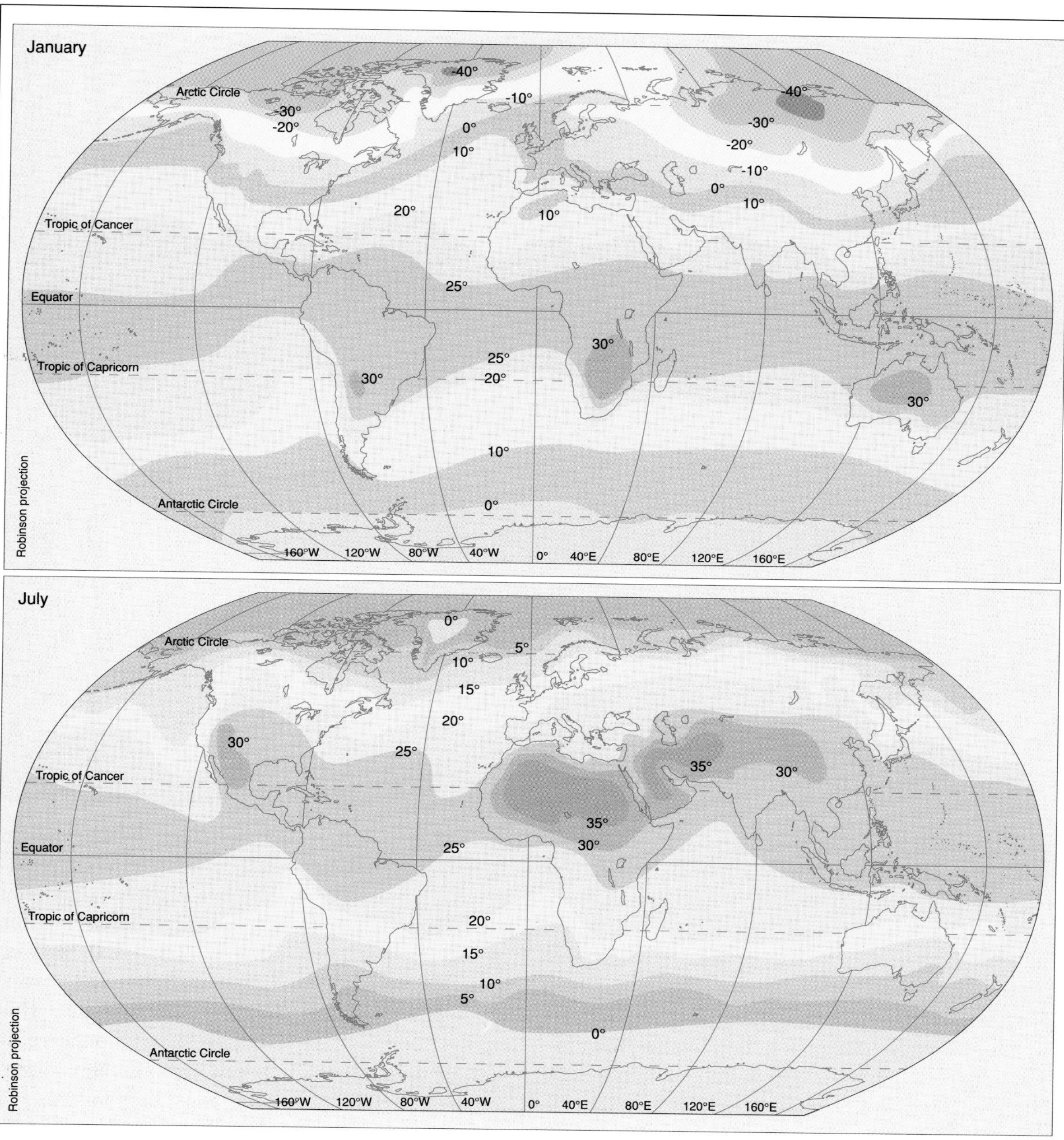

214 Distribution of the mean world temperature in the months of January and July. The isotherms, the lines that join up points with the same temperature, show a certain uniformity in an E-W direction due to the progressive decrease in insolation from the equator to the poles. This uniformity can be better seen in the southern hemisphere, below the 25th parallel, where there is more ocean than continent. In the northern hemisphere the isotherms show considerable deviations towards the north or the south when they cross continents to the oceans; especially in the month of January, when the contrast between the temperatures of the continents and the oceans is most marked. In general terms, one can state that there is a temperature gradient from the equator to the poles and an increase in the fluctuations in temperature in the same direction. The mean temperature in the northern hemisphere is 59.4°F (15.2°C) while in the southern hemisphere it is 37.9°F (3.3°C), but the difference between the means in January and July is 57.7°F (14.3°C) and 45.3°F (7.4°C) respectively. The maximum temperatures of the Earth are around 158°F to 176°F (70-80°C), taken at the surface of dry dark soils, in a calm atmosphere; they are 136°F (57.8°C) in the shade, while the minimums recorded are -108°F (-77.8°C) to –117.9°F (-83.3°C) in Antarctica. In more southern zones of the southern hemisphere there are no records of temperarure changes because of the lack of fixed observatories to record data continuously. *[Cartography: Editrònica, from various sources]*

Atmospheric and oceanic circulation

Atmospheric and oceanic circulation implies the transport of great quantities of heat and water between very distant points on the planet. In fact as regards the balance of radiation received and given off by the Earth's surface at different latitudes, we can see a clear surplus of heat at low latitudes and a negative balance at the high ones. In other words, at high latitudes more heat is lost than is received through radiation. These differences are compensated by the active transport of heat associated with oceanic currents and air masses. Atmospheric circulation is determined by these differences in warming, which means that air rises in zones near the equator and is replaced by colder and denser air from high latitudes. However, a single convection cell is not formed, but rather a descent of partially cooled down air takes place at medium latitudes. This apparently simple model of circulation is in reality complicated by the appearance of a deflecting force (*the Coriolis force*) derived from the movement of the Earth's rotation and which tends to divert paths towards the right in the northern hemisphere and in the opposite direction in the southern hemisphere.

Furthermore, zones dominated by the rising or falling of air become respectively zones of low and high pressure. This complicates the circulation model even further. Low pressures appear in the equatorial zone, in a band at middle to high latitudes and above the large continental masses, when they heat up intensely because of the strong sunshine. High pressures, on the other hand, have a tendency to form above oceans in subtropical latitudes and also above continents which

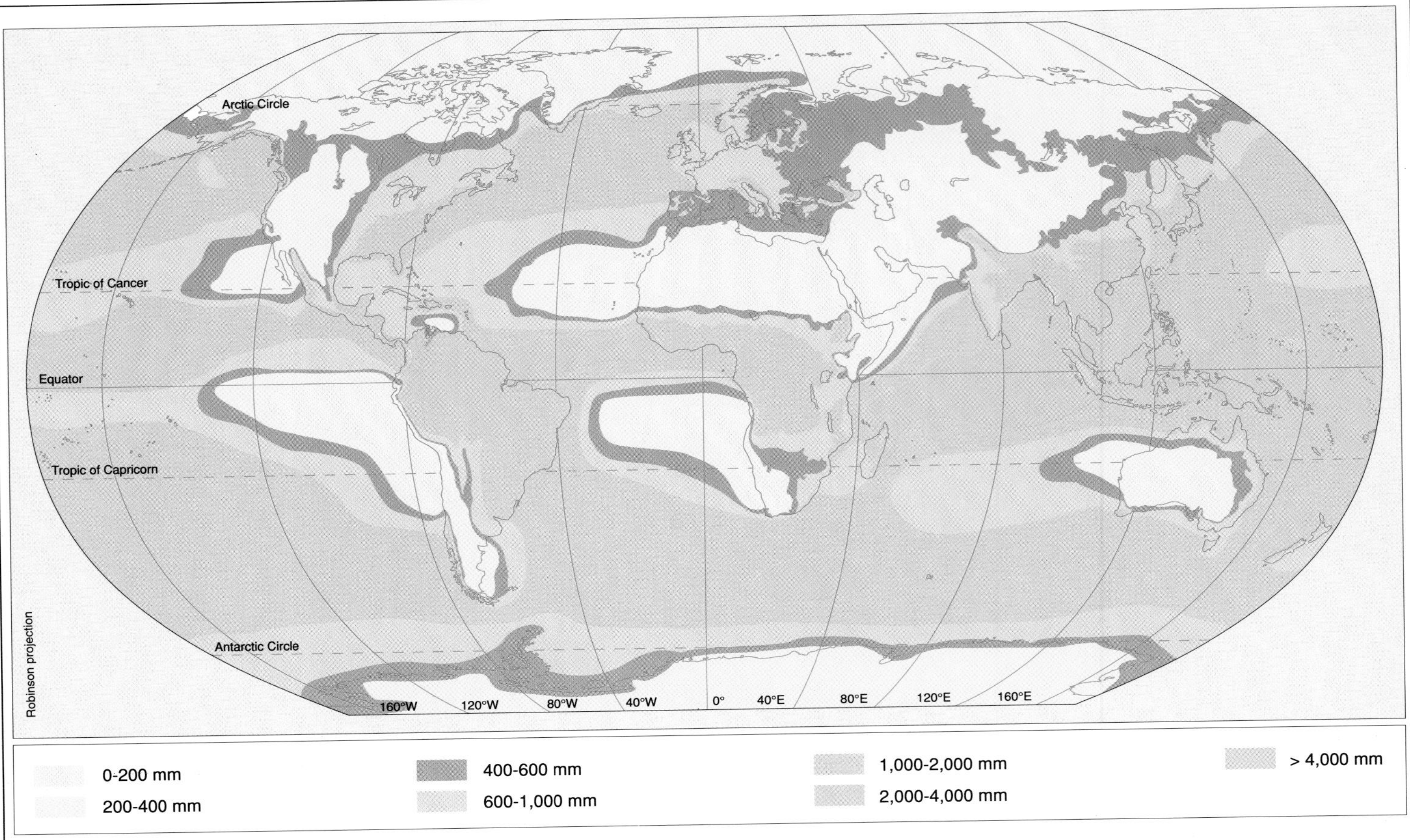

215 Mean annual precipitation. In the equatorial zone, rainfall is very abundant, generally more than 79 in (2,000 mm) annually, since the high temperatures and the large expanses of ocean produce a great amount of water vapor. In the centers of high pressure in the subtropics, rainfall is scarce: this is the reason for the deserts in North Africa, Arabia and Iran, South Africa, and the west coast of South America. The effect of the trade winds on a coastal chain of mountains produces orographic rainfall as in Central America and Madagascar, where the rainfall can exceed 79 in (2,000 mm) annually. The dry coastal belt of the Peruvian littoral and the Kalahari desert are situated to the east of the subtropical oceanic anticyclones, where the air descends in a parcel from above and is warmed because of the vertical movement (adiabatically). The rains of the subtropical zone are zenithal, while those of the extratropical temperate zone depend on wind circulation (cyclonic).
[Cartography: Editrònica]

have cooled down during the cold seasons. The effect of these zones of high and low pressure on atmospheric and oceanic circulation is considerable.

Wind has a tendency to go from high to low pressures, which is the same as saying that the direction of its movement is perpendicular to the isobars (lines which join points which are at the same pressure). The Coriolis force, however, diverts this trajectory by 90º, giving rise to a wind which moves parallel with the isobars. The friction of the wind over the planet's surface also helps to divert the wind, giving rise to models of cyclonic circulation (*low pressure*) and anticyclonic (*high pressure*), which in low-pressure areas become centers of convergence and rising of masses of air, and in high-pressure ones become centers of descent and divergence of cold air. This has important climatic effects as the rise and consequent cooling of masses of air is associated with the formation of clouds and precipitation, due to the condensation of humidity derived from the drop in temperature. On the other hand, in the case of the high ones, the descent of masses of air leads to warming by compression, giving rise to dry air, in other words, stable weather without precipitation.

Low pressures or storms formed at medium and high latitudes also lead to the mixture and interaction of polar masses of air with others of tropical origin. This contact, or boundaries, between different masses of air gives rise to so-called fronts, which are nothing more than contact surfaces between these masses of air in which condensation of water vapour becomes spectacularly active, which eventually leads to precipitation. The distribution of pressures affects, then, not only atmospheric circulation but also the distribution of precipitation on the planet.

Oceanic circulation, which also transports large quantities of heat from low latitudes to high ones, derives from the gradients of density and temperature of masses of water and the frictional drag caused by prevailing winds. Thus, warm currents are formed in an equator-pole direction and cold currents in the opposite direction. The prevailing atmospheric circulation, adjusted by the distribution of the centers of high and low pressures, also contributes to the frictional drag of masses of water. Finally, the Coriolis force diverts these currents in the directions just indicated, giving rise to more or less closed circuits which have a tendency to turn clockwise in the northern hemisphere and anticlockwise in the southern hemisphere.

The buffering effect of climatic gradients derived from oceanic currents is evidently much more

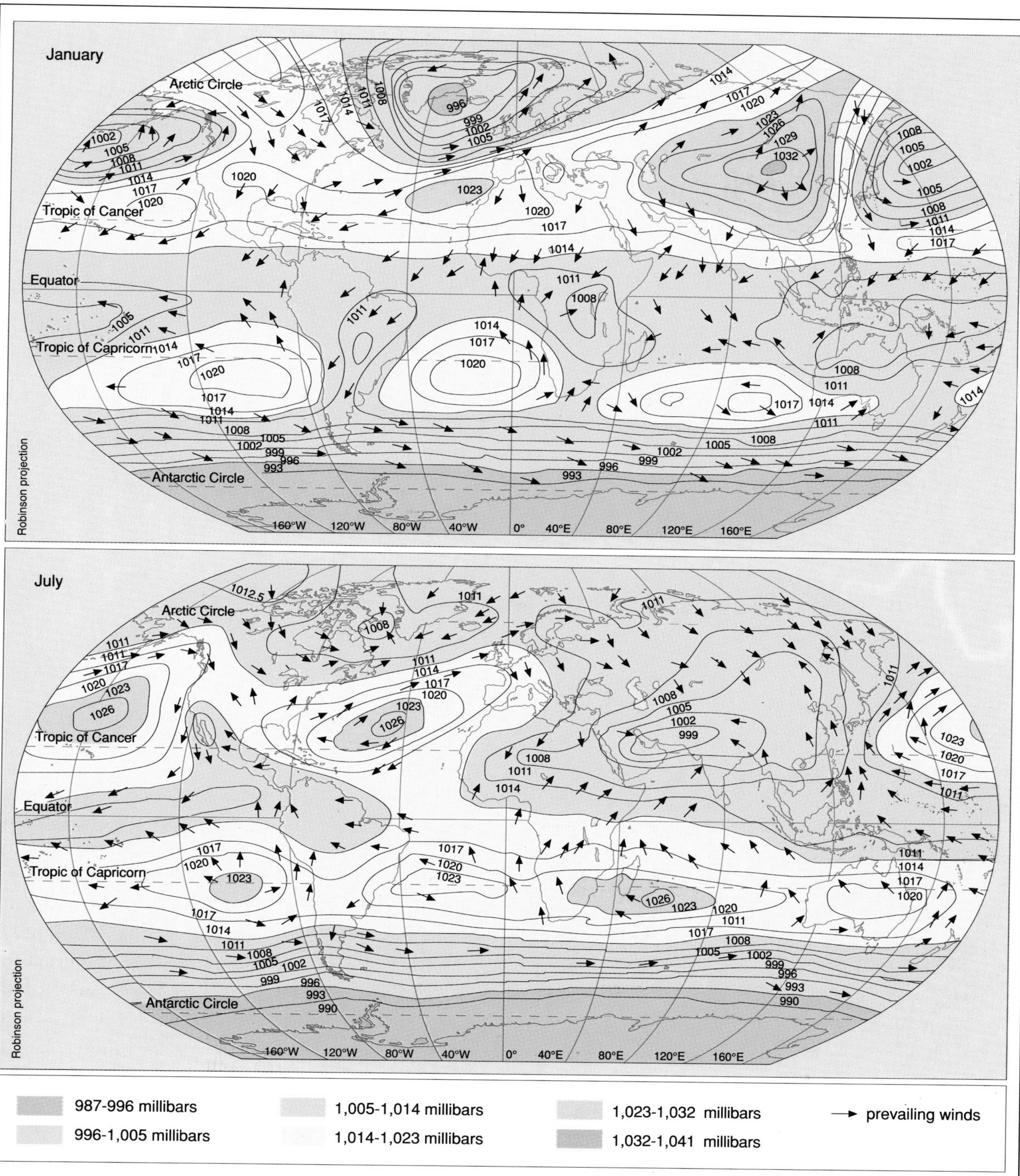

216 The circulation of the atmosphere and of the oceans is due to differences in insolation between regions at different latitudes and tends to redistribute the heat on a global scale. The atmosphere is heated up from beneath (at high pressure) and cools down above (at low pressure), while the sea warms up and cools in the same area, at the same pressure. For this reason convection cells in the atmosphere are vertical, while in the sea they are horizontal. The air of the atmosphere circulates between the equator and the poles, but recirculates also in each of the convection cells. *[Cartography: Editrònica, from various sources]*

important in continental zones near the coasts, while it is negligible in the interior of the large continental land masses. Atmospheric circulation, on the other hand, has effects which are felt in all the planet's zones.

Latitude and altitude

We could imagine that the distribution of climates follows a pattern that is closely associated with latitude, which would give rise to parallel homogeneous bands, from the equator to the poles. In reality, however, the distribution of climates follows a considerably more complicated scheme because of the effect that the variable proportions between seas and continents at different latitudes has over it.

We have already mentioned the effect of continental and oceanic masses on the distribution of low and high pressure areas, or rather, in relation to atmospheric and oceanic circulation. Furthermore, these masses also have direct effects on temperature and rainfall. In the interior of a large continental mass, temperatures becomes much lower in winter and higher in summer, increasing the thermal oscillation. Parallel with this, we find a decrease in precipitation over the continents at medium and high latitudes as a consequence of the blocking effect of continental anticyclones on

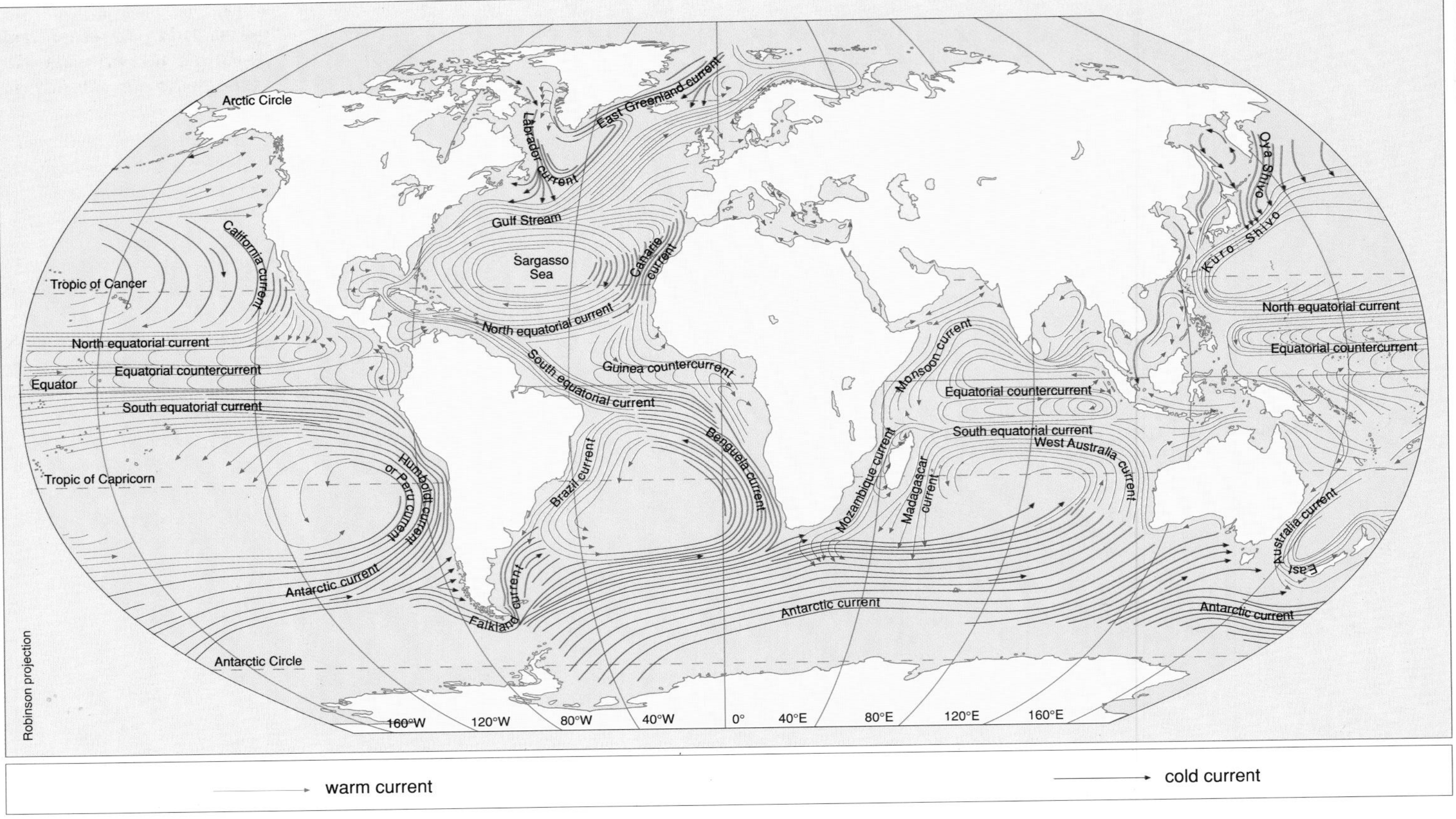

217 Surface circulation of oceanic water, in which the cold currents are indicated by blue arrows and the warm currents by red arrows. Note the circular type movements surrounding the subtropical anticyclones, at some 25° or 30° latitude N or S. An equatorial current indicates the trade wind belt (although the trade winds blow towards the NW and SW, the movement of the water follows the parallels). The N and S equatorial currents are separated by an equatorial countercurrent. At low altitudes and along the western edge of the continents, the equatorial current is directed towards the poles and creates a current parallel to the coast. As regards the poles in the northern hemisphere, where the Glacial Arctic Ocean is surrounded by continents, the cold water moves towards the equator along the western edge of the straits that connect it with the Atlantic basin. In the Antarctic region the there is an Antarctic polar current which moves clockwise. *[Cartography: Editrònica, from various sources]*

depressions. Continentality, then, is associated with drier climates, which are colder in winter and warmer in summer than those at similar latitudes in coastal areas. This means that the isotherms, or lines which join points with equal temperatures, are not parallel with the equator but are deformed by the effect of the continents. The unequal distribution of the continental masses in both hemispheres gives rise to much more oceanic climates, in other words, mild in the southern hemisphere and with a much more marked degree of continentality in the northern hemisphere. In fact, one part of this distortion can be attributed to the oceanic currents which, as warm waters are carried towards higher latitudes, moderate the climate of the coastal regions. In contrast, cold currents coming from high latitudes provoke climatic cooling in the zones they affect. The North Atlantic current, which heats up the British and Scandinavian coasts, and the Humboldt and Benguela currents, which cool down the southwestern coasts of Africa and South America respectively, are good examples of these effects.

Furthermore, within continents we still find the effects or distortions caused by altitude. Temperature decreases by some 1.1ºF (0.6ºC) for each 328 ft (100 m) of altitude and it is for this reason that mountain climates are colder than lower areas at the same latitude. This cooling down of the air facilitates the condensation of vapor and the formation of clouds and fogs which make mountain climates more humid.

An increase in altitude has often been compared to a displacement towards higher latitudes, both in terms of climatic effects and effects on the landscape, but this tends not to be so in the majority of cases. This simple scheme might be valid when dealing with modest differences in altitude, but it loses validity in cases of altitudinal gradients of thousands of meters. To begin with, above the level of condensation, the mountain climate becomes simultaneously drier and colder. Furthermore, the altitudinal gradient is not associated with a strong variation in the length of the day or night, that is, the total quantity of radiation received and its seasonal variation. All in all this means that high mountains have climatic conditions which are quite different from those of flat lands at higher latitudes, although there are some similarities.

The distribution of climates over the Earth depends, then, on latitude, continentality and altitude, but is also affected by the proximity of cold or warm oceanic currents. The variety of landscapes in the biosphere and their complex distribution are a consequence of this climatic distribution.

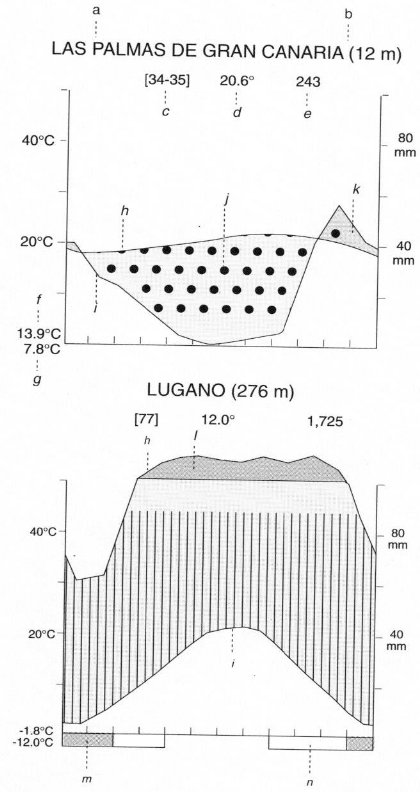

218 Pluviothermic diagrams bring together and relate the two principal climatic parameters, temperature and rainfall, based on their absolute annual values and annual distribution. A quick look at the diagram gives an intuitive idea of the climate of the place studied. The situation in a map of pluviothermic diagrams obtained in different parts of the world allows an easy comparison to be made of their respective climates and to distinguish homoclimatic areas, that is, areas of the world with the same climate. These are bioclimatic zones or domains. *[Diagram: Editrònica, from various sources]*

a: name
b: altitude above sea level
c: number of years of observation (temperature-precipitation)
d: mean annual temperature (in °C)
e: mean annual precipitation (in mm)
f: mean daily minimum temperature of coldest month (in °C)
g: extreme minimum temperature recorded (in °C)
h: mean monthly temperature curve
I. mean monthly precipitation curve
j: (dotted area): dry episode (h above i)
k: (striped area): wet episode (h below i)
l: (solid area): very wet episode (more than 100 mm/month, scale 1:10)
m: (blue band): cold period (months with mean daily minimum below 0°C)
n: (white band): period with frosts (months with absolute minimum below 0°C)

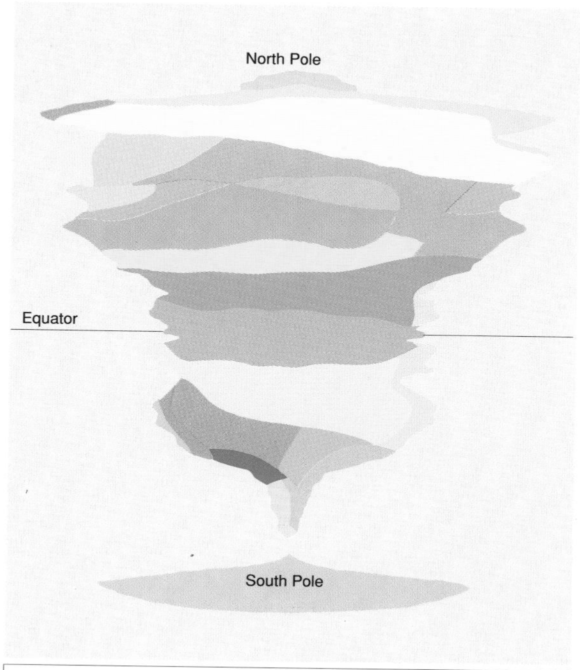

EXTRATROPICAL ZONES OF THE NORTHERN HEMISPHERE

- Hot desert
- Cold continental desert
- Semidesert or steppe
- Sclerophyllic woody vegetation with winter rains
- Steppe with cold winter
- Evergreen forest with warm temperate climate
- Deciduous forest, green in summer
- Oceanic forest
- Boreal conifer forest
- Subarctic birch forest
- Tundra
- Cold desert

TROPICAL ZONES

- Equatorial rainforest
- Equatorial rainforest with mountain rainfall determined by trade winds
- Deciduous tropical forest, green during the rainy season, or wet savannah
- Tropical scrub or dry savannah

EXTRATROPICAL ZONES OF THE SOUTHERN HEMISPHERE

- Coastal desert
- Cloudy desert
- Sclerophyllic forest with winter rains
- Semidesert
- Subtropical grassland
- Warm temperate rainforest
- Forest with cold temperate climate
- Semidesert with cushion vegetation or steppe
- Subantarctic tussock grassland
- Antarctic "inlandsis"

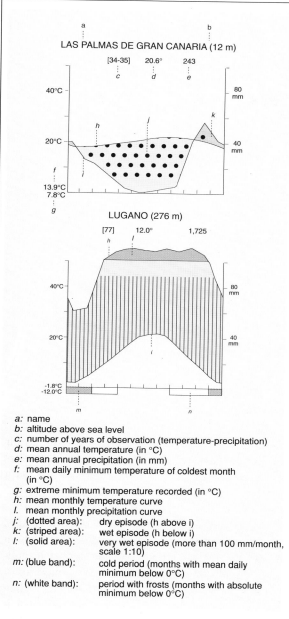

219 Distribution of land and sea by latitude in an ideal continent, in which the asymmetry of the vegetation zones in the northern and southern hemispheres, which coincides with equally irregular distribution of the climate, can be observed. The symmetry is maintained only at tropical latitudes, where it coincides in both hemispheres, but as one moves away from the equator, the asymmetry of the climate and the vegetation, and of land distribution, becomes more evident.
[Diagram: Biopunt, from H. Walter, 1976]

Types of climate

Many models for the definition and classification of climates have been tried, taking different climatic variables as their basis. Thus we can find classifications based on temperature, precipitation, or a combination of both. The most accurate and useful classifications as regards the interpretation of landscapes, are those that take into account both these variables and their distribution or variation throughout the year. The classifications derived from this methodology, such as the well-known Köppen-Geiger system, are of an empirical-quantitative nature; in other words, they start from measured variables and apply simple quantitative criteria like the value of the mean annual temperature, of thermic oscillation or of the annual rainfall. These sys-

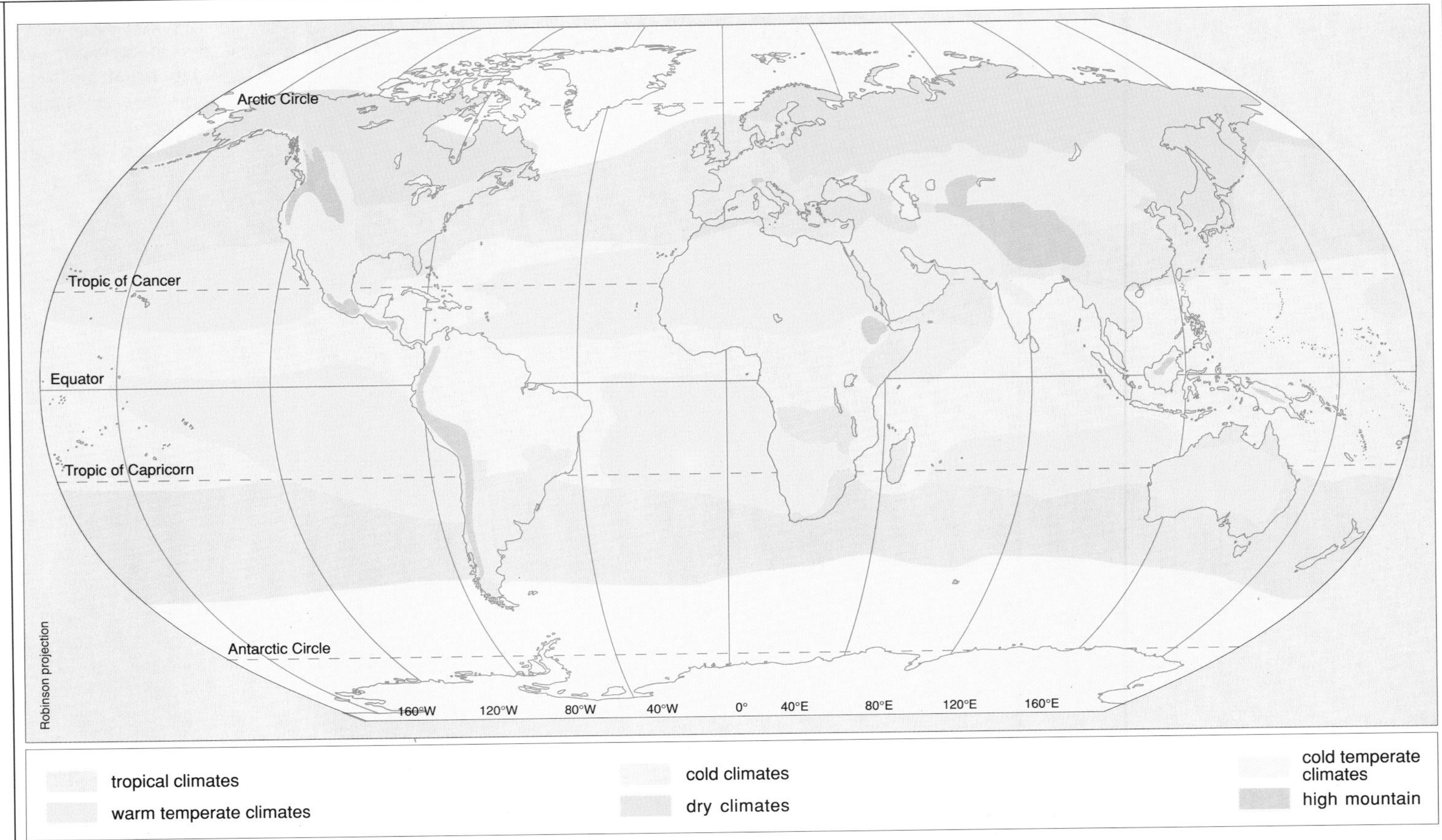

220 The climatic zones of the Earth, according to the classification of Köppen. The map shows the areas of the Earth with a similar climate and defines five major categories, as well as the high mountain. It allows one to appreciate that there is a certain symmetry on both sides of the equator, which is lost as one moves away from the equatorial belt. But there are asymmetrical conditions to the N and S of the equator, caused by the predominance of oceanic surface in the S hemisphere that affects the climate in the sense of making it cooler and more in equilibrium and leads to the temperate zone being little developed (only South America passes slightly the line of 40° latitude S). In the Southern hemisphere the equivalent of the boreal zone is lacking. *[Cartography: Editrònica, based on Strahler, 1984]*

tems are useful for the definition of large climatic units, but not so good for detecting more subtle variations which are often of great importance in modifying the landscape.

This sort of classification is based essentially on the climatic requirements of certain vegetation types, and divides the planet into the following climatic regions: the *equatorial zone* (high rainfall, hot temperatures and daily thermal oscillations which are greater than seasonal ones); the *tropical zone* (a perceptible seasonal oscillation of temperatures and rainfall, increasing during the warm season); the *arid subtropical zone* (temperatures which show a clear seasonal oscillation and very weak rainfall); the *transition zone* (with winter rains, a hot and dry summer and moderately cold and humid winters); the *temperate zone* (moderately cold summer and cold winters, but abundant rainfall of cyclonic origin throughout the year. The length of winter and the greater or lesser continentality determine the definition of some subzones); and the *arctic zone* (short, cold summer without nights, a long, cold and dark winter and weak rainfall spread out throughout the year).

Much more flexible classification methods have been developed which arrive at a much more accurate definition of the *bioclimate*, in other words of the conditions of cold and heat and humidity and aridity which affect living beings. It is clear that the same precipitation can give rise to biological conditions of dryness or humidity depending on the temperatures. Furthermore, the combination of the distribution of precipitation and temperature is also a factor which defines the bioclimate as the fact that the hottest or coldest seasons coincide with the rainy seasons is not without effect.

The phenomenon of microclimates

The microclimate or precise climatic conditions which organisms can tolerate at a specific location can be very different from the macroclimate which affects a particular zone. This depends not only on the size of the organisms but also on their position within the landscape. For example, small organisms which live deep down in the soil have a much more humid environment and with thermal oscillations which are much less marked than those which live on the soil's surface. Analogically, sunny areas will have much warmer and drier conditions than shady ones, converting a cold climate in a warm microclimate or a humid climate into a dry microclimate.

There are an infinite number of examples and they refer both to the aforementioned situation in space

221 The contrasts in landscape that correspond to local variations of the general climate in a particular area, can be very important as this photograph shows (Montseny, Catalonia]. In the northern hemisphere, on north-facing slopes, with relatively little sunshine, there are beechwoods that are deciduous, soft-leaved trees that like damp and cool conditions. In contrast, the south-facing slopes, under the Mediterranean sun, are covered with holm oaks, which are woods that are evergreen and coriaceous and tolerant of dry and hot conditions (see an autumnal view of this same zone in fig. 257). This kind of microclimatic change complicates considerably the structure of the landscape in areas with marked relief since it increases the diversity of ecological conditions. *[Photo: Ernest Costa]*

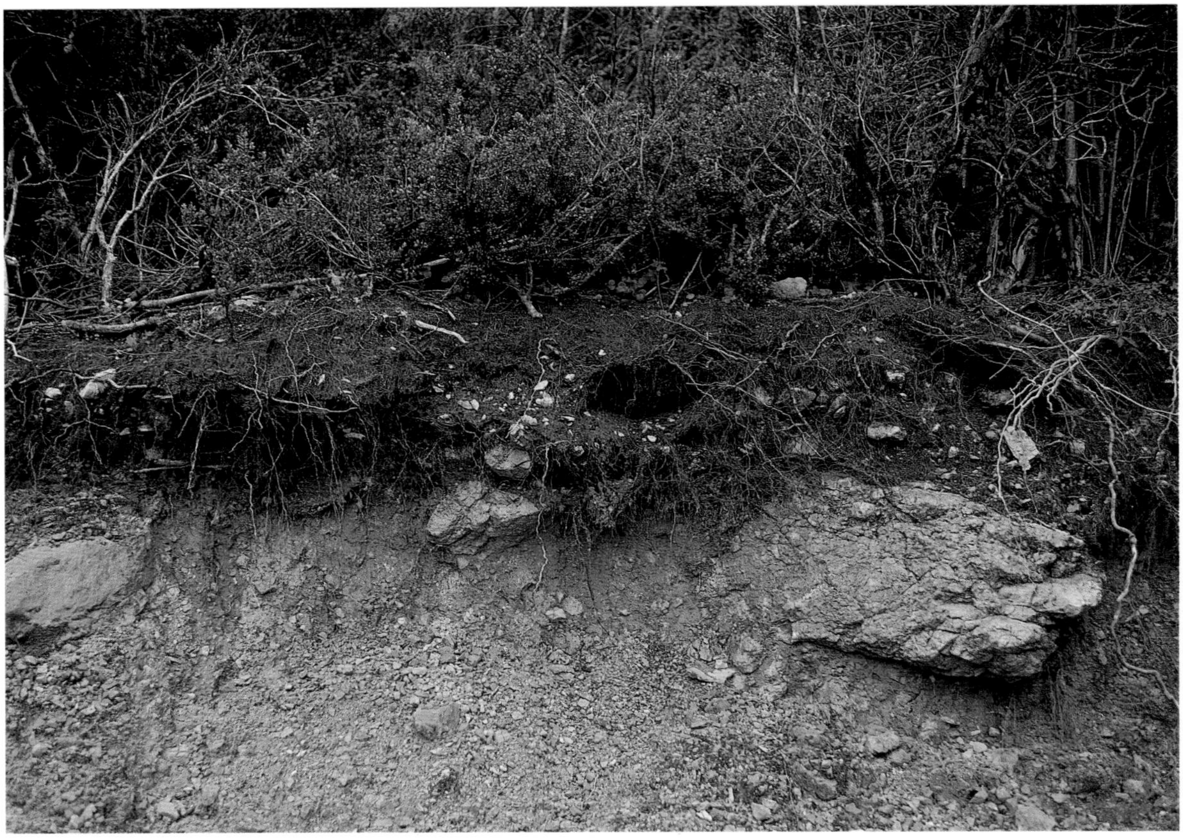

222 The presence of humus manifests itself in the darkening of the upper horizons of the soil by the phenomenon known as melanization. The speed of humification and the type of humus that ensues in a particular soil depends on the plant remains, the class of mineral substrate, and the climatic conditions.
[Photo: AGE Fotostock]

and to the vital strategy and the biological cycle of the organisms under consideration, as an organism can avoid unfavourable periods if there is a very short and reduced life cycle in those periods when the climatic conditions are less extreme. We will be able to comment on this when we analyse certain cases of adaptations to extremely dry or cold climates.

1.3 Edaphic factors

Plant growth requires a medium in which the roots can develop. This is only possible if the medium contains spaces which allow the roots to penetrate and then room for them to grow. In general this does not happen in rock which is normally a compact, hard and massive material, and when rock outcrops on the surface of an area, the growth of vegetation is impeded. Root penetration allows the plants to take root, but the system of spaces which allows the roots to penetrate must also contain air, so that the roots and other living organisms can breathe, and water, which transports nutrients in solution. The natural medium for plant growth is soil, because it satisfies these conditions. This is a functional conception of soil: throughout this chapter other concepts will be presented which will give an understanding, not only of soil's importance to life and to the biosphere, but also of its formation and its importance as a natural resource, and the need for its conservation.

From rocks to soil

Igneous and metamorphic rocks, which are formed in the heart of the lithosphere, have been subjected to either high temperatures or high pressure, or both simultaneously. When the materials lying on top of the rock break down and the rock breaks through to the surface, the conditions will be completely different to those which were present at its formation. The pressure of the material which lay above it, or lithostatic pressure, will have ceased, whilst at the same time the temperature will be much lower and there will be great differences in temperature during the day and during the course of the year. Contact with the atmosphere—which one must remember is an oxidising medium—and with water, will, however, be the most important factors in accelerating the transformation of rock at the earth's surface into more stable structures, under the conditions which characterise the biosphere. The changes brought about by these external factors, which lead to the formation of new materials, are called *weathering processes*.

Although the final product of weathering can not yet be called soil (those derived from compact rocks like

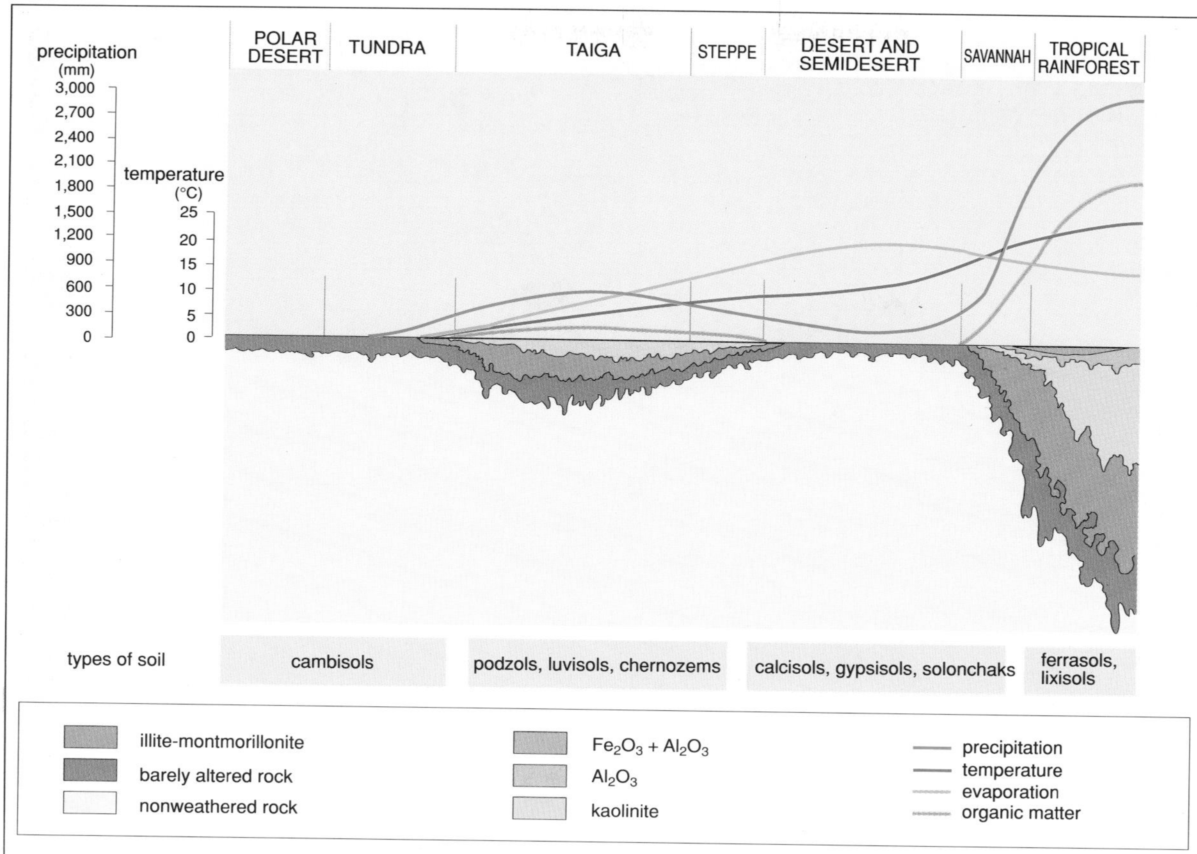

223 The weathering of soils and their components is shown in this diagram in which the environmental factors are indicated in a hypothetical transect going from the pole to the equator. Given that the temperature and degree of humidity decreases from the equator to the pole, the degree of weathering, like the decomposition of organic matter, is slower as the latitude increases in the Northern hemisphere. *[Diagram: Biopunt, from various sources]*

granite are often called *saprolites*, whilst those derived from less compact rocks, such as argillite [lutite], are often called *regoliths* which are often considered to include the soil), they nevertheless blend into and interact with soil forming (or edaphogenic) processes. Weathering does not end where edaphogenesis begins, but rather the two processes interact and take part in soil formation. The classical view of weathering in rocks and minerals established a division which, although pedagogically successful, was nevertheless a little inconsistent. Weathering was divided into three types: mechanical, chemical and even biological. The problem is one of scale in the first two cases, whilst in the last instance the role of certain agents is highlighted. Weathering processes, on the level of rock or large minerals causes materials to break down (*physical weathering*), whereas on the level of crystalline structure, this process takes place at a molecular or submolecular level (*chemical weathering*). In the first case, fragmentation could be considered a mechanical process where chemical or mineralogical changes in composition are not involved, whereas compositional change does occur when fragmentation takes place at a molecular or submolecular level.

Mechanical

The elimination of lithostatic pressure on a rock massif allows a degree of expansion. When it expands, the rock splits along a series of dilatation planes or expansion joints which are subparallel and perpendicular to the direction of pressure release. These planes occur every 3-10 ft (1-3 m) and can affect a mass of up to 66 ft (20 m) in depth. This type of process is typical in massive igneous rocks, in residual reliefs like "inselbergs," and explains the existence of large amounts of sandy soil above the granite, the formation of which is favoured by the passage of water along the fracture systems. The formation of typical granite landscapes, in which superimposed blocks can be seen, is related to this type of weathering by expansion. It should be pointed out, however, that although fragmentation favors the circulation of water throughout the rock mass, this circulation will also have repercussions at the molecular and submolecular level. Processes on one level or another act slowly and together, reinforcing each other's actions in the transformation of rocks and their mineral constituents.

Rocks that already lay on or near the surface are affected by heat transfer and temperature variations. The fact that rocks have a low heat conductivity and that the minerals which compose them have differing dilatation coefficients, suggests the existence of a process of chemical disintegration. The existence of such a process, called *thermoclasty* (insulation weathering), has been called into question because it

224 In cold zones, in the Chukchi peninsula (in the extreme east of Russia, asiatic zone of the Bering Strait), the cold provokes the fragmentation of the minerals in the soil by the formation of ice and its subsequent thawing; this phenomenon is known as *gelivation*. [Photo: Serguei A. Balandin]

has not been possible to reproduce it in the laboratory unless humidity is present: in other words, for such a process to be effective the existence of prior hydration or hydrolysis would seem to be necessary. Thermoclasty does not appear to explain spheroidal weathering in concentric layers (exfoliation or onion-skin weathering), common in rocks such as basanite. These instead seem to be due to the action of water. As regards heat transfer, and specifically in relation to physical change in water held in the rock, we find fragmentation due to the formation of ice (*gelivation* or *frost-wedging*). The more often the freeze-thaw cycle is repeated the more effective is the process. This process is more active in subarctic areas than in arctic regions, where thaws only occur once a year.

Rock can also be subjected to internal pressures from animals or the activity of organisms which live within it (*biomechanical processes*), or by the growth of salt crystals, which can cause the rock to fragment (*haloclasty*). These processes can be important in arid or semi-arid areas, as the phreatic layers can be saline, and also because the rocks themselves can contain a certain amount of salts which, on dissolving, precipitate inside the rock or on its surface, showing themselves as a white bloom (efflorescence). Alveolate weathering processes which operate on clays in semi-arid regions, such as the so-called "tafoni" of Corsica and Sardinia, can also be related to this type of crystal growth, as can the differentiated thermal expansion of salts held in the rock. In other environments, such as coastlines, these mechanisms can explain the rapid breakdown of schists.

Weathering by dissolving action is important in areas with gypsum ($CaSO_4{\cdot}2H_2O$). In general this process effects those soluble products resulting from weathering which can be transported vertically in solution (this is referred to as loss by leaching), or laterally along the surface. Both processes can be considered as part of the weathering system.

Chemical weathering

Fragmentation at the level of crystalline structure is due to exothermic chemical reactions, since weathering is a spontaneous process in nature. One of the principal processes is *hydration*, or combination with water molecules, which causes an increase in volume, thereby forming a new mineral. The change from anhydrite ($CaSO_4$) to gypsum ($CaSO_4{\cdot}2H_2O$) is a good example. Oxides of iron also play a part in processes of this type. The reaction of the mineral with water, or to put it in a more generic way, the reaction of the mineral with H^+ ions from various sources, a process known as *hydrolysis*, is the most important weathering process, because it affects all of the silicates and these are the principal rock-forming minerals. H^+ ions are able to enter into the crystalline structure and displace other ions such as, for example, the potassium ions (K^+) in orthoclase feldspars ($KAlSi_3O_8$), which then go into solution. The difference in size between the ions makes the structure unstable and liable to collapse.

The weathering of carbonated rocks requires the presence of carbon dioxide (CO_2) in the water to make its dissolution possible. Limestone, no matter how white it may appear nor how pure it may seem, will always contain silicates (clays) as impurities. These impurities are the materials left from which the soil will be formed once the carbonates have been lost by successive leaching of the bicarbonates into which the chalk has been transformed. The weathering of a rock with carbonic acid anhydride is called carbonation. The *rendzinas* and *terra rossa* originated in this way.

225 **Red earths** are fossil soils characterized by having an *A* horizon formed by impurities in the underlying calcareous rock, which undergoes a slow dissolution. The reddish color is caused by the high content of iron oxides, which were usually formed under past climatic conditions.
[Photo: David Badia / Biopunt]

The processes of oxidation-reduction (redox) also play a part in weathering, because rock can contain elements in a state of reduction. The iron of a biotite for example becomes unstable on contact with the atmosphere or with water and has a tendency to change, albeit slowly, from ferrous iron (Fe^{2+}) to ferric iron (Fe^{3+}) with an increase in volume which causes tensions within the rock of which the affected mineral forms part. The presence of chelating substances, which are liable to form coordination complexes with metallic ions, rather than causing the crystalline structure to collapse, weaken it, since they extract elements previously liberated by hydrolysis.

The result of weathering is a set of components, derived from the rock, some of which have been transformed to varying degrees, some of which are capable of reorganizing themselves *in situ*, thereby giving rise to minerals with new structures, and, finally, other, soluble, elements which can be transported by water. All of this shows just how complex the weathering system—or the process of transforming rocks into soil—really is.

Soil forming processes

A weathering process can be linked to a action-reaction model. The processes acting upon the rock will be of one type or another depending on the environmental conditions under which the system develops. Therefore the responses, that is to say the mineral components of soil in different parts of the biosphere at any given time, can also be completely different. There is not necessarily, therefore, a one-to-one correspondence between rock and regolith (or saprolite), nor between regolith (or saprolite) and soil. It should be remembered that weathering acts upon any type of material whatsoever, not just on *in situ* rocks, but also on transported materials and on soil itself. For that reason, by analogy, soil forming processes act upon a regolith or a saprolite, on transported material, or on previously existing soils. It is usual to talk about the mother rock in the first cases and parent material in the others. Not all the soils are the same, because the mother rock and the parent materials from which they are formed are not the same, and also because the weathering and soil formation systems evolve differently according to environmental conditions. The factors which control the system vary in importance according to geographical area, geomorphological position, and the stage reached in the soil forming process.

Since the beginning of soil science the principal factors involved in soil formation have been identified as climate, mother rock or parent material, living organisms (the vegetation and the soil biota), geomorphological position, and weather. This leads to a view of soil as a natural system whose origin is linked to the environment in which it was formed. Soil is a result of the continuous action of the climate and of living organisms on the parent material or mother rock, which occupies a particular place in the landscape. Its formation depends upon the length of time these factors have been at work and on their intensity.

In the humid tropical zone, for example, the processes of weathering and soil formation are usually very active because of the high temperatures (the rate of reaction doubles every 18ºF [10ºC]). Meanwhile the high rainfall means that the soil system loses its soluble elements by leaching as soon as they are liberated, thereby favouring the continuation of the reactions, and the final products will be the only ones that are possible under these conditions—clays poor in silicon (kaolinites), oxides of iron and aluminium (bauxites), etc. They are all acidic compounds, poor in bases and not very suitable for the sustaining natural vegetation or agriculture. On the other hand, if an area in a tropical region has poor drainage, leaching is slowed down and the products of weathering are resynthesised into new mineral components which are very different from the original ones. Silicon is not lost through leaching, and there might be bases like magnesium, and also possibly iron. Under these conditions the formation of silica-rich clays, such as smectites, is possible. The resultant soils, such as the vertisols, will be rich in swelling clays. These are fertile soils, though difficult to work. Likewise, it is the environmental conditions in which weathering and edaphogenesis take place which explain why the biosphere's mantle of soils is the way it is. These also explain why some areas are highly efficient and productive whilst others make life difficult for both plants and men, who, whether they know it or not, act upon extremely fragile ecosystems, the degradation of which could become irreversible.

Soil formation, then, is the combined result of processes which affect the weathering the rock and its component minerals; processes of decomposition of incorporated organic material; edaphic processes which affect all the constituents of the system; and processes of degradation (erosion, amongst others). The resulting soil is divided into horizontal layers called *horizons*, each of which have their own characteristics. The upper horizons are called the *A* horizons and they are generally darker, looser and richer in humus than the lower layers. The *B* horizons are layers where many of the products removed from the *A* horizon accumulate. They are generally more compact than the *A* horizons and often have more vivid coloring. They are often structured and enriched, due to the leaching action of water coming down through the upper layers, with humus, iron, clay, or calcium (illuviation), depending on the composition of the upper layers. Finally, *C* horizons are those layers that rest on the mother rock or the parent material and which have been produced directly by weathering of the latter.

Fresh organic material, which comes mainly from plant remains and, to a lesser degree, from the soil fauna, is rapidly transformed by the activity of organisms (animals and micro-organisms) which live in the soil. It was Darwin who, in 1881, drew attention to earthworms as being particularly effective in the processes that take place in soil. More specifically, they play a part in forming edaphic structure because by mixing mineral components and organic matter with secretions from their digestive tracts, through which a large amount of soil passes over the course of a year. Over a year an active earthworm population could process up to 40 Mg of soil. Earthworms, however, cannot tolerate acid soil conditions with a pH of less than 5, so that mixing of mineral components and organic matter does not take place in acid soils. Furthermore, in acid soils bacteria do not operate either, whereas such conditions are favorable to fungi. As a result organic material is not broken down quickly in acid soils and so it accumulates on the soil's surface, giving rise to an acidic leaf litter which is not very biologically active and which constitutes a mor-type 0 horizon (an 0 horizon being the name given to horizons which lie on top of the actual soil).

226 The horizons in the soil are formed by the joint action of physical, chemical, and biological processes. Weathering is the process of alteration of the rocks and minerals that are found on the surface of the Earth, since in these locations the materials are exposed to the characteristic climatic conditions of each zone.
[Photo: David Badia / Biopunt]

POORLY DEVELOPED KINDS OF HUMUS	
Peat	Formed by organic material that is poorly decomposed, caused by permanent waterlogging, which leads to anaerobic conditions and which allows only anaerobic bacteria and some fungi to develop.
Mor	Formed in cold or permanently humid conditions, on sandy soils that are poor in clay and cations, with acid leaf litter such as that of conifers or heathers; it is an acid type of humus with a high C/N ratio (over 30).
Moder	Formed when biological activity is reduced, basically, to that of microarthropods, and in which there are abundant fecal remains and plant fragments; it is slightly acid and a C/N ratio between 15 and 25.
Carbonated mull	Formed when calcium carbonate is so abundant in the soil that it affects the process of humification independently of climatic conditions, since it reacts with the organic material giving rise to highly polymerized molecules and intimately linked with clays; it is a black humus, slightly basic, with a C/N ratio around 10
WELL DEVELOPED KINDS OF HUMUS	
Mull	When the process of humification is very rapid and newly formed generally, the result is mull which is nearly neutral and with a C/N ratio of between 10 and 15; different types of mull are distinguished by the speed of mineralization, or rather by the rate of renewal.
Anmoor	When there is an alternation in the surface horizons between dryness and flooding, the process of humification becomes much slower and gives rise to a type of humus intimately linked to the mineral fraction up 30%.

227 Within its great diversity, the characteristics of humus are very good indicators of global environmental conditions, since they combine biotic and abiotic factors over long periods of time. For this reason, a classification of them into large families that correspond to different environmental conditions has been made. A distinction is made between little-developed humus (peat, mor, moder, carbonated mull) and developed humus (mull, anmoor).
[Source: data supplied by the author]

228 Determination of the texture classes of the soil, according to the classification of the International Society of Soil Science and of the USDA (United States Department of Agriculture); different particle sizes have to be taken into account in determining the textures, as indicated in the diagram. *[Diagram: Biopunt, from various sources]*

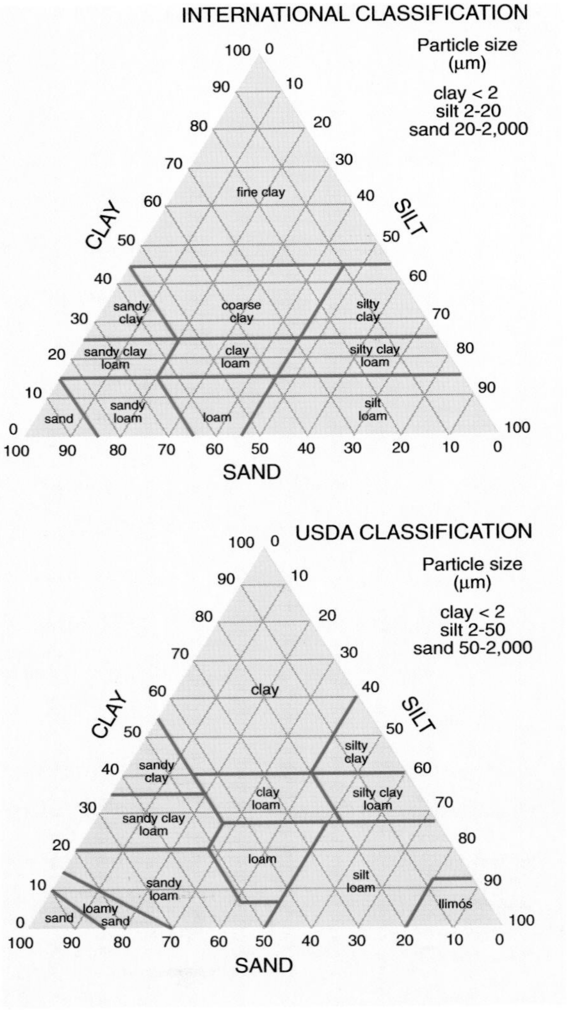

The processes affecting organic material in the soil are, firstly, the mineralisation of simple compounds such as carbon dioxide, water and ammonium, nitrate, sulphate and phosphate ions, etc; secondly, the transformation of nitrogenous substances (ammonification, nitrification, immobilization and denitrification); and lastly, humification. This latter process, controlled by environmental conditions, leads to the formation of humus, which may be "mull" in biologically active media with many bases, "moder," where conditions are intermediate, or "mor," in acid soils.

Soils and vegetation

The suitability of a soil for plant growth is determined by a series of characteristics. One of those characteristics on its own does not determine whether or not the soil is fertile: for example, roots can only take advantage of a balanced nutrient content if the soil has a suitable structure. Likewise, adequate porosity will be useless if there are problems of toxicity caused by a certain element.

Amongst the physical characteristics of soil, *texture* is important, texture being defined as the relative proportion by weight of different sized mineral particles in the soil. Texture, or granulometry, refers to those mineral particles measuring less than 2 mm (terra fina). These are divided into three classes, sand, silt and clay, although the limits between each class vary according to classification criteria. The results of granulometric analysis are represented in triangles named according to texture, in which soils are divided into textural classes. This classification indirectly provides information about other aspects of the soil: for instance, a sandy soil is, in principle, more permeable and aerated than an clayey soil, while a soil with a looser or more balanced texture holds more water available for plants.

The *structure* of the soil is the product of the arrangement of elemental particles into aggregates, separated by planes of weakness. These aggregates separate into individual pieces when a clod of earth is carefully broken up. The structure affects the characteristics of the largest spaces in the soil (macropores): a good aggregation helps root penetration, the aeration of the soil, and the capacity of water to infiltrate, whilst hindering erosion. The classical description of structure is based on the shape and size of the aggregates (prismatic, blocky, platy, crumb, etc.) and on their stage of development (weak, moderate, strong).

Porosity is the ratio of the total volume of pores to the total volume occupied by the soil. The movement of air and water in the soil, as well as root behavior, not only depend on the porosity of the soil, but also on the characteristics of the pores themselves, such as their shape, diameter, and their continuity or degree of connection between them. Thus, two soils with the same porosity values might behave completely differently depending on whether or not the interstitial voids are vesicles (unconnected cavities), or holes created by the soil's fauna, or fissures which are in contact with the exterior atmosphere and which can take water and nutrients to the roots.

The characteristics of the pores have a decisive influence on the properties of soil in relation to water. These properties include: *infiltration capacity*, which is the ability of a soil surface to absorb water; *hydraulic conductivity* (permeability), which is a measure of the soil's capacity to permit fluids to flow through it; and *hydric potential*, which measures the amount of energy with which water is retained within the pores. This latter factor is important because plant roots only have a limited ability to take in water. Thus, in a soil which has just been watered the roots

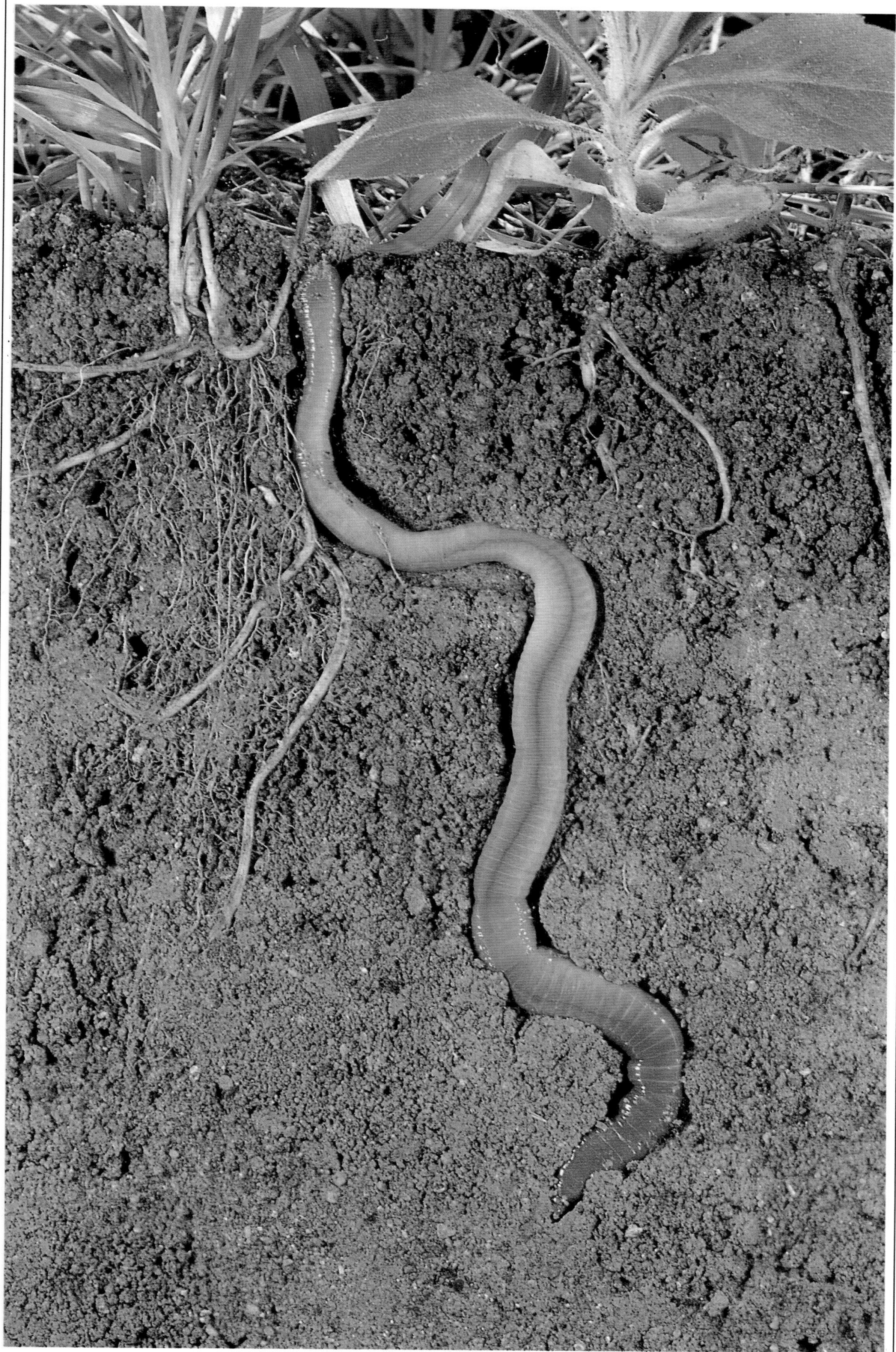

229 Both roots and the activity of soil fauna contribute considerably to the structure of soils; in particular conferring on them a spongy structure as shown in this profile. Slowly but relentlessly, the the movement of soil fauna, and even more their feeding and digestive activities, constantly turn over the soil particles. The roots, in a similar way, in opening up the way and absorbing nutrients and, and fauna enter into a profound interactive relationship and confirm that the soil is the interphase between the biosphere proper and the inanimate fraction (which is quantitatively dominant) of the planet.
[Photo: Anne and Jacques Six / Firo Foto]

will not have too much difficulty in absorbing water, but, as the water drains deeper into the soil, or evaporates, or is absorbed by the plants, the remaining water is retained around the soil particles with more energy, causing the hydric potential to become more and more negative until it reaches a certain level below which the roots will not be able to extract more water. The quantity of water retained by a soil between these two energy levels is traditionally called the *field capacity* (field moisture capacity) and the *wilting point*, is the available water capacity which in general reaches its optimum level in loosely textured soils.

In order to grow, plants need a certain amount of nutrients which they have to extract from the soil. The principal nutrients are nitrogen, phosphate and potassium. Smaller quantities of other elements are also essential for plant growth. When these elements are present they are absorbed by the roots in the form of ions in the soil solution. These elements come from a number of different sources; they might be the result of the mineralisation of organic material, or of the alteration or dissolving of the minerals which released them, or they might be the result of the activities of micro-organisms. These complex, interrelated processes determine the availability and mobility of nutrients at any given moment according to the characteristics of the soil. These characteristics include water content, the pH of the soil, and its redox potential, among others. One of the properties of soil which most affects the mobility of ions is the *base (cation) exchange capacity*: some soil components, such as clays and organic material, carry negative electric charges on their surface and these attract cations present in the soil solution. The absorbed cations are balanced with the cations in solution (forming a nutrient reserve). They also play a regulatory role in preventing ionic imbalance in the soil.

Soil nomenclature

The useful properties of soils are what actually interest its users who are not normally interested in their nomenclature. Nevertheless, the classification of soils allows us to order our knowledge of them. It makes it possible to generalise about one area by using experience acquired in another part of the biosphere, as long as the soils are similar, a fact which will be reflected in their having the same denomination. This is the main reason for classifying soils.

One of the first difficulties we come across in classifying soils is deciding on the criteria to use. It is necessary to define and choose a taxonomic system which is capable of expressing soil characteristics and which can be understood by other users. Systems based on the intrinsic properties of soils are, when applied, more objective, and are better when they are based on morphometry. Genetic classifications based on the genesis of the soil are more speculative since it is necessary to first of all infer their genesis before they can be established. There are two systems which give an overall view of the soils of the biosphere. The first of these is the Soil Taxonomy, and the other is the Soil Units System developed by FAO-UNESCO.

Soil Taxonomy

A system developed by the U.S. Department of Agriculture was presented to the scientific community at the International Soil Science Congress held in the United States in 1960. This came to be known informally as the Seventh Approximation and since then it has been revised a number of times to bring it up to date. The current version was published in 1975: Soil Taxonomy—a Basic System of Soil Classification for Making and Interpreting Soil Surveys, generally called simply Soil Taxonomy. (See also "Soil classification" in volume 11.)

230 Naming and characterization of the soil orders, according to Soil Taxonomy (1975).
[Source: data supplied by the authors]

ORDERS	CHARACTERISTICS
ENTISOLS (from recent)	Embryonic soils without diagnostic horizons (very little developed).
INCEPTISOLS (from inceptum, beginning)	Little developed soils, with one or more soil horizons of alteration or concentration but without accumulations or translocated materials, which are not carbonates or silica.
ALFISOLS (from pedalfer, aluminium and iron)	Soils with an argillic horizon with a medium to high base saturation.
ARIDSOLS (from aridus, arid)	Soils of dry areas or saline soils, with various horizons.
MOLLISOLS (from mollis, soft)	Soils with a thick mollic horizon.
VERTISOLS (from vertere, to turn over)	Soils with a high content of swelling clays; during dry periods, they form deep and wide cracks.
SPODOSOLS (from podzol, ashen soil)	Soils with an accumulation of amorphous materials, with iron and luminium compounds and humus in the horizons.
ULTISOLS (from ultimus, last)	Soils of subtropical zones with an argillic horizon and low base saturation (less than 35%).
OXISOLS (from oxide)	Soils of tropical zones, with horizons which are mixtures of mainly of kaolinite, hydrated oxides, and quartz, and with small amounts of weatherable minerals.
HISTOSOLS (from histos, web)	Organic soils

231 Naming and characteristics of the soil units in the FAO system (1989). *[Source: data prepared by the authors]*

UNITS	CHARACTERISTICS
HISTOSOLS folic, terric, fibric, thionic, gelic	Organic or peaty soils
LEPTOSOLS eutric, dystric, rendzinic, mollic, umbric, lithic, gelic	Not very deep soils
VERTISOLS eutric, dystric, calcic, gypsic	Developed soils on swelling clays, with cracks in dry periods
FLUVISOLS eutric, calcaric, dystric, mollic, umbric, thionic, salic	Young soils, developed on alluvial materials
SOLONCHAKS haplic, mollic, calcic, gypsic, sodic, gleyic, gelic	Very saline soils
GLEYSOLS eutric, calcic, dystric, andic, mollic, umbric, thionic, gelic	Hydromorphic soils
ANDOSOLS haplic, mollic, umbric, vitric, gleyic, gelic	Soils developed on volcanic materials and ash
ARENOSOLS haplic, cambic, luvic, ferralic, albic, calcaric, gleyic	Soils with a coarse, sandy texture
REGOSOLS eutric, calcaric, gypsic, dystric, umbric, gelic	Soils with an AC profile and an ochric A horizon
PODZOLS haplic, cambic, ferric, carbic, gleyic, gelic	Soils with a spodic B horizon
FERRALSOLS haplic, xanthic, rhodic, humic, geric, plinthic	Tropical soils with an oxic horizon
PLANOSOLS eutric, dystric, mollic, umbric, gelic	Soils with an albic horizon and an abrupt junction with an argillic B_{t2}horizon with low permeability
SOLONETZS haplic, mollic, calcic, gypsic, stagnic, gleyic	Sodic soils with a B_{t2} natric horizon
GREYZEMS haplic, gleyic	Soils with a mollic, partly whitish A horizon
CHERNOZEMS haplic, calcic, luvic, glossic, gleyic	Steppic soils with a mollic A horizon and C_k subsurface horizons
KASTANOZEMS haplic, luvic, calcic, gypsic	Steppic soils with a mollic A horizon and C_k or C_{cs} subsurface horizons
PHAEOZEMS haplic, calcaric, luvic, stagnic gleyic	Grassland soils with a mollic A horizon and without C_k or C_{cs} subsurface horizons
PODZOLUVISOLS eutric, dystric, stganic, gleyic, gelic	Soils with an albic A_2 horizon which forms tongues within a B_{t2} argillic horizon
NITOSOLS haplic, rhodic, humic	Tropical soils with illuviation of clay
ACRISOLS haplic, ferric, humic, plinthic, gleyic	Tropical and subtropical soils with an argillic horizon and low base saturation
LUVISOLS haplic, ferric, chromic, calcic, vertic, albic, stagnic, gleyic	Soils with an argillic horizon and high base saturation
CAMBISOLS eutric, dystric, humic, calcaric, chromic, vertic,ferralic, gleyic, gelic	Soils with a cambic horizon
CALCISOLS haplic, luvic, petric	Soils with a calcic or petrocalcic horizon
GYPSISOLS haplic, calcic, luvic, petric	Soils with a gypsic or petrogypsic horizon
LIXISOLS haplic, ferric, plinthic, stagnic, gleyic	Soils with an argillic horizon an low capacity for exchange of cations
ALISOLS haplic, ferric, humic, plinthic, stagnic, gleyic	Soils with an argillic horizon and low base saturation
PLINTHOSOLS eutric, dystric, humic, albic	Soils with plinthite
ANTHROSOLS aric, cumulic, phimic, urbic	Soils that have been heavily affected by humans

From its introduction the popular names used to designate soils in different countries were not used, though these names are still used today in other classifications. The Soil Taxonomy introduced a new nomenclature based on Greek and Latin roots, which is self-explanatory for a series of soil characteristics and environments. For instance, talking of an Australian soil called *quartzipsamment* it is possible to tell just from the, apparently cryptic, name and without ever having seen the soil itself, that it is a sandy soil (*psammos*, sand). Because it is a sandy soil we know that it will have a low water and nutrient storage capacity, a high level of hydraulic permeability and there will be a risk of wind erosion. We furthermore know that only the A and C horizons will be present, because it is an *entisol* (the order is indicated by the termination -ent, the element which forms the order); that its potential fertility is very low, given that all sand is formed from quartz (indicated by the prefix "quartz"); that plants, apart from specially adapted ones, will have difficulty living there; and that in order to be cultivated a nearby water source, fertilization and irrigation will be necessary.

Soil Taxonomy establishes six hierarchical levels of homogeneity which increase as they pass from the lowest categories, and it is capable of classifying soils on the level of plots. The levels are: order, suborder, great group, subgroup, family and series. The different categories are defined by the system according to the presence or absence of diagnostic soil horizons—the *epipedon* that forms at the surface, and the *endopedon* (or subsurface diagnostic horizon) that originates below the surface, and humidity and temperature regimes and other diagnostic characteristics. The system's main drawback is that it places humidity and temperature regimes very high on the scale and, in many parts of the world, this information is simply not available. Another drawback is that the system requires laboratory analysis. This is, at the same time, an advantage because the information given by a soil cartography based on this system is much fuller.

FAO Soil Units

At first the FAO (1971) did not intend to develop a soil classification system: the idea was simple to draw up a list of Soil Units to be used on maps that it was then

232 Comparison of soil classifications (p.p.=*pro parte*)
[Source: data prepared by the authors]

TRADITIONAL NAME	SOIL TAXONOMY	FAO SOIL UNITS
Alluvial soils	Fluvent	Fluvisols (p.p.)
Rendzinas	Lithic xerorthent Rendoll	Lithosols Renzinas
Sandy soils	Psamments	Arenosols Regosols
Hydromorphic soils	Aquents Aquepts Aqualfs	Gleysols Fluvisols (p.p.) Gleyic luvisols
Calcareous soils	Calcixerollic xerochrept	Calic cambisols
Brown soils	Ochrepts Umbrepts	Cambisols (p.p.)
Rankers	Umbrepts	Rankers Cambisols (p.p.)
Andosols	Andepts Andosols	Andosols
Brown alluvial soils	Xeralfs Ustalfs	Luvisols (p.p.)
Saline soils Solonchaks	Camborthids Halaquepts	Solonchaks Yermosols (p.p.) Xerosols
Chalky soils	Gypsiorthids Gypsic camborthids	Yermsols (p.p.)
Peats	Histosols	Histosols
Podzols	Orthods Humods	Orthic podzols Humic podzols
Red soils	Rhodoxeralfs Halpoxeralfs	Chromic luvisols
Crusty soils	Petrocalcic xerochrepts Paleorthids Palexeralfs	Calcic yermosols

HUMIDITY REGIME	YEARS	DRY DAYS		WET DAYS		MEAN TEMPERATURE OF SOIL AT 50 cm	
		ACCUMULATIVE	CONSECUTIVE	ACCUMULATIVE	CONSECUTIVE	ANNUAL	SUMMER-WINTER
Aquic	10/10	Some days saturated with st > 5°C					
Aridic or torrid	> 5/10	> 180		< 180	< 90		
Udic 1	> 5/10	< 90		> 270		< 22	> 5
2	> 6/10		< 45(s)				
Ustic 1	> 5/10	> 90		> 180	> 90	> 22	< 5
2	> 6/10		< 45(s)		> 45 (w)	< 22	> 5
Xeric	> 6/10		> 45(s)	> 180	> 45 (w)	< 22	> 5

233 Edaphic humidity regimes, determined by the number of years in which certain requirements of numbers of days with dry soil are met. [s=summer; w=winter; st=soil temperature.] *[Source: data prepared by the authors]*

producing with UNESCO. This is a compromise scheme which uses many of the Soil Taxonomy's concepts (for example, diagnostic horizons), although in labelling the soils many names from European classifications are used. It was conceived as a method of designating soils on a worldwide scale, which are then represented on small-scale maps. As it is not a classificatory system it is not hierarchical and it only establishes two categories. The higher of these is sometimes equivalent to the order in the Soil Taxonomy, whilst at other times it is the same as a group. The lower category is formed by intermediate soils or by soils with special horizons. The main advantage of this system compared with the Soil Taxonomy is its simplicity, although the latest revision by the FAO in 1989 made it considerably more complex and brought the two systems closer together. Nevertheless the FAO system still does not require as much information as the Soil Taxonomy, nor does it utilise humidity regimes and temperature in its classifications. In the following study of the soils of the biosphere the FAO system will be used because the maps that have been produced on a world scale have used this system. Wherever possible, however, correlations with the Soil Taxonomy will be made.

Edaphic models

By looking at soils on a global scale and comparing their distribution with the distribution of weathering-edaphogenic systems, climatic variation, vegetation and soils (the Strakhov diagram), we know that the processes of edaphogeneisis do not take place at random. It is therefore possible to establish edaphic models for the biosphere's main environment types. Although some of the processes outlined here are broadly associated with the world's principal climate types, they are not necessarily restricted to one climate type and can be found in other environments when the circumstances are right.

Edaphic model for well-drained, temperate and humid areas

In these areas edaphogenesis is controlled by the soil's *udic* regime which is dominated by percolation because precipitation exceeds evapotranspiration. Leaching affects the carbonates and other soluble products resulting from weathering. The level of decarbonisation reached depends on the type of parent material and the climate. The release of iron oxides by weathering allows these to combine with clays and organic material to form insoluble complexes. This process is called *brunifaction* and gives the soil a characteristically brown colour. It is typical of these environments which are characterised by a moderate degree of weathering, light acidification, the development of soils with an A B_w C profile and "mull" type humus. These, according to the FAO system, are *cambisols* (equivalent to *inceptisols* in the Soil Taxonomy). If the climate is Mediterranean the oxides of iron may rehydrate give the soil a reddish colour—a process called *rubifaction.*

REGIME	MEAN TEMPERATURE (mast)	SUMMER TEMPERATURE (JUNE, JULY, AUGUST) (mast)				
		minerals soils				organic soils
		not saturated p in summer		saturated p in summer		
Pergelic	< 0					frozen 2 months p after summer solstice
Cryic	0 < msst < 8	s/h 0	w/h 0	s/h 0	w/h 0 histic	not frozen p
		< 15	< 8	< 13	< 6	> 5 cm
Frigid	< 8	more than in critical regime				
Mesic	8 ≤ msst < 15					
Thermic	15 ≤ msst < 22					
Hyperthermic	msst ≥ 22					

234 Soil temperature is a factor that affects the agricultural use of soils, which the Soil Taxonomy quantifies according to the accompanying Table (temperatures taken at 20 in (50 cm) depth, or in lithic or paralithic contact, expressed in degrees Celsius). [p=in part; w/h=with horizon; s/h=without horizon; mast=mean annual soil temperature.] *[Source: data prepared by the authors]*

235 Podzols are the climatic climax in boreal zones, while in zones at lower latitudes they may be a seasonal climax. The very humid climatic conditions and the acidifying vegetation, generally of conifers, are favorable factors, but it is the very permeable rocks—which are poor in minerals and that are easily modified—that accelerate the process of podzolization.
[Photo: David Badia / Biopunt]

In more humid regions and with parent material which is poorer in bases, acidification progresses more rapidly, the organic material gives rise to *moder* humus, and the argiles disperse and can initiate a process of *illuvation* in which the clays migrate for purely physical reasons, transported in suspension from the upper part of the profile and deposited at a certain depth. The result is the formation of horizons of accumulated illuviated clays which are called *argillic endopedons*. In the FAO system these types of soil are called *luvisols*, and they are equivalent of *alfisols* in the Soil Taxonomy. Under conditions in which the bases are more thoroughly leached and where vegetation of resiniferous plants predominates the clays can become unstable, the collapse of crystalline structure can release iron and aluminium, and the soil can become acid. Organic material evolves slowly into *mor*-type humus whose components are able to form soluble or pseudosoluble chelates with the iron and aluminium, which can then move through the whole profile. This process is called *podzolization* and the resulting soil will be a *podzol* with an O A E $B_{h\,ir}$ type profile (equivalent to a *spodosol* in the STS system).

Edaphic model for arid and semiarid areas

Soils in arid and semiarid areas are characterized by the presence of components that are highly susceptible to weathering as long as there is sufficient water. In these soils percolation is never predominant and is sometimes absent (*xeric* or *arid* regimes). Under these conditions carbonates, chalk, or highly soluble salts may be present.

Carbonate accumulation processes are frequent, these being brought about by solubilisation-translocation and the precipitation of calcium carbonate within the soil itself. The result is the formation of calcite nodules (producing a calcic horizon) or typical calcareous crusts (*petrocalcic horizon*) which are impenetrable to roots. Typical profiles are A B_k C_k or even A B_{km} C_k, the soils are calcic cambisols according to the FAO system (*calcixerolic xerocrepts* in the Soil Taxonomy) or also xerosols, yermosols, or calcisols.

Chalk is a frequent component of soil in arid and semiarid areas. It is the protagonist in processes of *gypsification* which are characterized by the translocation of this component, giving rise to vermiform chalk or to more generalized accumulations in the form of gypsic or hypergypic horizons. The resulting soils can be gypsic xerosols or yermosols, or gypsisols in the FAO system (*gypsic xerocrepts* or *gypsiorthids* in the Soil Taxonomy).

In certain areas the landscape might favour the accumulation of more soluble salts (NaCl, Na_2SO_4, $MgCl_2$, etc.). Under these conditions the salinization processes only allow the establishment of plant communities comprising mainly halophytes (*Suaeda, Salicornia,*

Arthrocnemum among others). In the FAO system these soils are called solonchaks (salorthids or saline soils in the Soil Taxonomy). *Sodication* processes occur when there is a large increase in the percentage of sodium at the cation exchange sites (CEC>15%) and these give rise to sodic soils or solonetz in the FAO system (*natrixeralfs, natrustalfs* and others, in the Soil Taxonomy). The formation of these soils requires conditions of greater humidity so that other cations, such as calcium and magnesium, can be leached out.

Edaphic model for tropical humid regions

In humid tropical zones the soils are subjected to intense leaching due to the high rainfall (udic regimes). The vegetation provides large quantities of organic materials which, because they decompose rapidly, assure a rapid return of nutrients, an essential factor in soils which, in themselves, are not very fertile.

Ferrugination is an edaphogenic process in these regions, characterised by the release of oxides of iron and silicates which only allows the formation of clays, like kaolinite, which are poor in silicates and are typical of ultisols. *Ferralization* constitutes a more advanced degree of weathering and is the origin of laterites (called *ferrasols or oxisols* in the Soil Taxonomy) which are characterised by having horizons which are rich in hydrated iron and aluminium oxides. They are very poor soils that can give rise to ferruginous crusts if the iron oxide horizon remains on the surface due to erosion and the soil dries out. This is the reason for their use as building materials in tropical regions.

In those cases where the parent rock is a sandstone or a quartzite, which are poor in bases, leaching is so effective that the soil which develops is known under the FAO system as a tropical podzol (*spodosol* in the Soil Taxonomy).

Edaphic model for poorly drained areas

In closed depressions and in places where there is no exterior drainage, water accumulates and the phreatic layer breaks through or is very near to the surface of the soil. In these environments the soil is saturated with water (aquic moisture regime) and the respiration both of roots and micro-organisms, exhausts the dissolved oxygen to produce reducing environments (negative redox potentials). Under these conditions the process known as *gleyzation* or *gleying* can take place. This process involves the reduction of chemical compounds in the soil, such as the change of iron from ferric (Fe^{3+}) to ferrous (Fe^{2+}). Since the latter is soluble, the soil takes on green or gray tones (mottled) caused by the absence of iron. The resulting soils are

236 Soils with a high concentration of salts provoke an increase in osmotic pressure, which has a negative effect on the growth of most plants.
[Photo: David Badia / Biopunt]

237 Laterites are soils of humid tropical climates and originate from siliceous rock through an intense process of leaching, as a result, the humus tends to break down rapidly; with the appearance of ferruginous crusts and the impoverishment in organic matter and nutrient elements, these soils become sterile. *[Photo: Geoscience Features Picture Library]*

hydromorphic and are classified as gleysols in the FAO system (aquents in the Soil Taxonomy).

Under anoxic conditions the organic material decomposes very slowly, and in some extreme cases the accumulation of plant remains can give rise to organic soils called *histosols*. An example of these are the peat bogs that arise in water-saturated and base-poor environments and that provide perfect conditions for the growth of *Sphagnum*.

The Earth's edaphic mantle

The map of soils produced by the FAO-UNESCO (1971-1981) is the only one available which gives an overall view of the distribution of different soil types over the earth's surface. It is on a 1:5,000,000 scale. The map, which is the result of correlating existing information about soils from different countries, groups together very diverse data. It has brought together, under a single unified legend, maps of different scales, of different observational density and different classifications. Although the legend was later modified (FAO 1989), the map itself has not been modified, and it therefore shows soil distribution corresponding to the first edition of

238 The lack of aeration in hydromorphic soils does not allow the roots of plants nor microorganisms to breathe, due to the lack of oxygen. This favors anaerobic microorganisms and leads to certain chemical elements (such as iron) with more than a single valency to change to their reduced states. This process is known as gleying (or gleyzation). *[Photo: David Badia / Biopunt]*

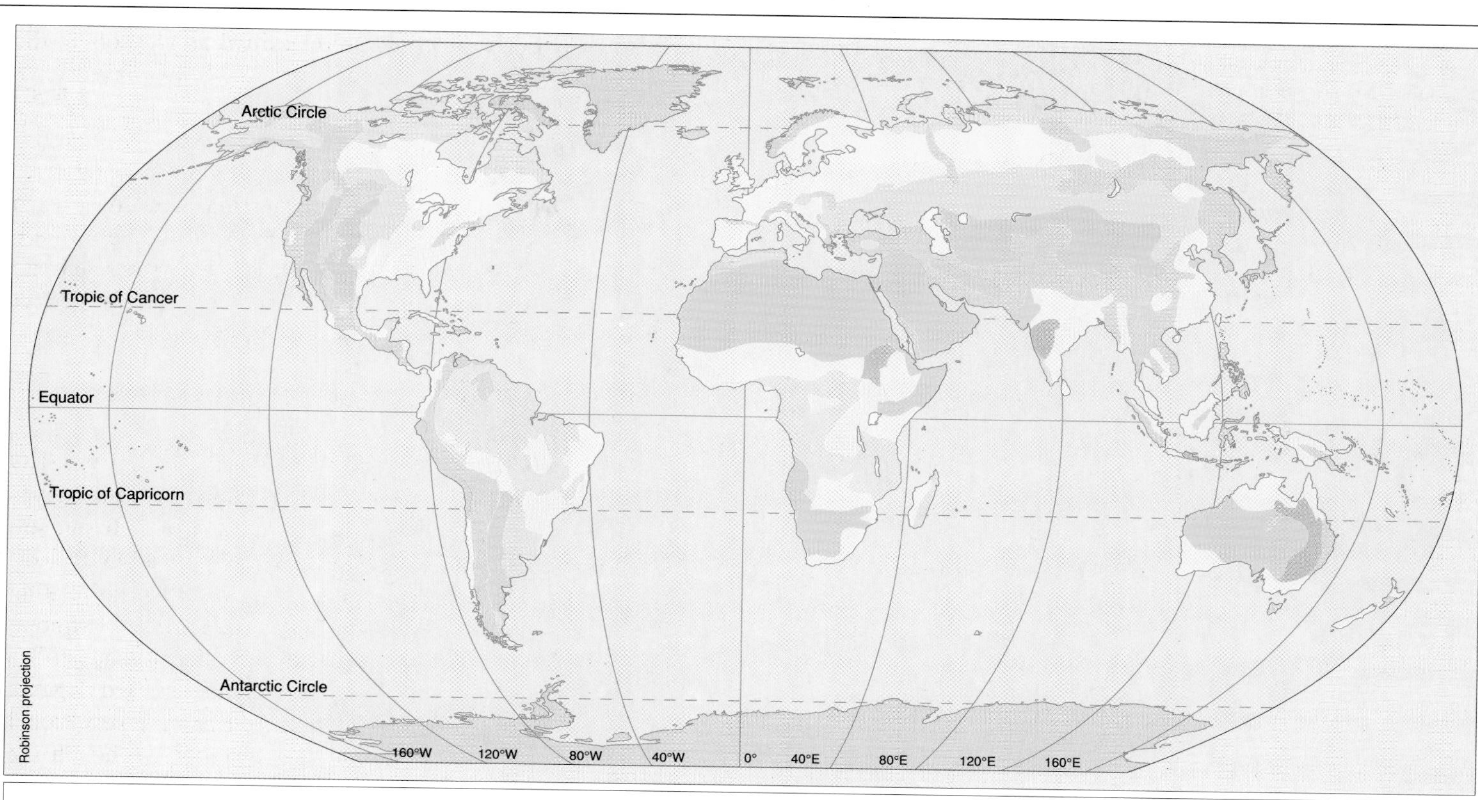

spodosols
alfisols
ultisols
oxisols
vertisols
mollisols
aridisols
tundra soils
highlands or perpetual snows

239 The great edaphic domains of the world established from the data of the Soil Conservation Service of the United States Department of Agriculture, and based on the criteria of the Soil Taxonomy.
[Cartography: Editrònica]

the legend (FAO 1971). There is no equivalent map based on the Soil Taxonomy classification system: only a schematic representation of orders and suborders on a worldwide basis has been produced, based on a map produced by the Soil Conservation Service of the United States Department of Agriculture. The FAO map allows us an overall view of the world's soils.

In tropical zones, where high temperatures and rainfall predominate, the harsh climatic conditions provoke a high degree of chemical interaction, which is reflected in the fact that the majority of soils in these areas are ferralsols, acrisols, and nitosols, with vertisols, andosols, cambisols, luvisols, arenosols, and litosols occupying a smaller surface area. The great deserts are almost totally made up of xerosols and yermosols which are characterized by a low level of development and by the accumulation of salts, carbonates or chalk.

The representative soils in the central areas of North America, Asia and, to a lesser extent, South America and northern Africa, are greyzems, chernozems, phaeozems and kastanozems (*mollisols* in the Soil Taxonomy). These have a surface horizon which is rich in organic material and a notable degree of biological activity. They are considered to be the best agricultural soils and they support the great, fertile meadowlands of the continental interiors, such as the Russian steppes, the American prairies, and the Argentinian pampas.

In wetter, colder regions such as northern Europe and Asia, *luvisols*, *podsols* and *podzoluvisols* are found, in which clays and/or organic materials have migrated to deeper horizons. They broadly correspond to the taiga zones.

Mediterranean regions are mostly occupied by *regosols, cambisols, alfisols* and *xerosols*, which reflect the particular characteristics of the Mediterranean climate, such as a warm dry season, the different geological and geomorphological characteristics, as well as the conditions which existed in the past.

The youngest soils, or soils which have undergone few edaphogenetic processes, are represented by regosols, fluvisols and arenosols (*entisols* in the Soil Taxonomy). They are common in the principal mountain chains (the Himalayas, the Alps, and the Andes) and throughout the great fluvial valleys, since the soils form on top of recent geological deposits. They are also found in deserts due to the extreme dryness.

From Hippocrates to Haeckel

Ernst Haeckel [AISA]

Ecology is a young scientific discipline, which had to wait until the year 1869 to receive a name: it was then that the German biologist, Ernst Haeckel, a disciple of Darwin, gave the name ecology to "the science of the economy, the customs, ways of life, the vital external relationships of organisms," in the opening pages of the first volume of *Generelle Morphologie der Organismen*, a book that was not exactly about ecology.

Unlike the majority of sciences in their formal sense today, ecology is not the fruit of a process of separation and specialization within a particular field of knowledge. It does not, like biochemistry, focus on a specific field within the broader area of chemistry, nor is it, like microbiology, a specialized field born of the advances our understanding of the microscopic world. Ecology stems, in fact, from the coming together and synthesis of strands of knowledge from many different sciences, and even embraces knowledge that is not strictly scientific, for example the information provided by country people, fishermen or hunters, with respect to the habitats and ways of life of many different plants and animals.

The fact that our species survived the first millennia of its existence shows that Palaeolithic man already boasted a fair measure of empirical knowledge regarding the workings of the systems, among which he lived or exploited. However, such knowledge possessed by primitive human societies was never scientifically formalized, but was, rather, passed on by word of mouth or by practical example, to become part of the general cultural baggage carried by different human societies or ethnic groups, or by a specific race or social group (hunters, shamans, priests, doctors, for example). In fact, one must look to the Greek medical schools of the fifth century B.C. to find the oldest evidence to have reached us of a certain "scientific" formalization of knowledge concerning the interaction of human life and the environment: in the treatise *On: Airs, Waters and Places* by the Asclepiad physician, Hippocrates (460?-377? B.C.). The Hippocratic tradition, which has greatly influenced western medical thinking, would thus be one of the earliest roots, to which ecology might be traced, together with the works on natural history of Aristotle (384-322 B.C.), another member of the Asclepiad group, and one who was responsible for *On the History of Animals*, and above all the work of Theophrastus (*c.* 372-288 B.C.), with his *History of Plants*. These works were to inspire all the European naturalists until the eighteenth century. Doctors and naturalists from early times to the Renaissance, agricultural writers and Roman, Arabic, and European veterinarians, navigators and fishermen, fish breeders and writers on the subject of falconry, all developed their respective fields of knowledge over the centuries, independently of one another, which does not mean that they did not occasionally share some ideas that we today might consider to be "ecological," but they were not aware of this common ground at the time. Thus, for example, medicine and botany were closely linked up until the beginning of the nineteenth century, but, even so, the environmental doctrine of Hippocrates was never applied to interpret the environmental conditions affecting the life of plants, but only those conditions affecting the life and health of humans.

Hippocrates [Mary Evans Picture Library]

Theophrastus [Mary Evans Picture Library]

Alexander von Humboldt on the Orinoco [Mary Evans Picture Library]

A new vision of nature emerged in the eighteenth century, and Carl von Linné introduced the concept of the "economy of nature." Linné, a deeply religious man who was still tied to the finalism and providentialism of current scholastic way of thought, saw the economy of nature as being the wise arrangement by the Creator of natural beings, in accordance with whom they tended to achieve common aims and to function interactively. This belief was reinterpreted along more secular and less providentialist lines by naturalists such as Alexander von Humboldt (1769-1859), who established the relationship between latitude and altitude and the distribution of plants, and Charles Lyell (1797-1875), who, in *Principles of Geology* (1832), referred to an economy within nature, in which divine providence is substituted by some material causes, and in which natural equilibria are the result of a linking process and of the constantly precarious balance held between opposing factors. In fact, since he followed this same line of thought, we should also mention a considerable part of the more "ecological" work of Charles Darwin (1809-1882), for example his studies into the structure, formation, and distribution of coral reefs (1842), the fertilization of plants by insects (1862), insectivorous plants (1875) or the formation of humus by earthworms (1881), or even the many references made in *On the Origin of Species* to competition between species and the effects caused by the introduction of new species.

Paradoxically, although it was a Darwinist, Haeckel, who gave ecology its name before the emerging discipline could consider itself to have been born, Darwinian thought made very limited impact upon the early

Charles Darwin [Mary Evans Picture Library]

shaping of ecology as an independent discipline. Some years would pass before various lines of study would converge: that of botanical, as followed by protagonists from Humboldt to Eugenius Warming (1841-1924), which would advance from simply recognizing the unequal distribution of plants in an area, to observing the relationship between them and environmental factors (including other plants and animals)—the line adopted by apologists of the secularized version of "the economy of nature"— one of whom, Karl Augustus Möbius, would introduce the concept of biocoenosis (1877), and the line followed by investigators of marine and continental waters.

At the beginning of the 20th century ecology emerged as a new discipline, offering a little more than just the name bestowed by Hæckel, but, nevertheless, still not very sure of its own paradigms. Thus, while botanical geography, from the roots of which ecology probably arose, split up into a number of schools, often very local, the theories of biotic communities or biocoenosis developed, and, from the field of demography, the statistical quantification of populations and the mathematical modeling of population dynamics were added. While some saw similarities between these communities and organisms with regard to their system of organization, others such as Arthur G. Tansley (1871-1955) reacted violently in the face of this organicism, and established the concept of an ecosystem as a new level of integration, which included both organisms and factors of their physical environment (1935). Finally, during the 1940s and 1950s, an ecological theory took definitive shape, principally due to the efforts of Raymond L. Lindeman (1915-1942), who introduced the study of material and trophic flows in ecosystems, which was later developed by the brothers Eugene P. (b.1913) and Howard T. Odum (b.1924).

Throughout the 1950s and afterwards, complexity began to be considered through the application of information theory, due, in particular, to the work of Ramon Margalef (b.1919) and of Robert H. MacArthur (1930-1972).

In parallel with the origins of the science of ecology, the concept of the biosphere developed from being a simple name to complement the words lithosphere, hydrosphere, and atmosphere appearing in the work *Das Anlitz der Erde*, (*The Face of the Earth*), by the Austrian geologist Eduard Suess (1831-1914), to become a clearly defined concept from the 1920s, thanks to the work of Vladimir Ivanovich Vernadskiy (1863-1945). However, little attention was paid to the latter's ideas outside what was then the Soviet Union until after his death, despite a commendable first translation into French of his principal work (*La Biosphère*), published in 1929. It was George Evelyn Hutchinson (b.1903), who, from the year 1948, promoted the concept of the biosphere and the holistic focus of ecology that derives from it, ideas which, since the 1960s and 1970s, thanks to the breakthroughs provided by remote sensors on satellites, have become accessible not only to specialists, but also to all who are even slightly interested in life on Earth, both now and in the future.

Charles Lyell [Mary Evans Picture Library]

2. Bioclimatic and edaphic domains: biomes

2.1 The biome concept

Each little zone of the biosphere is unique and unrepeatable. We can, however, compare different fragments in a search for regularities that allow us to make a classification of the major kinds of landscape, overlooking the differences due to local factors, whether past or present. Macroclimatic conditions lend themselves particularly to subdividing the biosphere into large units as the climate is the primary factor which influences all others, both edaphic and biotic.

To arrive at a definition and classification of the major units of the biosphere, we must add to the concept of a climatic zone or domain, another which encompasses biotic aspects. It is of little use to use fauna for this end, since although the distribution areas of most vertebrates are well known, the great mobility of these species and their tendency not to be confined to one region, gives them a character which is quite independent of climatic conditions. Vegetation, on the other hand, is particularly suitable due to its immobility and its clear dependence on climatology. We usually use the concept of *formation*, based more on physiognomy and phenology than on specific composition, which means that the same formation can stretch through different biogeographical regions as it is more a product of the climate than of evolutionary history. Despite the greater variability of soils, which are not useful for making a general classification because of the great influence of historical climatic conditions or of non-climatic factors, like the composition of the parent rock, the concept of plant formation is also related to edaphic, and even to geomorphological characteristics, to the extent that these are an expression of present-day climatic conditions as well as historical ones. So, we tend to classify the Earth's landscapes in large units or *biomes* starting from the concept of climatic domain and of formation, together with aspects of morphology, behavior and biological rhythm throughout the year, before arriving at a differentiation which can be considered natural.

Biomes are very large units, occupying areas of between thousands and millions of square kilometres. Within each large biome we can often find large areas with distinguishing features which clearly differentiate them from the rest and which are caused especially by special edaphic or climatic conditions. It is for this reason that we use the word *orobiomes* to refer to mountain areas influenced by a climate different from the general one, and *pedobiomes* to refer to developed fragments in peculiar edaphic conditions, normally in azonal or intrazonal soils.

The classification of the Earth's landscapes as large units or biomes is complex, especially when defining the boundaries, as no matter how much information we have on the features which define each biome, we cannot ignore the transitional band which separates two different biomes and which can be considered from various different points of view. We must not forget that these transitional zones are active and dynamic interphases which can change with the passing of time, above all when human activity leads to modifications which can shift to one side or another, of what was previously midway between the two. Intensive and extensive human activity has greatly complicated what was an already a varied panorama of the biosphere, whether by direct exploitation of the plant cover, through elimination and replacement by crops and grazing lands, irrigation, the introduction or elimination of species, or irreversible environmental degradation like erosion. However, the difficulties in defining the frontiers of the great biomes does not mean that a classification of this type is any less useful or interesting, since it represents a very understandable synthesis obtained by looking at the biosphere from a distance so as to grasp the broad similarities rather than the small differences.

2.2 The world's great biomes

Among all the possible classifications of the world's great biomes, we have opted for one which considers nine large units, some of which strictly correspond to a biome while others are sufficiently broad as to justify subdivision into

240 Epiphytism, a relationship in which the epiphyte does not harm the host but uses it only as a support, is an important phenomenon in tropical rainforests. In these, the humidity of the air allows mosses and lichens, and especially ferns, orchids, and bromeliads to grow on the trees without taking water from the soil. Evergreenness and richness are outstanding characteristics of the rain forests, in which there is a great exuberance of life.
[Photo: Waina Cheng-Oxford Scientific Films / Firo Foto]

areas, which can be clearly differentiated. In addition, some isolated systems with peculiar characteristics such as islands, caves, or marine systems, are treated separately.

Tropical forests: humid tropical lands

We usually distinguish two basic types of rain forest: lowland rain forests and the montane cloud forests. These latter are situated in areas which do not have a high rainfall but are influenced by clouds and mists of orographic origin which give them the necessary moisture. The rain forests and cloud forests are characterised by being evergreen and by the luxuriance of their living forms and their great taxonomic diversity. The difference between the two types of forest lies in the fact that the second has a relatively simpler structure and is much richer in epiphyts. The enormous vigor of the vegetation is reflected in the height which the trees can reach, up to 197 ft (60 m) tall, and the high values of phytomass per surface unit area, between 500 and 1,000 t/ha. The dominant leaves are of average size, soft and not very tough and contain a large number of stomata which facilitate transpiration. Their evergreen nature is achieved through a combination of truly perennial-leaved species with

241 The geographical interpretation of the various bioclimatic domains of the planet has given rise to many graphic interpretations. In fact, the differences between the various maps are more common and marked with regards the frontiers of the different climatic zones than with regards to the types of biomes considered; even so, it is still possible to find very different classifications, as a result of mixing or separating particular formations, thereby increasing or decreasing the number of biomes considered.
[Cartography: prepared from various sources with the help of the World Conservation Monitoring Center, Cambridge / Simon Blyth]

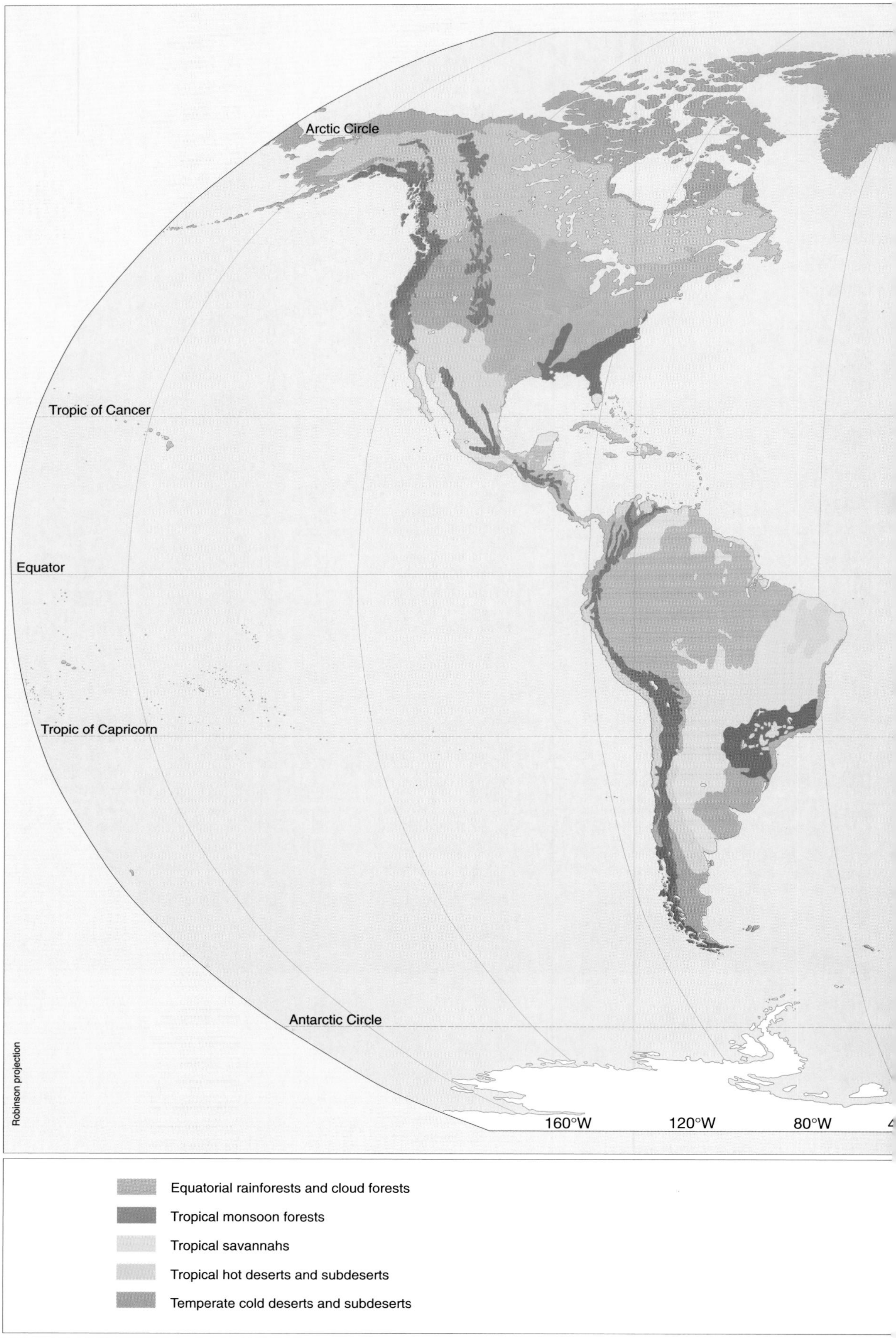

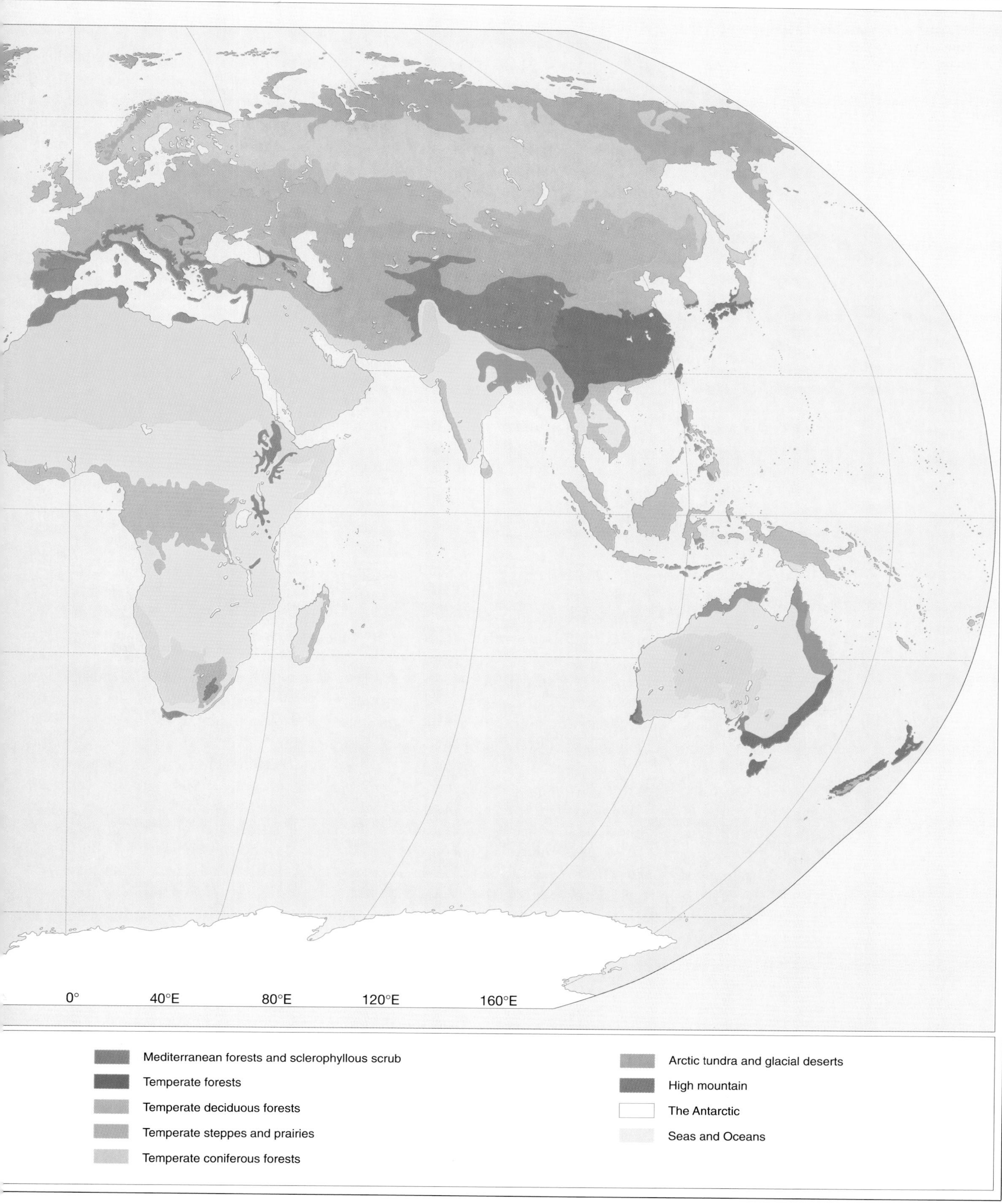

0°
40°E
80°E
120°E
160°E
Mediterranean forests and sclerophyllous scrub
Temperate forests
Temperate deciduous forests
Temperate steppes and prairies
Temperate coniferous forests
Arctic tundra and glacial deserts
High mountain
The Antarctic
Seas and Oceans

other deciduous ones but which behave asynchronically, even reaching a total lack of synchronism between individuals of the same species or between parts of the same individual.

As for taxonomic richness, we could say that the rain forests are the richest biomes in terms of species in the world. One very important reason for this is the long-term climatic stability in these regions; environmental conditions, which are very suitable for the development of life, have changed little since the Pleistocene. Great diversification, combined with their role as refuge for particular evolutionary lines which are in regression, has given rise to this explosion of diversity. The structure of the whole is very complex and is characterised by a lack of dominance of one particular species, a fact which is very evident when we look at the vegetation. The plants are arranged in differentiated strata, and there can be as many as five of them—three tree strata, one of shrubs and one herbaceous. In the tree layer, we can easily find up to 40 different species per hectare (1 hectare=2.5 acres) and in some cases there can be as many as 100, generally belonging to different families.

Most soils are Tertiary, even though we can also find recent volcanic soils and alluvial soils. The latosols are dominant, well leached and rich in iron and aluminium sesquioxides. Decomposition of the dead leaves is very intense and mineralized elements are rapidly absorbed through the roots which only occupy the upper layers of soil. The nutrient cycle is strongly controlled by the living fraction, which accumulates almost all the ecosystem's reserves. This combination of features means that the tropical forests are apparently very stable systems but with a low *resilience*; in other words, they have only a small capacity to resist modification or alteration or to return to their initial state. The forests have been called green deserts because of their deceptive lushness. They are not very suitable for exploitation and their replacement by agricultural crops uncovers the poor soils which rapidly become degraded, thereby impeding the system's later recovery.

The equatorial rain forests, which are the Earth's most developed and complex systems because of the favourable climatic conditions and their long-term stability, have a potential area of some 20 million square kilometers distributed along a belt around the equator. They are divided into three groups, one in the American continent, another in the African and a third fragmentary one in Malaysia.

Savannahs: the dry tropical lands

Under the umbrella term of savannahs, which has no precise geobotanical meaning, a whole range of tropical environments are considered, which go from deciduous and evergreen forests to dry semidesert herbaceous formations, via all sorts of intermediary formations with a shrub layer or a distinct tree layer. In general, we can make a first distinction between the savannah woodlands and the humid savannahs of South America, and the deciduous savannah woodlands and the dry savannahs which stretch throughout all continents in the area between the two tropics. As a whole, though, they are very varied physiognomically, including grassy plains with palm trees and acacias, spiny scrub of low trees, cactus formations, little groups of trees in grasslands, and semi-deciduous forests.

Climate has a role to play, undoubtedly very important, but edaphic factors are often the cause of the existence of a savannah or a savannah woodland rather than a closed wood, as water availability can be strongly influenced by the soil's characteristics and structure. We usually differentiate between *climatic savannahs*, *edaphic savannahs* and *flooded savannahs*. In the first case, the determining factor is the combination of rainfall and temperature; in the second, the dryness is caused by a sandy or stony soil which hardly retains the rain water, necessary, *a priori*, to maintain a deciduous forest; in the third case, the savannahs are found on soils with variable humidity, going from flooding to dryness. This panorama, already complex in itself, becomes even more difficult to interpret when human activity is present. Deforestation can give rise to the so-called *anthropogenic savannahs*, but in certain cases the process is reversed as the excessive amount of pasture in certain savannah formations provokes the development of woodland as the trees are more able to compete for water than are herbaceous plants.

As far as the flora is concerned, the wealth of species is not very great. Legumes and grasses are the most diversified families in these environments. There is a certain amount of convergence in the morphological characteristics of tree and shrub plants in these formations: corky barks, xeromorphic leaves and thorns on the trunks. The general structure of these systems is not very complex and the phytomass oscillates between 10 and 160 t/ha.

As regards faunistic richness, the most notable are the African savannahs as opposed to the American or Australian ones. They are, in general, areas with

large herbivores and carnivores, many of which migrate in search of water and food. The highest levels of the food chains are occupied by prestigious animals, whether herbivores (gazelles, giraffes and African zebra) or carnivores (South American wolves, Australian dingoes, lions and African leopards); also of note are the large flightless birds (cassowaries and emus in Australia, rheas in South America and ostriches in Africa).

Deserts: the dry lands

The Earth's dry lands are found in tropical and subtropical areas and are covered, for the most part, by deserts, semideserts and a whole range of transitions between these and the dry savannah-like formations or Mediterranean sclerophyllous formations. Some desert areas are, however, far distant from the subtropical domain and enter into the zones of great winter cold, so that in general terms we can make a distinction between hot deserts and semideserts, already mentioned, and cold deserts and semideserts, which are transitional between the temperate and arctic zones. The characteristic common to all deserts, whether cold or hot, is the rainfall which is erratically distributed and is considerably less than the potential evapotranspiration.

The main characteristic of deserts is the lack or scarcity of vegetation, which leads to a landscape dominated by geology. In deserts, the vegetation is restricted to areas where humidity builds up, giving rise to a so-called *contracted vegetation*. In contrast, in the semideserts, the vegetation is distributed evenly but is sparse, covering up to 25% of the soil, and is called *diffuse vegetation*.

In such extreme conditions, soils largely determine the availability of water for the vegetation. Clayey soils are much dryer than sandy ones, as the latter allow the water to penetrate more deeply, thus being protected from evaporation. This means that apparently dry and inhospitable soils which are sandy and stony are actually more humid deeper down. The salinization of soils due to the rise of salts by capillarity is a very common phenomenon. In these conditions, however, plants do not live in conditions of permanent water stress as the water supply per unit of transpiring surface area is similar in both arid regions and in humid regions. Aridity provokes an increase in the surface area of roots and a reduction in the transpiring surface area, as well as

242 The vegetation of the savannahs, herbaceous formations with scattered trees, shows the phenomenon of coevolution with the animals that live there. The acacias, in particular, share features in common with the majority of trees of these formations through morphological convergence: coiled trunks, corky bark, xeromorphic and coriaceous leaves, and spines on the trunks that prevent grazing by herbivores. The herbivores have shared their eating habits between the various strata of vegetation. In the photograph, a group of Waller's gazelle (*Litocranius walleri*) browse shoots and tender stems of *Commiphora* in a savannah-like wood in Kenya. These gazelles are able to stand on their hind legs to reach lower the branches. Other strata of the savannah-like vegetation serve as food for other animals. *[Photo: Mitch Reardone / Ph. Stone International]*

243 Desert plants, like this aloe (*Aloe dichotoma*) from the Namibian desert, survive with very little water but have devised various strategies to do so; some manage to obtain an amount of water that is comparable to what is normal for plants of temperate or even humid climates. In the particular case of succulent plants, the system consists of keeping the stomata of the leaves closed during the day to avoid transpiration, without having to limit photosynthesis; at night the stomata open and take in carbon dioxide with which they make organic acids that they use to undertake photosynthesis during the day. In short, they photosynthesize with little transpiration, which is the strategy of so-called C4 plants (see also figure 121). The succulent habit of the stems in the case of the plants in the photograph, is shared by various families, such as the Cactaceae, restricted to the American continent, the Euphorbiaceae, especially in the African deserts, Crassulaceae, and others. In the coastal desert of Namibia, which can be considered a cold desert because of the humidity and the almost total lack of rain, the vegetation consists of succulent plants and acacias; in the granitic areas, spiny euphorbias, succulent members of the geranium family (*Sarcocaulon*), and aloes (*Aloe dichotoma*) are dominant; there are extensive stony areas without vegetation, and where there are sand dunes, the leaves of the very bizarre welwitschia (*Welwitschia mirabilis*).
[Photo: H.R. Bramaz / Firo Foto]

giving rise to a series of adaptations related to the water regime. Thus, in arid regions, succulent plants occur which are capable of accumulating water in special organs: poikilohydrous plants which are capable of tolerating the drying up of their vegetative parts; stenohydrous plants with a considerable capacity to regulate the loss of water through the stomata; and ephemeral plants which have a short life span and develop during the short humid periods and spend the dry seasons in the form of seed. As far as fauna is concerned, the problems caused by aridity manifest themselves in the search for food in a rather unproductive environment and in the control of water loss due to respiration and excretion. Like the vegetation, the fauna is scarce in dry environments and shows different types of adaptations, whether behavioural (nocturnal rhythm, underground habits, diapause), morphological (small volume-surface area ratio, long snouts to avoid water loss) or physiological (solid excretions, tolerance to the partial dehydration of the tissues). As in the case of plants, animals are few and far between but they do not permanently go thirsty.

Cattle-raising has been a very important factor of change in the ecology of deserts, as the effect of the grazing of domestic herbivores is much more destructive than that of wild herbivores. The great carnivores have practically disappeared (American puma, Australian marsupial wolf, African lion) and as a large majority of the existing herbivores have been domesticated, little has been left of the deserts' original energy chain.

The Mediterranean lands: temperate regions with a dry summer period

The Mediterranean areas are characterized by a dry subtropical summer and a moderately mild and rainy winter. Under these climatic conditions, sclerophyllous

244 The dark, tough, persistent foliage of the bushes of *Aulax cancellata* is characteristic of the South African Mediterranean vegetation. Active all year round, the mediterranean vegetation can resist the winter cold and the long summer droughts due to its sclerophylly; a strategy which consists of adopting an active water regime, which consists of making the maximum use of the water that falls during the period when the vegetation is dormant, i.e. the winter, and at the same time saving as much of it as possible during the summer, through regulation transpiration, by closing its stomata.
[Phot: Colin Paterson-Jones]

and evergreen woods and scrublands develop. Mediterranean areas are found between the subtropical and temperate zones, on the western coasts of the continents: the Mediterranean basin proper, California, Chile, South Africa, and Australia.

The typical vegetation of these areas, which we usually describe as sclerophyllous, is xerophytic, in other words, made up of plants which are capable of regulating transpiration by closing their stomata, so avoiding excessive loss of water during the hot, dry season. Sclerophylly tends to be associated with good root development as the plants try to reach the deep layers of soil which contain water reserves. Under the conditions of extreme aridity, scrub replaces woodland and deciduous summer trees appear, as well as small-leaved aromatic shrubs.

Resistance to cold is a remarkable characteristic of the flora of sclerophyllous woodland and scrub, as many species tolerate temperatures way below the freezing point of water without suffering any damage. This is very important since although the winters are mild, occasional long cold spells occur because of the influence of colder neighboring zones.

Fire is a very important ecological factor for Mediterranean ecosystems because of the coincidence of hot and dry weather during the summer. Adaptation to fire has been translated into different types of adaptations which go from pyrophytism (plants rich in inflammable oils, fruits that only open in the case of fire, germination favoured by the exposure of the seeds to high temperatures) to being fire-resistant (incombustible corky barks, stumps which can re-sprout) in such a way that it is very difficult to explain the working of some Mediterranean ecosystems without taking into account the recurrent fires.

The fauna of Mediterranean regions does not have any special features. Apart from the presence of some endemics, it is not very different from that of the rest of the temperate zone. The role of these areas as a winter refuge for birds from colder regions is very important, above all in the case of the Mediterranean basin. On the other hand, the intense human modification of all these landscapes has provoked the rarity or loss of all the great carnivores and herbivores from these areas.

Mediterranean systems are especially fragile. Intense human action has greatly changed these landscapes, provoking a spectacular increase in forest fires and giving rise to serious problems of erosion which could convert many Mediterranean regions into semideserts. Erosion is especially serious under these climatic conditions as the loss of soil supposes a reduction in the water holding capacity and soil fertility. Furthermore, many of the Mediterranean soils were formed in more rainy epochs than the present one and this means that presentday edaphogenesis is extremely slow or nonexistent. This makes the problem of soil loss an even more serious matter.

Temperate forests: temperate lands that are neither cold nor dry

Temperate forests form in warm temperate regions, which are characterized by an abundant rainfall and ambient humidity, regularly distributed throughout the year or more concentrated during the hot season, a total absence of a dry season and a winter which is not very cold with only occasional frosts. They are typically evergreen broadleaved forests, even though needle leaf forests which grow under similar conditions could be included as well.

The most typical temperate forests are those of the Macaronesian region (the Canary islands, Madeira, the Azores and Cape Verde) and in the south east of China. We also find them in small patches in some eastern parts of the continents, (Japan, Australia, the southeast United States) as well as in some areas in the west of the American continent. In these latter zones we find, atypical examples of the valdivian forest, of giant conifer forests (sequoias) and *Araucaria* conifer forests.

The temperate forest is, in general, a dense woodland formation which is highly developed and has been described, in some cases, as a tropical forest outside the tropics, which gives a clear idea of its general appearance. The canopy can reach as high as 98 ft (30 m) and is made up of several different species from different families and genera, even though under difficult conditions and at the limits of their distribution area, the forest becomes poorer and the canopy tends to be monospecific, as in the case of the magellanic forests of *Nothofagus* or the needle-leaf *Araucaria* formations. Under the canopy there is an undergrowth formed of shrubs, lianas, and epiphyts. The richness of flora as a whole is notable, reaching 30-40 tree species per hectare. The phytomass is also considerable with values of as much as 200-500 t/ha. The greatest degree of development occurs in the Tasmanian eucalyptus forests which reach heights of up to 360 ft (110 m). The long dura-

245 The humid Japanese forests (in the Kyoto region in the photograph) corresponds to the most typical laurisilva, (i.e the moist woodlands of warm temperate climates), typical of the regions with a so-called Chinese climate (South China, Korea, and Japan) and the Macaronesian region (Canary Islands, Azores, Madeira, and Cape Verde). It consists of a transitional form of woodland in which evergreen dorsiventral-leaved plants form the greater part of the multispecies canopy, while the undergrowth is made up of small bushes, lianas, and many epiphytes.
[Photo: Photothèque Stone International]

tion of the vegetative period (7 to 10 months) as well as the favorable moisture conditions permit this development, combined with their evergreen character.

Woodlands: temperate lands with a cold winter and low rainfall

In the northern hemisphere, the temperate zone of humid summers and cold but not very long winters is the land of deciduous forests. These forests, which occur in the European, north American and Asiatic continents and are absent from the southern hemisphere, form magnificent changing landscapes, bright green in summer, and with yellowish or reddish autumn colouring, and bare trunks in winter.

The structure of the temperate deciduous forest is simple as it consists of a single tree layer of up to 98-131 ft (30-40 m) high with a shrubby, rather poor undergrowth and a herbaceous layer that develops in spring as it makes the most of the short favorable period before the trees grow their leaves, causing a drastic reduction in the amount of light that reaches the soil. The richness of the flora is much higher in the north American and Asiatic forests than in European. This is due to differential impoverishment of the flora caused by ice ages which was very high in the European continent because of the barriers represented by the transverse mountain ranges, and very low in other areas in which the mountain ranges are orientated north-south and permit migration and provide refuge. The tree layer, monspecific in European forests and plurispecific in the others, is a clear reflection of this phenomenon.

The fauna of temperate forests follows the rhythm established by the vegetation. With the arrival of the cold, migratory species leave, especially the birds. The small mammals, of which there are many, the reptiles and amphibians all tend to hibernate, as do many arthropods. The large mammals, which are relatively scarce, are the only ones which remain active throughout the year. In these forests, the deciduous leaf strategy derives from an adaptation to avoid the cold. Physiognomically speaking, the

246 The strategy adopted by deciduous temperate woodlands is clear and well known: it is not so much a question of adapting to the cold as avoiding it, by losing its leaves during the unfavorable period. This is the main feature of deciduous woodlands in temperate environments. The photograph shows the physiognomic aspect of the wood, which adopts four different aspects each year. During the year, nutrients all go through a phase of movement, a phase of storage in the leaf litter and in the wood, and a phase of chemical transformation and mineralization. One can deduce that in this system, the decomposer microfauna play a qualitatively and quantitatively important role, while the above-ground fauna has a more limited role; they have less biomass and both their presence and their activity are also interrupted by the winter resting period. *[Photo: AGE Fotostock]*

temperate deciduous forest is a system, with various phases which adopts a different aspect throughout the course of the year, with important consequences which are related to course of the nutrient cycles, as these pass through a phase of mass monement, a phase of storage in the layer of dead leaves and wood, and a phase of chemical transformation and mineralisation. It is for this reason that the microfauna which breaks down the system is of great importance, compared with the rather sparse presence of the surface fauna. These forests, which accumulate phytomasses of between 200 and 500 t/ha, develop on very rich and moist soils, in which the dead leaves play an extremely important part. In the areas that they occupy, they have for centuries undergone an intense exploitation, whether for their wood or for cattle grazing. Their structure, therefore, already simple in itself, has become even further simplified. In some cases, an irreversible impoverishment of the soils has led to the substitution of these forests by shrub communities, while in others they have been simply cleared to make way for crops on the fertile soils which support them.

The steppes and dry prairies

In the interior of the continents, in areas with a continental temperate climate, and far removed from the mitigating effect of the oceans, rain becomes scarce and temperatures take on more extreme values, both in summer and winter. In these dry, seasonally rigorous conditions, tree vegetation cannot develop and the landscape is dominated by herbaceous formations. This is the case of the Asiatic steppes, the north American prairies and the Argentinean *pampa* lands which make up the most extensive areas of this kind of formations. There is, however, some variation: thus,although in the case of the Asiatic steppes and the South American prairies, the climatic conditions are the clearest factors, in the case of the north American prairies the lack of tree and shrub vegetation is due to a combination of occasional exceptional droughts, recurrent fires, and an abundance of herbivores.

Steppe and prairie vegetation is typically herbaceous, and shrub elements only appear in zones of transition to other more wooded formations. Despite

247 The Eurasiatic steppe, as in the photograph, at 328 ft (100 m) altitude, W of Hujirt in Arhangay (Mongolia), is steppe par excellence; the term steppe comes from there and it represents the richest, most diverse and typical in the world. The vegetation of these biomes is emblematic steppe herbaceous, dominated by grasses, or shrubby and xerophytic and continental in nature.
[Photo: Paolo Koch / Firo Foto]

this simplicity, we can distinguish up to three sizes or layers which go from the tall grasses (up to 7 ft [2 m] high), those of average height (around 12 in [30 cm]) and tiny ones accompanied by mosses (4 in [10 cm] high). The richness and variety of flora is not inconsiderable as one can find up to 70 different herbaceous species there, sometimes dominated by grasses. The vegetation cover depends to a considerable extent on the rainfall, and for this reason it can vary considerably according to the zone and the year. The phytomass can reach values above 20 t/ha but one must bear in mind that up to 90% of this corresponds to roots which grow down in search of water.

The annual cycle is marked. When the snow melts, the soil's moisture content and the rising temperature lead to an explosive spring flowering of non-graminoid species which have spent the winter in the form of underground bulbs. At the beginning of summer, the landscape is a green meadow of grasses in active growth which end up flowering and drying out at the height of the season, not to revive until the coming spring, after having spent the winter covered with snow. In these climatic conditions, the production of organic matter is very high, both above and below ground, the latter making up the greater part of the phytomass. This gives rise to mostly chronozem soils which are very deep and rich in humus.

The fauna has to be adapted to the annual rhythm of these cold or torrid flat lands. It is a matter of searching for a balance with a herbaceous vegetation capable of producing large quantities of biomass during a short seasonal period but which, on the other hand, does not produce the same amount every year, depending on the climatic conditions. Herbivores abound here and are capable of travelling great distances in search of food, as different in aspect and strategy as those of the grasshopper, the Siberian crane or the American bison. Living in groups facilitates their defense against predators in these vast open spaces, and living in underground groups seems to be the most developed form of adaptation, adopted by animals as different as insects, reptiles and mammals. This strategy allows them to protect themselves both from predators and from the winter cold and the summer heat.

The great richness of the soils in the steppes and prairies has turned them into extensive cereal-growing areas where a large part of world production is concentrated, even though the considerable annual variability of the rainfall can give rise to important fluctuations in the production of these crops.

Boreal coniferous forests or taiga: the cold, wet lands

The cold and wet lands in the northern hemisphere, in which the polar cold and the accompanying rains and snow define the main climatic traits, are occupied by coniferous forests. This zone occupies an extensive belt of land, 50-60 degrees latitude, across the Euroasiatic and American continents. This belt is bordered in the north by the tundra and in the south by the temperate area of deciduous forest. The name taiga, originally applied to the Siberian coniferous forest, is used to describe this whole type of formation in general.

The sufficient rainfall allows for the development of tree vegetation, but the length of the winter, with monthly averages below 32ºF (0ºC) for more than half the year, combined with the presence of frosts almost all year round, favour needle-leaf perennials rather than any other strategy. The summer season is short and not very favourable and shedding leaves becomes an impossible luxury. The only solution is to grow leaves capable of resisting the winter colds and setting to work as soon as the favorable season starts.

The recency of this biocenosis, formed through the process of reconquering the northern lands after the glaciations, implies a lack of developed soils and a considerable poverty of species. Only a few species of trees form vast and monotonous dark green landscapes, dotted with the occasional deciduous trees in marginal zones. Where the climate becomes more continental, in the eastern Euroasiatic taiga, deciduous needle-leaf trees appear as the final and extreme form of resistance and adaptation. The shrub layer is equally poor and all over the soil we can find a carpet of cryptogams.

The taiga soils are cold, frozen and poor. The branches and evergreen canopies makes it difficult for solar radiation and snow to get through; the latter, paradoxically, acts as a protector of the soil against the cold (in direct contrast with the snow, the temperature does not usually fall below 23ºF [-5ºC], while the ambient temperature can drop to from -4ºF [-20ºC] to -22ºF [-30ºC]) . The soils freeze up to depths of 31 in (80 cm), and the trees have their roots in the upper layers which are the first to thaw. The low temperatures, the accumulation of water and the poor aeration make the decomposition of dead leaves difficult, which gives rise to accumulations of peat. In these conditions, being evergreen also represents a great advantage as it allows trees to retain nutrients in the

248 When the cold is very intense during much of the year and the vegetative period is reduced, without reaching such extremes that trees cannot grow, needle-leaved perennials dominate the landscape. The small and very hard leaves are able to resist the rigors of the cold winter and begin to photosynthesize as soon as the temperatures rise at the beginning of the favorable period. The crowns, which are conical in shape, are well able to resist heavy snowfalls without suffering the significant damage that the snow causes in trees with a rounded crown and branches that stick out from the trunk at an acute angle.
[Photo: Tom Tracy / Photothèque Stone International]

phytomass, which can then recycle them and thus become less dependent on the poor supply in the soil.

The composition of the fauna is relatively varied, as the fauna of the area is joined by fauna from neighboring biomes, which are too cold in summer or too hot in winter for some species. Here we find large herbivores that eat bark or lichens (eland, reindeer, caribou), rodents (rabbits and hares), birds with powerful beaks capable of breaking pine cones and pine nuts, small mammals, birds of prey and carnivores with sought-after skins (mink, marten, lynx, wolf and fox). The bear, omnivore par excellence, makes the most of all resources. In fact, the wealth of fauna is surprising in such a cold environment in which humans, present throughout the planet, only live as hunters and shepherds, as climatic and edaphic conditions do not permit the planting of crops.

Biomes of asphalt and concrete

Copacabana, Flamengo, Botafogo: these beaches, which are famous throughout the world, were once fringed by the dense Atlantic forest; now they find themselves surrounded by the skyscrapers, asphalt roads, and paved maritime promenades of the city of Rio de Janeiro. These areas of Atlantic forest are now occupied by chemical, cement, paper, glass, and food industries, all part of the second-most important industrial center in Brazil. And little by little, asphalt is making the biomes all over the world similar.

Toronto [Ramon Folch]

Mirror in a pub in London [Joan Biosca]

Rio de Janeiro [Eckart Pott / Bruce Coleman Limited]

Since its foundation by Estacio de Sá in 1565, Rio de Janeiro has been swallowing up the Atlantic coastal forest, which used to completely surround the south of the bay of Guanabara, thereby creating a breach of human origin in the temperate forest biome.

State highway U.S. 41 in Florida, runs across the state from east to west. This communication link was built over the swamps of the Everglades, a vast hydrological system, which was thus divided in two, seriously disturbing the natural flow of its waters; this is yet one more case among thousands, in which frag-

Street signs in Tokyo [AGE Fotostock]

ments of biomes are being replaced by asphalt.

All around the world, concrete and asphalt are cutting into and disrupting the different biomes that make up the biosphere, in the form of towns and communication routes. There have been roads since Roman times, and towns since the agricultural revolution of the fourth millennium B.C., but road building and urbanization, and their resultant impact upon the environment, made a dramatic advance from the middle of the nineteenth century. It was then that England, bowing to the irresistible pressure of the nascent industrial revolution, began to manufacture Portland cement, from which concrete was later derived, and then in Monaco, in 1902, Ernest Gugliemetti invented the current asphalting technique. Man's use of concrete and asphalt has had enormous repercussions upon what are often sizeable and important parts of biomes.

At the beginning of the 19th century, only the cities of Paris and London had more than one million inhabitants. At the beginning of the 20th century, New York and London already had more than five million, and Paris and Berlin more than two and a half million inhabitants. In the beginning of 1990 many cities around the world have gone beyond these figures: Tokyo, with 17 million, New York, with 16 million, and Los Angeles, with 11 million, are the largest cities of the industrialized countries, while Mexico and São Paulo, with 16 million, Shanghai with 12 million, and Buenos Aires, with 11 million inhabitants, are the largest urban centers of the Third World. At the moment, it is these cities of the Third World which are experiencing the fastest population growth, although this does not mean that the living conditions in these cities are improving at the same time.

All these large cities, especially those in industrialized countries, need means of communication in order to ensure the supply of food and fuel. Thus, in all countries, large connurbations, roads, motorways, railway lines and airports, link these urban areas with each other, and with rural areas. The final result is a transport network connecting the various departure and destination nodes (the cities), leading to the changes in the biomes and landscape already mentioned. Thus asphalt has become a new factor in ecology.

If ecology as a whole is a very young science, then urban ecology is even younger. In the last few years this specialist branch within ecology has been developing to the point that it is now offered as a separate subject at some universities, and some fairly comprehensive studies and analyses have already been made of cities such as Barcelona, Frankfurt, and Hong Kong.

Indeed, cities function like genuine ecosystems. It could be said that they have a biotic side (principally the gardens, parks, and humans) and an abiotic side (the sewers, streets, buildings, etc.). One can also talk of a nutrient flow and an energy flow. Thus, in a city, the vegetation in the parks and gardens, the street trees, and the seething mass of human beings make up the bulk of the ecosystem's biomass. The nutrients available to the city are food that is found in the surrounding rural areas, or sometimes abroad, and as manufactured products from outside the city itself. The communication routes (roads, motorways, railway lines) form the city's "roots." But, unlike a forest, the bulk of the energy consumed is of fossil, not solar, origin. This is the case of cities in industrialized countries, where the consumption of external energy far exceeds consumption of internal energy. In contrast, the opposite occurs in Third World cities: internal energy consumption is much greater than external energy consumption.

In contrast to natural ecosystems, cities do not possess a high level of *in situ* primary production to provide support for secondary production: heterotrophs dominate, and primary production is relegated to the rural areas that supply them with food: horizontal transport, so typical of animals, is taken to its extreme in the urban ecosystem (which was, after all, invented by a zoological creature...). Finally, it should be pointed out that, while in a "natural" ecosystem the nutrients are partly recycled within the same ecosystem, which we refer to as a nutrient cycle, in a city the nutrients are not recycled, and we would have to describe this as a nutrient flow, rather than cycle. Everyone is familiar with the enormous quantities of undigested waste generated by all cities, posing one of the most pressing problems of our age. In the same way that relief and soils introduce variety in the great biomes, leading to a concept of azonal biomes, humans take on a similarly influential role when they build cities. For this reason, the cities might be regarded as a new biome, which is, of course, azonal. The landscape is not determined by the vegetation, but by the structures raised by humans—the buildings. In the same way, the local climate is determined by the city itself, and thus frequent reference is made to the island of heat or thermal dome, which has a similar effect on weather conditions in all cities. Although all cities vary one from the other, and it must be remembered that biomes also display a high degree of internal variation, certain common characteristics of cities may be defined in accordance with the concept of the biome. For this reason, they could be regarded as a new azonal biome, which, considered as a whole, is large, but distributed in small patches throughout the biosphere.

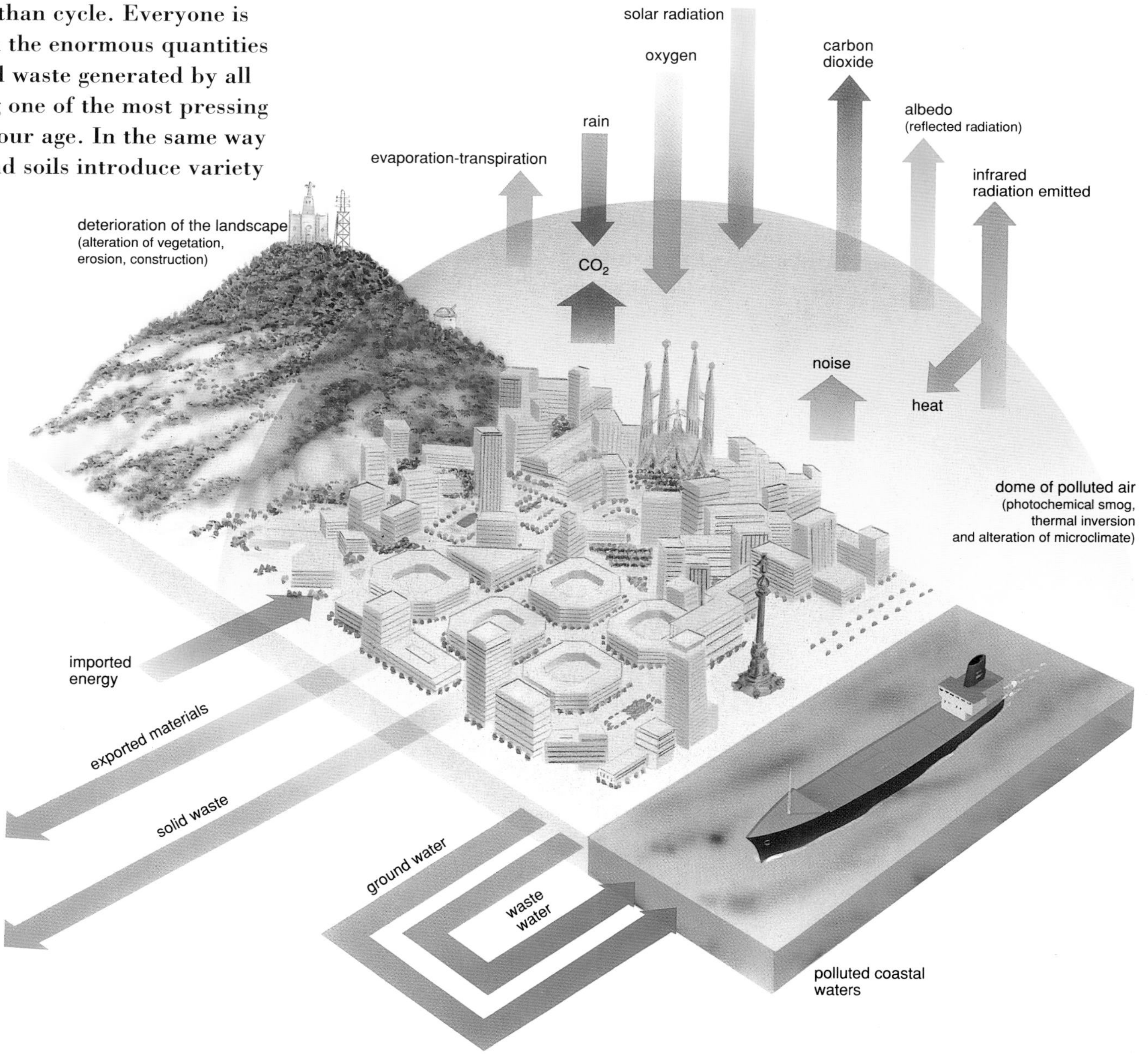

Entry and exit of energy to and from a city [Marcel Socias]

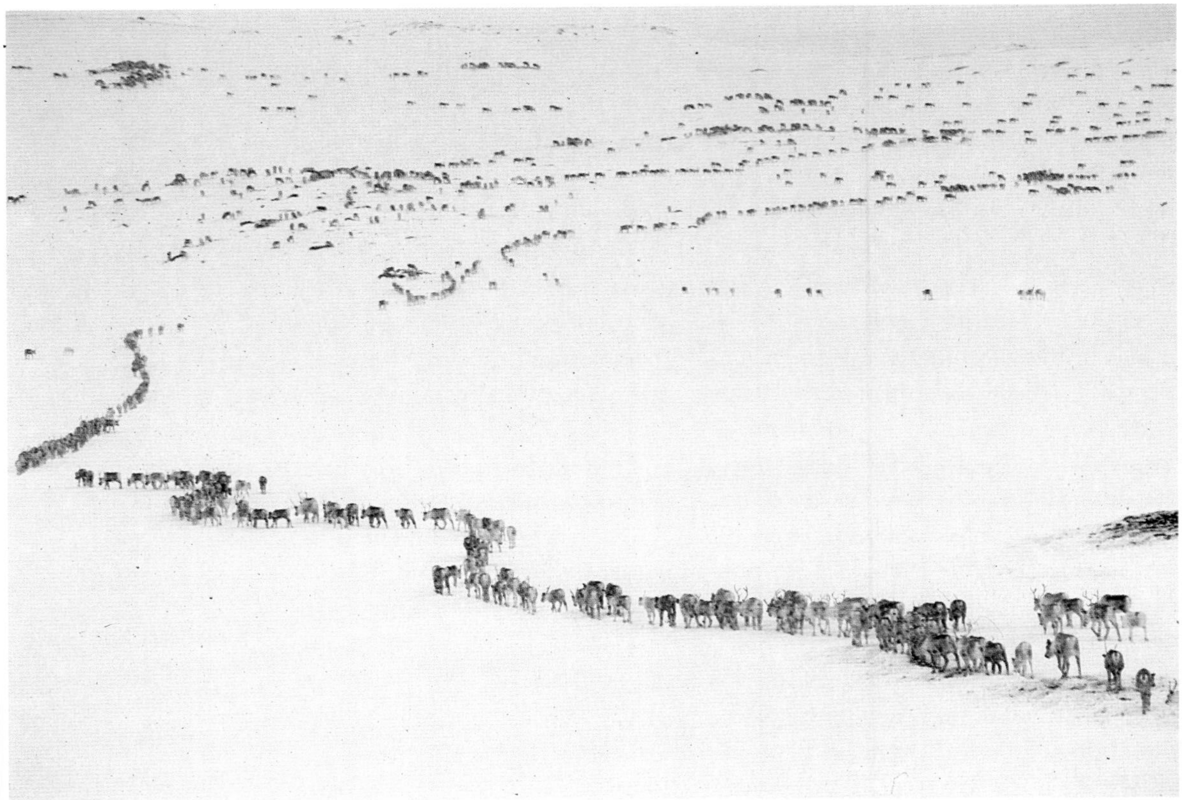

249 The young Arctic tundra formation, which has appeared since the ice retreated from the zone, occupies the coldest lands of the Northern Hemisphere. The reindeer (*Rangifer tarandus*), one of the most representative animals of the northern territories, is found throughout the Arctic region. The lifestyle of the reindeer is very much conditioned by the climatic conditions of the zones where it lives. In the northern winter, when the low temperatures linked with a drastic reduction in the hours of sunlight stops all plant growth and activity, the reindeer leave this biome and move south to occupy the taiga zone where more food is available. When the days lengthen, the reindeer move north again. In the short period of vegetative activity that the tundra experiences, the reindeer take advantage of the active growth of the vegetation to feed, as the rising temperatures make the snow disappear.
[Photo: Michael Friedel / Firo Foto]

The Arctic tundra: frozen boreal lands

The large, treeless tundra region occupies the coldest lands in the northern hemisphere, above 70 degrees latitude north, in other words, above the arctic polar circle. They are not very rainy areas (less than 200 mm per year) but they are not dry because of the low temperatures in the region. During more than half the year, the average daily temperatures remain below zero and the summer temperatures do not go up much due to the heat used in melting the snow and thawing the surface soil layers. The snow, which is not very abundant, is distributed irregularly because of the strong winds that sweep it away and expose wide clearings of soil to the rigors of winter. The arctic tundra represent the last vegetation formations in the northern limits of the northern hemisphere: nearer the pole the snow and permanent frost make plant life impossible.

Deep down, the soil is permanently frozen. The vegetation only occupies the top surface layer which thaws in summer. This surface layer, which varies between 13 ft (4 m) and only 6 in (15 cm), is followed by a layer called *permafrost*, a heritage of the glaciations, which can be as much as 1,476 ft (450 m) thick. The soils are very poor in organic material as under conditions as hard as these, biological productivity is very low and peat does not accumulate.

These conditions are only bearable for smallish plants which have surface roots and which are active during the summer season. These are lichens and other cryptogams, with dwarf long-lived (up to 200 years), slow-growing shrubs, which are sometimes capable of producing buds at the end of the favourable period. The seeds are very small and are normally disseminated through water and wind, as zoochory or animal dispersal represent too great a waste. The extremely low probabilities of germination justify the dominance of long-lived vegetation, since a strategy like that of annual plants does not make sense in an environment of this kind. There are even aperiodic species, with a development which lasts several years and which is interrupted, no matter what stage it is in, when winter arrives. This makes them independent of the short summer. The low elevation of the sun above the horizon during summer makes the sloping and stony soils heat up much more than the flat soils, so that they become genuine flower gardens which reflect the great importance that any small improvement has in such harsh conditions.

In these zones, herbivores play a role of primary importance. These are small rodents which spend the winter underground eating the tender parts of the vegetation covered by the snow, and deer which migrate annually when the long polar night arrives.

2.3 The seas and other "outsiders"

The general scheme that divides the planet primarily into large biomes leaves out some peculiar systems that, are sometimes quantitatively or qualitatively important. They are systems in which climatic factors are less important defining factors than others. In this sort of odds-and-ends box, we can place the marine systems and all the terrestrial coastal land systems which are influenced by salinity, together with terrestrial systems characterized by their isolation and as diverse as the Antarctic continent, high mountains, islands, lakes and caves.

The Antarctic domain

The immense Antarctic continent is almost a desert as far as plant life is concerned. The greater part of the surface area is permanently covered with ice and only in some marginal lands which thaw during summer do we find mosses, lichens, terrestrial algae and no more than three species of phanerogams. The marine systems which surround this continent are very productive and it is for this reason that there is a very abundant fauna (penguins, seals, etc.) which feeds in the waters and only uses the continent as a place to rest and nest, in other words as a purely physical, solid base and not as a productive landscape into which they become integrated.

The high mountain domain

As altitude increases, the climate becomes progressively colder and more humid and it is for this reason that mountainous regions present landscapes which are very different from the flat lands that surround them. The progressive change in climatic conditions is accompanied by a progressive change in the landscape, giving rise to what is called an altitudinal zonation of vegetation. This altitudinal zonation has often been compared to a shift to more extreme latitudes, but this comparison is not entirely true, as the conditions of sunlight, linked to latitude and not altitude, continue to be the ones that correspond to the area. Furthermore, on very high mountain ranges, when the height goes over a certain level, mists and

250 The Antarctic biome, which is found only in the Southern Hemisphere, is separated from the rest of the continents by extensive circumpolar oceans. This land area occupies some 5.3 million mi² (13.8 million km²) of which 98% is covered by ice. This means that the vegetation is scarce, but not the fauna. The richness of the waters that surround the Antarctic allows the growth of a large variety of animals. There are extensive populations, which make use of the continent only as a physical base for resting or for rearing young but not as a place to seek food. *[Photo: AGE Fotostock]*

251 The landscapes of high mountains show some common features that clearly distinguish them. On the one hand, high mountains are subjected to the influence of the climate of the lowlands that surround them, but have a peculiar and unique climate that stems from a combination of latitude and altitude. On the other hand, due to their isolation, the flora and fauna are highly specific. This, combined with the spectacular adaptations to the harsh environmental conditions and the relative simplicity of the landscapes, makes the presence or dominance of particular species or biological forms stand out, and results in the landscapes of high mountains being so peculiar and distinct from each other. *[Photo: Christer Fredriksson / Bruce Coleman Limited]*

mountain clouds disappear and the climate becomes dryer. This all goes to produce a series of conditions which are quite special and cannot be associated with any other zone on the planet. At the highest points of the great mountain ranges, other very important factors appear, such as the great intensity of solar radiation and the drying effects of the constant winds.

All these factors give rise to culminant landscapes made up of a shrub and herbaceous vegetation which is very resistant to the cold, dry conditions and high levels of insolation. In each case, though, local characteristics determine a considerable part of the vegetation's appearance as outside these great common environmental traits there are a multitude of differences between the tropical high mountains and those of medium or high latitudes. Biogeographically speaking, the uppermost parts of the high mountains are like islands or archipelagoes separated by impassable seas of low lands.

252 The geographical situation of an island and its topographical relief determine the diversity of environmental conditions that are found in the interior and which, in effect, means that landscapes corresponding to one or more kinds of biome are dominant there. However, other features such as overall size of the island, its distance from the nearest continent, and the time of its separation, determine the number of species that grow there, as well as the degree of endemism or differentiation shown by its flora and fauna in relation to continental species. The biological systems of the island evolve when they separate from the continent, or they build up and structure themselves slowly with colonizing species as, in the case of recently formed islands such as volcanic ones. *[Photo: AISA]*

253 Caves are systems in which the lack of light prevents the existence of primary products. Bats, which feed outside the caves and use them only as a place of rest or hibernation, constitute an important source of entry of organic material. Their feces are an importance source of food for many species of arthropod, which in turn serve as a food for other species of the cave system. The bats are not the only source of entry of organic material into the caves, but their abundance and their habit of concentrating in great numbers makes them a key element in the ecological functioning of many subterranean cavities. *[Photo: Josep Loaso]*

Isolated systems: islands, lakes, and caves

Islands, lakes, and caves are systems which are isolated from the biomes that include them. In these three cases, even more so than in the previous one, isolation is the essential factor which allows us to understand the structure and working of these systems.

Islands present landscapes which are certainly influenced by climatology, but the structure and composition of their ecosystems depend to a large extent on factors such as the age of the island, its surface area and its distance from the nearest continents. The total number of species, the degree of speciation and endemism, the diversity of the ecosystems and the variety of the environments depend more on these factors than on climatology. Islands are true biological laboratories which have allowed us to clarify many ecological and genetic mechanisms related to the occupation of space and to the process of speciation.

Lakes are aquatic systems influenced by their catchment basins, whose characteristics determine factors as important as temperature and water composition. But as in the case of the islands, their dimensions and history are factors that have to be taken into account when explaining the characteristics of their ecosystems. The relationship between their surface area and their volume, which determines the degree of interaction between the lake system and the terrestrial systems which surround it, is also an important factor. Their very pronounced boundaries have made them the paradigm of isolated systems in terrestrial or continental environments and, in fact, the first studies on the functioning of ecosystems were carried out in lakes.

Caves are the last example of systems in which isolation is a determining factor. Furthermore, they are very peculiar ecological systems as they lack primary producers and depend on the import of organic material synthesised in the bright, outside world, thus giving rise to biological systems formed exclusively by decomposers and secondary consumers which are well adapted to the general scarcity of resources that are found there. But the most interesting aspect of caves, apart from their isolation, is the constancy of the environmental conditions, characterised by their extremely high humidity and temperatures which hardly vary, even though they can be found in regions with a clearly seasonal climate. This has converted them, in temperate regions, into refuges for hypogeal fauna, which was abundant in the outside world in periods of hotter and more humid climates. The speciation due to isolation gives rise to nioendics which superimpose themselves on these paleoendemics or relics of previously more extensive faunas, giving rise to a series of faunistic groupings which are basic to our understanding the history of the changes in the outside environment.

Marine systems

Marine systems include both truly aquatic, and terrestrial systems which are heavily influenced by the presence of salt water. This is the case of the ecosystems of coastal salt marshes and mangroves in which the salinity of the waters is a factor which determines the structure and functioning of the vegetation, more than climatic factors do. Certainly, the composition of the flora and other aspects of the vegetational landscape, like the dominance of herbaceous plants, shrubs or trees, are clearly influenced by the climate. Mangroves, for example, are only found on tropical coasts protected by coral reefs and subjected to the effect of tides but not to the movements of the waves, but the water's salinity is clearly the factor that determined most of the properties and characteristics of these systems.

Marine systems are a world apart. They are not independent of environmental factors like temperature, but their structure and behavior have little to do with terrestrial systems. Coastal belts, which are neither very deep nor very extensive compared with the total area of the oceans, present systems or landscapes which can be classified or arranged in the same way as terrestrial biomes. Thus we can speak of tropical coral reefs or of Mediterranean benthonic communities just as we speak of tropical forests and Mediterranean sclerophyllous forests, even though the variability of the atmospheric conditions in marine environments is not as great as in the case of terrestrial ones and we can, therefore, distinguish fewer units.

The enormous areas of ocean, beyond these narrow coastal bands, behave in quite different ways. They are filled with landscapes which we could describe as transparent to the human eye, which is only capable of distinguishing organisms of a considerable size. Marine systems are dominated by microscopic primary producers, phytoplankton, which rapidly renew themselves and provide food for a second rung which is similarly dominated by minute organisms, zooplankton. Nutrients become sedimented and are dragged along by currents over distances of the order of hundreds or thousands of kilometres, contrasting with the short journeys that they make in terrestrial ecosystems.

Marine systems are basically influenced by the availability of nutrients, often associated with the upwelling of deep waters caused by strong currents. This source of subsidiary energy which returns sedimented nutrients to the sunlit layer is what determines whether a marine system is highly productive or whether it behaves like a terrestrial desert, as happens, in practise, in the greater part of the ocean surface. At all events, they are scarcely structured ecosystems, dominated by consumers and not by primary producers as happens in terrestrial systems. We, terrestrial organisms that we are, feel uncomfortable faced with these marine landscapes, which are too empty and immense. Perhaps this very notion of landscape is not particularly useful for describing and understanding these biological systems which occupy most of the planet.

254 The biological basis of marine systems is made up of microscopic organisms: plankton. Unlike terrestrial systems dominated by primary producers of considerable size and longevity, and having a very complex structure and a relatively slow dynamism, marine systems are much more dynamic. They have a base of primary producers that have a much more simple structure and high turnover rate. Marine landscapes, apart from not corresponding to the terrestrial notion of landscape because of their loose structure, are so dynamic that they can be considered landscapes almost without memory; influenced only by recent history and not by a long cumulative process as occurs in terrestrial ecosystems. *[Photo: Claude Carré]*

From one biome to another: animal migrations

White stork (*Ciconia ciconia*) [Oriol Alamany]

Animals are not as dependent on climatic conditions as plants. This does not mean that each biome does not have its own typical fauna, but that many animal species have a sufficiently wide tolerance to allow them to live in very different climatic zones.

This relative independence of environmental conditions is more marked in the case of the so-called "higher" animals—the birds and the mammals. This is natural since they are homoiothermal, i.e., they have the capacity to regulate their body temperature and maintain it at a higher level than that of their surroundings, which allows them to tolerate very different thermic conditions.

The mobility of animals is obviously a basic factor when it comes to avoiding the rigors of climate and reaching resources concentrated at certain points in space. If the resource in question is water, this supposes the capacity to survive in environments where its availability is very different and which therefore have a completely different vegetation. But this very mobility allows animals to travel great distances, whether on a daily or a seasonal basis, some of them so great that the animals travel between different biomes. The capacity to migrate is related to the size of organisms: the biggest have the greatest mobility. But the animal's mode of locomotion also plays an important role: the ability to fly, in the case of terrestrial organisms, and to swim strongly, in the case of marine organisms, allow greater mobility.

Cape buffalo (*Syncerus caffer*) in Botswana [Frans Lanting / Minden Pictures]

Mammals, including large ones, move over great distances, but rarely migrate from one biome to another. Bats, or chiropterans, due to their ability to fly, can undertake journeys of several hundred kilometers between their breeding and their wintering grounds. Many herbivores of the African savannahs, such as gnus (*Connochaetes*), also make seasonal journeys between areas within the same biome, making north-south migrations that allow them to avoid dry periods and take to advantage of distant pastures associated with the progressive advance of the monsoon rains. Some large mammals, such as the moose (*Alces alces*) and the reindeer (*Rangifer tarandus*), undertake migrations of a similar distance, but their position on the edge of two biomes means that they move from one to another: they exploit the pastures of the tundra during the short Arctic summer and pass the winter in the taiga feeding on lichens and the branches of trees such as the willow (*Salix*) and the birch (*Betula*). Some marine mammals migrate thousands of kilometers, as is the case with certain cetaceans and the seal (*Callorhinus alascanus*), which breeds in the Bering Sea and winters on the coasts of California, some 3,107 mi (5,000 km) away, which demonstrates the great mobility deriving from their form of locomotion.

The truly great migrations that fill the pages of treatises on natural history or books on the wonders of nature are those of animals that can fly or swim. A modest insect such as the monarch butterfly (*Danaus plexippus*) of North America undertakes seasonal migrations that take it from temperate to subtropical zones, traveling distances of some 3,728 mi (6,000 km). Birds are the migrators par excellence, the great travelers between different biomes. In the Palaearctic Region, of the 589 species of non-marine birds living there during the summer, around 40% winter in more southern bioclimatic zones. The biosphere is literally criss-crossed with bird migration routes, and it is not necessarily the largest who travel the most, size actually imposes many limitations on flight. The most spectacular migrations are undertaken by modest birds such as the sanderling (*Calidris alba*), which breeds in the Arctic tundra and winters in a large area up to 4,971 mi (8,000 km) away, or the Arctic tern (*Sterna paradisaea*), which breeds in the Arctic and winters in the southern hemisphere, even reaching the Antarctic. The limitations on bird migration thus derive more from the size of the planet than from their capacity to travel.

Monarch butterfly (*Danaus plexippus*) [Frans Lanting / Minden Pictures]

In marine systems, as we have already seen with the migrations of some aquatic mammals, we also find spectacular migrations covering hundreds or thousands of kilometers. This is the case of the tunnies, strong swimmers that move over great areas, breeding and wintering in completely distinct zones. Many smaller fish take advantage of currents, while others move about in pursuit of or seeking abundant feeding grounds. In some cases the migratory routes acquire truly spectacular dimensions, as is the case of the European eel (*Anguilla anguilla*), which spend their adult life in European rivers and breed in the western Atlantic, which obliges their young to undertake a return journey lasting three or four years.

Some of the advantages of migration are obvious: taking advantage of widely separated ecosystems ensures greater stability in the availability of resources and less dependence on possible fluctuations in either of them. On the other hand, in general terms, the areas exploited during breeding are ecologically less mature, and therefore more productive and changeable than the wintering grounds.

American sockeye salmon (*Oncorhynchus nerka*) [Jeff Foott / Bruce Coleman Limited]

The migration of European birds, which winter in Africa and breed in the higher latitudes, allows them to take advantage of productive periods in the more changeable climatic areas and at the same time avoid competition with sedentary African species, which is tolerable during the winter, but becomes critical when breeding increases the need for resources. Migration may involve higher mortality rates, but these can be compensated for by an increase in fertility; but there are exceptions to this general scheme, as in the case of the tuna (*Thunnus thynnus*), which breeds in the not very productive Mediterranean, and precisely during the summer when the shallow waters are poorer in plankton. Migration can include other more subtle advantages, such as the elimination of parasites, which are less resistant to climatic changes or incapable of adapting their life cycle to the periodic disappearance of their potential host. Despite this, there are cases of migratory behavior we are still unable to explain and that can seem absurd when we analyze the advantages and disadvantages, as in the examples of the eel or the Arctic tern. Some of these apparently absurd forms of behavior may be relics of the past that have survived into later changed conditions; we might thus, interpret the long journey of the eel as the result of a long, slow separation of the breeding and wintering grounds, due to the expansion of the Atlantic.

In any case, and leaving aside the possible reasons, animals cross the frontiers between biomes and gain access to a broader territory, not limited by climatic conditions.

3. The biosphere, a mosaic

3.1 Diversity within biomes

The biosphere is very complex, it resists being forced into simple classification schemes that have only a few categories, especially when we examine it closely. Scale of perception is a very important factor when determining the homogenous units which we can define on the Earth's living mantle. Thus, if we move far enough away, from the point of view of an observer in a satellite or a plane, the large units we define as biomes appear satisfactorily homogenous and with clear frontiers between them. As we move closer to the Earth, the panorama becomes more complex as we gradually appreciate the marked variability in space which the biosphere presents. It is not necessary to imagine the perception of an animal with much smaller dimensions than ours, to observe that on a human scale, the biosphere appears as a multi-colored mantle in which no two pieces are the same. The biosphere is a complicated mosaic in which different norms or regularities are observed depending on the distance of the observer from the Earth.

The observation and verification of this variability leads to a definition or recognition of subordinate units in the biomes. These units can be defined according to different criteria: whether they are strictly linked to the composition of the flora or fauna, or whether they refer to variables which define the structure and the functioning of these units, as in the case of the cover, or density, the biomass, production or the rate of turnover. In the first case, we take the presence of certain species as an indication of a set of environmental conditions, while in the second we pay more attention to the system's response as a whole.

Variability within biomes

The large units which we defined earlier can easily be subdivided according to physiognomic and structural characteristics. The degree of subdivision is variable as some present a much greater homogeneity than others. Thus, forests can be subdivided into tropical rain forests and montane cloud forests. But the montane cloud forests of America are different from those of Africa, for instance, because the species that comprise them are different. Biomes, then, must not be understood as discrete and real elements but rather as methodological reductions of a continuous reality.

On the other hand, a given biome's territory can feature all kinds of geographical and edaphic unevenness (rivers, lakes, cliffs, etc.) which introduce sharp and sudden modifications into the location's ecological parameters. This leads to changes in the species composition, as well as in the structure and functioning of the ecosystems in the biome, to such an extent that at the heart of one and the same biome quite different formations can co-exist.

Thus, for both biogeographical and ecological reasons, biomes are far from homogenous, although formations within biomes tend to more similar to each other than to formations in other biomes. This is all reflected in the names commonly used to describe many of these formations. In the world of savannahs and savannah-type woods, for example, we find names such as *espinal*, *caatinga*, *sertao*, *campo*, *barbaçuai*, *miombo*, and so on: the local people see these as very different areas and that is why they give them different names, but on a global scale they all formations typical of the dry tropical biome.

Microenvironments

Within the landscape we can also define lesser units associated with a finer level of structure, which depends on microclimatic conditions. Factors such as the relief make the depth of the soil and the insolation change in a very marked way within relatively small distances. This means that under certain homogenous macroclimatic conditions, variable factors like the availability of water and nutrients, average temperature, thermal variation and the availability of light, show sharp gradients. These gradients involve changes which can affect the degree of development of a type of vegetation, and

255 Phenomena are perceived differently according to the scale at which they are observed. On the scale of the accompanying photograph, one can see on this rock covered with lichens, a unique community where a number of elements repeat themselves in space in a more or less regular manner, while a more detailed view of a small fragment of this rock would make different species observable (in this case species of the genera *Rhizocarpon, Lecidella, Pertusaria, Aspicilli, Hafellia,* etc.) and would show that there is a solution of continuity going from one species to the neighboring one. The same happens with biomes and the diversity within them: the biome which appears to be homogeneous at the scale at which it can be seen from a satellite analagous to (our view of the lichens that cover the rock), can appear very polymorphic when seen from one of its subunits (the view at the scale of a small arthropod inhabiting one of the lichen species).
[Photo: AISA]

256 Valley bottoms, because of the greater availability of humidity coupled with the greater quality, or depth, of the soil, and the rainfall, have a different appearance from that of the slopes. In some cases, this microenvironmental difference causes a relatively slight difference in landscape, since the conditions remain similar and allow the presence of similar or identical biological forms. In particular situations, however, the differences lead to a major contrast as in the case of a zone that is near the boundary between two biomes, a zone in which a small difference represents the crossing of a threshold. In the photograph, the severe degradation of the slopes by erosion drastically reduces the water retention capacity of the soil. In this situation, in a matter of a few meters one passes from a degraded zone to a riparian wood.
[Photo: Ernest Costa]

can even determine more important structural changes, like the disappearance of the tree layer or the substitution of one formation for another. Under general conditions of Mediterranean climate, for example, orientation and relief determine the presence of shrub formations, or of sclerophyllous woods, under similar rainfall conditions.

These effects linked to the microclimate are of considerable importance in boundary zones or zones of transition between biomes. Under these conditions, a small variation can imply a drastic change in the landscape as a boundary or limit is crossed. The borders between biomes or formations are less definable as we get closer to them, that is, as we observe them in greater detail. Edaphic conditions or the relief, when they present important variations, gives rise to borders which are anything but straight-edged or showing a smooth transition.

257 Each biome corresponds to a major biological strategy of adaptation to the prevailing climatic conditions; which in the case of the habitat shown in the photograph, (Ripollès, Osona, Catalonia) involves the installation of sclerophyllous woods, that is, trees with small, tough, evergreen leaves, adapted to tolerating the small amount of water available and the marked summer drought characteristic of the Mediterranean climate. However, within a biome, there may be penetrations by other biomes, due to variations in, for example, altitude or slope: this will also be the case in this landscape where intrusions of the biome corresponding to temperate deciduous woodland are found in hollows or on cool, damp slopes (see also figure 221). Normally in the contact zones between two biomes, or in mountains subjected to several altitudinal climatic changes, this kind of interpenetration of biomes may be found.
[Photo: Ernest Costa]

Limits and gradients

Environmental conditions can present more or less gradual transitions, depending on the characteristics of the relief. Thus in the case of an abrupt relief, there will be very marked transitions which will tend to give rise to very marked and defined limits in the landscape. On the other hand, in a smooth and homogenous relief, the transitions will also be smooth and give rise to gradual changes. In the first case, and especially in border zones between different formations or biomes, we will find a patchwork landscape, made up of clearly differentiated units. In the second case, we will find a landscape dominated by gradients with changes which lead almost imperceptibly from one type of landscape to another. These differences give rise to several different ways of understanding and describing landscapes. In the European continent, with a very marked relief, crossed by transverse mountain ranges and with considerable climatic differences, associated with a greater or lesser

258 Of the main remote sensing satellites, among the most sophisticated are the series of French SPOT (Satéllite pour l'Observation de la Terre) satellites, which allow us to obtain data from the Earth's surface at a resolution of 33 ft (10 m). The significance of environmental problems today has led to the design of satellites that will allow us to follow the state of the biosphere to decide courses of action to improve the global environment. For example, the European Space Agency (ESA) has a satellite, the ERS-1 devoted exclusively to obtaining information about the environment; it has been designed in such a way that the operationally important data can be transmitted to users in less than three hours. The data obtained from the last generations of satellites, the ERS, for example, allow one to make weather and marine forecasts; monitor the development of frosts; detect the causes of pollution; assist agriculture, forestry, and fishing; and explore mineral resources. (a) MSS: Multi-Spectral Scanner; (b) TM: Thematic Mapper; (c) Sea Wide Field Sensor; (d) Thermal Infra Red; (e) Synthetic Aperture Radar; (f) Coastal Zone Color Scanner; (g) Heat Capacity Mapping Mission; (h) European Remote Sensing Satellite; (i) Active Microwave Instrument; (j) Wind Scattometer; (k) Radar Altimeter; (l) Along Track Scanning Radiometer; (m) Microwave Sounder; (n) Marine Observation Satellite (Japanese); (o) Multispectral Electronic Self-Scanning Radiometer; (p) Microwave Scanning Radiometer; (q) Indian Remote Sensing Satellite; (r) Linear Imaging Self Scanning.
[Source: data supplied by the author]

SATELLITE	TYPE OF DETECTOR/SENSOR	RESOLUTION	AREA COVERED	REPETITION	BAND SPECTRUM	ALTITUDE
LANDSAT 1	MSS (a)	80 m	185 km	18 days	500-600 nm	910 km
(1972-1980)					600-700 nm	
					700-800 nm	
					800-1,100 nm	
LANDSAT 2	MSS (a)	80 m	185 km	18 days	500-600 nm	910 km
(1975-1982)					600-700 nm	
					700-800 nm	
					800-1,100 nm	
LANDSAT 3	MSS (a)	80 m	185 km	18 days	500-600 nm	910 km
(1978)					600-700 nm	
					700-800 nm	
					800-1,100 nm	
		120 m			10,400-12,500 nm	
LANDSAT 4	MSS (a)	80 m	185 km	18 days	500-600 nm	705 km
(1982)					600-700 nm	
					700-800 nm	
					800-1,100 nm	
	TM (b)	30 m			450-520 nm	
					520-600 nm	
					630-690 nm	
					760-900 nm	
					1,550-1,750 nm	
					2,080-2,350 nm	
		120 m			10,400-12,500 nm	
LANDSAT 5	MSS (a)	80 m	185 km	18 days	500-600 nm	705 km
(1984)					600-700 nm	
					700-800 nm	
					800-1,100 nm	
	TM (b)	30 m			450-520 nm	705 km
					520-600 nm	
					630-690 nm	
					760-900 nm	
					1,550-1,750 nm	
					2,080-2,350 nm	
		120 m			10,400-12,500 nm	
LANDSAT 6	Panchromatic		185 km	16 days	500-900 nm	705 km
(1991)	TM (b)	30 m			450-520 nm	
					520-600 nm	
					630-690 nm	
					760-900 nm	
					1,550-1,750 nm	
		120 m			2,080-2,350 nm	
					10,400-12,500 nm	
	SeaWIFS (c)				433-453 nm	
					490-510 nm	
					555-575 nm	
					655-675 nm	
					745-785 nm	
					843-887 nm	
					10,500-11,500 nm	
					11,500-12,500 nm	
	TIR (d)				3,530-3,930 nm	
					8,200-8,750 nm	
					8,750-9,300 nm	
					10,200-11,000 nm	
					11,000-11,800 nm	
SEASAT	SAR (e)	25 m	90 km	162 days	23.5 cm	790 km
(June 1978-October 1978)						

SPOT 1 (1986)	Multispectral	20 m	60 km	26 days	500-590 nm	832 km
					610-680 nm	
					790-890 nm	
	Panchromatic	10 m			510-730 nm	
SPOT 2 (1990)	Multispectral	20 m	60 km	26 days	500-590 nm	832 km
					610-680 nm	
					790-890 nm	
	Panchromatic	10 m			510-730 nm	
NIMBUS 7 (October 1978)	CZCS (f)	800 m	1,566 km	6 days	430-450 nm	955 km
					510-530 nm	
					540-560 nm	
					660-680 nm	
					700-800 nm	
					1,050-1,250 nm	
HCMM (April 1978) (g)	HCMR 1	500 m	716 km	16 days	550-1,100 nm	620 km
	HCMR 2	600 m			10,500-12,500 nm	
METEOSAT		2.5-5 km	variable	30 min	400-1,100 nm	3,900 km
					5,700-7,100 nm	
		120 m			10,500-12,500 nm	
ERS - 1(h) (July 1991)	AMI (i)	30 m	100 km	3 days	C 5.3 GHz	785 m
	WS (j)	50 cm			C 5.3 GHz	
	RA (k)	10 cm			Ku 13.8 GHz	
	ATSR (l)	1 km	500 km	35 days	1,600 nm	
					3,700 nm	
					11,000 nm	
					12,000 nm	
	MS (m)	20 km			23.8 GHz	
					36.5 GHz	
ERS - 2(h) (April 1995)	AMI (i)	30 m	100 km	3 days	C 5.3 GHz	785 m
	WS (j)	50 cm			C 5.3 GHz	
	RA (k)	10 cm			Ku 13.8 GHz	
	ATSR (l)	1 km	500 km	35 days	1,600 nm	
					3,700 nm	
					11,000 nm	
					12,000 nm	
	MS (m)	20 km			23.8 GHz	
					36.5 GHz	
MOS-1 (n) (February 1987)	MESSR (o)	900 m a	100 × 90 km	17 days		
		2,700 m				
	MSR (p)	32 m			23 GHz	
		23 m			31 GHz	
IRS-1A (q) (March 1988)	LISS (r)	72.5 m a	148-74 km	22 days	4,500-5,200 nm	
		36.25 m			5,200-6,800 nm	
					6,200-6,800 nm	
					7,700-8,600 nm	

degree of continentality, and sitting between three large, different biomes, some landscape ecologists have described its structure as a mosaic. They use descriptive methods which define and distinguish between clearly differentiated and neighboring units, formed by groups of related species which are placed in a systematic category, in a scheme which is similar to the arrangement and classification of species. In the American continent, on the other hand, made up of large areas of relatively homogenous relief or broken by N-S mountain ranges, the landscapes change gradually. In this case the methods of description that have been developed are directed more towards the study of gradients than to that of borders, as they are faced with landscapes made up of different units of broad belts along which some species are gradually replaced by others, in a smooth transition between different types of landscapes or formations. It is perhaps for this reason that European and American phytosociology constitute two completely different schools as far as methodology goes. They provide, like the landscapes, responses to the different distribution of environmental conditions in space.

The perception of the biosphere

Seeing is one thing and perceiving quite another. In the past, and even today, human beings did not perceive many of things they could see. At the other extreme, technology allows us to perceive many things we cannot see. It is a question not only of the senses, but also of sensors and of scale.

It is said that we cannot see the wood for the trees: it is no good looking at things too closely, i.e., on an inappropriate scale. To change the scale of a map is to alter, not its dimensions, but the level of detail with which we consider the features portrayed and thereby the nature of the concepts given in the legend: if we simply enlarge the map of a city, the plans of its buildings do not appear.

At a scale of 10^{-18} m, for example, we enter the world of subatomic particles. We need enormous particle accelerators, large research teams and sophisticated computer systems to study reality at such a level. The bosons Z^0, W^+ and W^-, observed by the team of Carlo Rubbia and S. Van der Meer at CERN (Conseil Européen pour la Recherche Nucléaire) won them the Nobel Prize for Physics in 1984. In contrast, the atomic world postulated in 1922 by their fellow Nobel Prize winner Ernest Rutherford dealt with units of a diameter 40,000 times larger, that is, around 10^{-14} m (although still far too small for us to perceive).

Eukaryotic cells have a membrane that separates the cytoplasm from the extracellular environment. It regulates the exchange of substances between the cytoplasm and the outside environment and enables cells to build into tissues. Cellular biologists use the electronic microscope to observe it: the scale of observation in this case is around 10^{-8} m. Eyes, those marvellous organs that allow animals to perceive part of the electromagnetic spectrum, stand at a higher level of biological integration than the subcellular, cellular, and histological levels. The human eye is a few centimeters in diameter, as are the other organs situated on the head, the nose, the ears, and the mouth. When we examine these organs it is at a scale of 10^{-2} m. At the other end of the scale, thanks to remote detection by satellite we can now see terrestrial phenomena at a previously impossible scale of 10^2-10^3 m.

[ESA - Science Photo Library / AGE Fotostock]

ERS-1 satellite [ESA]

Satellites allow us to monitor various ecological parameters of a discrete ecosystem, such as a river basin, or a large part of a biome, such as the rainforests of South America. We can detect, for example, the great plumes of smoke made by fires in stretches of the Amazon jungle. And even more: on July 19, 1969, Neil Armstrong and Edwin "Buzz"Aldrin Jr. were the first humans to set foot on the moon, and the first to be astounded by the view of the Earth from that distance. Our blue planet, a little over 7,457 mi (12,000 km) in diameter, was a breath-taking sight above the lunar horizon. The two astronauts were observing, perceiving, reality at a scale of 10^4 m.

In the future, when we can travel to the stars, astronauts will be able to reach a point where it will be possible to observe the whole solar system, the diameter of which is 10^9-10^{10} m. The scale of the object perceived will be greatly increased in relation to the Earth observed from the moon. With the aid of powerful telescopes, such as those of Mount Palomar in California, or the orbiting Hubble telescope, we can already observe large stellar bodies that are great distances away such as galaxies or groups of galaxies. The Local Group is the name given to a group of 18 to 20 galaxies including the Milky Way, in which the Earth is situated. This group of galaxies has a diameter between 10^{18} and 10^{20} m, staggeringly big in comparison with the 10^{-18} m of subatomic particles: a practically unimaginable difference of 10^{36} m! However, we do not need to go so far. At the moment, the remote sensing systems which allow us to perceive realities of 10^3 m have already revolutionized our vision of the biosphere.

Aerostatic dirigible balloon [Philippe Plailly - Science Photo Library / AGE Fotostock]

All bodies with a temperature above that of absolute zero absorb, reflect, or emit electromagnetic energy at different frequencies, wavelengths, intensities, etc., according to their physico-chemical properties. With the right instruments we can thus obtain valuable information about the nature of an object by studying the radiation it emits or reflects. This is the principle of remote sensing, a technique that collects information from the electromagnetic energy emitted or reflected by objects, not only within the visible range of the spectrum, but also on shorter (ultraviolet) and longer (near infrared, thermal infrared, microwaves) wavelengths.

Remote sensing includes relatively classical techniques such as aerial photography and photogrammetry alongside other more modern ones, such as the use of multispectral chambers in orbital satellites. These chambers, which do not use film, capture electromagnetic signals emitted by the surface of the Earth using electronic detectors, digitize them, and transmit them radioelectronically. The signal, once transformed by electronic imagery, can be visualized in false color for later study. The electromagnetic radiation coming from an object can either be observed passively, or radiation can be directed at it to see how it modifies it (e.g., radar and sonar).

In order to learn more about the functioning of the planet, the atmosphere, the hydrosphere, lithosphere, and biosphere, we need data obtained by satellite using remote sensors. We can discover the rate of deforestation in the Amazon basin over a period of time by taking infrared photographs of the forest cover at different time intervals over the period under consideration. A satellite can also provide us with an indication of the amount of chlorophyll produced by the oceans, which will indicate the level of activity of marine phytoplankton. A country that wants to engage in regional planning can obtain a map of soil uses from the interpretation and processing of data obtained by different types of remote sensing. The best known are the maps used in television weather forecasts, where we can see the progression of the clouds across our country during the last 24 hours. This is nothing more than data obtained by satellite and processed by computer.

259 Often the transformation of the land by humans is so profound that it is difficult to imagine what the landscape looked like before human intervention. In some places and situations, such a reconstruction is very difficult, such as in the zones of transition between different biomes and in territories that have been subject to change for centuries. In many cases, human activity is an environmental factor that shapes the landscape as effectively as climatic or edaphic factors. *[Photo: A. Tovy / Index]*

3.2 Humanized biomes

The mosaic formed by the biosphere's landscapes has become more and more complex. Humans have gradually transformed these landscapes and have introduced new factors that cause variation. The influence the human race has had on nature has changed considerably throughout its history, as has been pointed out in previous chapters. For a long time the heavy consumption of external energy has allowed humans to change the biosphere radically, to such an extent that today it is impossible to understand the distribution and structure of landscapes without taking human intervention into account.

The general trend for changes in the biosphere introduced by humans, as far as modification and transformation of landscapes is concerned, consists of a process of simplification and the introduction of new factors affecting spatial distribution. Structural simplification stems directly from exploitation which, in ecological terms, consists of a rejuvenation of ecosystems that places them in less mature though clearly much more productive states. The exploitation of forests to obtain wood, the conversion of forests to pasture or crop lands and the harvesting of fish resources are all different examples of the above-mentioned trend. In fact, whenever humans add a trophic level to an ecosystem, the lower levels experience a rejuvenation. Such rejuvenation, the reverse of the trend that leads ecosystems to their most mature states, encourages so-called opportunist species—ones that grow quickly and that are well-adapted to environmental fluctuations—because of their high reproductive capacity in particular. Humans, when transforming the landscape through exploitation, directly or indirectly benefit certain species whose role which was at first slight becomes pronounced and dominant. That causes a loss of diversity or, in other words, a reduction in the total number of species, accompanied by an increase in dominance of a few. If we compare the appearance of a forest, a pasture and a monoculture treated with insecticides, we get an extremely clear example of this series of transformations.

Exploited and exploitable ecosystems

Some ecosystems are clearly preadapted to exploitation. In other words, they experience structural and functional transformations of minor significance as a result of the extraction of resources. This is the case in systems previously adapted to fluctuating conditions, naturally dominated by opportunist species capable of rapidly rebuilding their populations. Formations dominated by herbaceous plants, like steppes and grasslands, and marine systems associated wiith areas of nutrient blooming are

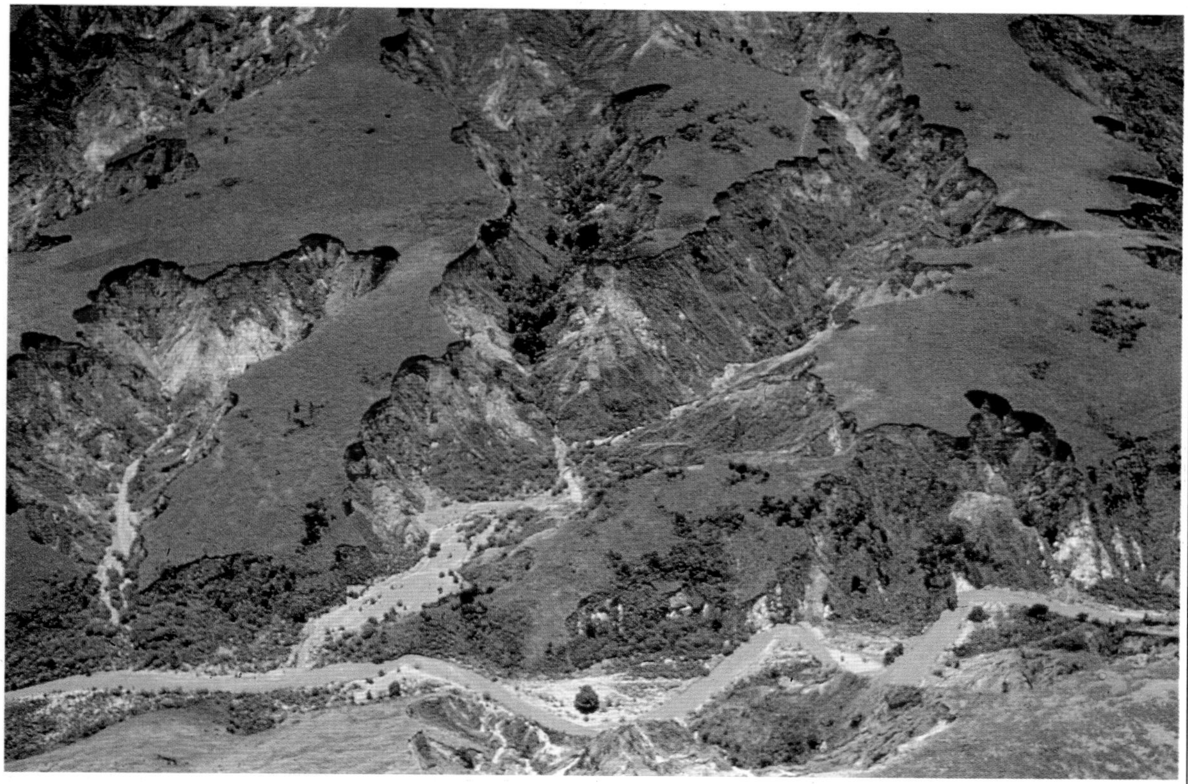

260 Some ecosystems, such as tropical forests, are very sensitive to the changes introduced by humans in the course of exploitation. The great fragility of tropical ecosystems—apparently so abundant and productive—combined with techniques for exploitation, and management methods imported from temperate biomes, which have been shown to be quite unsuitable for application outside the environmental conditions in which they were designed, have led to the irreversible destruction of large areas of tropical forest, such as those of Madagascar shown in the photograph. In many cases, however, this destruction is caused purely and simply by overexploitation, which takes only immediate benefits into account.
[Photo: Frans Lanting / Minden Pictures]

good examples of this. Humans effectively replace the action of grassland fires and large herbivores by transforming them into cereal farms whose structure is not that much simpler than that of the initial ecosystem; less drastic, but equally effective, is the straightforward changeover from the original herbivores to herds of domestic livestock. In the case of fishing grounds near nutrient blooms, humans exploit fish species that have an extremely high reproductive capacity and relatively short life span so that the populations can be rebuilt very rapidly.

In other cases, some characteristics of ecosystems make them better suited to certain types of exploitation. For example, the rich, deep soils in temperate deciduous forests can be turned into crop lands without any problem whatsoever, so long as the periodic application of fertilizers replaces the nutrients drained by the harvests. In this case, part of the system (the soil) copes well with exploitation, although the system as a whole suffers a far-reaching modification that turns it into something completely different.

A third case is systems that cannot cope with exploitation at all, and not necessarily because of difficult environmental conditons. This is the case of tropical rain forests and tropical coral formations. In both cases the ecosystems provide extremely favourable conditions and have a very substantial species and structural richness that cannot be matched by any other ecosystem on the planet. They are stable systems in stable conditions, though very sensitive to fluctuations and alterations. Most of the species that make up these ecosystems have a long life span and a relatively low reproductive capacity. The species are also very well adapted to particular environmental conditions. The system as a whole has a low level of resilience, in other words, it cannot readily recover from changes. In the case of tropical rain forests, the problem is worsened because of the structure of the soils: they are very poor in nutrients and not at all resistant to intense leaching by rain, an action that would be generated should the vegetation cover be removed. The model of agricultural exploitation from middle latitudes is obviously unsuitable for application in tropical rainy climates. Similarly, fishing exploitation in nutrient rich areas cannot be applied to coral reefs in warm seas.

Deliberate and involuntary alterations

Modifications made to the landscape by humans go far beyond simple transformations that stem from the extraction of resources or the replacement of vegetation by crops and pastures. In fact, unsuitable exploitation or overexploitation can lead to irreversible changes in a system as a result of degradation. This is the case, for example, of the overexploitation of wood in Mediterranean forests, excessive grazing or the cultivation of steep slopes within the same biome. Each one of these actions gives rise to intense erosion that destroys the already poor Mediterranean soils, which are often fossil soils or soils whose formation is extremely slow. Therefore, when these forms of exploitation are abandoned, because they are no longer productive, the original systems cannot be recovered; the degradation they have suffered prevents this from happening.

In very densely populated areas of the planet, territorial transformations go much further, as the effect of humanizing amounts to serious alteration of the landscape, changing it so as to adapt it to communication routes, housing, and other structures, all of which gives rise to new landscapes that only a few species are capable of sharing with man.

Furthermore, there are many alterations that are not caused by voluntary intervention, but are side-effects stemming from other actions. This is the case of the pollution and eutrophication of waters, the pollution of soils caused by the dumping of waste, the disappearance of species that cannot survive certain alterations in their environment, the side-effects caused by insecticides, atmospheric pollution, radioactive contamination or forest fires, to name but a few. Whether voluntary or not, the alterations are anthropic, induced by humans in the fabric of the biosphere.

Man's far-reaching tentacles

The human species represents but a small part of the biosphere's total biomass, yet its importance is by no means proportional to this minuscule fraction. Most of the planet's landscapes are humanized or, in other words, transformed directly or indirectly by man's activities. However, even in those landscapes where the human population is not permanent or is very sparse, the traces of humans are always present. The side-effects of pollution, of radioactive waste or of synthetic chemicals, for example, manage to reach all four corners of the earth.

Humans have changed, upset and complicated the mosaic of the biosphere that was itself already very complex. Humans have fragmented landscapes, causing a reduction in biological diversity but a multiplication of frontiers. They have directly or indirectly favoured some species, increasing their areas of distribution, whilst bringing about the disappearance of others, that were unable to tolerate the disturbances. They have humanized and disfigured the Earth's living mantle, either for their own benefit or as a consequence of side-effects which, although undesirable, have not been avoided. Therefore, as far as crops and livestock are concerned, with their associated weeds, fodder-producing plants, plagues and parasites, today's world displays a considerable level of homogeneity, due to what some authors have termed *ecological imperialism*, referring to the great success of the effects of colonization over the past 500 years by civilizations coming from temperate European biomes. Andean lands in Argentina and Chile, for example, are full of crops, trees, shrubs and animals that are typically European, which have displaced the indigenous flora and fauna to a lesser or greater extent.

Insular systems or those that are largely isolated have been hit particularly badly by the effects of these massive introductions of species connected with the colonization process. New Zealand, for example, which has been separate from the Australian continent for 100 million years and whose indigenous flora is 89% endemic, and which developed in the absence of large herbivores, saw its vegetation severely disturbed when European livestock were introduced in 1840. Some European plants, accidental human travelling companions, like furze (*Ulex europaeus*), bramble (*Rubus fruticosus*), broom (*Sarothamnus scoparius*) and the tree lupin (*Lupinus arboreus*), spread throughout New Zealand as if it were totally unoccupied, displacing vegetation that was incapable of competing with them. The rabbit, a permanent companion of European colonizers, has repeatedly plagued insular systems or those that are largely isolated. The 24 rabbits introduced into Australia in 1874 gave rise to a population of hundreds of millions in just a few years because of the absence of predators and diseases to control them. The introduction of foxes helped to keep numbers down but caused, as an indirect consequence, many marsupial populations to become rare, chiefly because they were not adapted to defend themselves against a predator of that type.

The same *biogeographical revolution* caused by man in some insular systems made them uninhabitable, as happened during the fifteenth century on the Atlantic island of Porto Santo (Madeira), when the colonizers were forced to leave by the uncontrollable population of rabbits. Donkeys introduced into Fuerteventura (Canary Islands) during the sixteenth century almost caused a similar exodus. In other cases, the biogeographical disturbance is more discreet and is limited to the disappearance of a few species without endangering the overall functioning of the systems. In the case of the island of Kerguelen, for example, sheep

261 The case of rabbits introduced by the Europeans into the continent of Australia for game, is probably the best known of the biological invasions caused by the continuous traffic of species that humans have practiced either voluntarily or involuntarily for a variety of reasons. In Australia, a modest game animal became converted, in the absence of predators and without competitors that could stop it, into a veritable pest both for agriculture and for the natural ecosystems of the continent. The large population densities reached means that, even today, the rabbit destroys crops and makes the regeneration of natural vegetation difficult.
[Photo: Brendan Beirne / Auscape International]

COUNTRY	NUMBER OF NATIVE SPECIES	NUMBER OF INTRODUCED SPECIES	PERCENTAGE OF INTRODUCED SPECIES
Antigua and Barbuda	900	180	10
Australia	15 - 20,000	1,500 - 2,000	10
Austria	3,000	300	10
Finland	1,250	120	10
France	4,400	500	11
Guadeloupe	1,668	149	9
Hawaii	12 - 13,000	228	17.5 - 19
Java	4,598	313	7
New Zealand	1,790	1,570	47
Spain	4,900	750	15

262 The percentages of introduced species in various floras. Bearing in mind the intense and indiscriminate traffic in species that humans have undertaken as a result of the links between the different continents and the lands of the planet, the percentage of introduced species in the floras of different countries can be considered as giving an indication of the susceptibility to invasion of different environments. Thus, in contrast to percentages in the 15-20 percent range in continental zones, we find other areas that have much higher rates of introduction, such as 20% in the Hawaiian islands and the 47% in the territory of New Zealand area have been isolated for a long time. One has to take into account, however, that these percentages do not give a clear idea of the degree of environmental change caused by these invasions, since, sometimes a single species can cause drastic changes if it gives rise to very large and extensive populations.
[Source: Drake et al. *(1989)]*

introduced in 1952 caused the virtual disappearance of two species of its flora (*Pringlea antiscorbutica* and *Azorella selago*) and the increase in numbers of a third (*Acaena ascendens*), which was rejected by the livestock and favoured by the lack of competition. The biogeographical revolution does not necessarily mean a reduction in the number of species: on the island of Réunion, for example, although the 5 indigenous species of mammals, 33 birds and five reptiles, were reduced to two, 14 and two respectively, they share their environment with 11 introduced species of mammals, 19 birds and 10 reptiles.

This general connectivity between biomes around the world is also taken advantage of by opportunist species and others with a high dispersion capacity. Ports and airports constitute recolonization centers from which new distribution areas open up for these new travellers. The Argentinean ant *Iridomyrmex humilis*, for example, appeared in New Orleans in 1891, in Madeira, Portugal, California, Cape Town and Chile between 1905 and 1910, on the Riviera in 1920, in Naples in 1936, in Melbourne, Hawaii and Australia between 1940 and 1950, and in Majorca in 1953, which just goes to show how it took advantage of transoceanic shipping lines. Outbreaks of malaria in the surroundings of European airports which have heavy traffic with tropical zones, caused by transporting mosquitos that transmit the disease, emphasizes the dangers that some of these small biogeographical revolutions can hold for man. Many sea organisms like molluscs and crustaceans also travel from one place to another by sticking to the hulls of ships or by simply being present in the waters used to fill ballast tanks. They then colonize areas far away from their initial ones. This spread can bring closely-related species into contact and, when crossed, give rise to new hybrids that can be viable or successful. The hybrid grass *Spartina*

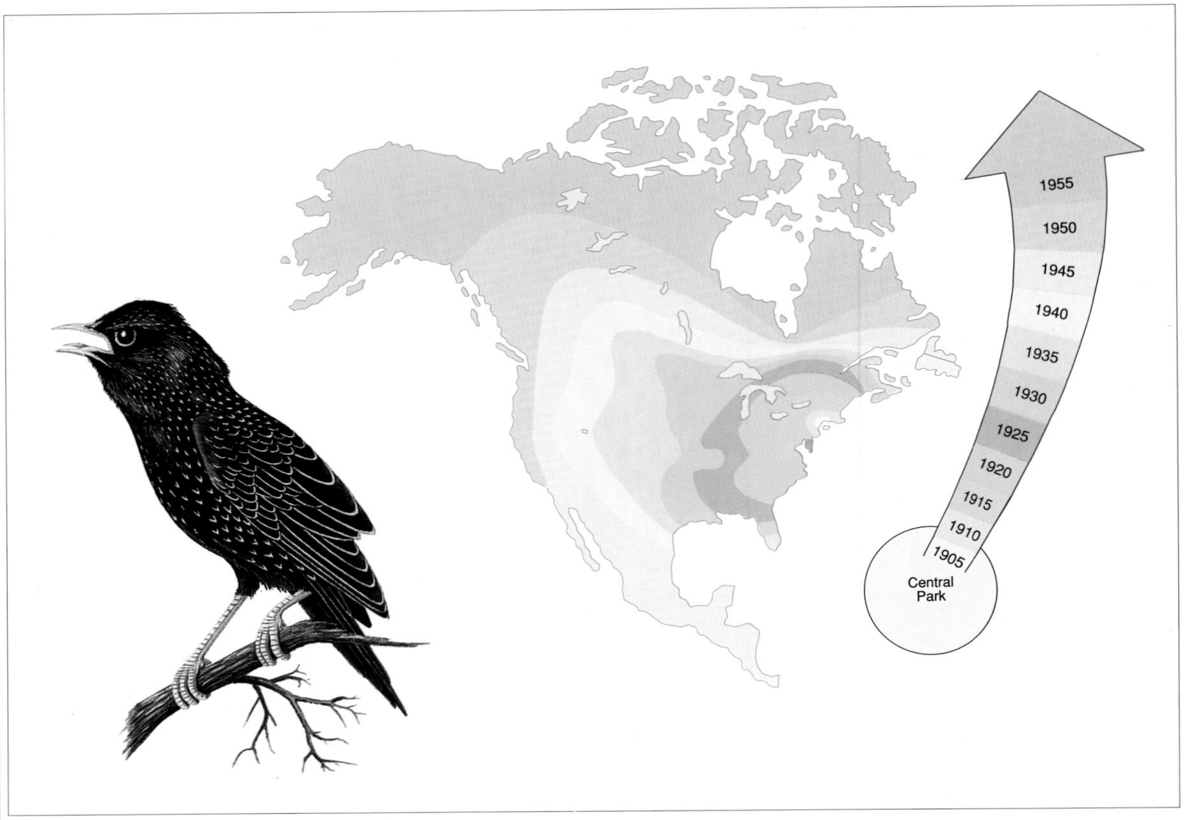

263 The common starling (*Sturnus vulgaris*) was introduced in North America in 1891, when 100 specimens were released in Central Park, New York. Its great capacity to compete with native species for food meant that in only 50 years it spread throughout nearly the whole of North America. Humans were the vehicle, facilitating a transatlantic journey that they could never have managed by themselves, but once in North America their great competitive capacity allowed them to spread rapidly.
[Diagram: Biopunt, from Attenborough, 1989]

townsendi, for example, has successfully colonized large zones of the European Atlantic coastline.

Humans do not only link the continents by transport routes but also physically modify some of the biogeographical barriers and even eliminates them. This is the case of the Suez canal, that has brought the waters of the Mediterranean into contact with those of the Red Sea, enabling 24 species of fish to pass from the latter to the former. In other cases, humans create peculiar environments within the biomes, that reproduce different climatic conditions, and involuntary transportation of species does the rest. Greenhouses in the temperate zone, for example, create a replica of tropical environments, and diverse species of seaweed, arthropods and Turbellaria typical of warm climates can be found in them.

The North American Indians called the plantain (*Plantago lanceolata*), very common along roadsides, "English foot," because it was associated with the presence of the colonizers. This close relationship emphasises the opportunist species' capability of rapidly colonizing altered habitats. In the last few centuries, these species have also become the privileged members of a biosphere that is ever more simplified and without frontiers. The old and absurd intercontinental bridges that paleontologists and biogeographers postulated in order to explain obvious relationships between species of different continents or separate specific areas, before the theory of continental drift provided a more realistic basis, have become much more of a reality, profuse than anyone would have dared to imagine. Humans have set in motion a biogeographical revolution whose consequences cannot easily be foreseen, full of notable events like the invasions by donkeys, rabbits and pigs, or like the tremendous thistle invasions of the Argentinian Pampa, or the orange groves that Charles Darwin found on the islands in the estuary of the Paraná River. But there is also a far less spectacular side, consisting of changes that are more subtle yet no less radical or irreversible. Humans are homogenizing and simplifying the biosphere, changing the specific composition of ecosystems and modifying landscapes. The biosphere has and will never be the same since humans learned to interpret the ocean winds and brought what had, in the distant past, been just one continent together again.

The end-product is a mosaic of virgin landscapes (the scarcest element), slightly altered landscapes (not very abundant), landscapes modified by forestry, livestock and agricultural exploitation (very abundant), highly modified or directly urbanized (found everywhere), and even completely eroded or destroyed landscapes (more and more frequent). The biosphere, complex by nature, is becoming even more diverse and difficult to interpret. In any event, however, this extremely humanized biosphere is the one we are left with. And it is, after all, the biosphere we now see.

264 The human-induced alteration of most forest landscapes of the world is seen clearly in this wood in the Azores (island of São Miguel); none of the dominant species there belongs to the native flora of the archipelago. In effect, the original laurisilva, which presumably covered nearly the entire area before humans arrived, was almost totally destroyed by repeated fires in the first years of settlement by the Portuguese and later the Dutch (in the fifteenth and sixteenth centuries). Native laurisilva has been replaced by crops, pasture, forest plantations, or buildings. Thus lush "pine" woodland is in fact a plantation of the Asian conifer *Cryptomeria japonica*, and the undergrowth is covered by the spontaneous Asian exotic *Hedychium gardnerianum* (Zingiberaceae), which was introduced to the archipelago accidentally, and by the hydrangea (*Hydrangea opuloides*), a third introduction from eastern Asia, which escaped from the hedges of the livestock enclosure. Today one can find similar kinds of landscape throughout the world, which are stable as this case, or might be in the need of constant human attention. *[Photo: Ramon Folch]*

Protecting areas against the extinction of species

How many species inhabit the biosphere? Five, 10, 20 or 30 million? So far, some 1.4 million living species have been described, of which 750,000 are insects, 250,000 plants, 41,000 vertebrates, the rest are divided between invertebrates, fungi, algae, and microorganisms.

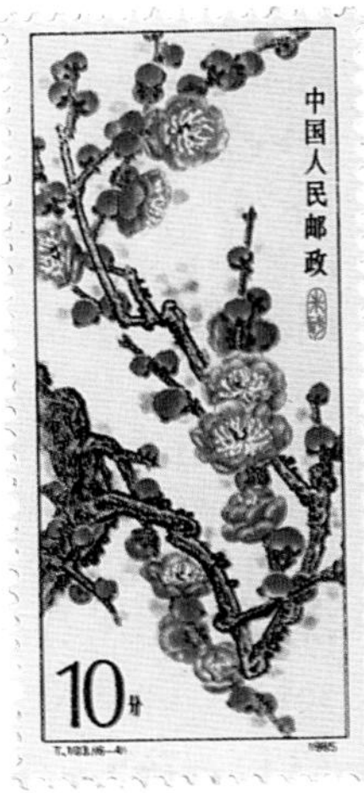

[Jordi Vidal]

Spring by Guiseppe Arcimboldi [AISA]

Recent findings in the tropical rainforests, which are estimated to contain half of the planet's extant species, leads us to believe that there are between five and 30 million of them in the biosphere as a whole. This means we have still only discovered a proportion of them. But biodiversity is not important simply at the level of species. Biodiversity begins at the lowest level of biological integration, the molecular level, and extends to that of the ecosystem and the biome. The genetic level is very important when we talk about the current crisis of biodiversity. The genetic diversity of individuals in a population is the key to the population's ability to survive environmental changes. In many cases of speciation, the genetic differences become so great that it is difficult to say when a population still belongs to the "old" species and when it has become a "new" one.

The fact is that human activity, particularly in this century, has been so intense and so extensive that this enormous biodiversity has begun to decrease alarmingly. Roads, motorways, railway lines, commercial ports and marinas, ski stations, hydroelectric power stations, the cutting down of forests, extensive monocultures, mining, hunting, wildlife collecting, pollution, etc., all contribute to this loss of biodiversity. The exponential increase in the human population (six billion human beings now inhabit the Earth) has increased these activities consider-

ably, to the extent where the repercussions can already be felt on a global scale.

The modification or disappearance of habitats is often caused by the fragmentation of ecosystems. For example, the modification of stretches of a forest, and the development of the most accessible or productive areas leaves it fragmented into parcels that vary in size and degree of isolation. According to the theory of island biogeography, as an island of forest becomes smaller and more isolated from the main body, so the number of species in it decreases until a new equilibrium is reached. This principle is applicable to many other ecosystems. This progressive fragmentation of ecosystems due to human activity causes the extinction of many species. As a result, the number of species in a region, and in the biosphere as a whole, decreases.

We are witnessing a wave of extinction of species that is unprecedented in the history of life on Earth. The current rate of extinction of species is comparable to, or greater than, the great mass extinctions at the beginning of the Triassic or the end of the Cretaceous. If we calculate the yearly average of species that have become extinct over the last 600 million years, we find that the current extinction rate is 10,000 times higher. Solving this serious problem requires all sorts of measures, from action on an individual level to major international decisions, and from creating recovery programs for species to the integrated land management of a territory. A historic step forward in this process was the creation, more than a hundred years ago, of the first protected areas.

In 1865 an extensive natural area was designated for the first time as an area

[Jordi Vidal]

of restricted use for the preservation of nature and the spiritual uplift of the public. This was the Yosemite National Park in California. Thus the concept of a National Park was born, although the term itself would not be employed until seven years later. It was in 1872 that Yellowstone, the first National Park in the world to be recognized as such, was established, also in the United States. Both parks were born from a desire to safeguard the riches of nature at a time when the West was being ravaged by pioneers. The idea was to preserve the area's natural and scenic wonders: the great canyons, the spectacular geysers, a rich fauna, waterfalls, etc. At the same time, there was a desire to compete with the old continent of Europe, to have something comparable to the marvelous works of architecture in Europe. After Yellowstone and Yosemite other parks "appeared:" the Everglades, Grand Canyon, Glacier, etc., the "jewels in the crown" of American nature, all destined to enjoy a less vulgar fate than the spectacular Niagara Falls (to take a nearby example), where commercial exploitation has grown to gigantic proportions.

The concept of the National Park was exported from the United States to the rest of the world, and there are now hundreds of them in many different countries. It is a brilliant and fertile idea that has spread far and wide—a good idea, but ambiguous in its objectives. American legislation established that the National Parks were set up "for the preservation of nature and the enjoyment of present and future generations." That is, National Parks were simultaneously meant to preserve the environment and provide recreation centers in the midst of nature, uses that were often mutually exclusive. This ambiguity has been a definite source of conflict in all the National Parks subsequently created

Bullock Museum, London [Mary Evans Picture Library]

around the globe. This situation has forced the IUCN—the World Conservation Union— to develop a series of new definitions of environmental protection that satisfy the different needs and possibilities of each country.

One of the limitations inherent in the concept of the National Park is that humans are not included as an integral part of nature. Partly as a response to this limitation, and partly in response to other definitions of protection that have appeared, the concept of a Biosphere Reserve was born in 1971. The idea was reinforced by the Mexican biologist Gonzalo Halffter within the framework of the activities of UNESCO's MAB ("Man and Biosphere") programme. The Biosphere Reserves in practice include humans and human activities as integral parts of the territory. They attempt to preserve a reality, not to create fenced-off preserves or nature sanctuaries. At the same time, the concept includes a strategic plan for establishing a network of reserves across the entire biosphere (see annex 2), in which all ecosystems without exception must be included. Thus the Biosphere Reserves differ from the National Parks in their incorporation of multiple functions within a unique conceptual framework, in the idea of an international network, and because they consider the human population to be a basic element. It is the aim of the Biosphere Reserves to demonstrate that it is possible to make development compatible with the preservation of the environment; they also seek to contribute to the conservation of the biological and ecological heritage of the biosphere, and promote the exchange of experience and research through their international logistical network.

In the words of UNESCO: "The Biosphere Reserves form an international network of protected areas in which an integrated concept of conservation is applied, combining preservation of ecological and genetic diversity with research, environmental monitoring, teaching, and training. The Biosphere Reserves are selected as representative examples of the world's ecosystems."

3.3 Climatic change: the greenhouse effect

It is said that a new climatic change is taking place due to an increase in the Earth's average temperature. It is also believed that human action on the Earth is one of the main causes of this change: gases emitted by industries, cars, forest fires, cattle raising, paddy fields, etc., are making the greenhouse effect worse. In 1863 Svante Arrhenius, a Swedish chemist and the founder of modern chemistry, had already foreseen this. There is a great deal of truth and a great deal of speculation about this subject.

The hypothesis of a man-made climatic change

Although natural factors contribute, current climatic change is caused mainly by human action. Carbon dioxide and methane emissions increase the concentrations of these gases in the Earth's atmosphere, provoking the greenhouse effect. Short-wave radiation coming from the Sun warms up the Earth's surface, but the later emission of long wave radiation by the Earth cannot escape to outer space as these gases absorb it and reflect it back again to Earth.

It is very difficult, though, to separate this human-made climatic change from natural climatic change, that is, from normal fluctuations of the climate. The Earth has undergone climatic changes, some of them very considerable, throughout history. Separating the increase in temperatures observed this century from the planet's normal fluctuations is very difficult. Until the last few decades, meteorological data were scarce and collected by a variety of instruments, which makes interpretation very difficult. To this we must add that data from so few years do not allow us to be certain as to whether the increase in temperature which has been observed is due to the effect of humans, to natural causes, or an error in available data.

To evaluate the validity of the data, climatologists and physicists of the atmosphere use huge supercomputers to construct climatic models. The models are computer programmes which simulate a real phenomenon, in this case atmospheric circulation. These models are used to try and predict what would happen to the Earth's climate if different variables were changed, like the composition of the different gases in the atmosphere. However, the results vary: some models predict an increase in the average global temperature of 5-9ºF (3-5ºC), while others foresee a much smaller increase of only 1-2ºF (0.5-1ºC). The fact is that these models, although extremely complex (supercomputers have to be used to make the very complex and long mathematical calculations), are still too simple as they cannot take into account the myriad of complex processes which take place in the atmosphere and the oceans. For example, clouds, an extremely important atmospheric factor (their presence or absence can lead to marked changes in the terrestrial albedo), are not taken into consideration.

Even though the different models and different teams of researchers cannot come to an agreement over the degree of temperature change, they do agree on the qualitative aspect of this change. Most models agree in predicting an increase in the Earth's average temperature. This prediction also fits in with the meteorological data which we have available. These data show a generalized increase in temperatures. Thus, even though we are using data and models which are not ideal, we can assert, with a high degree of certainty, that the climate is tending to warm up.

The possible agents of the change

The possible natural causes are numerous and plausible. Thus, raising the enormous plains of Tibet and the western part of north America provoked important physical and chemical changes in the atmosphere which helped to shape modern climatic trends. In the past, important climatic changes could have been provoked by large changes in the relief of the land and the configuration of the continents. We can find another cause in the modification of the geometry of the Earth's orbit and the inclination of the Earth's axis, since orbital variations modify the climate as they alter the quantity of solar energy which the Earth receives at different latitudes and in different seasons. The existence of a connection between the history of the glacial periods and orbital variations has recently been demonstrated. Solar activity varies every eleven years. During these cycles the number of sun spots and eruptions changes. When the cycle is longer, solar activity decreases and that, in turn, makes the Earth's temperature fall. Although the formation of great plains and the geometrical changes in the Earth's orbit explain the climatic change only on a very large time scale, the change in solar activity could partly explain it on a much smaller time scale, of the order of 10 years.

265 The large urban and industrial centers act as a focus for pollution and suffer especially from its effects, because of the accumulation of gases and particles under certain weather conditions. This high frequency of pollution—as well as creating poor environmental conditions from a health point of view—leads to certain changes such as the increase in the number of days with mist and rain and an increase in mean temperatures. This shows clearly how human activities can lead to important environmental changes.
[Photo: Bruno Barbey / Zardoya]

However, part of the increase in temperature recorded this century is certainly due to the increase in the concentration of greenhouse gases, an increase produced by humans. Some of the gases which make up the atmosphere, mainly carbon dioxide (CO_2), methane (CH_4) and water vapour (H_2O) are the so-called *greenhouse* [*effect*] gases. The short-wave radiation coming from the Sun can penetrate the atmosphere and warm up the Earth's surface, its oceans and continents. The Earth's surface, like any heated body, radiates heat—infrared radiation. Only infrared radiation of between 8 and 12 μm can traverse the atmosphere and escape to outer space. The remaining, two thirds to three quarters of the radiation emitted by Earth, is trapped by those gases, which act like a heat trap, or like a screen that stops the Earth's radiation from escaping. Humans, through their activity, increases the concentration of these gases in the atmosphere and therefore increases the greenhouse effect, causing the Earth's temperature to rise.

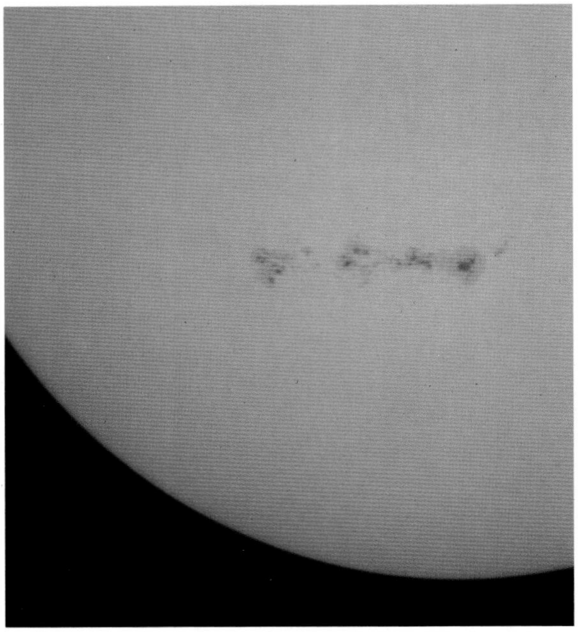

266 Sun spots are an indication of the amount of activity at different points and regions of the star that is found at the center of the solar system. The number and extent of the sun spots, which are a measure of the amount of radiation that reaches the surface of the planet, varies from year to year, but follow a cycle of about 11 years. The effects of these variations on processes such as photosynthesis and the growth of plants has been shown. There is no doubt that they contribute to the variation in the meteorological conditions of the whole planet from year to year. *[Photo: John Bova-Photo Researchers, Inc. / AGE Fotostock]*

One of the factors that most complicates the greenhouse effect is cloud cover. Clouds are water vapor and, as we have mentioned before, prevent long-wave radiation escaping into space. But clouds also increase the terrestrial albedo and, therefore, the reflection of solar rays back into outer space. Thus, with respect to climatic change, clouds present two opposite effects at the same time. On the one hand, they stop infrared radiation from escaping to outer space, and on the other hand they stop short-wave radiation from reaching the Earth's surface. The result of all this can be very variable, from a net gain to a net loss of heat, and depends on the type of cloud. Some clouds contribute more to the Earth's albedo, while others contribute more to the trapping of heat in the lower atmosphere. The high cirrus-type clouds which are flat on top and very bright, reflect more radiation coming from the Sun than they absorb from the Earth. On the other hand, cumulus-type clouds have the opposite effect. This added complexity due to the clouds is one of the most problematic factors when attempting to construct climatic models with computers that are capable of predicting future climatic changes with a degree of certainty.

Not only the clouds affect the global terrestrial albedo; human activity also directly modifies the nature of the Earth's surface, changing its albedo. The whole process of desertification due to human action is the most revealing example of this. When a rain forest is cut down and the soil is left exposed, the albedo suffers an important change and the reflection coefficient is much higher. These changes in the albedo of the Earth's surface change the proportion of energy retained versus energy reflected back into outer space in the form of short-wave radiation, and this has an effect on the thermal balance.

The possible consequences of climatic change

The phenomenon of the greenhouse effect and its accentuation through human action is extremely complicated. There are many factors which come into play. Which is a natural phenomenon with many variables, the links between them are still not well understood. For example, the increase in greenhouse effect gases increases the temperature on the Earth and, in turn, the amount of water vapour in the atmosphere. But no-one knows if this increase in water vapour contributes to an even greater increase in the temperature on Earth or on the contrary to a reduction of the same, thus counterbalancing the greenhouse effect. Evidently the consequences of one or the other are very different. The consequences associated with this climatic change induced by man can be catastrophic from the point of view of human societies. The extent of the catastrophe depends on whether the global climate heats up by between 0.9ºF (0.5ºC) or 1.8ºF (1ºC) or whether the rise in temperature is considerably greater, of between 7.2ºF (4ºC) and 9ºF (5ºC). Although predictions can have a high margin of error, the consequences if this climatic change were to occur, would be very great. It is a case where the uncertain predictions are coupled with a very real and serious risk. In other words, although we cannot affirm whether what has been forecast will happen or not, the consequences if it did happen are so great that they deserve the highest consideration.

A global increase in temperature does not mean that this increase would be uniform everywhere, at all latitudes and altitudes. In some places it will be more marked than in others. It has been predicted that temperatures will remain more or less the same at low latitudes while the biggest changes will take place at mid and high latitudes, winter temperatures at mid and high latitudes could rise to more than double the global average; summer temperatures would rise also, but less. We can understand the magnitude of this change if we consider that a temperature change of 1.8ºF (1ºC) is equivalent to a latitudinal change of 62-93 mi (100-150 km). Furthermore, it is believed these climatic changes would be irreversible on a human timescale.

A change of this type would make the forests migrate northwards. For example, it has been forecast that, because of the higher temperatures, the taiga would migrate to higher and consequently

267 The seriousness of the effects caused by a climatic change, though small, has led to the investment of considerable resources into the collection and processing of information about climatic variables. Observation satellites, which for some years have been gathering data on the planet, provide vast quantities of data that are very useful for weather forecasting and essential for studying trends in climate change. The meteorologists and students of climatic change are always faced with the uncertainty as to whether the flitting of the wings of a butterfly in Asia will provoke a cyclone in the Caribbean: more seriously, they have to deal with phenomena that they cannot forecast, at least for periods of more than 24 to 48 hours. *[Photo: Center for Medium Range Weather Forecast]*

milder latitudes which are currently covered in tundra. It is not so simple, however as the vegetation's ability to adapt does not only depend on temperature but on edaphic conditions. It has also been forecast that in north America the limits of the prairies and the forests would move northwards at a speed of between 62 and 93 mi (100 and 150 km) per decade. We shall have to see if the edaphic factors help in this process or not, if the genomes of the species will be adaptable enough to perform such a rapid migration. If the climatic change does take place it is probable that the ecosystems will not have time to adapt to it, which could lead to important disturbances in them, with unpredictable consequences.

One of the most serious consequences is the rise in sea level: between 13 and 23 ft (4 and 7 m) as a consequence of the partial melting of the polar icecaps. We only have to remember that a large proportion of human settlements are situated in coastal regions throughout the world to get some idea of the magnitude of this phenomenon: cities like Barcelona or New York would be partially flooded. There is no doubt that this would lead to an important human displacement: millions and millions of people throughout the world would have to move to other areas. A considerable proportion of the surface area of the continents would end up under water, and very valuable areas would be lost. The combination of all these changes on a global scale would provoke an even greater human pressure on the environment than at present and could well be accompanied, in the worst cases, by social conflict and even war.

Change, Gaia and Humans

Supposing that global warming is a reality, we could face this situation in two radically different ways. We could let the Earth warm up and adapt to it, or we could take preventive measures. In either case, the costs associated with these measures are very high. It is therefore absolutely essential to lend all possible support to research in this area to clarify the situation, and so that the measures taken can be founded on a sound scientific basis. Adapting to an increase in temperature means taking corrective measures, like developing different types of crops suitable for the new climate, putting up flood barriers along coasts, feeding the oceans with carbon dioxide so that it turns into calcium carbonate and joins the marine sediments and reduces the quantity of carbon dioxide in the atmosphere, and so on. As for preventing climatic change, we could try to reduce the emissions of greenhouse gases, use more energy efficient technologies (cars that use less fuel, better insulated housing, etc.), change to alternative sources of energy (solar and tidal power, geothermic or nuclear power), and replant barren zones so that the vegetation absorbs more carbon dioxide, and so on. Whatever the case, one thing is certain: Gaia, if it really exists, will restore the dynamic balance which it never loses: humans, however may not.

Depletion of the ozone "layer"

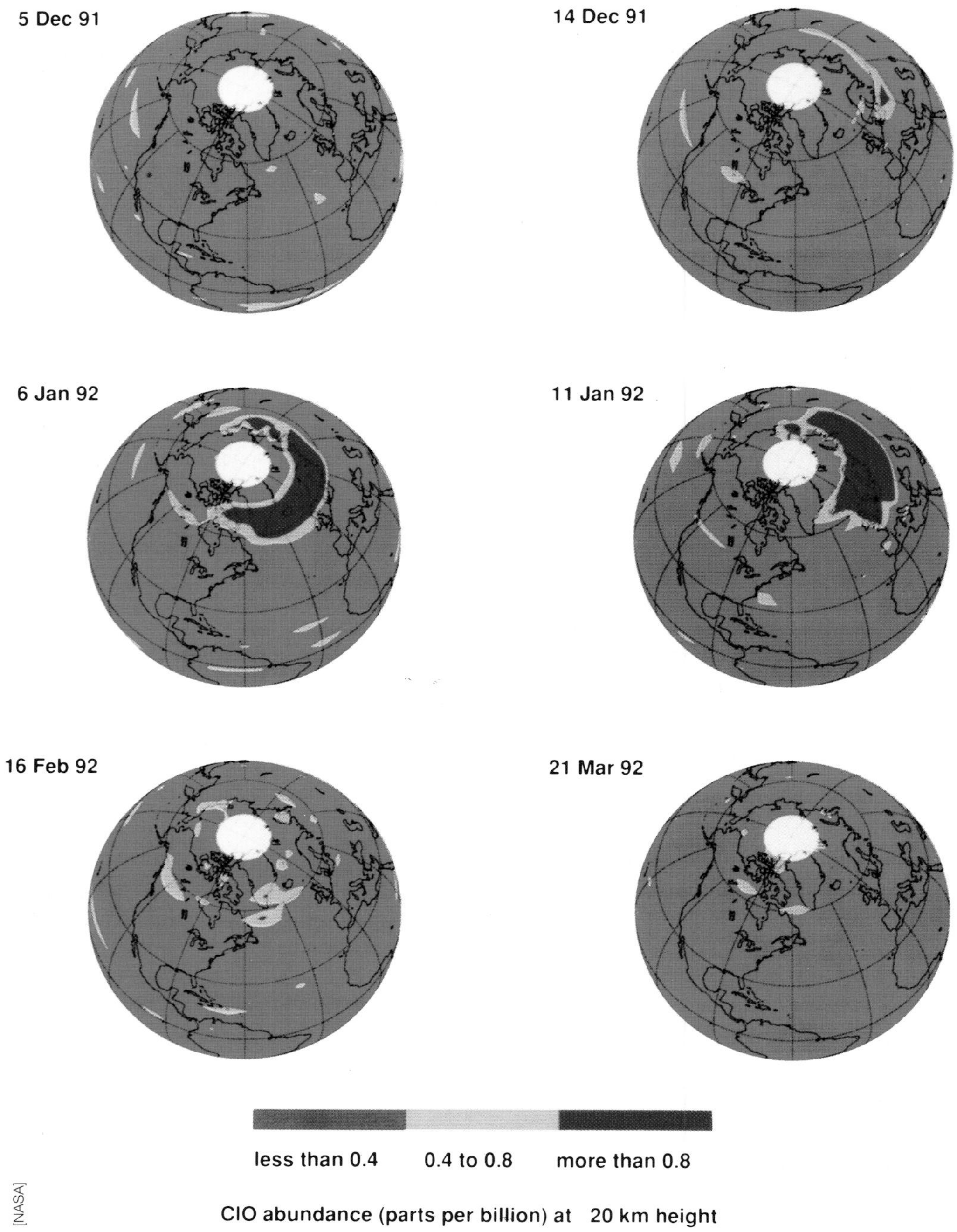

[NASA]

The intensification of the greenhouse effect due to human activity has become a serious matter of international concern. But the consequences of discharging gases into the atmosphere harbors other dangers, such as the depletion of the ozone layer.

Although the possible destruction of stratospheric ozone had been hinted at in the 1970s, it was not until 1985 that the phenomenon was actually observed. A team of British researchers using data provided by NASA discovered that a decrease in the concentration of stratospheric ozone was occurring every spring over the Antarctic, a kind of hole in what we rather incorrectly call the ozone layer. It should be pointed out that the data that led to this discovery had been available for some time but had not been sufficiently analyzed.

Ozone (O_3), an allotropic form of oxygen, forms a "layer" in the stratosphere between 49,200 and 180,400 ft (15,000 and 55,000 m), with densities that vary according to altitude. This layer is of vital importance for life on Earth since it protects living creatures against ultraviolet radiation from the sun. Ozone is formed by the action of this radiation on oxygen molecules (O_2). Oxygen molecules are split into two reactive atoms, which subsequently combine to form a molecule of ozone. This molecule is unstable and short-lived, but is produced continuously.

Ozone can be destroyed by many reactions. Nitric oxide, the radical hydroxyl, and chlorine and bromine atoms act as catalytic agents for the destruction of ozone. They remove an oxygen atom from the ozone molecule, thereby forming an oxide and a molecule of oxygen. The oxide then looses its oxygen, which combines with another such atom to form a new oxygen molecule. In this way the catalytic agent is reconstituted, and is ready to catalyze another reaction. The net result of these reactions is the transformation of an oxygen atom and a molecule of ozone into two oxygen molecules. The same catalytic agent can therefore destroy many ozone molecules.

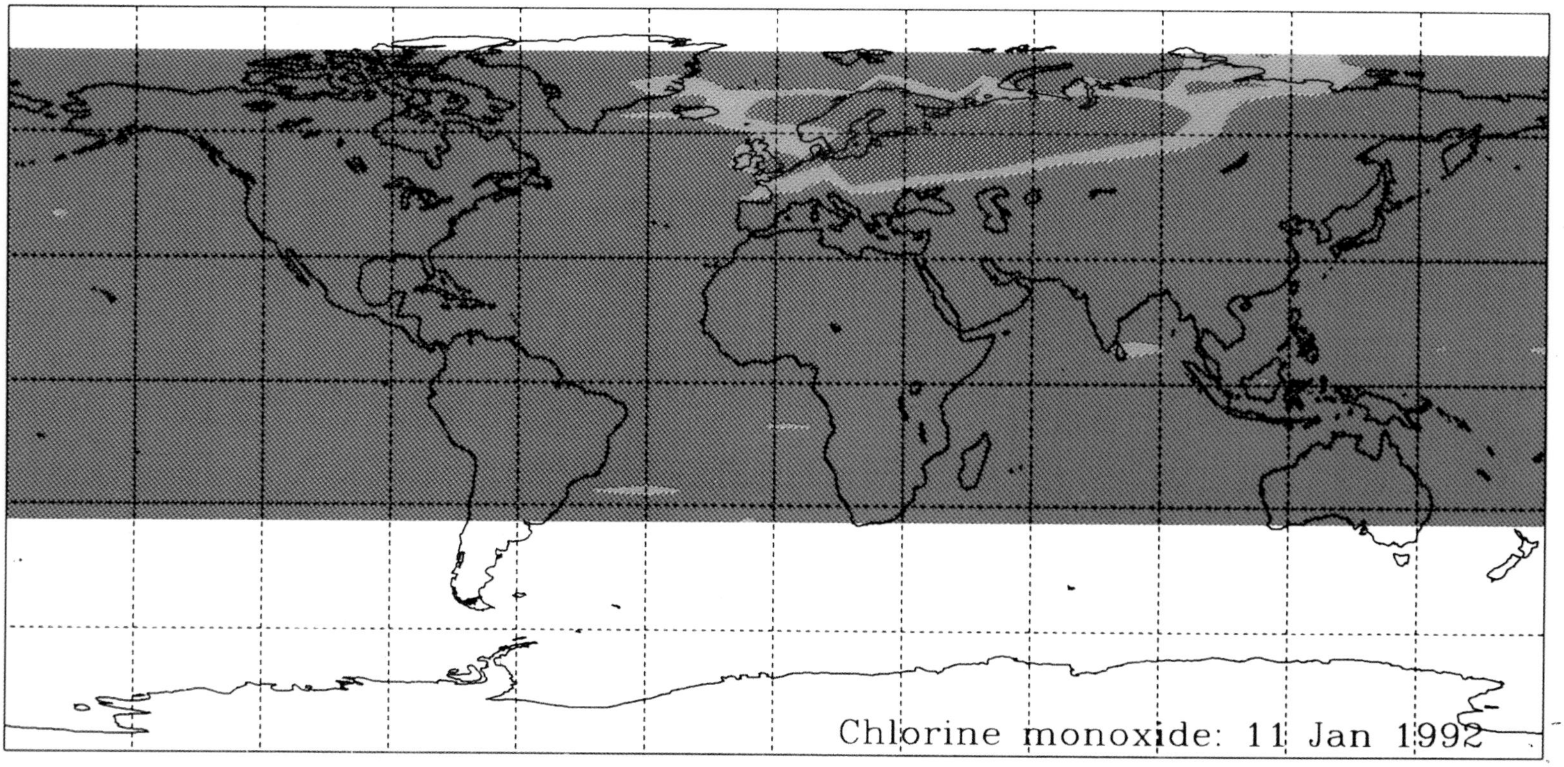

The ozone hole over the Antarctic forms in annual cycles. It is at its greatest during the Antarctic spring, when there is a remarkable 60% loss of ozone at the place where the hole is. We know that the agent responsible for the destruction of stratospheric ozone in the Antarctic is the dichlorine oxide dimer $(Cl0)_2$, and that oxygen atoms do not take part. It appears that there is another important reaction responsible for the destruction of ozone. The atmospheric weather in the Antarctic greatly aids in the destruction of ozone in that area. The prevailing winds in the Antarctic make temperatures of -121°F (-85°C) possible in the lower stratosphere, favoring the formation of the dimer of chlorine monoxide. When the sun's rays arrive in the spring, reactions with dichlorine oxide and bromine rapidly destroy the ozone. The intense cold helps form stratospheric clouds, which also contribute to the process. The prevailing winds at the South Pole follow the parallels and therefore prevent mixture with air from the north, allowing the hole to remain. A considerable depletion of the ozone layer has also been observed in the Arctic, although it has not yet reached proportions comparable with that of the Antarctic. In comparison with the latter, the maximum loss recorded in the Arctic hole is only 10%. The loss of ozone in the middle latitudes is comparable in both hemispheres. However, the thinning of the ozone layer in the Arctic and middle latitudes of the northern hemisphere is far more alarming because of the large human population there. On the 40°N latitude, on which cities such as New York and Madrid are situated, a thinning of 8% in the ozone layer at the end of winter and the spring has been observed. This truly worrying fact has lead to a great deal of money and human resources being recently channeled into the study of the phenomenon at northern latitudes. This is the European Experiment on Stratospheric Arctic Ozone. The objective is the collection of exhaustive data on Arctic ozone in order to understand the extent of the problem.

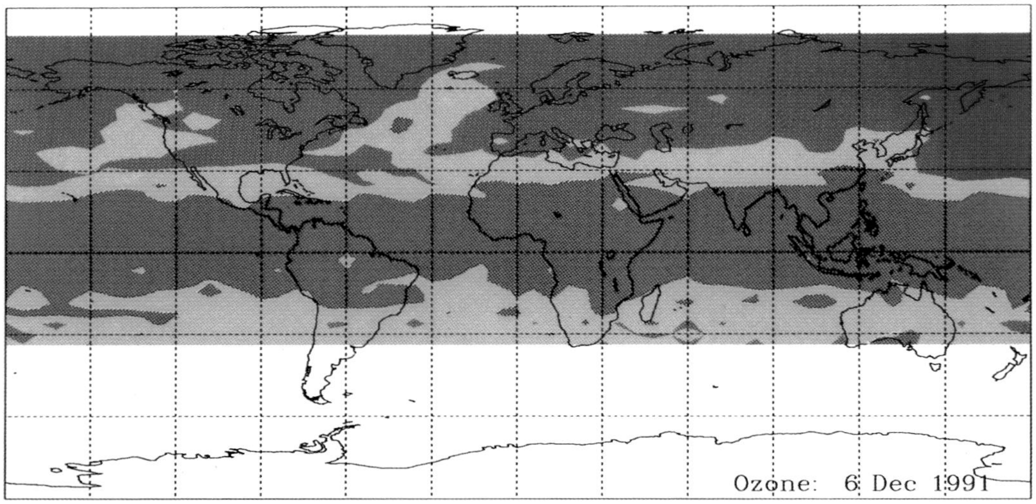

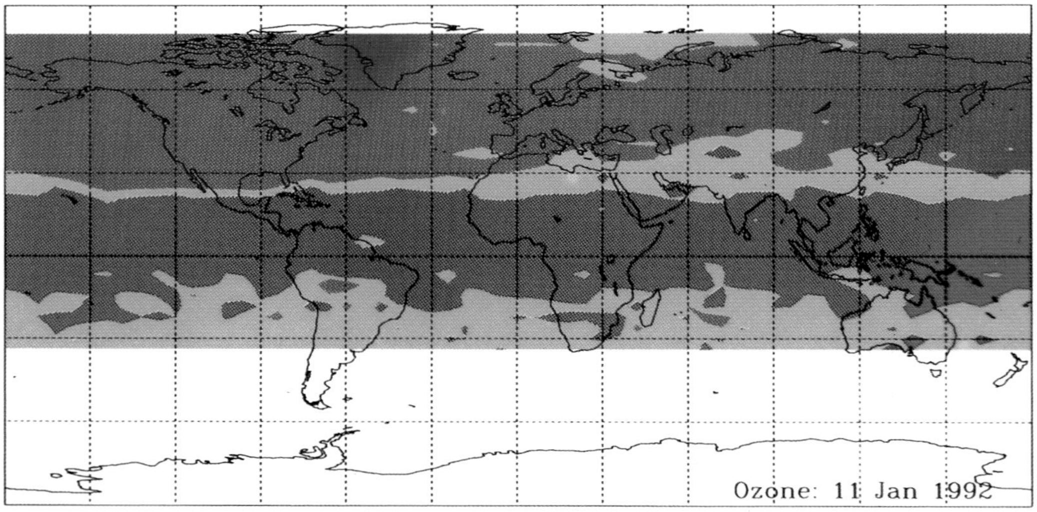

[NASA]

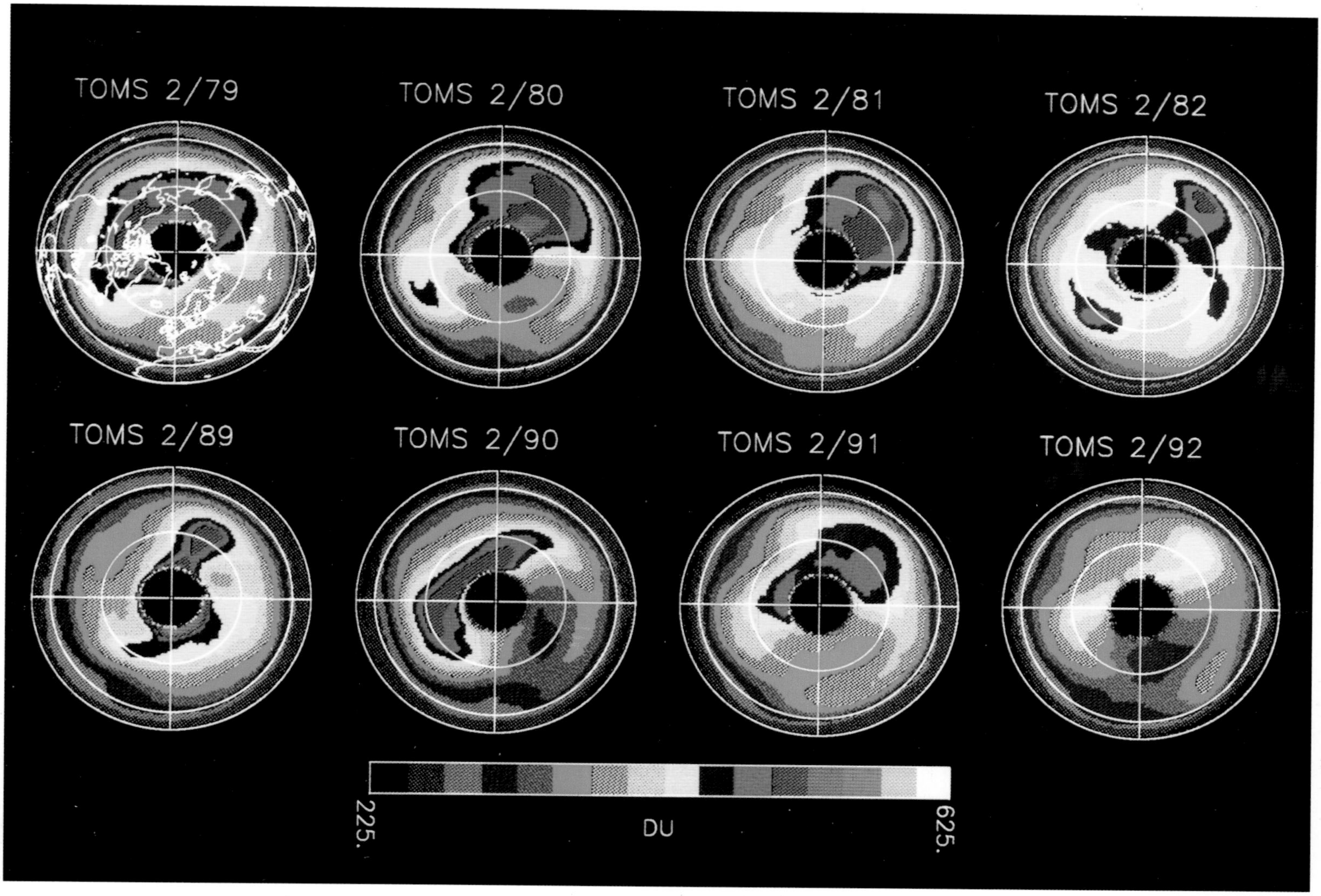

[NASA]

Fears that the destruction of the ozone layer could lead to a rise in skin cancer led to the Montreal Protocol. On September 16 1987, in an unprecedented accord without parallel in the annals of international diplomacy, countries and industries from all over the world signed a treaty deciding to significantly reduce production of various chemical products that destroy ozone. These products are the chlorofluorocarbons (CFCs) and halons, which are, however, extremely useful in certain economic activities. They are the gases that propel aerosols, allow air-conditioners to function, and which can be used to clean computer circuits. The most notable aspect of the treaty was its imposition of substantial economic costs in the short term in order to protect human health and the natural environment against future dangers that have still not been completely proven. The Montreal Protocol revealed the current environmental reality: that nations must work together in the face of global dangers, since this is the only way man will be able to deal with the ever more numerous global environmental problems. States must, in short, accept common responsibility for the administration of the planet. After all, they certainly accept it in all other areas.

Bibliography

ADENA – WWF (1984–85). *Enciclopedia de la Naturaleza'* Debate – Itaca – Círculo de Lectores, Madrid – Barcelona. 24 vols.
ALLABY, M. (1988). *Macmillan Dictionary of the Environment.* Macmillan Press Ltd., London – Basingstoke. 423 p.
ALLEGRE, C. (1983). *L'écume de la Terre.* Fayard, Paris. 338 p.
ANDERSON, M.S. (1966). *18th Century Europe.* Oxford University Press, Oxford.
ANKAR, S. (1977). *Soft–bottom ecosystems of Northern Baltic proper with especial reference to the macrofauna.* Contributions Askoe Laboratory University, Stockholm fasc. 19, 62 p.
ATTENBOROUGH, D. (1989). *The Atlas of the Living World.* Weidenfeld and Nicholson, London. 220 p.
BAILES, K.E. (ed.) (1985). *Environmental History.* University Press of America, Lanham – London. 697 p.
BARIGOZZI, C. (ed.) (1986). *The origin and domestication of cultivated plants.* Elsevier, Amsterdam – Oxford – New York – Tokyo. 218 p.
BARRAU, J. (1975). "L'homme dans le milieu naturel." In: J. Barrau *et al.* (eds.), *Environnement et qualité de vie*, p. 21–58. Guy Le Prat Éditeur, Paris.
BAZZAZ, F.A. AND E.D. FAJER (1976) "La vida de las plantas en un mundo enriquecido con CO_2." *Investigación y Ciencia*, 186:6–13. Barcelona.
BEADLE, G.W. (1977). "The origins of *Zea mays*". In: C.A. Reed (ed.), *Origins of Agriculture*, p. 615–635. Mouton, The Hague – Paris. 1013 p.
BERTRANPETIT, J. AND L.L. CAVALLI–SFORZA (1991). "A genetic reconstruction of the history of the population of the Iberian Peninsula". *Ann. Hum. Genet.*, 55: 51–67. London.
BOTKIN, D.S., M.J. CASWELL, J.E. ESTES AND A.A. ORIO (1989). *Changing the global environment.* Academic Press, San Diego.
BRADBURY, I. (1991). *The Biosphere.* Belhaven Press, New York – London. 203 p.
BRAMWELL, A. (1989). *Ecology in the 20th Century. A History.* Yale University Press, New Haven – London. 292 p.
BRAQUE, R. (1988). *Biogéographie des Continents.* Masson, Paris. 470 p.
BRIMBLECOMBE, P. AND C. PFISTER (1990). *The Silent Countdown. Essays in European Environmental History.* Springer–Verlag, Berlin – Heidelberg – New York. 265 p.
BRONSON, B. (1977). "The Earliest Farming: Demography as Cause and Consequence". In: C.A. Reed (ed.), *Origins of Agriculture*, p. 23-48. Mouton, The Hague – Paris.
BURGES, A. AND F. RAW (1971). (eds.) *Biología del suelo.* Omega. Barcelona. 589 p.
CAIRNS–SMITH, A. G. (1985). *Seven clues to the origin of life.* Cambridge University Press. Cambridge.
CALDWELL, J.R. (1977). "Cultural Evolution in the Old World and the New, Leading to the beginnings and Spread of Agriculture." In: C.A. Reed (ed.), *Origins of Agriculture*, p. 77–88. Mouton, The Hague – Paris.
CAMARASA, J.M. (1981). "El biotopo de la especie humana". In: E. Lluch (ed.), *Geografia de la sociedad humana. Una perspectiva planetaria. Estructuración político–ideológica y organización territorial*, 2: 369–405. Planeta, Barcelona.
CANDOLLE, A. DE (1896). *Origine des plantes cultivées.* Felix Alcan Éditeur, Paris. 379 p.
CARACCIOLO, A. (1988). *L'ambiente come storia. Sondaggi e proposte di storiografia dell'ambiente.* Il Mulino, Bologna. 94 p.
CARTER, G.F. (1977). "A Hypothesis Suggesting a Single Origin of Agriculture". In: C.A. Reed (ed.), *Origins of Agriculture*, p. 89–133. Mouton, The Hague – Paris. 1013 p.
CAVALLI–SFORZA, L.L. (1992). "Genes, lenguas y pueblos". *Investigación y Ciencia*, 194:4–11. Barcelona.
CHINERY, M. *et al.* (1988). *Killers of the world.* Salamander Books Ltd.
CLEYET–MERLE, J.–J. (1990). *La préhistoire de la pêche.* Éditions Errance, Paris. 195 p.
CLOUD, P.E. (1986). *Oasis in Space: Earth History from the Beginning.* W. W. Norton & Company, New York – London. 508 p.
CLOUDSLEY–THOMPSON, J.L. (1977). *Man and the Biology of Arid Zones.* Edward Arnold (Publishers) Ltd., London.
CLUB DE BARCELONA (1990). *Poblacions, societats i entorn.* Barcanova, Barcelona. 313 p.
COLINVAUX, P. (1978). *Why Big Fierce Animals are Rare.* Princeton University Press, New York.
CORELL, R.W. AND P.A. ANDERSON (1991). *Global Environmental Change.* Springer–Verlag, Berlin – Heidelberg – New York. 264 p.
COWEN, R. (1990). *History of Life.* Blackwell Scientific Publications, Boston. 470 p.
CRESPO, M. (1988). *Atlas de Botànica. Flora i vegetació.* Edibook, Barcelona. 87 p.
CRITCHFIELD, H.J. (1974). *General Climatology.* Prentice–Hall, Inc., Englewood Cliffs.
CROSBY, A.W. (1986). *Ecological imperialism. The biological expansion of Europe, 900–1900.* Cambridge University Press, Cambridge.
DANCHIN, A. (1990). *Une aurore de pierres.* Éditions du Seuil, Paris. 281 p.
DARYLL FORDE, C. (1934). *Habitat, Economy and Society.* Methuen & Co., London.
DEBEIR, J.C., J.P. DELÉAGE AND D. HÉMERY (1986). *Les servitudes de la puissance. Une histoire de l'energie.* Flammarion, Paris. 428 p.
DEBUSCHE, M., S. RAMBAL AND J. LEPART (1987) *Le changement de l'occupation des terres en région méditerranée humide: évaluations des conséquences hydrologiques. Acta Oecol.; Oecol applic*, 8:317–332.
DEL CASTILLO, M. (1988). "Another approach to the world biogeography of the families of inland fishes." *Systemathic Zoology*, 37: 34–46.
DELÉAGE, J.P. AND D. HEMERY (1989). "De l'écohistoire à l'écologie–monde". *Homme et Société*, 91–92: 13–30. Paris.
DEMANGEOT, J. (1987). *Les milieux 'naturels' du globe.* Masson, Paris. 250 p.
DERRY, T.K. AND T.I. WILLIAMS (1960). *A Short History of Technology. From the Earliest Times to A. D. 1900.* Clarendon Press, Oxford.
DIGARD, P.P. (1988). "Jalons pour une anthropologie de la domestication animale". *Homme et Société*, 38(4): 27–58. Paris.
DILLEHAY, T. D. AND M. B. COLLINS (1988). "Early cultural evidence from Monte Verde in Chile". *Nature*, 333: 150–152. London.
DRAKE, J.A., H.A. MOONEY, F. DI CASTRI, F.J. KRUGER, M. REJMANEK AND M. WILLIAMSON (ed.) (1989). *Biological Invasions: A global perspective.* John Wiley and sons, Chichester. 525 p.
DROUIN, J.M. (1991). *Réinventer la nature. L'écologie et son histoire.* Desclée de Brouwer, Paris. 208 p.
DURRELL, L. (1986). *State of the Ark. An Atlas of conservation in action.* Doubleday and Co., Inc.
ECOLOGICAL SOCIETY OF AMERICA (1991). "The Sustainable Biosphere Initiative: an Ecological Research Agenda". *Ecology*, 72 (2): 371–412. Durham.
ENGBECK, J.H. (1976). *The enduring giants.* University Extension, The University of California – Berkeley. 120 p.
EPSTEIN, H. (1971). *The origin of domestic animals in Africa.* Africana Publishing Corporation, New York – London – Munich. 2 vols. 573;pl719 p.
ESTEBAN AMAT, A. AND I. PARRA VERGARA (1984). "L'últim cicle glacial–interglacial a les terres mediterrànies a partir de les anàlisis pol·líniques". *Revista Catalana de Geografia*, 0 : 47–60. Barcelona.
FAO (1971–81). *FAO–UNESCO Soil Map of the World.* Esc. 1: 5 000 000. Vols. 1–10. UNESCO, Paris.
FAO (1985). *El Estado Mundial de la Agricultura y la Alimentación.* FAO.
FAO (1989). "Soil Map of the World. Revised Legend". *World Resources Report*, 60. Rome.
FEREMBACH, D., C. SUSANNE AND M.C. CHAMLA (1987). "*L'homme, son évolution, sa diversité. Manuel d'anthropólogie physique*". Editions du CNRS⁄Doin éditeurs, Paris.
FLOS, J. (1984). *Ecología: entre la magia y el tópico.* Omega, Barcelona. 120 p.
FOLCH, R., T. FRANQUESA AND J.M. CAMARASA (1984). "Generalitats". In: R. Folch (dir.) *Història Natural dels Països Catalans. Vol. 7, Vegetació*, p. 13–63. Enciclopèdia Catalana, SA, Barcelona.
FONTBOTÉ, J.M. (1986). "La geologia dels Països Catalans en el marc de la Mediterrània Occidental". In: R. Folch (dir.), *Història Natural dels Països Catalans. Vol. 1, Geologia I*', p. 50–82. Enciclopèdia Catalana, SA, Barcelona.
FOX, D.L. (1979). *Biochromy. Natural Coloration of Living Things.* University of California Press, Berkeley – Los Angeles – London. 248 p.
GAYRARD–VALY, Y. (1990). *Les fossiles: empreinte des mondes disparus.* Gallimard, Paris. 208 p.
GLADIKIH, M., N.L. KORNIETZ AND O. SOFFER (1992). "Viviendas de huesos de mamut en la llanura rusa". *Investigación y Ciencia*, 1(100): 84–91. Barcelona.
GODARD, O. AND I. SACHS (1975). "L'environnement et la planification". In: J. Barrau *et al.* (eds.), *Environnement et qualité de vie*, p. 207–247. Guy Le Prat Éditeur, Paris.
GORMAN, C. (1977). "A Priori Models and Thai Prehistory". In: C.A. Reed (ed.), *Origins of Agriculture*, p. 321–356. Mouton, The Hague – Paris.
GOUDIE, A. (1981). *The Human Impact. Man's Role in Environmental Change.* Basil Blackwell Publisher Ltd., Oxford.
GOULD, S.J. (1989). *Wonderful Life. The Burgess Shale and the Nature of History.* W. W. Norton & Company, New York – London.
GUIDON, N. AND G. DELIBRIAS (1986). "Carbon–14 dates point to man in the Americas 32,000 years ago". *Nature*, 321: 769–771. London.
GUILLE–ESCURET, G. (1989). *Les sociétés et leurs natures.* Armand Colin, Paris. 183 p.
HAINARD, J. AND R. KAEHR (1987). *Des animaux et des hommes.* Musée d'Ethnographie, Neuchâtel. 221 p.
HALFFTER, G. (1991). "El concepto de Reserva de la Biosfera". *Mem. Sem. Cons. Div. Biol. Mexico*, 1: 1–25.
HALLAM, A. (1973). *A Revolution in the Earth Sciences. From Continental Drift to Plate Tectonics.* Oxford University Press, Oxford.
HARLAN, J.R. (1975). *Crops and Man.* American Society of Agronomy, Inc. ⁄ Crop Science Society of America, Inc., Madison (WI).
HARLAN, J.R., J.M.J. DE WET AND A.B.L. STEMLER (eds.) (1976). *Origins of African Plant Domestication.* Mouton, The Hague – Paris. 498 p.
HARLAN, J.R. (1977). "The Origins of Cereal Agriculture in the Old World". In: C.A. Reed (ed.), *The origins of Agriculture*, p. 357–384. Mouton, The Hague – Paris.
HARRIS, D.R. (1977). "Alternative Pathways Toward Agriculture". In: C.A. Reed (ed.), *Origins of Agriculture*, p. 179–243. Mouton, The Hague – Paris.
HAUDRICOURT, A.G. (1988). *La technologie, science humaine.* Éditions de la Maison des Sciences de l'Homme, Paris. 347 p.
HAUDRICOURT, A.G. (1988). "Que savons–nous des animaux domestiques". *Homme et Société*, 28(4): 72–83. Paris.
HAUDRICOURT, A.G. AND L. HÉDIN (1987). "L'Homme et les Plantes Cultivés". A.M. Métailié, Paris. 281 p.
HENDERSON–SELLERS, J. R. AND P. J. ROBINSON (1986). *Contemporary Climatology.* Longman Group.
HERRERO MOLINO, C., M.J. JIMÉNEZ ARMESTO, G. MORELLÓN BLANCO AND A. STERLING CARMONA (1989). *Madre Tierra ¿Por qué Conservar?* ICONA, Madrid. 232 p.

HERRE, W. AND M. RÖHRS (1977). "Zoological Considerations on the Origins of Farming and Domestication". In: C.A. Reed (ed.), *The Origins of Agriculture*, p. 245–280. Mouton, The Hague – Paris.

HIGHAM, C.F.W. (1977). "Economic Change in Prehistoric Thailand". In: C.A. Reed (ed.), *Origins of Agriculture*, p. 385–412. Mouton, The Hague – Paris.

HO PING–TI (1977). "The Indigenous Origins of Chinese Agriculture". In: C.A. Reed (ed.), *Origins of Agriculture*, p. 413–484. Mouton, The Hague – Paris.

HUECK, K. (1978). *Los bosques de Sur–América.* Sociedad Alemana de Coop. Técnica, Ltda. (GTZ), Eschborn. 476 p.

HUTCHINSON, G.E. (1965). *The Ecological Theater and the Evolutionary Play.* Yale University Press, New Haven.

IUCN/UNEP/WWF (1991). *Caring for the Earth. A Strategy for Sustainable Living*, IUCN/UNEP/WWF, Gland. 228 p.

JONES, D. L., A. COX, P. CONEY AND M. BECK (1983). "El crecimiento de Norteamérica". *Investigación y Ciencia*, 76: 30–45. Barcelona.

JUSTICE, C.O., J.R.G. TOWNSHEND, B.N. HOLBEN AND C.J. TUCKER (1985). "Analysis of the phenology of global vegetation using meteorological satellite data". *Int. J. Rem. Sens.*, 6(8): 1271–1318.

KABAKER, A. (1977). "A Radiocarbon Chronology Revelant to the Origins of Agriculture". In: C.A. Reed (ed.), *Origins of Agriculture*, p. 957–980. Mouton, The Hague – Paris.

KLEIN, R.G. (1989). *The Human Career. Human Biological and Cultural Origins.* University of Chicago Press, Chicago – London. 524 p.

KLEIN, R.G. (1992). "The Archeology of Modern Human Origins". *Evolutionary Anthropology*, 1(1): 5–14. New York.

KNOLL, A.H. (1986). "Geological evidence for early evolution". *Treb. Soc. Cat. Biol.*, 39: 113–141. Barcelona.

KOMAREK, P. (1987). *Environnement et droits de l'homme.* UNESCO, Paris. 178 p.

KUBIENA, W.L. (1952). *Claves sistemáticas de suelos.* Institut de Edafología, CSIC, Madrid.

KÜPPERS, B.O. (1990). *Information and the Origin of Life.* MIT Press, Cambridge – London. 215 p.

LACOSTE, Y. (1959). *Les pays sousdéveloppés.* Presses Universitaires de France, Paris.

LACOSTE, A. AND R. SALANON (1969). *Éléments de biogéographie.* F. Nathan Ed., Paris. 189 p.

LANGANEY, A. (1988). *Les Hommes.* Armand Colin, Paris, 252 p.

LATHRAP, D.W. (1977). "Our Father the Cayman, Our Mother the Gourd: Spinden Revisited, or a Unitary Model of the Emergence of Agriculture in the New World". In: C.A. Reed (ed.), *Origins of Agriculture*, p. 713–751. Mouton, The Hague – Paris.

LAWRENCE, B. (1967). "Early domestic dogs". *Zeitschreift für Säugetierkunde*, 32: 44–59

LAWRENCE, B. (1968). "Antiquity of large dogs in North America". *Tebiwa, Journal of the Idaho State University Museum*, 11: 43–49.

LAZCANO, A. (1986). "Prebiotic evolution and the origin of cells". *Treb. Soc. Cat. Biol.*, 39: 73–103. Barcelona.

LAZCANO, A., G. E. FOX AND J. ORÓ (1991). "Life before DNA: The Origin and Evolution of Early Archean Cells". In: R. P. Mortlock (ed.), *The Evolution of Metabolic Functions.* Telford Press, Caldwell.

LEAKEY, R.E. (1980). *The Making of Mankind.* The Rainbird Publishing Group Ltd., London.

LEARMONTH, A. (1988). *Disease Ecology.* Basil Blackwell, Oxford – New York. 456 p.

LEMÉE, G. (1967). *Précis de Biogéographie.* Masson & Cie., Paris. 358 p.

LENCO, M. (1975). "Les groupes socio–économiques". In: J. Barrau *et al.* (eds.), *Environnement et qualité de vie*, p. 169–206. Guy Le Prat Éditeur, Paris.

LEROY, C. (1975). "L'homme dans le milieu social". In: J. Barrau *et al.* (eds.), *Environnement et qualité de vie*, p. 59–128. Guy Le Prat Éditeur, Paris.

LE ROY–LADURIE, E. (1967). *Histoire du climat depuis l'An Mil.* Flammarion, Paris. 379 p.

LEVER, C. (1985). *Naturalized Mammals of the World. Longman*, London – New York. 487 p.

LEWINGTON, A. (1990). *Plants for People.* Natural History Museum Publications, London. 232 p.

LIETH, H. AND R.H. WHITTAKER (1975). *Primary Productivity of the Biosphere.* Springer–Verlag — Berlin – Heidelberg – New York. 339 p.

LINCHARDUS, J., M. LINCHARDUS–ITTEN *et al.* (1983). *La protohistoire de l'Europe.* Presses Universitaires de France, Paris.

LOCQUIN, M. V. (1987). *Aux origines de la vie.* Fayard. Paris.

LUMLEY, H.D. (1982). *Origine et evolution de l'homme.* Museum National d'Histoire Naturelle, Paris. 255 p.

MACNEISH, R.S. (1977). "The Beginning of Agriculture in Central Peru". In: C.A. Reed (ed.), *Origins of Agriculture*, p. 753–801. Mouton, The Hague – Paris.

MALDONADO, A. (1986). "Evolution of the Mediterranean basins and a detailed reconstruction of the Cenozoic paleoceanography". In: R. Margalef (ed.), *Western Mediterranean*, p. 17–59. Pergamon Press, Oxford.

MANNERS, I. R. AND M. W. KESELL (1974). *Perspectives on Environment*. Association of American Geographers.

MANNION (1991). Global Environmental Change.

MARGALEF, R. (1962). *Comunidades naturales.* Inst. Biologia Marina, Univ. Puerto Rico, Mayagüez (Puerto Rico). 469 p.

MARGALEF, R. (1974) *Ecología.* Omega, Barcelona. 951 p.

MARGALEF, R. (1980). *La biosfera: entre la termodinámica y el juego.* Omega, Barcelona. 236 p.

MARGALEF, R. (1981). *Ecología.* Ed. Planeta, SA, Barcelona. 252 p.

MARGALEF, R. (1985). *L'ecologia.* Diputació de Barcelona, Servei del Medi Ambient, Barcelona. 126 p.

MARGALEF, R. (ed.) (1986). *Western Mediterranean.* Pergamon Press, Oxford.

MARGALEF, R. (1990). "Les xarxes en ecologia". In: *Club de Barcelona, Poblacions, societats i entorn*, p. 151–180. Barcanova, Barcelona.

MARGALEF, R. (1990). "Viure a la Terra: dels límits i de les regles del joc". In: *Club de Barcelona, "Poblacions, societats i entorn*, p. 21–55. Barcanova, Barcelona.

MARGALEF, R. (1991). *Teoría de los sistemas ecológicos.* Publicacions de la Universitat de Barcelona, Barcelona. 290 p.

MARGULIS, L. (1985). *Early Life.* Jones & Barlett Publishers, Boston.

MARGULIS, L. (1989). "The ancient microcosmos of planet Earth". In: D. Osterbrock & P. Raven (eds.), *Origins and Extinctions*, p. 83–107. Yale University Press, New Haven.

MARGULIS, L., D. CHASE AND R. GUERRERO (1986). "Microbial Communities". *BioScience*, 36 (3): 160–170. Dunedin.

MARGULIS, L. AND R. GUERRERO (1986). "Not 'origin of life' but 'evolution in microbes'". *Treb. Soc. Cat. Biol.*, 39 : 105–112. Barcelona.

MARGULIS, L. AND R. GUERRERO (1989). "From planetary atmospheres to microbial communities: a stroll through space and time". In: D. S. Botkins, M.J. Caswell, J.E. Estes & A.A. Orio (eds.). *Changing the global environment*, p. 51–67. Academic Press, San Diego.

MARGULIS, L. AND R. GUERRERO (1990). "From origins of life to evolution of microbial communities: a minimalistic approach". In: C. Ponnamperuna & F.R. Eirich (eds.), *Prebiological self organization of matter*, p. 261–267. A. Deepak Publishing.

MARGULIS, L. AND R. GUERRERO (1991). "Kingdoms in turmoil". *New Scientist*, 1761: 46–50. London.

MARGULIS, L. AND M. McMENAMIN (1990). "Kinetosome–centriolar DNA: Significance for endosymbiosis theory". *Treb. Soc. Cat. Biol.*, 41: 5–16. Barcelona.

MARGULIS, L. AND D. SAGAN (1986). *Microcosmos. Four billion years of microbial evolution.* Summit Books, New York. 302 p

MARGULIS, L. AND D. SAGAN (1988). *Garden of microbial delights. A practical guide to the subvisible world.* Harcourt Brace Jovanovich Publishers, Boston – San Diego – New York. 229 p.

MARGULIS, L. AND K. W. SCHWARTZ (1982). *Five Kingdoms. An illustrated guide to the Phyla of Life on Earth.* W.H. Freeman & Company, New York.

MARTÍNEZ ALIER, J. (1984). *L'ecologisme i l'economia. Història d'unes relacions amagades.* Edicions 62, Barcelona. 318 p.

MARTIN, P.S. AND R.G. KLEIN (1984). *Quaternary Extinctions.* University of Arizona Press, Tucson. 892 p.

MATHUR, H.S. (1988). *Essentials of Biogeography.* Pointer Publishers, Jaipur. 352 p.

MAURIZIO, A. (1932). *Histoire de l'Alimentation Végétale.* Payot, Paris. 663 p.

MELLARS, P. AND C. STRINGER (1989). *The Human Revolution.* Princeton University Press. Princeton.

MOLNAR, S. (1983). *Human Variation. Races, Types, and Ethnic Groups.* Prentice–Hall, Inc., Englewood Cliffs. 253 p.

MOOR, A.W., R.F. ISBELL AND K.H. NORTHCOTE (1983). "Classification of Australian soils" In: *Division of Soils. Soils: an Australian viewpoint*, p. 253–266. CSIRO –Academic Press, Melbourne– London.

MORIN, E. (1977). *La méthode. 1. La Nature de la Nature.* Éditions du Seuil, Paris. 410 p.

MORTLOCK, R.P. (ed.) (1991). *The evolution of metabolic function.* Telford Press, Caldwell.

MOSCOVICI, S. (1968). *Essai sur l'histoire humaine de la nature.* Flammarion, Paris. 604 p.

NATIONAL ACADEMY OF SCIENCES (1990). *One Earth, one Future. Changing global environment.* NAS, Washington, D. C.

NEEDHAM, J. (1969). *La science chinoise et l'Occident*, Éditions du Seuil. Paris. 253 p.

NELSON, H. AND JURMAIN, R. (1988). *Introduction to Physical Anthropology.* West Publishing Company, Saint Paul.

OLIVIER, G. (1975). *L'écologie humaine.* Presses Universitaires de France, Paris. 128 p.

OPARIN, A.I. (1986). "La vida: una de les formes del moviment de la matèria". *Treb. Soc. Cat. Biol.*, 39: 15–36. Barcelona.

ORÓ, J., S.L. MILLER AND A. LAZCANO (1990). "The origin and early evolution of life". *Ann. Rev. Earth Planet Sci.*, 18: 317–356.

OSTERBROCK, D. AND P. RAVEN (1989). *Origins and Extinctions.* Yale University Press, New Haven.

PACCINO, D. (1972). *L'imbroglio ecologico.* Einaudi, Turin. 271 p.

PEÑUELAS, J. (1988). *De la biosfera a la antroposfera. Una introducción a la ecología.* Barcanova, Barcelona. 287 p.

PEPPER, D. (1984). *The Roots of Modern Environmentalism.* Routledge, London – New York. 246 p.

PERELMAN, R. (1975). "L'homme et son habitat". In: J. Barrau *et al.* (eds.), *Environnement et qualité de vie*, p. 129–168. Guy Le Prat Éditeur, Paris.

PFISTER, C. (1988). "Fluctuations climatiques et prix cerćaliers en Europe du XVIe au XXe siècle". *Annales ESC*, 1: 25–53.

PIRES–FERREIRA, J.W., E. PIRES–FERREIRA ANDD P. KAULICKE (1976). "Preceramic Animal Utilization in Central Peruvian Andes". *Science*, 194 (4264): 483–490. London.

POIRIER, J. (dir.) (1972). *Ethnologie régionale.* Gallimard, Paris. 2 vols. 1608 ;pl 1632 p.

PONNAMPERUNA, C. AND EIRICH, F. R. (eds.) (1990). *Prebiological self organisation of matter.* A. Deepak Publishing. Hampton.

PORTA, J. AND R, JULIÀ (eds.) (1985). *Els sòls de Catalunya. Àrea Meridional de Lleida.* DARP, Barcelona. 332 p.

PORTA J., J.M. ALCAÑIZ, E. CASTELLS, R. CRUAÑAS, R. DANÉS, M.T. FELIPÓ, J. SÁNCHEZ AND N. TEIXIDOR (1985). "Sòl". In: R. Folch (dir.), *Història Natural dels Països Catalans. Vol. 3, Recursos geològics i sòl*, p. 271–435. Enciclopèdia Catalana, SA, Barcelona.

PORTA, J., J.M. ALCAÑIZ, E. CASTELLS, R. CRUAÑAS, R. DANÉS, M.T. FELIPÓ, J. SÁNCHEZ AND N. TEIXIDOR (1987). *Introducció al coneixement del sòl. Sòls dels Països Catalans*. Associació d'Enginyers Agrònoms de Catalunya – Fundació Enciclopèdia Catalana, Barcelona. 166 p.

POSTMAN, N. (1985). *Amusing Ourselves to Death. Public Discourse in the Age of the Show Business*. Viking Penguin Inc., New York. 221 p.]

PRICEL, D. H. (1990). *Atlas of World Cultures: A Geographic Guide to Ethnografic Literature*. Sage Publications, Newbury Park – London – New Delhi. 156 p.

RAMOS, A. (coord.) (1987). *Diccionario de la Naturaleza. Hombre, Ecología, Paisaje*. Espasa–Calpe, Madrid. 1016 p.

RASCHKE, E. (1989). "Die Stralungshauhalt der erde" *Naturwissenschaften* 76: 351–357.

READER, J. (1988). *Man on Earth*. William Collins Sons and Co. Ltd., London. 256 p.

REDMAN, C.L. (1977). "Man, Domestication, and Culture in Southwestern Asia". In: C.A. Reed (ed.), *The Origins of Agriculture*, p. 523–542. Mouton, The Hague – Paris.

REED, C.A. (ed.) (1977). *Origins of Agriculture*. Mouton, The Hague – Paris. 1013 p.

REED, C.A. (1977). "Origins of Agriculture: Discussions and Some Conclusions". In: C.A. Reed (ed.), *Origins of Agriculture*, p. 879–953. Mouton, The Hague – Paris.

RENFREW, C. (1987). *Archaeology and language. The puzzle of indo–european origins*. Jonathan Cape Ltd – London.

RICHERSON, P.J. AND R. BOYD (1990). "Fets per a la velocitat, no per al confort. La teoria darwiniana i la cultura humana". In: Club de Barcelona. *Poblacions, societats i entorn*, p. 57–101. Barcanova, Barcelona.

RIERA I MORA, S. (1990). "Història de la vegetació al Pla de Barcelona en els darrers 9000 anys. Anàlisi pol·línica de l'antic estany del Cagalell". *Rev. Cat. Geogr.*, 13: 57–68. Barcelona.

RIOUX, J.P. (1971). *La révolution industrielle*. Éditions du Seuil, Paris. 251 p.

ROUGERIE, B AND N. BEROUTCHACHVILI (1991). *Géosystèmes et paysages*. Armand Colin, Paris. 302 p.

ROUGERIE, G. (1969). *Géographie des paysages*. Presses Universitaires de France, Paris. 128 p.

ROUGERIE, G. (1988). *Géographie de la Biosphère*. Armand Colin, Paris. 288 p.

RUDLOFF, W. (1981). *World–Climates*. Wissenschaftliche Verlagsgessellschaft mbH, Stuttgart. 632 p.

RUHLEN, M. (1987). *A guide to world languages. Vol 1: Classification*. The Library of Congress. Stanford University Press, Stanford. 433 p.

SABBAGH, C. *et al.* (1991). *On a marché sur la Terre*. ICS/Muséum National d'Histoire Naturelle, Paris. 223 p.

SAHLINS, M. (1972). *Stone Age Economics*. Aldine Publishing Company, Chicago.

SÁNCHEZ, G. AND C. ZABALETA (1982). *Curso de meteorología y oceanografía*. Dirección General de la Marina Mercante, Madrid. 498 p.

SÁNCHEZ–MONGE, E. (1981). *Diccionario de plantas agrícolas*. Servicio de Publicaciones Agrarias, Ministerio de Agricultura, Madrid. 467 p.

SCHOPF, J. W. (1983). *Earth's earliest Biosphere*. Princeton University Press, Princeton.

SEPKOWSKI, J.J. (1976). "A kinetic model of Phanerozoic taxonomic diversity. I. Analysis of marine orders". *Paleobiology*, 4: 223–251. Menlo Park.

SEPKOWSKI, J.J. (1979). "A kinetic model of Phanerozoic taxonomic diversity. II. Early Phanerozoic families and multiple equilibria". *Paleobiology*, 5: 222–251. Menlo Park.

SEPKOWSKI, J.J. (1984). "A kinetic model of Phanerozoic taxonomic diversity. III. Postpaleozoic families and mass extinctions". *Paleobiology*, 10: 246–267. Menlo Park.

SERPELL, J. (1986). *In the company of animals*. Basil Blackwell, Oxford – New York. 215 p.

SIGAUT, F. (1988). "Critique de la notion de domestication". *Homme et Société*, 28(4): 59–71. Paris.

SIMMONS, I.G. (1982). *Ecología de los recursos naturales*. Omega, Barcelona. 463 p.

SMITH, F. H. AND F. SPENCER (1984). *The Origin of Modern Humans. A World Survey of the Fossil Evidence*. Alan R. Liss., Nova York.

SOIL SURVEY STAFF (1975). *Soil Taxonomy*. SMSS, Washington.

SOIL SURVEY STAFF (1990). "Keys to Soil Taxonomy". 4a ed. *SMSS Techn. Monograph*, 6. Blacksburg, Virginia.

STERN, T. AND U. BRINK (1991). "Sounding the bottom of the world". *New Scientist*, 1784: 41–43. London.

STRAHLER, A.N. (1984). *Geografía Física*. Omega, Barcelona. 767 p.

TAKHTAJAN, A. (1986). *Floristic Regions of the World*. University of California Press, Berkeley – Los Angeles – London. 522 p.

TALLIS, J.H. (1990). *Plant Community History. Long–term changes in plant distribution and diversity*. Chapham & Hall, London – New York – Tokyo – Melbourne – Madras. 398 p.

TERMIER, H. AND G. TERMIER (1960). *La trame géologique de l'histoire humaine*. Masson et Cie., Paris.

TESTARD, A. (1982). *Les chasseurs–cueilleurs ou l'origine des inégalités*. Société d'Ethnographie, Paris. 254 p.

THOMPSON, J.I. (1987). *Gaia: a way of knowing*. The Lindisfarne Association, Inc., New York.

TINDALE, N.B. (1974). *Aboriginal tribes of Australia*. University of California Press, Berkeley – Los Angeles – London. 404 p.

TRINKAUS, E. AND W. H. HOWELLS (1980). "Neandertales". *Investigación y Ciencia*, 41: 60–72. Barcelona.

TUDGE, C. (1991). *Global Ecology*. Natural History Museum Publications, London. 173 p.

UDVARDY, M.D.F. (1975). *A Classification of the Biogeographical Provinces of the World*. IUCN, Morges (Switzerland). 49 p.

UNEP (1991). *Environmental Data Report*. 1991–92. Basil Blackwell, Oxford. 408 p.

VALENTINE, J.W. AND E.M. MOORES (1970). "Plate–tectonic regulation of faunal diversity and sea level: a mode"'. *Nature*, 228: 657–659. London.

VALLADAS, H., H. CACHIER, P. MAURICE, F. BERNALDO DE QUIROS, J. CLOTTES, V. CABRERA VALDÉS, P. UZQUIANO AND M. ARNOLD (1992). "Derect radiocarbonic dates for prehistoric paintings at the Altamira, El Castillo and Niaux caves". *Nature*, 357(6373): 68–70. London.

VAN DOBBEN, W.H. AND R.H. LOWE–MCCONNELL (1975). *Unifying Concepts in Ecology*. Dr. W. Junk B. V., The Hague – Wageningen. 397 p.]

VIDAL, G. (1983). "Microorganismos planctónicos fósiles". *Investigación y Ciencia*, 83: 8–19. Barcelona.

VIERS, G. (1968). *Éléments de climatologie*. Fernand Nathan, Paris. 224 p.

WALTER, H. (1973). *Vegetationszonen und Klima*. Verlag Eugen Ulmer, Stuttgart.

WALTER, H. AND S.W. BRECKLE (1985). *Ecological Systems of the Biosphere. 1. Ecological Principles in Global Perspective*. Springer Verlag, Berlin – Heidelberg – New York – Tokyo. 242 p.

WEINER, D.R. (1988). *Models of Nature. Ecology, Conservation and Cultural Revolution in Soviet Russia*. Indiana University Press, Bloomington – Indianapolis. 312 p.

WESTBROEK, P. (1991). *Life as a Geological Force*. W. W. Norton & Company. New York – London. 240 p.

WHITTAKER, R.H. (1970). *Communities and Ecosystems*. MacMillan, New York – London. 87 p.

WILSON, E.O. (1988). *Biodiversity*. National Academy Press, Washington, D.C. 521 p.

WING, E.S. (1977). "Animal Domestication in the Andes". In: C.A. Reed (ed.), *The Origins of Agriculture*, p. 837–860. Mouton, The Hague – Paris.

WINTERHALDER, B. AND E.A. SMITH (eds.) (1981). *Hunter–Gatherer Foraging Strategies*. The University of Chicago Press, Chicago – London. 268 p.

WOESE, C.R., O. KANDLER AND M.L. WHEELIS (1991). "Towards a natural system of organisms: proposals for the domains Archea, Bacteria and Eucaria". *Proc. nat. Acad. Sci. USA*, 87: 4576. Washington.

WOOD, B. (1976). *The evolution of early man*. Peter Lowe, ed. 124 p.

WORLD RESOURCES INSTITUTE (1990). *World Resources. 1990–91. A Report of the World Resources Institute in collaboration with the United Nations Environment Programme and the United Nations Development Programme*. Oxford University Press, Oxford – New York. 383 p.

WORSTER, D. (1985). *Nature's Economy*. Cambridge University Press, Cambridge

WRIGHT, H.E.J. (1977). "Environmental Change and the Origin of Agriculture in the Old and New Worlds". In: C.A. Reed (ed.), *Origins of Agriculture*, p. 281–320. Mouton, The Hague – Paris.

WU, R. AND S. LI (1983). "El hombre de Pequín". *Investigación y Ciencia*, 83 (August 1983): 48–57. Barcelona.

Indexes

Species' index

This index contains the scientific and common names of the species mentioned in the text. The number refers to the page or pages where the name appears in the main text. Page numbers in italics refer to illustrations. As this first volume is introductory, this index only contains references to species about which more information is supplied.

Thematic index

The biosphere in the human age 235

Authorship and source of the illustrations

Pictures and maps:

- Biopunt (Barcelona), 43, 46, 62, 71, 75, 89, 90, 98, 106, 107, 108, 113, 114, 115, 117, 119, 124, 127, 128, 140, 142, 146, 147, 150, 155, 156, 158, 162, 163, 168, 169, 170, 173, 176, 180, 181, 182, 187, 192, 197, 220, 228, 250, 258, 265, 268, 271, 273, 274, 285, 315, 327, 331, 336, 392
- Bonner, Aina, 207, 275
- Corbera, Jordi (Barcelona), 28, 120, 137, 249
- Editrònica (Barcelona), 29, 31, 40, 63, 65, 79, 148, 151, 152, 154, 157, 159, 165, 166, 171, 185, 187, 188, 190, 198, 208, 210, 222, 223, 224, 227, 242, 251, 264, 272, 284, 288, 291, 293, 294, 295, 296, 322, 323, 324, 325, 326, 327, 328, 345
- Martínez, Albert, 30, 32
- Puche, Carles (Sant Celoni), 120, 121
- Socias, Marcel (Barcelona), 367
- World Conservation Monitoring Centre (Cambridge), 352

Photographs:

- Abbas / Magnum / Zardoya (Barcelona), 167
- AF Photographic Library / Zardoya (Barcelona), 39
- AGE Fotostock (Barcelona), 35, 42, 78, 82, 95, 103, 110, 116, 118, 131, 133, 153, 175, 194, 203, 213, 218, 221, 262, 267, 287, 314, 316, 321, 330, 360, 366, 369
- Agelet, Antoni (Balaguer), 172, 298
- AISA (Barcelona), 83, 204, 260, 269, 280, 346, 371, 379, 395
- Alamany, Oriol (Barcelona), 374
- Alfred-Wegener-Institut für Polar-und Meeresforschung (Bremerhaven), 31
- Allison, Glen / Photothèque Stone Intenational (Barcelona), 208
- Álvarez, Walter-Science Photo Library / AGE Fotostock (Barcelona), 59
- American Museum of Natural History (New York), 129
- Ancient Art & Architecture Collection (Pinner), 101
- Anderson, A.E. / American Museum of Natural History (New York), 129
- Amos, James L. / National Geographic Society (Washington DC), 38
- Atkins, Kathie / Oxford Scientific Films / Firo Foto (Barcelona), 201
- Badia, David / Biopunt (Barcelona), 333, 335, 342, 343, 344
- Balandin, Serguei A. (Moscow), 332
- Barbey, Bruno / Magnum / Zardoya (Barcelona), 167
- Barbey, Bruno / Zardoya (Barcelona), 399
- Bartel, Alex / Science Photo Library / AGE Fotostock (Barcelona), 202
- Beirne, Brendan / Auscape International (Redfern Hill, NSW), 391
- Biophoto Associates / Science Source / AGE Fotostock (Barcelona), 104
- Biosca, Joan (Barcelona), 364
- Blasi, Miquel (Barcelona), 64
- Bova, John / Photo Researchers, Inc. / AGE Fotostock (Barcelona), 400
- Bramaz, H.R. / Firo Foto (Barcelona), 356
- Bridgeman / Index (Barcelona), 243
- British Museum (London), 244
- Burgess, Jeremy / Science Photo Library / AGE Fotostock (Barcelona), 177, 195
- Burri, René / Magnum / Zardoya (Barcelona), 178
- Campillo, R. / Zardoya (Barcelona), 193
- Carbó, Joaquim / SCM, 193
- Carbonell, Eudald (Tarragona), 270
- Carré, Claude, 373
- Carreras, Elisabet, 183
- Centre for Medium-Range Weather Forecast (Reading), 401
- Cheng, Waina / Oxford Scientific Films / Firo Foto (Barcelona), 351
- Chillmaid, Martyn / Oxford Scientific Films / Firo Foto (Barcelona), 86
- Christer, Fedriksson / Bruce Coleman Limited (Uxbridge), 370
- CLB-TPS / Index (Barcelona), 317
- CNRI / Science Photo Library / AGE Fotostock (Barcelona), 111
- Coll. Musée de l'Homme (Paris), 281
- Comellas, Antoni (Terrassa), 218
- Costa, Ernest (Fontcoberta), 225, 329, 380, 381
- Da Rocha Filho, Rubens / Image Bank (Barcelona), 199
- Dowsett, A.B. / Science Photo Library / AGE Fotostock (Barcelona), 87
- Durfort, Mercè (Barcelona), 184
- Edmond, John / Massachusetts Institute of Technology (Cambridge, MA), 44
- Edwards, Dianne (Cardiff), 123
- ESA (Darmstadt), 160, 386
- ESA / Science Photo Library / AGE Fotostock (Barcelona), 385
- European Centre for Medium-Range Weather Forecast (Reading), 401
- Feldman, Gene / NASA GSFC / Science Photo Library / AGE Fotostock (Barcelona), 191
- Ferrer, Xavier (Barcelona), 91, 218
- Ferrés, Lluís (Barcelona), 171
- Firo Foto (Barcelona), 82, 213, 261
- Fogden, Michael & Patricia (Dunblane), 218, 232
- Folch, Ramon / ERF (Barcelona), 179, 211, 246, 364, 393
- Foott, Jeff / Bruce Coleman Limited (Uxbridge), 377
- Foto Rambol / ECSA (Barcelona), 212
- Photothèque Stone International (Barcelona), 52, 229, 359
- Freeman, Michael / Bruce Coleman Limited (Uxbridge), 263, 384
- Friedel, Michael / Firo Foto (Barcelona), 368
- Fuson, P. / Magnum / Zardoya (Barcelona), 83
- Geoscience Features Picture Library (Wye), 344
- Gifford, Jane / Photothèque Stone International (Barcelona), 73
- Greenaway, Frank / Bruce Coleman Limited (Uxbridge), 193
- Grossman, Shelly / AGE Fotostock (Barcelona), 283
- Guerrero, Ricard (Bellaterra), 88
- Gunter Ziesler / Bruce Coleman, 49
- Index (Barcelona), 95, 308, 310, 311
- Index / Stock International, Inc., 145
- Institut Pasteur / CNRI (Paris), 90
- Koch, Paolo / Firo Foto (Barcelona), 247, 361
- Koskas, R. / Photothèque Stone International (Barcelona), 54
- Kristof, Emory / National Geographic Society (Washington DC), 33
- Land, Martin / Science Photo Library / AGE Fotostock (Barcelona), 51
- Lanting, Frans / Minden Pictures (Aptos, CA), 375, 376, 389
- Latova, José (Madrid), 312
- Lessing, E. / Zardoya (Barcelona), 80, 82, 83, 289
- Loaso, Josep (Barcelona), 371
- Lowler, Wayne / Auscape International (Redfern Hill, NSW), 72
- MacQuitty, William / Camera Press / Zardoya (Barcelona), 299
- Mary Evans Picture Library (London), 68, 81, 139, 277, 278, 301, 347, 348, 349, 397
- Mear, Roger / Photothèque Stone International (Barcelona), 61
- Moczydlowska, Vidal & Rudavskaia, 105
- Morrison, Reg / Auscape International (Redfern Hill, NSW), 58, 94, 97, 119
- Murti, Gopal -Science Photo Library / AGE Fotostock (Barcelona), 214
- NASA (Washington DC), 402, 403, 404, 405
- NASA GSFC / Science Photo Library / AGE Fotostock (Barcelona), 147
- Nationalmuseet of Copenhagen (Copenhagen), 209
- National Museum of Kenya (Nairobi), 256, 267
- Novosti (London), 66, 67
- Paterson-Jones, Colin (Newlands), 357
- Philippe Plailly / Science Photo Library / AGE Fotostock (Barcelona), 215, 387
- Pott, Eckart / Bruce Coleman Limited (Uxbridge), 365
- Prenzell, Fritz / Bruce Coleman Limited (Uxbridge), 241
- Radovan, Zev (Jerusalem), 290
- Reader, John / Science Photo Library / AGE Fotostock (Barcelona), 253, 254, 257
- Reardone, Mitch / Photothèque Stone Intenational (Barcelona), 355
- Révy, J.C. / CNRI (Paris), 77
- Richardson, Jim / West Light / AGE Fotostock (Barcelona), 68
- Ronan, Ann / Image Select (Watford), 48, 245, 282, 302, 303
- Root, Alan / Survival Anglia (Long Hanborough), 125
- Science Photo Library / AGE Fotostock (Barcelona), 252
- Seynes, R. de / Firo Foto (Barcelona), 135
- Shaw, John / Bruce Coleman Limited (Uxbridge), 221
- Shear, William (Sydney, VA), 125
- Six, Anne & Jacques / Firo Foto (Barcelona), 337
- ST-TCL / Index (Barcelona), 149
- Stammers, Sinclair / Science Photo Library / AGE Fotostock (Barcelona), 37
- Steven, Austin James / Bruce Coleman Limited (Uxbridge), 261
- Stolp, Heinz (Bayreuth), 108
- Tannenbaum, A. / Sygma / Contifoto (Barcelona), 130
- Taylor, Kim / Bruce Coleman Limited, 200
- TCL / Index (Barcelona), 27
- Terry, Sheila / Science Photo Library / AGE Fotostock (Barcelona), 138
- The Library of Congress (Washington DC), 292
- The Needham Research Institute (Cambridge), 239, 300
- Torrella, Francesc (Murcia), 90, 92, 99
- Tovy, A. / Index (Barcelona), 47, 388
- TPS / Index (Barcelona), 109

- Tracy, Tom / Photothèque Stone International (Barcelona), 363
- Turner, Peter / Image Bank (Barcelona), 132
- Tuttle, Merlin D. / Bat Conservation International, Inc. (Austin, TX), 199
- University of Moscow (Moscow), 161
- US Department of Energy / Science Photo Library / AGE Fotostock (Barcelona), 205
- Vidal, Jordi (Barcelona), 102, 272, 304, 305, 306, 307, 394, 396
- Vidal, Jordi / ECSA (Barcelona), 37, 50, 51, 128, 131, 134, 267
- Vioujard, Christian / Gamma / Flash Press (Madrid), 276, 278, 279
- Wolf, Hans / Image Bank (Barcelona), 175
- Zardoya (Barcelona), 189, 214, 349
- Ziesler, Gunter / Bruce Coleman, 49